Automatic Control Systems

PRENTICE-HALL ELECTRICAL ENGINEERING SERIES

WILLIAM L. EVERITT, *Editor*

ANNER *Elements of Television Systems*
ARMINGTON AND VOLZ *An Introduction to Electric Circuit Analysis*
BALABANIAN *Network Synthesis*
BENEDICT *Introduction to Industrial Electronics*
BLACKWELL AND KOTZEBUE *Semiconductor-Diode Parametric Amplifiers*
DAVIS AND WEED *Industrial Electronic Engineering*
DEKKER *Electrical Engineering Materials*
DUNN AND BARKER *Electrical Measurements Manual*
EVANS *Experiments in Electronics*
FETT *Feedback Control Systems*
FICH *Transient Analysis in Electrical Engineering*
FICH AND POTTER *Theory of A-C Circuits*
FLORES *Computer Logic: The Functional Design of Digital Computers*
FOECKE *Introduction to Electrical Engineering Science*
GOLDMAN *Information Theory*
GOLDMAN *Transformation Calculus and Electrical Transients*
HERSHBERGER *Principles of Communication Systems*
JORDAN *Electromagnetic Waves and Radiating Systems*
KUO *Automatic Control Systems*
LO, ET AL *Transistor Electronics*
MARTIN *Electronic Circuits*
MARTIN *Physical Basis for Electrical Engineering*
MARTIN *Ultra High Frequency Engineering*
MOSKOWITZ AND RACKER *Pulse Techniques*
NIXON *Handbook of Laplace Transformation; Tables and Examples*
NIXON *Principles of Automatic Controls*
PARTRIDGE *Principles of Electronic Instruments*
PUMPHREY *Electrical Engineering*, 2nd
PUMPHREY *Fundamentals of Electrical Engineering*, 2nd
REED *Electric Network Synthesis*
REED *Foundation for Electric Network Theory*
RIDEOUT *Active Networks*
RUSSELL *Modulation and Coding in Information Systems*
RYDER, F. L. *Creative Engineering Analysis*
RYDER, J. D. *Electronic Engineering Principles*, 3rd
RYDER, J. D. *Electronic Fundamentals and Applications*, 2nd
RYDER, J. D. *Networks, Lines and Fields*
SHEDD *Fundamentals of Electromagnetic Waves*
SKODER AND HELM *Circuit Analysis by Laboratory Methods*, 2nd
SOOHOO *Theory and Application of Ferrites*
STOUT *Basic Electrical Measurements*, 2nd
THOMSON *LaPlace Transformation*, 2nd
VAIL *Circuits in Electrical Engineering*
VAN DER ZIEL *Noise*
VAN DER ZIEL *Solid State Physical Electronics*
VAN VALKENBURG *Network Analysis*
VON TERSCH AND SWAGO *Recurrent Electrical Transients*
WARD *Introduction to Electrical Engineering*, 3rd
WARFIELD *Introduction to Electronic Analog Computers*
WEED AND DAVIS *Fundamentals of Electron Devices and Circuits*

Automatic Control Systems

BENJAMIN C. KUO

Associate Professor of Electrical Engineering
University of Illinois

Prentice-Hall, Inc.

Englewood Cliffs, N.J.

To My Father and Mother

Preface

The primary aim of this book is to give the reader a reasonably complete understanding of the various principles and techniques utilized in the analysis and design of feedback or automatic control systems.

Most of the material has been used by the author in a number of servomechanism courses at both the undergraduate and the graduate levels at the University of Illinois. The book is so prepared that it can be used as a textbook for either a first or an intermediate course in servomechanisms.

The first two chapters give the basic concept and a review of the mathematical background of control systems. In Chapter 2, the general gain formula of the signal flow graph technique is covered and extended to the block diagram methods. This treatment allows the evaluation of the transfer function of a complex block diagram configuration without using the usually tedious block diagram reduction technique. Chapter 3 covers the basic feedback theory. The concept of feedback is presented from a general viewpoint so that the reader will understand why feedback is incorporated into a physical system and the effects of feedback in the system.

Throughout the book, both the frequency response method — using the Nyquist criterion, Bode plot, Nichols chart, and the s-plane — and the root locus technique are emphasized with equal importance. The author feels that in practical design, one technique does not replace the other.

In Chapter 8, the generalized root locus–root contour technique is treated extensively. The root contours are defined as the roots of the characteristic equation of a closed-loop system when parameters other than the forward gain are varied. The root contour technique has proved to be a very useful tool in the design of linear feedback control systems, since, in general, optimum design relies on the choice of suitable values for other parameters as well as the forward gain. The book shows that the construction of the root contours follows virtually the same rules devised for the construction of the conventional root locus diagrams.

In Chapter 9, the design of the compensation of feedback control systems is effected by both the frequency domain technique and the root contour technique. Again, the root contours indicate clearly the effects of phase-lead and phase-lag compensations on the performance of feedback control systems. A systematic procedure is also outlined for the design of feedback compensation by the root contour method.

Chapter 10 covers the theory of sampled-data systems and the z-transformation. The signal flow graph technique also is extended to the studies of systems with sampled-data. Chapter 11 gives an introduction to nonlinear systems; because of space limitations, only the describing function and the phase plane methods are discussed.

The author wishes to express his sincere appreciation to Dean W. L. Everitt for his encouragement and interest in the preparation of the manuscript. The author also owes a debt of gratitude to Prof. G. E. Anner and Mr. D. Humpherys for their valuable suggestions.

Benjamin C. Kuo

Table of Contents

1 Introduction to Feedback Control Systems   1

1.1 The Control Systems, 1
1.2 The Basic Elements of a Servomechanism, 4
1.3 Types of Servomechanisms, 6
1.4 The Analysis and Design of Feedback Control Systems, 6

2 Equations and Models of Linear Systems   10

2.1 Models and Mathematical Representation of Physical Systems, 10
2.2 Linear versus Nonlinear Equations, 11
2.3 Equations of Electrical Systems, 12
2.4 Mechanical Systems, 21
2.5 Equations of Mechanical Systems, 25
2.6 Gear Trains, 29
2.7 Transfer Function and Impulse Response of Linear Systems, 32
2.8 Block Diagrams, 37
2.9 Signal Flow Graphs, 41
2.10 Application of the Signal Flow Gain Formula to Block Diagrams, 52

3 General Feedback Theory   58

3.1 What is Feedback? 58
3.2 The Effects of Feedback, 59
3.3 Mathematical Definition of Feedback, 72
3.4 The Sensitivity Function, 78
3.5 Impedance and Admittance Functions, 80

4 Components of Feedback Control Systems   88

4.1 Introduction, 88
4.2 Transducers and Error-Sensing Devices, 89
4.3 Servo Motors, 101
4.4 Modulators and Demodulators, 112
4.5 Servo Amplifiers, 115

5 Time Response of Feedback Control Systems   120

5.1 Introduction, 120
5.2 Typical Test Input Signals for the Transient Analysis of Feedback Control Systems, 120
5.3 Time Domain Performance Characteristics of Feedback Control Systems, 122
5.4 Transient Response of Feedback Control Systems, 123
5.5 Transient Response of a Second-Order System, 127
5.6 Transient Response of a Positional Servomechanism, 130
5.7 Effects of Derivative and Integral Controls on the Transient Performance of Feedback Control Systems, 138
5.8 Steady-State Response of Feedback Control Systems — Steady-State Error, 145
5.9 The Generalized Definition of Error Coefficients (The Error Series), 151
5.10 Stability of Linear Feedback Control Systems, 155

6 The Frequency Response Method   170

6.1 Introduction, 170
6.2 The Polar Plot, 171
6.3 The Bode Plot (Corner Plot), 172
6.4 The Magnitude versus Phase Shift Plot, 181
6.5 Frequency Response of Feedback Control Systems, 183
6.6 Frequency Domain Specifications, 185
6.7 M_p and ω_p for a Second-Order System, 186

7   The Nyquist Criterion   194

7.1   Introduction, 194
7.2   "Encircled" and "Enclosed," 196
7.3   The Principle of the Argument, 197
7.4   The Nyquist Path, 200
7.5   The Nyquist Criterion and the GH-Plot, 201
7.6   The Application of the Nyquist Criterion, 204
7.7   The Effects of Additional Poles and Zeros of $G(s)H(s)$ on the Shape of the Nyquist Locus, 213
7.8   Systems with Transportation Lags, 218
7.9   Relative Stability from the Nyquist Diagram — Gain Margin and Phase Margin, 222
7.10 Conditionally Stable Systems, 229
7.11 The Constant M Loci in the G-Plane, 231
7.12 The Constant Phase Shift Loci in the G-Plane, 235
7.13 The Constant M and N Loci in Gain-Phase Plane (The Nichols Chart), 236

8   The Root Locus Technique   246

8.1   Introduction, 246
8.2   The Root Loci (Definition), 248
8.3   The Construction of the Root Loci, 250
8.4   Some Other Important Properties of the Root Locus, 271
8.5   Root Locus of Conditionally Stable Systems, 276
8.6   The Generalized Root Locus Diagrams (The Root Contours), 280

9   Compensation of Feedback Control Systems   300

9.1   Why Is Compensation Necessary? 300
9.2   Types of Compensation, 302
9.3   Frequency Domain Design versus s-Plane Design, 305
9.4   Series Compensation with D-C Networks, 306
9.5   Feedback Compensation, 353

10   Sampled-Data Feedback Control Systems   360

10.1 Introduction, 360
10.2 The Sampling Process, 362
10.3 Mathematical Analysis of the Sampling Process, 364
10.4 Interpretation of the Sampling Process in the Frequency Domain, 371
10.5 Data Reconstruction (Hold Circuit), 373
10.6 The z-Transform Method, 378
10.7 The Pulse Transfer Function, 387

10.8   The z-Transform Analysis of Sampled-Data Systems, 390

10.9   Signal Flow Graphs of Sampled-Data Systems, 394

10.10 Limitations of the z-Transform Method, 405

10.11 The Routh-Hurwitz Criterion Applied to Sampled-Data Systems, 409

10.12 Design and Compensation of Sampled-Data Systems, 419

10.13 Response of Sampled-Data Systems between Sampling Instants, 427

10.14 Summary, 431

11   Nonlinear Systems   435

11.1   Introduction, 435

11.2   The Phase Plane Method, 437

11.3   Application of Phase Plane Technique to On-Off Control Systems, 441

11.4   Application of Phase Plane Technique to Systems with Coulomb Friction, 451

11.5   Phase Plane Diagram of Systems with Ramp Input, 454

11.6   The Describing Function Technique, 455

11.7   Describing Functions of Common Nonlinear Elements in Feedback Control Systems, 467

11.8   The Application of Describing Function to Stability Analysis of Nonlinear Systems, 470

APPENDIX A.   Laplace Transformation   479

A.1   Complex Variables and the s-Plane, 479

A.2   The Laplace Transform, 482

A.3   Partial Fraction Expansions, 491

Index   499

1

Introduction to Feedback Control Systems

1.1 The Control Systems

In recent years, automatic control systems have assumed an important role in the development of modern civilization and technology. Domestically, automatic thermostats in furnaces and air conditioners regulate the temperature and the humidity of modern houses for comfortable living. Industrially, automatic control systems are employed to improve both the quantity and the quality of manufactured products. In modern weapons systems, the applications of control systems have become overwhelmingly important.

The basic control system may be described by the simple block diagram shown in Fig. 1-1. The output variable c is controlled by the input variable

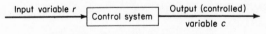

Fig. 1-1. The basic control system.

r through the elements of the control system. For instance, the angular position of the steering wheel of an automobile controls the direction of the front wheels. In this case, the position of the steering wheel is the input, and the direction of the front wheels is the output; the control system elements are composed of the steering mechanisms.

1

Open-Loop Control Systems (Non-feedback Systems)

Not all types of control systems can provide satisfactory performances. The open-loop control systems represent the simplest and most economical type of control systems. However, since they are usually inaccurate and unreliable, they are not generally preferred. The control adjustment of an open-loop system must depend on human judgment and estimate. For instance, a furnace for home heating without thermostatic control is an open-loop control system. If the furnace is equipped with a timing device, the human operator must estimate the amount of time required for the furnace to operate in order to reach the desired temperature and must set the timer accordingly. When the preset time is up, the furnace is turned off; however, it is quite likely that the room temperature is either above or below the desired value. An "automatic" washing machine is also an open-loop system, because the amount of wash time is entirely determined by the judgment and estimation of the human operator. A true automatic washer would check the cleanliness of the clothes constantly and turn itself off when the desired degree of cleanliness was reached. Figure 1-2 illustrates

Fig. 1-2. A typical diagram of an open-loop system.

the block diagram of a basic open-loop control system. A small input signal r is amplified by the amplifier, whose output actuates the powering device; the output of the powering device, in turn, drives the controlled variable c.

Another important disadvantage in the performance of open-loop systems is that the systems do not adapt to variations in environmental conditions or to external disturbances. Perhaps an experienced person can estimate correctly the exact amount of operating time for the furnace to provide a certain temperature in the house, but if the doors or windows are opened and closed intermittently during the operating period, the final temperature of the house definitely will not be the desired temperature. Missing in the open-loop systems is a link or feedback path between the output and the input signals for a more satisfactory control. In order to obtain accurate control, the actual output must be fed back and compared with the "desired output" (input signal), and an actuating signal proportional to the difference of the output and the input must be sent through the system to correct the error.

Closed-Loop Control Systems (Feedback Control Systems)

A system with a feedback path like that described in the last paragraph is a closed-loop system. Human beings are probably the most complicated and sophisticated feedback control systems in existence. For instance, when a person reaches for a book on the desk, his brain sends out a signal to his arm to reach for the book. His eyes serve as a sensing device which feeds back the exact position of his hand continuously. The distance between his hand and the book is the error. However, if he is told to reach for the book and then is blindfolded, he can only reach toward it, estimating its exact position. It is quite possible that he may miss the book by a large margin. With his eyes blindfolded, the feedback loop is broken, and he is

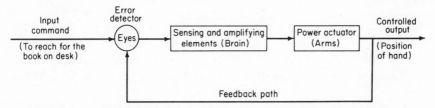

Fig. 1-3. Block diagram of human being as a closed-loop system.

operating as an open-loop system. The example of a human being as a feedback control system is described by the block diagram in Fig. 1-3. Figure 1-4 shows the block diagram of another closed-loop system, whose

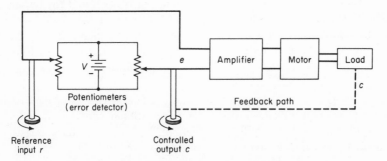

Fig. 1-4. A closed-loop system for positioning a load.

function is to position a load. In this case, a pair of potentiometers are used to detect the error between the actual position of the load (output) and the reference input, which is the desired position of the load. The error voltage e which appears at the potentiometer terminals is amplified and then sent to cause the motor to rotate in such a direction that the error signal is eventually reduced to zero. If the reference input shaft is suddenly given an angular displacement of R units* as shown in Fig. 1-5a, the typical output

---

*This is usually referred to as a step displacement test signal in the analysis of feedback control systems.

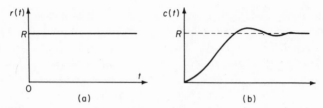

Fig. 1-5. Typical step response of a feedback control system. (a) Step displacement input; (b) Output system response.

response of the system as a function of time is as shown in Fig. 1-5b. Due to electrical and mechanical inertia, the output displacement cannot respond instantaneously, but will, rather, move gradually toward and sometimes oscillate about the desired position before reaching its final steady state.

Although a closed-loop system can offer more accuracy in control than an open-loop system, it is also capable of being unstable. In most feedback control systems, if the gain is too high, the system may tend to "overcorrect" the error, and its output may oscillate without bound. An unstable linear system is considered useless. Another important consideration is that the final output of a feedback control system usually does not exactly equal the references input. In other words, because of friction and the features of feedback, the system may have a steady-state error. It will be shown later that the steady-state error can usually be reduced by increasing the gain of the system. In a very rough sense, we can say that to design feedback control systems essentially is to find a compromise between two contradictory factors: *stability* and *accuracy*.

The foregoing discussion of the significance and effects of feedback is, of course, oversimplified. From feedback amplifier theories, it is known that feedback also has significant effects on such system characteristics as bandwidth, impedance, sensitivity, and distortion, as well as stability and accuracy. In fact, in the analysis and design of feedback control systems, all these factors are important and should be considered. A more quantitative discussion of feedback theory will be given in Chapter 3.

1.2 The Basic Elements of a Servomechanism

The name "servomechanism," or "servo" for short, has been used quite freely in the literature of feedback control systems. Strictly speaking, servomechanisms merely represent a particular group of feedback control systems whose controlled outputs are mechanical positions. From the basic concept of closed-loop control systems, feedback control systems may be defined: *systems comprising one or more feedback loops which compare the controlled signal c with the command signal r; the difference (e = r − c) is used to drive c into correspondence with r.* A servomechanism, on the other hand, is defined as a feedback control system in which one or more system signals represent mechanical motion*. However, since "servomechanism" and "servo" have been frequently used in a very broad sense, in this text "servo system" and "feedback control system" are used interchangeably.

The elements of a basic servo system can be schematically represented by the closed-loop block diagram shown in Fig. 1-6. The block diagram

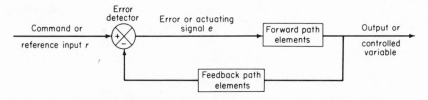

Fig. 1-6. Basic block diagram of a servo system.

consists of a forward path, a feedback path, and an error-sensing device. A more detailed diagram of a servo system is illustrated in Fig. 1-7. In general, the forward path of a servo system may consist of the following

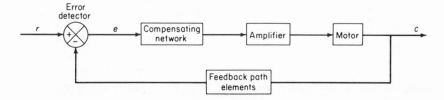

Fig. 1-7. Block diagram illustrating the basic components of a servo system.

elements: (1) error-sensing device (error detector), (2) amplifier, (3) servomotor, (4) compensating networks, etc. The feedback path usually consists of transducers and compensating networks. The error detector compares the reference input with the actual output or some function of the output signal, and sends out a signal proportional to the difference. Compensating networks are often needed in the forward path, the feedback path, or both, to improve the performance of the system. A servo system with only its minimum required components seldom gives satisfactory performance.

---

*IRE Standards on Terminology for Feedback Control Systems, *Proc. IRE,* January, 1956.

1.3 Types of Servomechanisms

Feedback control systems (or servo systems) may be classified in a number of ways.* According to the nature of the control system signals flowing in the systems, they can be classified into the following three types:

(1) *Continuous-Data Feedback Control Systems*

A continuous-data system is one in which the signals at various parts of the system are all continuous functions of time. The continuous data may either be modulated, in which case the system is referred to as an a-c carrier servo system, or unmodulated, when the system is called a d-c system. The features and characteristics of a-c and d-c servo systems will be discussed in the forthcoming chapters. For instance, the system used for positioning a load in Fig 1-4 is a typical continuous-data d-c system; the signals appearing in the system are all unmodulated and of low frequency.

(2) *Relay-Type Feedback Control Systems*

In a relay-type (on-off type) servo system, the full power of the motor is applied as soon as the error signal is large enough to operate the relay. In this type of system, the signals in part of the system are rectangular waves whose polarity depends on that of the error signals. A relay-type system is also a nonlinear system, because its operation can only be described by nonlinear differential equations. The thermostatic control of a furnace is a very common example of an on-off control system. The furnace is turned either "on" or "off," depending upon whether the room temperature is below or above the preset reference.

(3) *Sampled-Data Feedback Control Systems*

In a sampled-data control system, the control signal is sampled at intermittent intervals, and the signals in at least part of the system are in the form of a pulse train. A radar tracking system is an example of a sampled-data control system. Information on the azimuth and the elevation is obtained in pulsed-data form by means of the scanning operation.

1.4 The Analysis and Design of Feedback Control Systems

The analysis and design of feedback control systems are usually carried out by using either linear or nonlinear techniques. Strictly speaking, linear systems do not exist in practice, since all physical systems are nonlinear to some extent. Therefore, linear feedback control systems are idealized

---

*H. L. Hazen, *Theory of Servomechanisms*, J. Franklin Inst., 1934, pp. 218, 279; H. M. James, N. B. Nichols, R. S. Phillips, *Theory of Servomechanisms*, McGraw-Hill Book Company, New York, 1947, pp. 2–8.

systems. When the magnitudes of the actuating signals are limited to a range in which system components are considered linear, these components may be represented by their linear models and counterparts. But when the actuating signals are extended outside the range of linear operations, the feedback control system becomes nonlinear. For instance, electronic servo amplifiers often possess saturation effect when the applied signal becomes too large; the magnetic fields of servo motors also have saturation proper-·ties. There are other inherent nonlinearities, such as backlash between gears and the hysteresis effects in some components, whose occurrence does not depend entirely on the size of the actuating signals. The relay-type control mentioned in the last section represents another kind of nonlinearity which is introduced purposely into a system. The techniques of solving nonlinear feedback control system problems are very involved and not yet unified at present. Some of the frequently used techniques* are as follows: the describing function method, the phase plane method, and the perturbation method. Quite often, analog and digital computers are required to simulate the nonlinear system characteristics.

Because the control systems engineer is confronted with an extremely wide range of physical systems, there are no definite steps that will lead to definite solutions of all the physical problems in existence. However, in general a systematic analysis of most control systems can be conducted by the following principal steps:

(1) Mathematical representation of the system
(2) Study of the mathematical model
(3) Evaluation of system characteristics from the results

The problems in the design and synthesis of control systems are usually more involved. In general, successful designs of most control systems rely on the following steps:

(1) Preliminary study of the design problem and examination of design specifications
(2) Mathematical representation of the fixed parts of the system
(3) Study of the model of the fixed parts
(4) Design of compensating networks and elements so that system meets design requirements
(5) Construction and testing of a prototype system

The mathematical aspects of the analysis and design of linear feedback control systems are usually carried out in either the time domain or the frequency domain. The time-domain analysis involves the evaluation of the transient and steady-state responses when typical test signals, such as

---

*R. Cosgriff, *Nonlinear Feedback Control Systems*, McGraw-Hill Book Company, New York, 1958; Y. H. Ku, *Analysis and Control of Nonlinear Systems*, The Ronald Press Co., New York, 1958.

step, ramp, and parabolic functions, are applied to the system. The transient response refers to the manner in which the system arrives at the steady-state conditions. In particular, for a step function input, the servo system should approach the steady-state in the most rapid but least oscillatory way. A response with a slow response time or excess overshoot and oscillation about the steady-state value is undesirable (Fig. 1-8). The

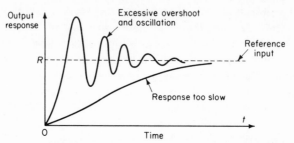

Fig. 1-8. Typical time responses of a servo system.

steady-state response indicates the accuracy of the servo system. An ideal steady-state response of a servo system should correspond with the reference input.

In the frequency-domain analysis, the steady-state response of the system is evaluated when the input is a sinusoidal signal. Because any periodic input function can be represented by a Fourier series, and an aperiodic input function can be expressed by a Fourier integral, the steady-state response of a given linear control system to any arbitrary function of time can be determined by the principle of superposition once the frequency response of the system is known. The essential characteristic of a linear system is that when the input is a sinusoid, the output response also varies sinusoidally, and at the same frequency. For a nonlinear system, the output will, in addition, contain higher harmonics or subharmonics.

The method of Laplace transformation is a very powerful tool in the analysis and design of linear systems. In the time-domain analysis, the system differential equations are "transformed" into algebraic equations in s, the Laplace operator. The output transform variable is solved for by using ordinary algebraic manipulations; the time response is then obtained through the use of the inverse Laplace transformation. The differential equation method, however, does not show how the system can be improved, so it is not very useful in the design of linear systems. Nevertheless, the design of servo systems based on the time-domain characteristics is not entirely impossible. The root locus technique introduced by Evans* has

*W. R. Evans, "Graphical Analysis of Control Systems," *Trans., AIEE*, vol 67, pp. 547–551, 1948; W. R. Evans, "Control System Synthesis by Root Locus Method," *Trans., AIEE*, Vol. 69, pp. 66–69, 1950

been proved to be very useful in the design and analysis of linear feedback control systems. It will be shown that the transient behavior of linear systems is uniquely determined by the roots of the characteristic equation of the system, which are also poles of the closed-loop transfer function, $C(s)/R(s)$. The conventional root locus diagram contains the plot of the loci of the characteristic equation roots when the loop gain of the system is varied from zero to infinity. The root contour diagram consists of the plot of the variations of the characteristic equation roots when parameters other than the loop gain are varied. The advantage of the root locus (or contour) method is that the root loci (or contours) not only indicate the transient behavior, but also take into account the sinusoidal behavior of a linear system.

The frequency response method of design is especially popular among servo engineers. The contributions made by Nyquist*, Bode,† and others have made the design of linear systems in the frequency domain very appealing. In simple words, the design method in the frequency domain involves the reshaping of the Nyquist plot or the Bode plot of the open-loop transfer function.

---

*H. Nyquist, "Regeneration Theory," *Bell System Tech. Jour.*, Vol. 11, January, 1932.
†H. W. Bode, *Network Analysis and Feedback Amplifier Design*, D. Van Nostrand Company, Inc., New York, 1945.

2

Equations and Models of Linear Systems

2.1 Models and Mathematical Representations of Physical Systems

The first step in the process of analysis of a physical system is to derive a mathematical model from which the features of the system may be studied. In a very broad sense, a model may be regarded as a means of representing the interrelationships between system components and ideas. Generally speaking, a model of a physical system may take any appropriate form. The following catagories are the most useful and common:

(1) Direct analog: Scaled or unscaled replicas and analog models

(2) Graphical representation: Block diagrams, signal flow graphs

(3) Mathematical representation: Differential equation, transfer function relation, matrix representation, etc.

A direct analog is a scaled or unscaled replica of a physical system; the necessity of this representation stems from many situations in which circumstances make direct study of the actual system virtually impossible. For instance, network analyzers are used as models of electric power distribution systems, with power generators simulated by voltage generators, and transmission lines and electric loads by combinations of resistances, inductances, and capacitances. Although the actual power systems operate on 60 cycles, some network analyzers are designed to operate at 10,000 cycles in order to reduce component size and, thus, save space and cost. Another typical example is the use of models in the study of water systems and the effectiveness of dams at various locations in controlling the flow of waters.

Representation of a physical system by mathematical expressions and pictorial means allows the control engineer to use the available mathematical and topological tools, such as differential equations and block diagrams. In practice, circumstances usually do not allow an exact mathematical representation of a complex system, but if valid assumptions are made on the system properties, much valuable information on the system can be gained from the approximated treatment. To clarify the statement just made: we should realize the fact that all physical systems are nonlinear to some extent, and the mathematical treatment of nonlinear systems is extremely difficult. Therefore, it is often necessary to assume that the system under study behaves linearly over the range of operation. In some cases, the assumption of linearity is quite valid over a large operating range. Under certain conditions, however, the assumption of linearity may depart greatly from the actual happenings. Strictly speaking, a linear system simply does not exist; it is only for the sake of simplifying the mathematics involved that the linear equivalence of a physical system is introduced.

Once the physical system is replaced by its linear model, the system equations are derived by applying various appropriate physical laws. For electrical systems, there are, for instance, Ohm's law, Kirchhoff's laws, Lenz's law, etc.; in mechanics, there are Newton's laws of motion.

An equation describing a physical system usually involves integrals and differentials, and is called a linear integro-differential equation. The solution of a linear integro-differential equation may be obtained by either the classical or the operational method.* The steps involved in the study of physical systems by linear and nonlinear analysis can be described by the flow diagram shown in Fig. 2-1.

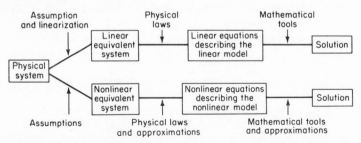

Fig. 2-1. Flow diagram describing the process of linear and nonlinear study of physical systems.

---

*M. F. Gardner and J. L. Barnes, *Transients in Linear Systems*, Vol. I, John Wiley & Sons, Inc., New York, 1942.

2.2 Linear Versus Nonlinear Equations

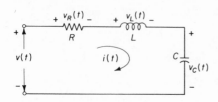

Fig. 2-2. *R-L-C* circuit.

At this point, it is necessary to define mathematically the difference between a linear and a nonlinear system. *A linear system is a system which satisfies the principle of superposition.* The equations which describe a linear system are linear equations, and, therefore, also satisfy the principle of superposition. Consider the *RLC* circuit shown in Fig. 2-2. If the circuit elements *R*, *L*, and *C* are independent of the voltage and current, the equations

$$v_R(t) = Ri(t)$$

$$v_L(t) = L\frac{di(t)}{dt} \tag{2-1}$$

$$v_c(t) = \frac{1}{C}\int_0^t i(t)\,dt$$

and

$$v(t) = v_R(t) + v_L(t) + v_C(t)$$

$$= Ri(t) + L\frac{di(t)}{dt} + \frac{1}{C}\int_0^t i(t)\,dt \tag{2-2}$$

are all linear equations; that is, equations of the first degree. If *R*, *L*, and *C* are all constants, Eq. (2-2) is called a linear integro-differential equation with constant coefficients. If any one (or more) of the elements, the resistance *R*, for example, is a function of time — the independent variable — Eq. (2-2) then becomes an equation with time-variant coefficient (or coefficients). It can be shown* that an equation with time-variant coefficients is still a linear equation. However, if one of the elements, *R*, *L*, *C*, is a function of the dependent variable *i(t)*, the equation becomes a nonlinear equation.

Some examples of nonlinear equations are

$$y(t) = \frac{d^2x}{dt^2} + 5\left(\frac{dx}{dt}\right)^2 + 2x \tag{2-3}$$

$$y(t) = \frac{d^2x}{dt^2} + 3x\frac{dx}{dt} + 2x \tag{2-4}$$

Equation (2-3) is nonlinear because it is of the second *degree*, and Eq. (2-4) has a coefficient which is a function of *x*.

---

*Y. H. Ku, *Analysis and Control of Nonlinear Systems*, pp. 6–8, The Ronald Press Co., New York, 1958.

2.3 *Equations of Electrical Systems*

The mesh and node equations of an electrical network are formulated from the two laws given by Kirchhoff. Kirchhoff's voltage law is a relation of the sum of the instantaneous voltages of the elements in a loop. It states: *In any loop the sum of the voltage drops must equal the sum of the voltage rises.*

Kirchhoff's current law relates to the sum of instantaneous currents at a node. It states: *The sum of currents flowing into a node equals the sum of current flowing out.**

Equations For Passive Networks

As an example of the loop analysis of an electric network with passive elements, consider the network of Fig. 2-3. The network has three independent meshes (loops) and the three mesh currents, i_1, i_2, i_3, have been assigned positive directions as shown. The three mesh equations, based on Kirchhoff's voltage law, are

$$\text{Mesh 1:} \quad v(t) = R_1 i_1(t) + \frac{1}{C_1}\int_0^t i_1(t)dt - \frac{1}{C_1}\int_0^t i_2(t)\,dt \quad (2\text{-}5)$$

$$\text{Mesh 2:} \quad 0 = -\frac{1}{C_1}\int_0^t i_1(t)\,dt + \left(\frac{1}{C_1}+\frac{1}{C_2}\right)\int_0^t i_2(t)\,dt + L_1\frac{di_2(t)}{dt}$$
$$-\frac{1}{C_2}\int_0^t i_3(t)\,dt \quad (2\text{-}6)$$

$$\text{Mesh 3:} \quad 0 = -\frac{1}{C_2}\int_0^t i_2(t)\,dt + R_2 i_3(t) + \frac{1}{C_2}\int_0^t i_3(t)\,dt \quad (2\text{-}7)$$

The same network of Fig. 2-3 can be analyzed by writing the node equations based on Kirchhoff's current law. The network with the nodes indicated is shown in Fig. 2-4. In this case, there are two independent nodes, therefore only two node equations (as compared with three mesh equations) are necessary:

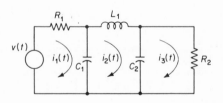

Fig. 2-3. Three-mesh network.

$$\text{Node 1:} \quad \frac{v(t)}{R_1} = \frac{1}{R_1}v_1(t) + C_1\frac{dv_1(t)}{dt} + \frac{1}{L_1}\int_0^t v_1(t)\,dt - \frac{1}{L_1}\int_0^t v_2(t)\,dt \quad (2\text{-}8)$$

$$\text{Node 2:} \quad 0 = -\frac{1}{L_1}\int_0^t v_1(t)\,dt + C_2\frac{dv_2(t)}{dt} + \frac{1}{L_1}\int_0^t v_2(t)\,dt + \frac{1}{R_2}v_2(t) \quad (2\text{-}9)$$

*It is assumed that the reader is already familiar with Kirchhoff's laws, therefore no detailed explanations of the laws are given here. The fundamentals of writing network equations are covered in any standard textbook on network analysis; for example, *Network Analysis* by M. E. Van Valkenburg, Chap. 3, Prentice-Hall, Inc., Englewood Cliffs, N. J., 1955.

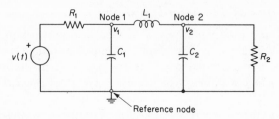

Fig. 2-4. Two-node network (same network as in Fig. 2-3).

It is possible to systematize our approach to network analysis by writing mesh and node equations in the form of general network equations. For an N-mesh network, Kirchhoff's voltage equations may be written in the general form as

$$v_k = \sum_{j=1}^{N} a_{kj} i_j \qquad (k = 1,2,3,\ldots,N) \quad (2\text{-}10)$$

where

$$a_{kj} = \pm \left(R_{kj} + L_{kj} \frac{d}{dt} + \frac{1}{C_{kj}} \int_0^t dt \right) \quad (2\text{-}11)$$

For $k \neq j$, R_{kj} = total resistance common to meshes k and j

L_{kj} = total inductance (including mutual) common to meshes k and j

C_{kj} = total capacitance common to meshes k and j

and for $k = j$, a_{kk} represents the total self-impedance in mesh k. All self-impedance terms, a_{kk}, are positive, since Eq. (2-10) is written as the sum of the voltage rises equals the sum of the voltage drops. The common impedance terms, a_{kj} $(k \neq j)$, are positive if i_k and i_j are assumed to be in the same direction in the elements common to both meshes; otherwise they are negative.

The notations used in Eq. (2-11) can be further simplified if we let p be the differential operator* denoting d/dt, and $1/p$ be the integral operator denoting $\int_0^t dt$. Then

$$a_{kj} = \pm \left(R_{kj} + L_{kj} p + \frac{1}{C_{kj} p} \right) \quad (2\text{-}12)$$

In a similar manner, Kirchhoff's current equations for an M-node network may be written as

$$i_k = \sum_{j=1}^{M} b_{kj} v_j \quad (k = 1,2,3,\ldots,M) \quad (2\text{-}13)$$

---

*It can be easily shown that the differential operator p is identical to the Laplace transform operator s if the initial conditions are zero.

where the b's are given by

$$b_{kj} = \pm \left(\frac{1}{R_{kj}} + C_{kj}\frac{d}{dt} + \frac{1}{L_{kj}}\int_0^t dt \right) \tag{2-14}$$

or

$$b_{kj} = \pm \left(\frac{1}{R_{kj}} + C_{kj}p + \frac{1}{L_{kj}p} \right) \tag{2-15}$$

For $k \neq j$, b_{kj} represents the total admittance connected between node j and node k. For $k = j$, b_{kk} represents the sum of all admittances connected to node k. Since the left side of Eq. (2-13) represents the sum of currents flowing into a node and the right side is the sum of the currents flowing out, the self-admittance terms, b_{kk}, are all positive, and the common admittance terms, b_{kj} $(k \neq j)$, are negative.

When the Laplace transformation* is applied to Eq. (2-10) and Eq. (2-13) with zero initial conditions, all the p operators in a_{kj} and b_{kj} are replaced by the Laplace transform operator s. Then, Eqs. (2-10) and (2-13) become algebraic transform equations for mesh and node analysis respectively, and are given by

$$V_k(s) = \sum_{j=1}^{N} a_{kj}(s)\, I_j(s) \quad (k = 1,2,3,\ldots,N) \tag{2-16}$$

$$I_k(s) = \sum_{j=1}^{M} b_{kj}(s)\, V_j(s) \quad (k = 1,2,3,\ldots,M) \tag{2-17}$$

Simultaneous equations of the form of Eqs. (2-16) and (2-17) can be solved with the help of determinants and Cramer's rule. The solution to the set of simultaneous equations of Eq. (2-16) is given by Cramer's rule as

$$I_1(s) = \frac{D_1}{\Delta^M}, \quad I_2(s) = \frac{D_2}{\Delta^M}, \quad \ldots, \quad I_j(s) = \frac{D_j}{\Delta^M}, \quad \ldots, \quad I_N(s) = \frac{D_N}{\Delta^M} \tag{2-18}$$

where Δ^M is the mesh network determinant, given by

$$\Delta^M = \begin{vmatrix} a_{11} & a_{12} & \ldots & a_{1N} \\ a_{21} & a_{22} & \ldots & a_{2N} \\ . & . & & . \\ . & . & & . \\ a_{N1} & a_{N2} & \ldots & a_{NN} \end{vmatrix} \tag{2-19}$$

and D_j is the determinant formed by replacing the jth column of Δ^M by the column of $V_k(s)$'s $(k = 1, 2, 3, \ldots, N)$, or simply

$$D_j = \sum_{k=1}^{N} (-1)^{j+k} V_k(s) \Delta_{kj}^M \tag{2-20}$$

---

*The Laplace transform theory and applications are given in Appendix A.

The determinant Δ_{kj}^M is called the "minor" of the element a_{kj} and is obtained by crossing out the kth row and jth columns of Δ^M. If we multiply the minor Δ_{kj}^M by $(-1)^{k+j}$, we have the "cofactor" of a_{kj}, i.e.,

$$\text{Cofactor of } a_{kj} = (-1)^{k+j} (\text{minor of } a_{kj}) \tag{2-21}$$

Therefore, Eq. (2-20) can also be written as

$$D_j = \sum_{k=1}^{N} V_k(s) \, (\text{cofactor of } a_{ki}) \tag{2-22}$$

Once the transform currents are obtained from Eq. (2-18), the currents as functions of time are obtained by means of the inverse Laplace transform.

As an example of the application of Cramer's rule the network analysis, we shall now solve for the three currents in the network of Fig. 2-3. The mesh determinant of the network is

$$\Delta^M = \begin{vmatrix} R_1 + \dfrac{1}{C_1 s} & -\dfrac{1}{C_1 s} & 0 \\[2ex] -\dfrac{1}{C_1 s} & \dfrac{1}{C_1 s} + \dfrac{1}{C_2 s} + L_1 s & -\dfrac{1}{C_2 s} \\[2ex] 0 & -\dfrac{1}{C_2 s} & R_2 + \dfrac{1}{C_2 s} \end{vmatrix} \tag{2-23}$$

The solutions for $I_1(s)$, $I_2(s)$, and $I_3(s)$ are

$$I_1(s) = \frac{D_1}{\Delta^M} = \frac{V_1 \Delta_{11}^M - V_2 \Delta_{21}^M + V_3 \Delta_{31}^M}{\Delta^M} = \frac{\Delta_{11}^M}{\Delta^M} V(s) \tag{2-24}$$

$$I_2(s) = \frac{D_2}{\Delta^M} = \frac{-V_1 \Delta_{12}^M + V_2 \Delta_{22}^M - V_3 \Delta_{32}^M}{\Delta^M} = -\frac{\Delta_{12}^M}{\Delta^M} V(s) \tag{2-25}$$

$$I_3(s) = \frac{D_3}{\Delta_M} = \frac{V_1 \Delta_{13}^M - V_2 \Delta_{23}^M + V_3 \Delta_{33}^M}{\Delta^M} = \frac{\Delta_{13}^M}{\Delta^M} V(s) \tag{2-26}$$

where

$$\Delta_{11}^M = \begin{vmatrix} \dfrac{1}{C_1 s} + \dfrac{1}{C_2 s} + L_1 s & -\dfrac{1}{C_2 s} \\[2ex] -\dfrac{1}{C_2 s} & R_2 + \dfrac{1}{C_2 s} \end{vmatrix} \tag{2-27}$$

$$\Delta_{12}^M = \begin{vmatrix} -\dfrac{1}{C_1 s} & -\dfrac{1}{C_2 s} \\[2ex] 0 & R_2 + \dfrac{1}{C_2 s} \end{vmatrix} \tag{2-28}$$

$$\Delta_{13}^M = \begin{vmatrix} -\dfrac{1}{C_1 s} & \dfrac{1}{C_1 s} + \dfrac{1}{C_2 s} + L_1 s \\[2ex] 0 & -\dfrac{1}{C_2 s} \end{vmatrix} \tag{2-29}$$

Equations For Active Networks

The mesh and node equations for passive networks derived in the preceding section can be generalized to include such active elements as vacuum tubes and transistors. The study of active networks and systems is of special importance to servo engineers, since all feedback control systems involve active elements.

Let us consider the vacuum tube circuit in Fig. 2-5a. A vacuum tube is

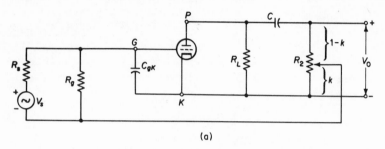

(a)

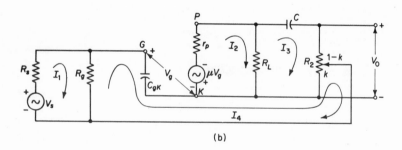

(b)

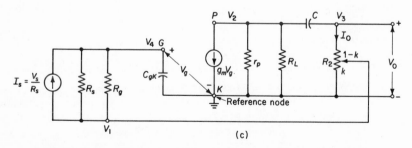

(c)

Fig. 2-5. Vacuum tube circuit and its linear equivalent circuits. (a) Vacuum tube circuit; (b) Voltage source linear equivalent circuit for mesh analysis; (c) Current source linear equivalent current for node analysis.

known to have nonlinear characteristics. But for class A_1 operation, and small exciting signals, the tube may be represented by a linear incremental equivalent model. The linear mesh and node equivalent circuits are given in Fig. 2-5b and Fig. 2-5c, respectively. With the mesh currents assumed as shown, the mesh equations of the circuit are

$$V_s(s) = (R_s + R_g)I_1(s) - R_gI_4(s) \tag{2-30}$$

$$- \mu V_g(s) = (r_p + R_L)I_2(s) - R_LI_3(s) \tag{2-31}$$

$$0 = - R_LI_2(s) + \left(R_L + R_2 + \frac{1}{sC}\right)I_3(s) - k\,R_2I_4(s) \tag{2-32}$$

$$0 = - R_gI_1(s) - k\,R_2I_3(s) + \left[R_g + k\,R_2 + \frac{1}{sC_{gk}}\right]I_4(s) \tag{2-33}$$

Also, from Fig. 2-5b,

$$V_g(s) = \frac{1}{sC_{gk}}I_4(s) \tag{2-34}$$

Substituting Eq. (2-34) into Eq. (2-31), and rearranging, we have

$$0 = (r_p + R_L)I_2(s) - R_LI_3(s) + \frac{\mu}{sC_{gk}}I_4(s) \tag{2-35}$$

The mesh network determinant is written directly from the above equations.

$$\Delta^M = \begin{vmatrix} R_s + R_g & 0 & 0 & - R_g \\ 0 & r_p + R_L & - R_L & \dfrac{\mu}{sC_{gk}} \\ 0 & - R_L & R_L + R_2 + \dfrac{1}{sC} & - k\,R_2 \\ - R_g & 0 & - k\,R_2 & R_g + k\,R_2 + \dfrac{1}{sC_{gk}} \end{vmatrix} \tag{2-36}$$

Similarly, for the nodes assigned as shown in Fig. 2-5c, the network determinant for node analysis is

$$\Delta^N = \begin{vmatrix} \left(\dfrac{1}{R_s} + \dfrac{1}{R_g} + \dfrac{1}{(1-k)R_2}\right) & 0 & \dfrac{-1}{(1-k)R_2} & -\left(\dfrac{1}{R_s} + \dfrac{1}{R_g}\right) \\ 0 & \left(\dfrac{1}{r_p} + \dfrac{1}{R_L} + Cs\right) & - pC & g_m \\ \dfrac{-1}{(1-k)R_2} & - pC & \left(pC + \dfrac{1}{(1-k)R_2}\right) & 0 \\ -\left(\dfrac{1}{R_s} + \dfrac{1}{R_g}\right) & 0 & 0 & \left(\dfrac{1}{R_s} + \dfrac{1}{R_g} + sC_{gk}\right) \end{vmatrix} \tag{2-37}$$

The major significance of the Δ's of an active network is that they are no longer symmetrical about their principle diagonals, as they are in the case of passive networks [Eq. (2-23)]. The solution of the mesh currents from Δ^M and the node voltages from Δ^N can be conducted in the same way as described before.

The voltage gain, current gain, input and output impedances of the network can also be expressed in terms of the network determinants and their minors. These are evaluated as follows:

Voltage Gain (V_o/V_s)

From Fig. 2-5b, the output voltage can be written as

$$V_o(s) = [I_3(s) - kI_4(s)]R_2 = \left(\frac{\Delta_{13}^M}{\Delta^M} + k\frac{\Delta_{14}^M}{\Delta^M}\right)R_2 V_s(s) \qquad (2\text{-}38)$$

Hence the voltage gain is

$$\frac{V_o(s)}{V_s(s)} = \left(\frac{\Delta_{13}^M}{\Delta^M} + \frac{k\Delta_{14}^M}{\Delta^M}\right)R_2 \qquad (2\text{-}39)$$

Current Gain (I_o/I_s)

As shown in Fig. 2-5c, the current I_o is given by

$$I_o(s) = [V_3(s) - V_1(s)]\frac{1}{(1-k)R_2} \qquad (2\text{-}40)$$

But

$$V_3(s) = -I_s(s)\frac{\Delta_{13}^N}{\Delta^N} - \frac{\Delta_{43}^N}{\Delta^N}I_s(s) \qquad (2\text{-}41)$$

$$V_1(s) = -I_s(s)\frac{\Delta_{11}^N}{\Delta^N} - \frac{\Delta_{41}^N}{\Delta^N}I_s(s) \qquad (2\text{-}42)$$

Substituting of Eq. (2-41) and Eq. (2-42) into Eq. (2-40), we have the current gain

$$\frac{I_o(s)}{I_s(s)} = \frac{-\Delta_{13}^N - \Delta_{43}^N + \Delta_{11}^N + \Delta_{41}^N}{\Delta^N(1-k)R_2} \qquad (2\text{-}43)$$

Input Impedance

The input impedance of a network is defined as the impedance seen at the input terminals of the network with all external (independent) sources replaced by their internal impedances. Referring to the node equivalent circuit of Fig. 2-5c, the input impedance is computed by considering I_s as an input source and the voltage across the input terminals as the resultant output signal (see Fig. 2-6a), therefore

$$Z_{in} = \left.\frac{V_4(s) - V_1(s)}{I_s(s)}\right|_{R_s \to \infty} \qquad (2\text{-}44)$$

hence

$$Z_{in} = \left.\frac{\Delta_{14}^N + \Delta_{44}^N + \Delta_{11}^N + \Delta_{41}^N}{\Delta^N}\right|_{R_s \to \infty} \qquad (2\text{-}45)$$

Referring to the mesh equivalent circuit of Fig. 2-5b, the input impedance is computed as the reciprocal of the input admittance, Y_{in}, and Y_{in} is
computed by applying a voltage source across the input terminals and
measuring the resultant current I_1 (see Fig. 2-6b). In this case, it is con-

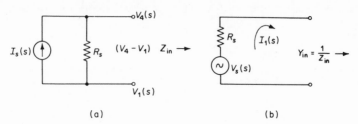

Fig. 2-6. Input terminals of mesh and node equivalent circuit.
(a) Node circuit; (b) Mesh circuit.

venient to express Z_{in} as a function of the Δ's and minors of the network.
Therefore:

$$Z_{in} = \frac{V_s(s)}{I_1(s)} - R_s = \frac{\Delta^M}{\Delta_{11}^M} - R_s = \frac{\Delta^M}{\Delta_{11}^M}\bigg|_{R_s = 0} \qquad (2\text{-}46)$$

It can readily be shown that the quantities in Eqs. (2-45) and (2-46) are
identical.

Output Impedance

The output impedance can be obtained in much the same manner as the
input impedance, except now the current or voltage source is applied at the
output terminals. Referring to Fig. 2-5c, the output impedance is given by

$$Z_{out} = \frac{V_3(s)}{I_3(s)}\bigg|_{I_s = 0} \qquad \text{(open circuit)} \qquad (2\text{-}47)$$

where I_3 is a current source applied at the output terminals, as illustrated
in Fig. 2-7a. Hence

$$Z_{out} = \frac{\Delta_{33}^N}{\Delta^N} \qquad (2\text{-}48)$$

As for the mesh equivalent circuit, it is necessary to apply a voltage
source V_o at the output terminals and compute the resultant current I_5 that
flows through the source (see Fig. 2-7b). The output impedance of the
network is

$$Z_{out} = \frac{V_o(s)}{I_5(s)}\bigg|_{V_s = 0} \qquad (2\text{-}49)$$

However, with the addition of this external voltage source V_o, we have
introduced a new mesh into the circuit of Fig. 2-5b. This means that the

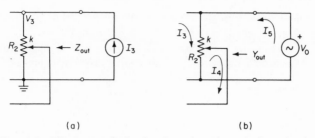

Fig. 2-7. Output terminals of node and mesh equivalent circuits.
(a) Node circuit; (b) Mesh circuit.

network determinant Δ^M is modified; all elements associated with the new mesh are altered, and a new row of elements are added, namely,

$$V_o(s) = 0 \quad 0 \quad R_2 - k\,R_2 \quad R_2 \tag{2-50}$$

We shall call this new determinant $\Delta^{M'}$. Then

$$Z_{\text{out}} = \left.\frac{V_o(s)}{I_s(s)}\right|_{V_s=0} = \frac{\Delta^{M'}}{\Delta_{55}^{M'}} \tag{2-51}$$

2.4 Mechanical Systems

Most feedback control systems contain mechanical elements as well as electrical elements. Mechanical systems also possess nonlinear properties, but when they are linearized, the method of analysis is similar to that of electrical networks.

The equations of a mechanical system are often directly or indirectly formulated from Newton's law of motion, which states that the algebraic sum of forces (torques) acting on a body is equal to the mass (inertia) of the body times its acceleration (angular acceleration).

The motion of mechanical elements can be described as translational, rotational, or a combination of both. These types of motion will be discussed separately in the following sections.

(1) *Mechanical Elements of Translational Motion*

The motion of translation is defined as a motion along a straight line. The variables which are used to describe translational motion are acceleration, velocity, and displacement.

Mechanical systems with translational motion are usually composed of the following elements:

(a) *Mass M*. Mass is considered to be an element which stores the kinetic energy of translational motion. It is analogous to inductance of electrical systems. If W is the weight of the body shown in Fig. 2-8a, and g is the acceleration of the body due to gravity, mass is given by

$$M = W/g \qquad (2\text{-}52)$$

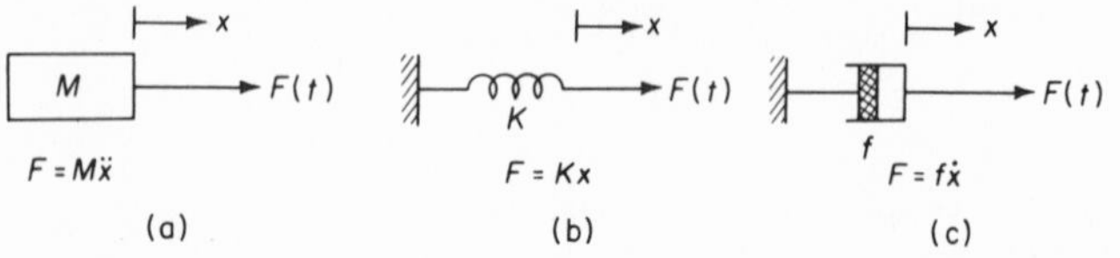

Fig. 2-8. Linear mechanical elements. (a) Mass-force system; (b) Hookean spring; (c) Frictional dashpot.

Now assume that a force $f(t)$ is acting on the body in the x-direction, and the acceleration of the body is a, from Newton's second law of motion:

$$f(t) = Ma = M\frac{d^2x}{dt^2} \qquad (2\text{-}53)$$

(b) *Linear Spring.* Spring is considered to be an element which stores potential energy. It is analogous to the capacitance in electrical systems. In practice, of course, all springs are nonlinear to some extent. A linear spring is one which obeys Hooke's law; that is, the spring is described by

$$\text{force} = \text{spring constant } x \text{ displacement} \qquad (2\text{-}54)$$

or simply $\qquad\qquad F = Kx \qquad\qquad\qquad\qquad (2\text{-}55)$

The spring constant (stiffness) K is defined as the force required to deform the spring linearly by a unit amount against the elastic restoring force. The model representation of the linear spring is shown in Fig. 2-8b.

(c) *Friction.* Although only linear frictional force will be considered in linear design and analysis considerations, in general, frictional force encountered in moving bodies may be considered to consist of three components: the static friction (stiction), the Coulomb friction, and viscous friction (linear friction).

Static Friction. This is a frictional force which exists only when the velocity of the body is zero. In other words, static friction is a force which tends to prevent the body from beginning to move, a phenomenon which is easily observed and experienced in our daily lives. The sign of the static frictional force changes with the change in direction of velocity. Mathematical descriptions of static friction are given by Eq. (2-56) and Fig. 2-9a.

$$\text{Static friction } F_s = \pm\, (F_s)_{\dot{x}=0} \qquad (2\text{-}56)$$

Viscous Friction. This is a frictional force which opposes motion, and its magnitude is considered to be directly proportional to the velocity. If f

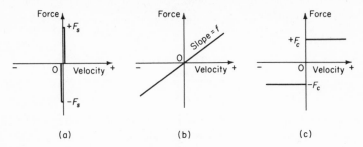

Fig. 2-9. Linear and nonlinear frictional forces. (a) Static friction; (b) Viscous friction; (c) Coulomb friction.

is the coefficient of viscous friction, the force required to overcome this friction when the velocity of the body is v is

$$F_v = f\frac{dx}{dt} = fv \tag{2-57}$$

A symbolic model representation of the viscous friction is the *dashpot* shown in Fig. 2-8c. Figure 2-9b illustrates the functional relation between F_v and velocity.

Coulomb Friction. Coulomb friction is considered to be a constant frictional force which does not vary with velocity, but the sign of the force changes with the reversal in direction of velocity. Mathematical descriptions of Coulomb friction are given by Eq. (2-58) and Fig. 2-9c.

$$F_c = \pm F_c = F_c\left(\frac{v}{|v|}\right) \tag{2-58}$$

Similar to electrical networks, mechanical systems can also be analyzed by means of the mesh and node methods. This statement, of course, needs clarification, since it is not obvious how the names "mesh" and "node" can be used for mechanical systems. In this case, the two names simply refer to the two possible forms of equations that a mechanical element may have. For instance, the equation of a force-mass system can be written either as

$$F = M\frac{dv}{dt} \tag{2-59}$$

or

$$v = \frac{1}{M}\int_0^t F\,dt \tag{2-60}$$

Equation (2-59) is called the mesh form, while Eq. (2-60) is the node form.

The units of mechanical elements are given in Table 2-1; the symbols, mesh and node equations are given in Table 2-2.

Table 2-1.

	Elements	Units		
		CGS	MKS	English
Active elements	Force F	dyne	newton	pound	ounce
	Velocity v	cm/sec	meter/sec	ft/sec	in./sec
Passive elements	Mass M	gram	kilogram	pound	ounce
	Stiffness K	dyne/cm	newton/m	pound/ft	ounce/in.
	Viscous friction f	$\dfrac{\text{dyne}}{\text{cm/sec}}$	$\dfrac{\text{newton}}{\text{m/sec}}$	$\dfrac{\text{pound}}{\text{ft/sec}}$	$\dfrac{\text{ounce}}{\text{in./sec}}$

Table 2-2.

	Elements	Symbols	Mesh equation	Node equation
Active elements	Force F	$\rightarrow F$	. . .	. . .
	Velocity v	$\rightarrow v$	. . .	. . .
Passive elements	Mass M	Mass	$F = M\dfrac{d^2x}{dt^2}$	$v = \dfrac{1}{M}\displaystyle\int_0^t F\,dt$
	Stiffness K	Spring	$F = Kx$	$v = \dfrac{1}{K}\dfrac{dF}{dt}$
	Viscous friction f	Dashpot	$F = f\dfrac{dx}{dt}$	$v = \dfrac{1}{f}F$

(2) *Mechanical Elements of Rotational Motion*

The motion of rotation of a body is defined as motion around a fixed axis. The variables generally used to describe rotational motion are angular acceleration α, angular velocity ω, and angular displacement θ. Table 2-3 gives the units of the elements in rotational motion. Table 2-4 describes the symbols and equations of the elements.

Table 2-3.

	Elements	Units			
		CGS	MKS	English	
Active elements	Torque T	dyne-cm	newton-m	pound-ft	ounce-in.
	Angular velocity	rad/sec	rad/sec	rad/sec	rad/sec
Passive elements	Moment of inertia J	gram-cm^2	Kg-m^2	slug-ft^2	oz-in.^{2} = $2.59 \cdot 10^{-3}$ oz-in.-sec^2
	Stiffness S	$\dfrac{\text{gram-cm}}{\text{rad}}$	$\dfrac{\text{newton-m}}{\text{rad}}$	$\dfrac{\text{pound-ft}}{\text{rad}}$	$\dfrac{\text{ounce-in.}}{\text{rad}}$
	Friction f	$\dfrac{\text{gram-cm}}{\text{rad/sec}}$	$\dfrac{\text{newton-m}}{\text{rad/sec}}$	$\dfrac{\text{pound-ft}}{\text{rad/sec}}$	$\dfrac{\text{ounce-in.}}{\text{rad/sec}}$

Table 2-4.

	Elements	Symbols	Mesh equation	Node equation
Active elements	Torque T	T ⟶	. . .	. . .
	Ang vel	ω ⟶	. . .	. . .
Passive elements	Moment of inertia J		$T = J\dfrac{d^2\theta}{dt^2}$	$\omega = \dfrac{1}{J}\displaystyle\int T\,dt$
	Stiffness S		$T = S\theta$	$\omega = \dfrac{1}{S}\dfrac{dT}{dt}$
	Friction f		$T = f\dfrac{d\theta}{dt}$	$\omega = \dfrac{d\theta}{dt} = \dfrac{T}{f}$
	Gear train		$\dfrac{T_1}{T_2} = \dfrac{N_1}{N_2} = \dfrac{\theta_2}{\theta_1}$	$\dfrac{T_1}{T_2} = \dfrac{N_1}{N_2} = \dfrac{\theta_2}{\theta_1}$

2.5 Equations of Mechanical Systems

In the preceding section, mathematical relations and models for linear mechanical elements have been obtained. The linear analysis of any mechanical system essentially involves first the representation of the system by a model containing interconnecting linear elements, and then the

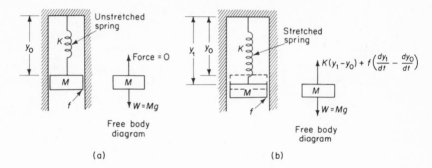

(a)   **(b)**

Fig. 2-10. Mass-spring-friction system. (a) System under unequilibrium state; (b) System under equilibrium state.

equations relating these linear elements, written in the same way as those for an electrical network.

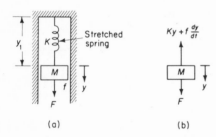

(a)   **(b)**

Fig. 2-11. Force applied to mechanical system under equilibrium. (a) System originally under equilibrium; (b) Free body diagram.

Consider the mechanical system with mass, linear spring, and viscous friction in Fig. 2-10a. Let the unstretched length of the spring be y_0, and the system is not under equilibrium condition, as indicated by the free body diagram in Fig. 2-10a. The system has reached the state of equilibrium in Fig. 2-10b; the weight of the body is balanced by the stretched spring, and the length of the spring has been increased to y_1. If a force $F(t)$ is applied to the system under the equilibrium condition, as depicted in Fig. 2-11, the differential equation of the system is given by

$$F(t) = M \frac{d^2y}{dt^2} + f \frac{dy}{dt} + Ky \qquad (2\text{-}61)$$

where y is the displacement of the mass measured from reference y_1. The gravitational effect does not appear in Eq. (2-61) at all; the system is influenced only by the applied force F. Thus, if a system is assumed to be originally in the state of equilibrium, the gravitational force is not considered in writing the system equations. For this reason, the systems in

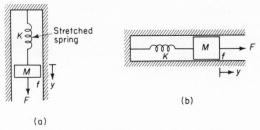

(a)

(b)

Fig. 2-12. Equivalent mechanical systems.

Fig. 2-12a and Fig. 2-12b are described by the same equations if the system in Fig. 2-12a is under equilibrium originally.

EXAMPLE 2-1. Consider the mechanical system with translational motion shown in Fig. 2-13a. Since the spring is stretched when it is sub-

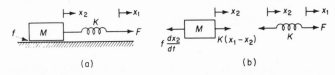

(a)

(b)

Fig. 2-13. Mechanical system of Example 2-1. (a) Mass-spring-friction system; (b) Free body diagrams.

jected to a pulling force F and the mass M also displaces, two displacements, x_1 and x_2, must be designated at the ends of the spring. The free body diagrams of the system are given in Fig. 2-13b. From these free body diagrams the differential equations of the system are written as

$$F = K(x_1 - x_2) \tag{2-62}$$

$$K(x_1 - x_2) = M\frac{d^2x_2}{dt^2} + f\frac{dx_2}{dt} \tag{2-63}$$

When the last two equations are rearranged and Laplace transformed, with zero initial conditions, the following transform equations are obtained:

$$F(s) = KX_1(s) - KX_2(s) \tag{2-64}$$

$$0 = -KX_1(s) + (Ms^2 + fs + K)X_2(s) \tag{2-65}$$

Since the last two equations are algebraic, the solution of X_1 and X_2 can be effected by use of Cramer's rule. The mesh determinant of the system is given by

$$\Delta^M = \begin{vmatrix} K & -K \\ -K & Ms^2 + fs + K \end{vmatrix} \tag{2-66}$$

EXAMPLE 2-2. In this example, the equations for the mechanical system in Fig. 2-14 are to be written. The free body diagrams for the two masses are shown in Fig. 2-14b. The positive directions of the displacements, x_1

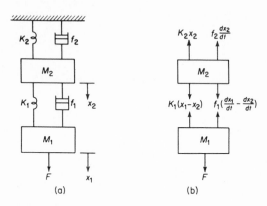

Fig. 2-14. Mechanical system in Example 2-2.

and x_2, are as indicated in the figure. The equations describing the motion of the system are formulated by writing Newton's force equations for the two free body diagrams. Usually, there is no need to write the equations in differential form and then to take the Laplace transform of the equations. With the transform relations in mind, we can always write out the Laplace-transform equations directly from the system diagrams. In this case, the two transformed equations are:

$$F(s) = (M_1 s^2 + f_1 s + K_1)X_1(s) - (f_1 s + K_1)X_2(s) \qquad (2\text{-}67)$$

$$0 = -(f_1 s + K_1)X_1(s) + (M_2 s^2 + f_2 s + K_2 + f_1 s + K_1)X_2(s) \qquad (2\text{-}68)$$

EXAMPLE 2-3. The rotational system shown in Fig. 2-15a consists of a disk with moment of inertia J mounted on a shaft. The friction on the shaft bearing is described by the viscous frictional coefficient f. The stiffness of

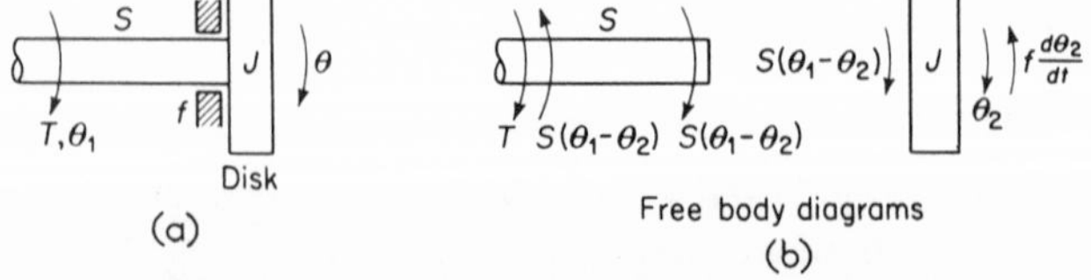

Fig. 2-15. Rotational system in Example 2-3.

the shaft is S, and a torque $T(t)$ is applied at the end of the shaft in the direction as shown. We can tell that this system is a counterpart of the system of Fig. 2-13 in the rotational sense. Therefore, it is necessary to assign two angular displacements, θ_1 and θ_2, at the opposite ends of the shaft. The free body diagrams of the shaft and the disk are constructed in Fig. 2-15b. The Laplace-transform equations of the system are obtained readily as:

$$T(s) = S\Theta_1(s) - S\Theta_2(s) \qquad (2\text{-}68a)$$

$$0 = - S\Theta_1(s) + (Js^2 + fs + S)\Theta_2(s) \qquad (2\text{-}69)$$

It is easy to see that Eqs. (2-68a) and (2-69) are of the same form as Eqs. (2-64) and (2-65).

2.6 Gear Trains

Gear trains are used in control systems to attain torque magnification and speed reduction. Like the transformers used in electrical networks for the optimum matching of impedance and power levels, gear trains in mechanical systems are also regarded as matching devices used to attain maximum power transfer. Two gears are shown coupled together in Fig. 2-16. The gear with N_1 (number of) teeth is called the primary gear (analogous to the primary windings of an electric transformer), and the gear with N_2 teeth is called the secondary gear.

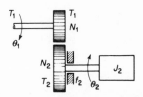

Fig. 2-16. A gear train system.

The relationships between torque T, angular displacement θ, and the teeth number N, of a gear train are derived from the following facts:

(1) The number of teeth on the surface of the gears is proportional to the radius of the gears; i.e., $r_1 N_2 = r_2 N_1$ (r = radius of gear).

(2) The linear distance traveled along the surface of each gear is the same; therefore, $\theta_1 r_1 = \theta_2 r_2$.

(3) The work done by one gear is equal to that of the other; $T_1\theta_1 = T_2\theta_2$.

From the relations given above, we have

$$\frac{T_1}{T_2} = \frac{\theta_2}{\theta_1} = \frac{N_1}{N_2} \qquad (2\text{-}70)$$

Notice that this expression closely resembles the voltage-current-turns ratio relation of an ideal transformer in electrical networks. An ideal transformer is simply an idealized element used to describe certain relationships between a set of variables in electrical systems. An ideal transformer does not exist in its strictest sense physically. Similarly, Eq. (2-70) must also have been derived under an idealized situation. In practice, all gear trains have some amount of backlash between the coupled gear teeth, and when two gear teeth are in contact there certainly will be friction. Keeping the backlash small will inevitably increase friction and wear out the gear teeth quickly, but excessive amount of backlash is known to have an adverse effect on the stability of a servo system.

Once the linear relations between the gear train variables are defined, the equations of a mechanical system with gear trains can be written in the same way as described before. Referring to Fig. 2-16, we find that the torque equation for the secondary side of the gear train is

$$T_2 = J_2 \frac{d^2\theta_2}{dt^2} + f_2 \frac{d\theta_2}{dt} \tag{2-71}$$

where T_2 is the torque developed at the secondary gear. The inertia of the gears and shafts are assumed to be negligible.

By the use of Eq. (2-70), it is possible to write Eq. (2-71) as

$$T_1 = J_2 \left(\frac{N_1}{N_2}\right)^2 \frac{d^2\theta_1}{dt^2} + f_2 \left(\frac{N_1}{N_2}\right)^2 \frac{d\theta_1}{dt} \tag{2-72}$$

Equation (2-72) indicates clearly that the original system can be represented by the equivalent system shown in Fig. 2-17, with the system equation given by

$$T_1 = J_1 \frac{d^2\theta_1}{dt^2} + f_1 \frac{d\theta_1}{dt} \tag{2-73}$$

where $\qquad J_1 = J_2(N_1/N_2)^2 \tag{2-74}$

and $\qquad f_1 = f_2(N_1/N_2)^2 \tag{2-75}$

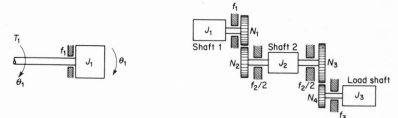

Fig. 2-17. Equivalent system of Fig. 2-16.   **Fig. 2-18.** Multiple-gear train system.

are regarded as the equivalent inertia and friction referred to the primary shaft.

The concept of equivalent inertia, friction, and torque, just described, can also be extended to a multiple-gear train system, as shown in Fig. 2-18. The inertia J_3 and friction f_3 at the load shaft are referred to shaft 2, and the equivalent quantities are

$$J_{2\mathrm{eq}} = J_2 + J_3(N_3/N_4)^2 \tag{2-76}$$

$$f_{2\mathrm{eq}} = f_2 + f_3(N_3/N_4)^2 \tag{2-77}$$

The equivalent inertia and friction at shaft 2 are now referred to shaft 1, resulting

$$J_{1eq} = J_1 + J_{2eq}(N_1/N_2)^2 = J_1 + J_2(N_1/N_2)^2 + J_3(N_1N_3/N_2N_4)^2 \qquad (2\text{-}78)$$

$$f_{1eq} = f_1 + f_{2eq}(N_1/N_2)^2 = f_1 + f_2(N_1/N_2)^2 + f_3(N_1N_3/N_2N_4)^2 \qquad (2\text{-}79)$$

Similarly, the inertia and friction at shaft 1 can be referred to the load shaft. Thus

$$J_{3eq} = J_3 + J_1(N_2N_4/N_1N_3)^2 + J_2(N_4/N_3)^2 \qquad (2\text{-}80)$$

$$f_{3eq} = f_3 + f_1(N_2N_4/N_1N_3)^2 + f_2(N_4/N_3)^2 \qquad (2\text{-}81)$$

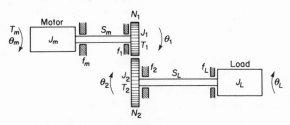

Fig. 2-19. Motor-load system with gear train.

From these examples, we can conclude that the equivalent inertia or friction of a system referred to a common shaft is found by multiplying each inertia or friction by the square of the total gear ratio between the inertia or friction and the common shaft.

The following example illustrates th' writing of the equations of a typical gear train system.

EXAMPLE 2-4. Consider the mechanical system shown in Fig. 2-19, in which a load is driven by a motor through a gear train. The motor has moment of inertia J_m; the viscous friction coefficient at the motor bearing is denoted by f_m; the torque developed by the motor is T_m. The torsional spring constants of the motor shaft and the load shaft are S_m and S_L respectively. The moments of inertia of the gears are assumed to be J_1 and J_2 respectively.

The free body diagrams of the gear train system and the associated torque equations are given in Fig. 2-20.

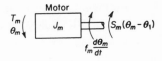

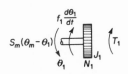

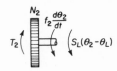

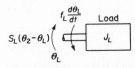

Fig. 2-20. Free body diagrams and system equations of motor-load-gear-train system in Fig. 2-19.

2.7 Transfer Function and Impulse Response of Linear Systems

As shown in the preceding sections, the system variables of a linear system model are related by linear differential equations. Usually, these linear differential equations provide a complete description of the system, and, for any given excitation, the system output response is obtained by solving these equations. However, it is apparent that the differential equation method of describing a system is rather cumbersome and of little practical use in design.

A simplification of linear system description is possible if the "transfer function" and the "impulse response" concepts are introduced. These modes of description are simply related, and each offers advantages in different fields of application and circumstances.

The transfer function concept is not a new one; it has been used to describe the Laplace-transform relationship between excitation and response of electrical networks with two or more terminal pairs. For any linear system, "transfer function" is defined as the ratio of the Laplace transform of the output variable to the transform of the input variable, with all initial conditions assumed to be zero. Consider that a linear system is described by the following differential equation:

$$a_0 \frac{d^n c}{dt^n} + a_1 \frac{d^{n-1} c}{dt^{n-1}} + \cdots + a_{n-1} \frac{dc}{dt} + a_n c = b_0 \frac{d^m r}{dt^m} + b_1 \frac{d^{m-1} r}{dt^{m-1}} + \cdots$$
$$+ b_{m-1} \frac{dr}{dt} + b_m r \quad (2\text{-}82)$$

where c is the output variable and r is the input variable, the a's and the b's are constants. Taking the Laplace transform on both sides of Eq. (2-82), and assuming zero initial conditions, we have

$$(a_0 s^n + a_1 s^{n-1} + \cdots + a_{n-1} s + a_n) C(s) = (b_0 s^m + b_1 s^{m-1} + \cdots$$
$$+ b_{m-1} s + b_m) R(s) \quad (2\text{-}83)$$

According to definition, the transfer function of the system is the ratio of $C(s)$ to $R(s)$; therefore

$$G(s) = \frac{C(s)}{R(s)} = \frac{b_0 s^m + b_1 s^{m-1} + \cdots + b_{m-1} s + b_m}{a_0 s^n + a_1 s^{n-1} + \cdots + a_{n-1} s + a_n} \quad (2\text{-}84)$$

The characteristics of a linear system depend solely on the properties of system elements, therefore the transfer function $G(s)$ is a property of the system elements only, and is independent of excitation and initial conditions. It should be pointed out that transfer function is not defined for a nonlinear system, although with certain approximations, "pseudo-linear transfer functions" may be defined for particular types of nonlinearities.

The following examples are given to show how transfer functions for linear systems are derived.

EXAMPLE 2-5. A simple mass-spring-friction system is shown in Fig. 2-21. Consider that the applied force F is the input and the displacement of

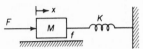

Mass-spring-friction system

Fig. 2-21. Mass-spring-friction system.

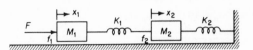

Fig. 2-22. Mechanical system in Example 2-6.

the mass, x, is the output of the system. The differential equation relating these two variables is

$$F = M\frac{d^2x}{dt} + f\frac{dx}{dt} + Kx \qquad (2\text{-}85)$$

Taking the Laplace transform on both sides of the last equation and assuming zero initial conditions, we have

$$F(s) = (Ms^2 + fs + K)X(s) \qquad (2\text{-}86)$$

The transfer function of the system is given by

$$G(s) = \frac{X(s)}{F(s)} = \frac{1}{Ms^2 + fs + K} \qquad (2\text{-}87)$$

EXAMPLE 2-6. For complex systems which involve a multiple number of simultaneous equations, it is more convenient to employ the methods of determinants in arriving at the transfer functions. Consider the mechanical system shown in Fig. 2-22. The Laplace-transform equations of the system are

$$F(s) = (M_1s^2 + f_1s + K_1)X_1(s) - K_1X_2(s) \qquad (2\text{-}88)$$

$$0 = -K_1X_1(s) + (M_2s^2 + f_2s + K_1 + K_2)X_2(s) \qquad (2\text{-}89)$$

The determinant of the system is directly obtained from Eqs. (2-88) and (2-89).

$$\Delta = \begin{vmatrix} M_1s^2 + f_1s + K_1 & -K_1 \\ -K_1 & M_2s^2 + f_2s + K_1 + K_2 \end{vmatrix} \qquad (2\text{-}90)$$

If F is considered to be the input and x_2 to be the output, the transfer function relating $F(s)$ and $X_2(s)$ is given by

$$G(s) = \frac{X_2(s)}{F(s)} = -\frac{\Delta_{12}}{\Delta} = \frac{K_1}{(M_1s^2 + f_1s + K_1)(M_2s^2 + f_2s + K_1 + K_2) - K_1^2}$$
$$(2\text{-}91)$$

Similarly, if the variable x_1 is considered to be the output of the system, the transfer relation between F and x_1 is given by

$$G(s) = \frac{X_1(s)}{F(s)} = +\frac{\Delta_{11}}{\Delta} = \frac{M_2s^2 + f_2s + K_1 + K_2}{(M_1s^2 + f_1s + K_1)(M_2s^2 + f_2s + K_1 + K_2) - K_1^2} \tag{2-92}$$

More examples concerning the derivation of transfer functions of physical systems are given in the material on servo components in Chapter 4.

In the analysis problem, the transfer function of a system is known and the transformed output response is found from the equation

$$C(s) = G(s)R(s) \tag{2-93}$$

The output time response is obtained by taking the inverse Laplace transform of $C(s)$. If the input signal of a linear system is a unit impulse function* $r(t) = \delta(t)$, the Laplace transform of the impulse function is unity.

The transformed output of the system is given by

$$C(s) = G(s) \tag{2-94}$$

Taking the inverse Laplace transform on both sides of the last equation yields

$$c(t) = g(t) \tag{2-95}$$

where $g(t)$ is the inverse Laplace transform of $G(s)$ and is called the *impulse response* (or weighting function) of the linear system. Therefore, when a unit impulse is applied to a linear system, the output is the impulse response of the system. *The Laplace transform of the impulse response gives the transfer function $G(s)$.* This means that, theoretically, complete description of a linear system may be obtained by exciting the system with an impulse function and measuring the output (impulse) response. In practice, although a true impulse cannot be generated physically, a pulse with a very narrow pulse width (much less than the significant time constants of the system) usually provides a suitable approximation.

The derivation of $G(s)$ in Eq. (2-84) is based on the knowledge of the system differential equation, and the solution of $C(s)$ from Eq. (2-93) also assumes that $R(s)$ and $G(s)$ are all available in analytical forms. This is not always possible, for quite often the input signal $r(t)$ is not Laplace transformable or is only available in the form of experimental data. If such a situation should occur, in order to analyze the system we would have no alternatives but to work with the time functions $r(t)$ and $g(t)$. Let us con-

---

*Refer to Appendix A for the definition and properties of a unit impulse.

sider that the excitation function sketched in Fig. 2-23a is applied to a
linear system, as shown in Fig. 2-24; the output response $c(t)$ is to be

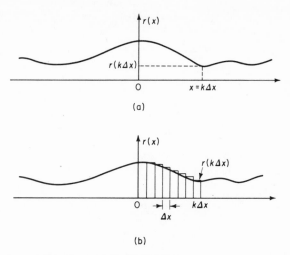

(a)

(b)

Fig. 2-23. (a) Input signal of a linear system; (b) Input signal represented by sum of rectangular pulses.

determined. In Fig. 2-23, the input signal is denoted as a function of x,
which is a dummy time variable; this is necessary since t is considered to be
a fixed quantity in the process. For all practical purposes, we may assume
that the signal extends from minus infinity to plus infinity in time. Now

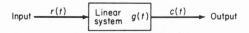

Fig. 2-24. Linear system.

consider that the signal is approximated by the sequence of pulses of pulse
width Δx, as shown in Fig. 2-23b. In the limit, as Δx approaches zero,
these pulses become a sequence of impulses, and the impulse at time $k \, \Delta x$
has a strength (area) $\Delta x \cdot r(k \, \Delta x)$, which is the area of the pulse at $k \, \Delta x$.
Also, when we let Δx become smaller, we have to increase k proportionally,
so that the value $k \, \Delta x$ stays constant and equals x, which is a particular
point on the time axis. We now compute the response of the linear system,
using this impulse approximated signal. When only the impulse at time
$x = k\Delta x$ is considered, the system response is given by

$$x \cdot r(k \, \Delta x) \, g(t - k \, \Delta x) \qquad (2\text{-}96)$$

which is the impulse strength multiplied by the system impulse response,
delayed by $k \, \Delta x$. By use of the superposition principle, the total response

due to $r(t)$ is obtained by adding the responses to each of the impulses from $-\infty$ to $+\infty$. Therefore,

$$c(t) = \lim_{\substack{x \to 0 \\ N \to \infty}} \sum_{k=-N}^{N} r(k\,\Delta x)\, g(t - k\,\Delta x)\, \Delta x \qquad (2\text{-}97)$$

or

$$c(t) = \int_{-\infty}^{\infty} r(x)\, g(t - x)\, dx \qquad (2\text{-}98)$$

For all physical systems,

$$g(t) = 0 \qquad\qquad t < 0 \quad (2\text{-}99)$$

that is, response does not precede excitation. The response for a physically realizable system now becomes

$$c(t) = \int_{-\infty}^{t} r(x)\, g(t - x)dx \qquad (2\text{-}100)*$$

Equation (2-100) gives the value of the output response at time t when the input $r(t)$ and the impulse response $g(t)$ of a linear system are known. The expression is given the name "convolution integral" and is denoted by

$$c(t) = r(t) * g(t) \qquad (2\text{-}101)$$

or

$$c(t) = r(t) \text{ convolves into } g(t) \qquad (2\text{-}102)$$

The time functions $r(t)$ and $g(t)$ in the convolution process may be interchanged, since basically there is no difference between the two. The convolution integral can also be written as:

$$c(t) = g(t) * r(t) = \int_{-\infty}^{t} g(x)\, r(t - x)\, dx \qquad (2\text{-}103)$$

and for physically realizable systems $g(t)$ satisfies Eq. (2-99). It can be shown that

$$c(t) = \int_{0}^{\infty} g(x)\, r(t - x)\, dx \qquad (2\text{-}104)$$

The evaluation of the impulse response of the controlled process or system is an important step in a class of systems called the "adaptive control systems"†. From a critical point of view, the dynamic characteris-

---

*If $(r)t$ is zero for $t < 0$, the limits of the integral are from 0 to t.

†H. L. Groginsky, "On the Design of Adaptive Systems," *IRE Conv. Rec.*, pt. 4, March, 1958, pp. 160–167.

tics of most control systems vary to some extent during the lifetime of the control operation. This may be caused by simple deterioration of components due to wear and tear, drift in operating environments, etc. For instance, the transfer characteristic of a guided missile in flight will vary in time due to the change of mass and atmospheric conditions. Thus the control system designed under the assumption of known transfer characteristic may fail to provide satisfactory guidance, should the dynamic characteristic variation become large. In order that the system may have the ability of self-modification or self-adjustment in accordance with varying parameters and environment, it is necessary that the system's transfer characteristic be identified at all times. One of the methods of identification is to measure the impulse response of the controlled process continuously, so that design parameters may be adjusted accordingly to attain optimum control at all times.

We have covered in this section the concept of transfer function and impulse response of linear systems. The two quantities are closely related by the Laplace transformation, and contain essentially the same amount of information about the system. But in the analysis and design of feedback control systems, the transfer function idea is more useful.

2.8 Block Diagrams

Because detailed schematic diagrams are difficult to draw for complex systems, a shorthand symbol called the *block diagram* is often used by control engineers. The combination of block diagram and transfer function of a physical system provides a pictorial representation of the cause-and-effect relationship between the input and output of the system. For instance, the block diagram representation of the transfer relation in Eq. (2-93) is shown in

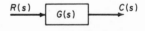

Fig. 2-25. Block diagram.

Fig. 2-25. The arrows on the diagram imply that the block diagram has a unilateral property (just as an electronic amplifier); that is, signal can only pass in the direction of the arrows.

Although all systems (with one input and one output) may be denoted by a single block connected between the input and the output, the advantage of the block diagram concept lies in the fact that feedback control systems are composed of many non-interacting elements whose transfer functions are determined independently. An entire system may, then, be represented by the interconnection of the blocks of the individual elements, so that their contributions to the over-all performance of the system may be evaluated. The simple configuration shown in Fig. 2-25 is actually the basic building block of a complex block diagram. For instance, the block dia-

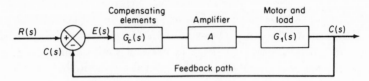

Fig. 2-26. Block diagram of a feedback control system.

gram of a typical feedback control system is shown in Fig. 2-26. Each block in the diagram represents an independent element of the system.

Block Diagrams of Feedback Control Systems

One of the vital organs of a feedback control system is the sensing device, which operates on signals coming from different parts of the system. Some of the most important types of sensing devices are discussed in Chapter 4. The sensing operations are denoted by the block diagram notations shown in Fig. 2-27. The operations only of addition and subtrac-

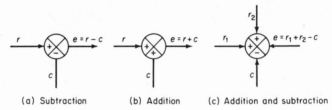

(a) Subtraction   (b) Addition   (c) Addition and subtraction

Fig. 2-27. Block diagrams of sensing devices.

tion are considered here. The output of the sensing device is shown to be equal to the algebraic sum of the input signals.

Some of the important terminology used in the block diagrams of feedback control systems are defined with reference to Fig. 2-28.

$R(s)$ = reference input

$C(s)$ = output signal (controlled variable)

$B(s)$ = feedback signal

$\mathcal{E}(s)$ = actuating signal

$G(s) = C(s)/\mathcal{E}(s)$ = forward path transfer function, or open-loop transfer function

$M(s) = C(s)/R(s)$ = Closed-loop transfer function

$H(s)$ = feedback path transfer function

$G(s)H(s)$ = loop gain*

---

*"Loop gain" refers to the situation when the feedback loop is broken at any point (feedback or forward path), and a signal of unity strength is sent through the opened terminal; the signal returned at the other end is, of course, $G(s)H(s)$. In some literature, this is also called the open-loop transfer function.

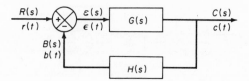

Fig. 2-28. Basic block diagram of a feedback control system.

The closed-loop transfer function, $M(s) = C(s)/R(s)$, can be expressed as a function of $G(s)$ and $H(s)$. From Fig. 2-28, we have

$$C(s) = G(s)\mathcal{E}(s) \tag{2-105}$$

and

$$B(s) = H(s)C(s) \tag{2-106}$$

The actuating signal is given by

$$\mathcal{E}(s) = R(s) - B(s) \tag{2-107}$$

Substituting Eq. (2-107) into Eq. (2-105) yields

$$C(s) = G(s)R(s) - G(s)B(s) \tag{2-108}$$

Substituting Eq. (2-106) into Eq. (2-108), we have

$$C(s) = G(s)R(s) - G(s)H(s)C(s) \tag{2-109}$$

from which, the closed-loop transfer function is given by

$$\frac{C(s)}{R(s)} = \frac{G(s)}{1 + G(s)H(s)} \tag{2-110}$$

The block diagrams of complex feedback control systems usually contain several feedback loops, and the evaluation of the system transfer functions directly from the block diagrams is usually tedious. The transfer function of a complex block diagram configuration is obtained by use of the block diagram reduction technique.* The block diagram of the system is first reduced to the basic form of Fig. 2-28, and then the transfer function is written from Eq. (2-110). Some of the important block diagram reduction manipulations are given in Table 2-5. No attempt is made here to cover all the possibilities.

EXAMPLE 2-7. The block diagram of a multiple feedback loop system is given in Fig. 2-29. The closed-loop transfer function of the system, $C(s)/R(s)$, is determined in the following by means of the block diagram reduction technique.

---

*T. D. Graybeal, "Block Digram Network Transformation", *Elec. Eng.*, vol. 70, pp. 985–990, 1951; R. A. Bruns and R. M. Saunders, *Analysis of Feedback Control Systems*, McGraw-Hill Book Company, pp. 259–290, 1955.

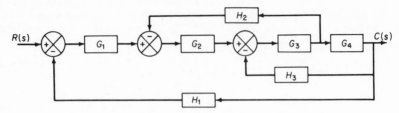

Fig. 2-29. Multiple-loop feedback control system.

Block Diagram Reduction Procedure

(1) The take-off point (starting point) of the block H_2 is moved to the output point of G_4 by use of rule 4 in Table 2-5 (see Fig. 2-30a).

(2) The loop which consists of G_3, G_4, and H_3 in Fig. 2-30a is recognized as the basic form of Fig. 2-28 and thus can be replaced by a single block with the transfer function $G_3G_4/(1 + G_3G_4H_3)$ (see Fig. 2-30b).

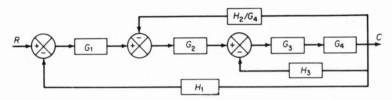

Fig. 2-30a. Block diagram reduction of system in Fig. 2-29.

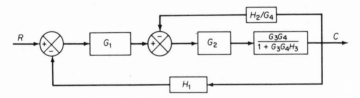

Fig. 2-30b. Block diagram reduction of system in Fig. 2-30a.

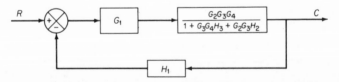

Fig. 2-30c. Block diagram reduction of system in Fig. 2-30b.

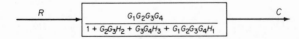

Fig. 2-30d. Block diagram reduction of system in Fig. 2-30c.

(3) Similar to the last step, the minor loop in Fig. 2-30b, consisting of the blocks G_2, H_2/G_4, and $G_3G_4/(1 + G_3G_4H_3)$, is replaced by a single block with gain $G_2G_3G_4/(1 + G_3G_4H_3 + G_2G_3H_2)$ (see Fig. 2-30c).

(4) The block diagram in Fig. 2-30c is of the basic form, and its transfer function is readily determined as

$$\frac{C(s)}{R(s)} = \frac{G_1G_2G_3G_4}{1 + G_2G_3H_2 + G_3G_4H_3 + G_1G_2G_3G_4H_1} \qquad (2\text{-}111)$$

2.9 Signal Flow Graphs

Block diagrams may be used conveniently as a shorthand symbol for the portrayal of complex systems, and they provide cause-and-effect relationship between input and output of a system. In general, however, the blocks which they contain have such complicated transfer functions that detailed study of the system — in regard to the flow of signals from point to point, and the effects of variations in system parameters on such system performance functions as gain, impedance, and sensitivity — frequently cannot be made directly from the block diagram representation.

The signal flow graph introduced by S. J. Mason* is capable of giving a more detailed representation of a complex system than a block diagram. For feedback systems, the signal flow graph not only illustrates the passage of signals through the systems, but also gives a clear indication of the feedback paths in the systems.

For sampled-data systems, the "pulsed-signal-flow graph" and the "composite signal flow graph" are shown to be useful in the evaluation of the sampled and the unsampled outputs (see Chapter 9).

A signal flow graph of a system is a network with junction points called nodes; the nodes are connected by paths, called branches, which have directions†. A signal travels along a branch only in the direction of the arrow.

Consider that a system is described by the set of equations‡   (2-112)

---

*S. J. Mason, "Feedback Theory — Some Properties of Signal Flow Graphs," *Proc. IRE*, Vol. 41, No. 9, pp. 1144–1156, September, 1953.

†It is important to note that the terms "network," "node," and "branch" used here do not have the same meaning as those used in network analysis.

‡The set of equations may represent integro-differential equations; i.e., x_j and x_k either are functions of time, or they may be transformed equations in which case x_j and x_k and t_{kj} are functions of s, and should be capitalized. It should also be noted that, in the present case, the system equations are written in the form:

Effect at $j = \Sigma$ (transmission from k to j)(cause at k)

These are unlike the network equations we wrote in the past, whose form is

Excitation (cause) at $k = \Sigma$ (transmittance from k to j)(response at j)

$$x_j = \sum_{k=1}^{N} t_{kj}x_k \qquad (j = 1, 2, \ldots, N)$$

Table 2-5.

Rules	Original network	Equivalent network
1 Cascaded elements	$R \rightarrow \boxed{G_1} \rightarrow \boxed{G_2} \rightarrow C$	$R \rightarrow \boxed{G_1 G_2} \rightarrow C$
2 Addition and subtraction	$R \rightarrow \boxed{G_1} \rightarrow \otimes \rightarrow C$, $\boxed{G_2}$	$R \rightarrow \boxed{G_1 \pm G_2} \rightarrow C$
3 Moving a starting point in front of an element	$R \rightarrow \boxed{G} \rightarrow C$	$R \rightarrow \boxed{G} \rightarrow C$, $\boxed{G}$
4 Moving a starting point behind an element	$R \rightarrow \boxed{G} \rightarrow C$	$R \rightarrow \boxed{G} \rightarrow C$, $\boxed{1/G}$
5 Moving a summing point ahead of an element	$R \rightarrow \boxed{G} \rightarrow \otimes \rightarrow \varepsilon$, $C \uparrow$	$R \rightarrow \otimes \rightarrow \boxed{G} \rightarrow \varepsilon$, $\boxed{1/G} \leftarrow C$
6 Moving a summing point behind an element	$R \rightarrow \otimes \rightarrow \varepsilon \rightarrow \boxed{G} \rightarrow$, $C \uparrow$	$R \rightarrow \boxed{G} \rightarrow \otimes \rightarrow \varepsilon$, $\boxed{G} \leftarrow C$

where the coefficient t_{kj} is called the "transmission" or "transmission function" representing the contribution of variable x_k to the value of variable x_j. If the variables are represented as nodes, and t_{kj} as directed branches, Eq. (2-112) implies that the system equations may be portrayed by a signal flow graph. The construction of the flow graph is basically a matter of following the *cause* and *effect* relations through the system relating each variable in terms of itself and the other variables. For instance, the equation

$$x_2 = t_{12} x_1 \tag{2-113}$$

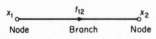

Fig. 2-31. Signal flow graph for $x_2 = t_{12} x_1$.

is represented by the signal flow graph shown in Fig. 2-31. Node x_1 and node x_2 represent the variables x_1 and x_2 respectively, and the branch directing from node x_1 to node x_2 expresses the dependence of x_2 upon x_1 (but not the reverse). The branch may also be interpreted as a unilateral amplifier of gain t_{12}, so that when a signal x_1

appears at its input, the signal is multiplied by the gain of the branch t_{12}, and a signal of strength $t_{12}x_1$ is delivered at node x_2.

As another example, consider the set of equations of a certain system:

$$x_2 = t_{12}x_1 + t_{32}x_3$$

$$x_3 = t_{23}x_2 + t_{43}x_4$$

$$x_4 = t_{24}x_2 + t_{34}x_3 + t_{44}x_4 \qquad (2\text{-}114)$$

$$x_5 = t_{25}x_2 + t_{45}x_4$$

The signal flow graph for the system is constructed as shown in Fig. 2-32. The nodes x_1, x_2, x_3, x_4, and x_5 are located in order from left to right. The first equation states that x_2 depends upon two signals, $t_{12}x_1$ and $t_{32}x_3$; the flow

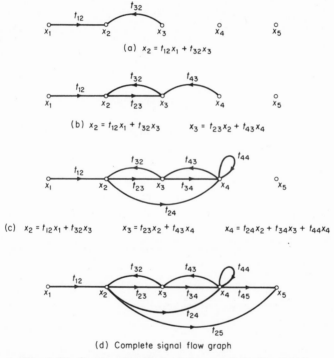

Fig. 2-32. Construction of signal flow graph for Eq. 2-114.

graph representing this equation is shown in Fig. 2-32a. The second equation states that x_3 depends upon $t_{23}x_2$ and $t_{43}x_4$; on the flow graph shown in Fig. 2-32a, a branch of gain t_{23} is drawn from node x_2 to x_3, and a branch of gain t_{43} is drawn from x_4 to x_3 with the directions of the branches indicated by the arrows (Fig. 2-32b). Similarly, with the consideration of the third equation, Fig. 2-32c is obtained. The complete signal flow graph is shown in Fig. 2-32d. The loop with gain t_{44} represents the dependence of x_4 upon itself.

Basic Properties of Signal Flow Graphs

At this point, it is best to summarize some of the important properties of the signal flow graph.

(1) The nodes represent variables of a system. Normally, the nodes are arranged from left to right, following a succession of causes and effects through the system.

(2) The branch directing from node x_k to x_j represents the dependence of the variable x_j upon x_k, but not the reverse.

(3) Signals travel along branches only in the direction described by the arrows of the branches.

(4) A signal x_k traveling along a branch between nodes x_k and x_j is multiplied by the gain of the branch t_{kj}, so that a signal of $t_{kj}x_k$ is delivered at node x_j.

Definitions for Signal Flow Graphs

The following terms are frequently used in connection with the signal flow graphs:

(1) *Input Node (Source):* A node which has only outgoing branches. (Example: node x_1 in Fig. 2-32.)

(2) *Output Node (Sink):* A node which has only incoming branches. (Example: node x_5 in Fig. 2-32d.) However, this condition is not always met by an output node. For instance, the signal flow graph shown in Fig. 2-33a illustrates that the output node also has an outgoing branch. In

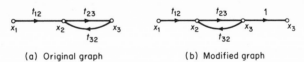

(a) Original graph   (b) Modified graph

Fig. 2-33. Realization of signal flow graph in which no branch leaves the output node.

order to meet the specified condition, it is necessary to introduce an additional branch of unit gain and an additional variable, as shown in Fig. 2-33b.

(3) *Path:* Any continuous, unidirectional, succession of branches traversed in the indicated branch directions. (Example: x_1-x_2-x_3-x_4-x_5; x_2-x_3-x_4; x_2-x_3-x_2; etc. in Fig. 2-32d.)

(4) *Forward Path:* A path from the input node to the output node, along which no node is encountered more than once. (Example: x_1-x_2-x_3-x_4-x_5; x_1-x_2- through t_{24}-x_4-x_5, or x_1-x_2- through t_{25}-x_5 in Fig. 2-32d.)

(5) *Feedback Path (Loop):* A path which originates and terminates on the same node, along which no node is encountered more than once. (Example: $x_2\text{-}x_3\text{-}x_2$; $x_3\text{-}x_4\text{-}x_3$; $x_4\text{-}x_4$ through t_{44}; however, $x_2\text{-}x_3\text{-}x_4\text{-}x_3\text{-}x_2$ is not a feedback path, since x_3 is encountered twice in Fig. 2-32d.)

(6) *Path Gain:* The product of the branch gains encountered in traversing the path. (Example: $t_{12}t_{23}t_{34}$ for path $x_1\text{-}x_2\text{-}x_3\text{-}x_4$ in Fig. 2-32d.)

(7) *Loop Gain:* The product of all the branch gains of the branches forming that loop. (Example: $t_{23}t_{32}$ for loop $x_2\text{-}x_3\text{-}x_2$; $t_{34}t_{43}$ for loop $x_3\text{-}x_4\text{-}x_3$; and t_{44} for loop $x_4\text{-}x_4$ in Fig. 2-32d.)

Simple Signal Flow Graph Algebra

(1) Addition

(a) The value of the variable represented by a node is equal to the sum of all the signals entering the node. In Fig. 2-34a, the value of x_j is equal to the sum of the signals transmitted through the n incoming branches; i.e.

$$x_j = \sum_{k=1}^{n} t_{kj}x_k \tag{2-115}$$

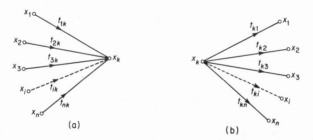

Fig. 2-34. (a) Node as a summing point; (b) Node as a transmitting point.

(b) The value of the variable represented by any node is transmitted on all branches leaving the node. In Fig. 2-34b, the signal flow graph shows that the signal x_k is transmitted to all n branches which are leaving the node. Thus

$$x_1 = t_{k1}x_k$$

$$x_2 = t_{k2}x_k$$

$$\tag{2-116}$$

$$x_n = t_{kn}x_k$$

(2) Multiplication

A series connection of branches with gains t_{12}, t_{23}, t_{34}, $\cdots$, $t_{(n-1)n}$, as shown in Fig. 2-35a, can be replaced by a single branch with gain equal to $t_{12}t_{23}t_{34} \cdots t_{(n-1)n}$; or

$$x_n = t_{12}t_{23}t_{34} \cdots t_{(n-1)n}x_1 \qquad (2\text{-}117)$$

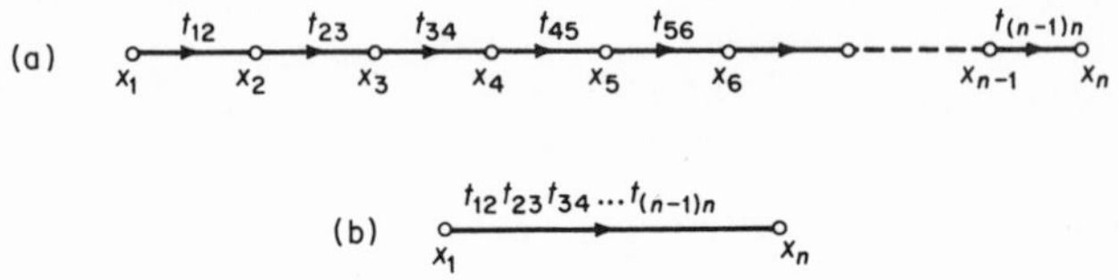

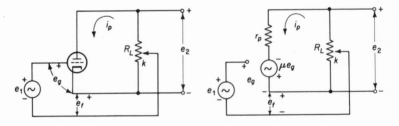

(a)

(b)

Fig. 2-35. Signal flow graph showing the multiplication of branch gains.

The following examples illustrate the construction of the signal flow graph of a physical system.

EXAMPLE 2-8. For the feedback amplifier circuit shown in Fig. 2-36a,

(a) Feedback amplifier circuit   (b) Linear incremental equivalent circuit

Fig. 2-36. Circuit to illustrate construction of signal flow graph.

the linear incremental equivalent circuit is given in Fig. 2-36b. One set of equations describing the system performance may be written as

$$e_g = e_1 - e_f \qquad (2\text{-}118)$$

$$e_f = \frac{\mu k R_L}{r_p + R_L}\, e_g \qquad (2\text{-}119)$$

$$e_2 = -\frac{e_f}{k} \qquad (2\text{-}120)$$

In these last equations, the variables e_1, e_g, e_f, and e_2 are chosen, and the corresponding signal flow graph is constructed and shown in Fig. 2-37a. In this flow graph, the feedback path from e_f to e_g clearly indicates the effect of the feedback signal directed from the output to the grid input. Normally, the equations for any physical system may take a variety of forms. If a set

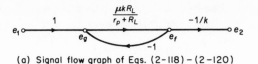

(a) Signal flow graph of Eqs. (2-118)–(2-120)

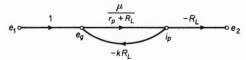

(b) Signal flow graph of Eqs. (2-121)–(2-123)

Fig. 2-37. Signal flow graphs for feedback amplifier.

of variables, e_1, e_g, i_p, and e_2, are chosen in the same circuit, the equations may be written as

$$e_g = e_1 - ki_pR_L \tag{2-121}$$

$$i_p = \frac{\mu e_g}{r_p + R_L} \tag{2-122}$$

$$e_2 = - i_pR_L \tag{2-123}$$

The signal flow graph corresponding to Eqs. (2-121) to (2-123) is constructed and shown in Fig. 2-37b. This shows that it is possible to construct different signal flow graphs for the same system, depending upon the method of writing the system equations.

EXAMPLE 2-9. Consider the ladder network shown in Fig. 2-38a, whose output voltage e_0 is to be determined. If the branch currents and node

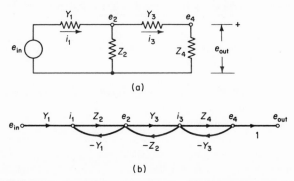

(a)

(b)

Fig. 2-38. (a) A passive ladder network; (b) Signal flow graph of a passive ladder network.

voltages are designated as shown in the circuit, one possible set of independent equations is

$$i_1 = (e_{in} - e_2)Y_1 \tag{2-124}$$

$$e_2 = (i_1 - i_3)Z_2 \tag{2-125}$$

$$i_3 = (e_2 - e_4)Y_3 \tag{2-126}$$

$$e_4 = i_3Z_4 = e_{out} \tag{2-127}$$

With the variables e_{in}, i_1, e_2, i_3, e_4, e_{out} arranged from left to right in order, the signal flow graph is shown in Fig. 2-38b. The method of using the general gain formula to solve for the expression e_{out}/e_{in} is given in the following section.

The General Gain Formula for Signal Flow Graph

In solving for the functional relation between the input and output variables (nodes) on a signal flow graph, a general gain formula* has been derived which permits writing down of the functional relation by inspection. The formula is

$$M = \sum_k \frac{M_k \Delta_k}{\Delta} \tag{2-128}$$

where M_k = gain of the kth forward path $\tag{2-129}$

$$\Delta = 1 - \sum_m P_{m1} + \sum_m P_{m2} - \sum_m P_{m3} + \cdots \tag{2-130}$$

P_{mr} = gain product of the mth possible combination of r non-touching loops.† $\tag{2-131}$

Or $\Delta = 1 -$ (sum of all individual loop gains) $+$ (sum of gain products of all possible combinations of two non-touching loops) $-$ (sum of the gain products of all possible combinations of 3 non-touching loops) $+ \cdots$ $\tag{2-132}$

Δ_k = The value of Δ for that part of the graph not touching the kth forward path. $\tag{2-133}$

This general gain formula may seem formidable to use at first glance, but the following examples will show that the actual application of the formula is quite straightforward.

S. J. Mason, "Feedback Theory — Further Properties of Signal Flow Graphs," *Proc. IRE*, Vol. 44, No. 7, pp. 920–926, July, 1956.

†Two loops or two parts of a signal flow graph are said to be non-touching if they do not have any common nodes.

EXAMPLE 2-10.   Consider, in the last example, that the functional relation between e_{out} and e_{in} is to be determined by using the general gain formula. The signal flow graph for the ladder network shown in Fig. 2-38a

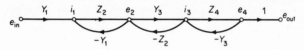

(a) Signal flow graph of passive ladder network

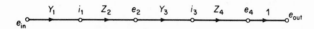

(b) The forward path of the flow graph

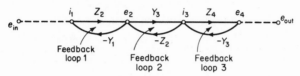

(c) The three individual feedback loops

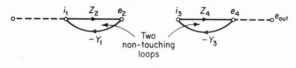

(d)

Fig. 2-39. Identification of quantities in the general gain formula for signal flow graph of Example 2-9.

is redrawn in Fig. 2-39a. The following conclusions are obtained by inspection from the given signal flow graph:

(1) There is only one forward path (Fig. 2-39b); the forward path gain is
$$M_1 = Y_1 Z_2 Y_3 Z_4 \qquad (2\text{-}134)$$

(2) There are three individual feedback loops (Fig. 2-39c); the loop gains are
$$P_{11} = - Z_2 Y_1 \qquad (2\text{-}135)$$
$$P_{21} = - Z_2 Y_3 \qquad (2\text{-}136)$$
$$P_{31} = - Z_4 Y_3 \qquad (2\text{-}137)$$

(3) There are two non-touching loops, as shown in Fig. 2-39d. The loop gains of these two loops are
$$- Z_2 Y_1 \quad \text{and} \quad - Z_4 Y_3 \qquad (2\text{-}138)$$

Hence P_{12} = gain product of the first (and only) possible combination of two nontouching loops = $Z_2 Z_4 Y_1 Y_3$.

(4) There are no 3-non-touching loops, 4-non-touching loops, etc., thus

$$P_{m3} = 0, \quad P_{m4} = 0, \quad \ldots$$

From Eq. (2-130):

$$\Delta = 1 - (- Z_2 Y_1 - Z_2 Y_3 - Z_4 Y_3) + (Z_2 Z_4 Y_1 Y_3) \qquad (2\text{-}139)$$

(5) All the three feedback loops are in touch with the forward path, hence

$$\Delta_1 = 1 \qquad (2\text{-}140)$$

Substituting the quantities in Eq. (2-134) through (2-140), the output-input voltage relation of the ladder network is

$$\frac{_oe_{ut}}{e_{in}} = M = \frac{M_1 \Delta_1}{\Delta} = \frac{Y_1 Y_3 Z_2 Z_4}{1 + Z_2 Y_1 + Z_2 Y_3 + Z_4 Y_3 + Z_2 Z_4 Y_1 Y_3} \qquad (2\text{-}141)$$

EXAMPLE 2-11. As a second example, consider the signal flow graph shown in Fig. 2-32d, which is redrawn in Fig. 2-40a. The functional relation between the output variable x_5 and the input variable x_1 is to be determined by means of the general gain formula. The following conclusions are obtained by inspection from the given signal flow graph:

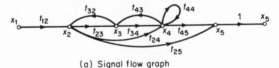

(a) Signal flow graph

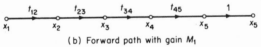

(b) Forward path with gain M_1

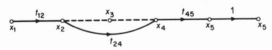

(c) Forward path with gain M_2

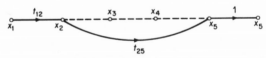

(d) Forward path with gain M_3

(e) Feedback loop P_{11}

Fig. 2-40. Signal flow graphs showing the application of the general flow graph gain formula.

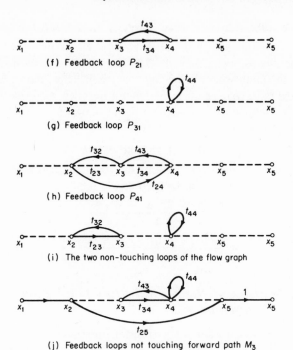

(f) Feedback loop P_{21}

(g) Feedback loop P_{31}

(h) Feedback loop P_{41}

(i) The two non-touching loops of the flow graph

(j) Feedback loops not touching forward path M_3

Fig. 2-40 (cont.) (f-j). Signal flow graphs showing the application of the general flow graph gain formula.

(1) There are three forward paths (Figs. 2-40b,c,d); the forward path gains are

$$M_1 = t_{12}t_{23}t_{34}t_{45} \qquad \text{(for } x_1\text{-}x_2\text{-}x_3\text{-}x_4\text{-}x_5) \quad (2\text{-}142)$$
$$M_2 = t_{12}t_{24}t_{45} \qquad \text{(for } x_1\text{-}x_2\text{-}x_4\text{-}x_5) \quad (2\text{-}143)$$
$$M_3 = t_{12}t_{25} \qquad \text{(for } x_1\text{-}x_2\text{-}x_3) \quad (2\text{-}144)$$

(2) There are four individual feedback loops (Figs. 2-40e,f,g,h) with loop gains

$$P_{11} = t_{23}t_{32} \qquad \text{(for } x_2\text{-}x_3\text{-}x_2) \quad (2\text{-}145)$$
$$P_{21} = t_{34}t_{43} \qquad \text{(for } x_3\text{-}x_4\text{-}x_3) \quad (2\text{-}146)$$
$$P_{31} = t_{44} \qquad \text{(for } x_4\text{-}x_4) \quad (2\text{-}147)$$
$$P_{41} = t_{24}t_{43}t_{32} \qquad \text{(for } x_2\text{-}x_4\text{-}x_3\text{-}x_2) \quad (2\text{-}148)$$

(3) There are two non-touching loops, as shown in Fig. 2-40i. The loop gains of these two loops are

$$t_{23}t_{32} \quad \text{and} \quad t_{44} \qquad\qquad\qquad (2\text{-}149)$$

Hence P_{12} = gain product of the first (and only) possible combination of two non-touching loops = $t_{23}t_{32}t_{44}$ (2-150)

(4) There are no 3-non-touching loops, 4-non-touching loops, etc., hence

$$P_{m3} = P_{m4} = \cdots = 0$$

From Eq. (2-130): $\Delta = 1 - (t_{23}t_{32} + t_{34}t_{43} + t_{44} + t_{24}t_{43}t_{32}) + t_{23}t_{32}t_{44}$ (2-151)

(5) The first forward path (path gain $= M_1$) is in touch with all the four feedback loops, hence $\Delta_1 = 1$. The second forward path (path gain $= M_2$) is also in touch with all the four feedback loops, hence $\Delta_2 = 1$. The third forward path (path gain $= M_3$) is not in touch with the two feedback loops, x_3-x_4-x_3 (loop gain $= t_{34}t_{43}$), and x_4-x_4 (loop gain $= t_{44}$), but is in touch with the other two loops (Fig. 2-40j), hence

$$\Delta_3 = 1 - (t_{34}t_{43} + t_{44})$$ (2-152)

Substituting the quantities obtained in Eq. (2-142) through Eq. (2-152) into the general gain formula, the expression for x_5/x_1 is

$$M = \frac{x_5}{x_1} = \frac{M_1\,\Delta_1 + M_2\,\Delta_2 + M_3\,\Delta_3}{\Delta}$$

$$= \frac{t_{12}t_{23}t_{34}t_{45} + t_{12}t_{24}t_{45} + t_{12}t_{25}(1 - t_{34}t_{43} - t_{44})}{1 - t_{23}t_{32} - t_{34}t_{43} - t_{44} - t_{24}t_{43}t_{32} + t_{23}t_{32}t_{44}}$$ (2-153)

2.10 Application of the Signal Flow Gain Formula to Block Diagrams

Although the evaluation of the transfer function of a multi-loop system by the reduction technique from a block diagram is not difficult, it has been shown to be a tedious process. Due to the similarity in the topology of the block diagram and the signal flow graph, it is possible to apply the general gain formula given by Eq. (2-128) directly to a block diagram. However,

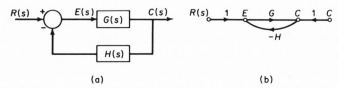

(a)   (b)

Fig. 2-41. Equivalent signal flow graph of a block diagram of a simple feedback control system. (a) Block diagram; (b) Signal flow graph.

given any block diagram, it is also convenient to draw its equivalent signal flow graph and then apply the gain formula to the flow graph.

To illustrate how the equivalent signal flow graph may be constructed from a block diagram, in Fig. 2-41b the equivalent flow graph of the block diagram of a simple feedback system is given. Note that, since the nodes on the flow graph are interpreted as summing points of all incoming signals to the node, the negative feedback is represented by assigning a negative sign for the feedback path gain H.

The block diagram of a more complex system is shown in Fig. 2-42a. The equivalent signal flow graph for this block diagram is shown in Fig.

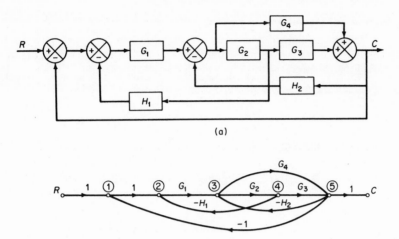

(a)

(b)

Fig. 2-42. A block diagram and its equivalent signal flow graph.
(a) Block diagram; (b) Signal flow graph.

2-42b. By applying the general gain formula to the signal flow graph of
Fig. 2-42b, the closed-loop transfer function of the feedback control system is

$$\frac{C(s)}{R(s)} = M(s) = \frac{G_1G_2G_3 + G_1G_4}{1 + G_1G_2H_1 + G_2G_3H_2 + G_1G_2G_3 + G_4H_2 + G_1G_4} \quad (2\text{-}154)$$

Problems

2-1. Write the differential equations for the electric networks of Fig. 2P-1.

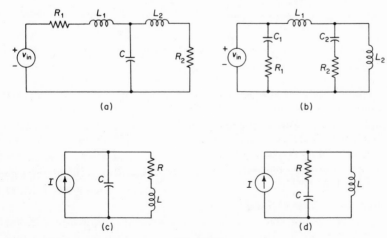

Fig. 2P-1

2-2. (a) Write the mesh and node network determinants for the circuit of Fig. 2P-2. Write the voltage gain V_0/V_s in Δ form.

(b) Find the following quantities in Δ form:

I_0/I_s, V_0/V_s, I_0/V_s, Z_{in} and Z_{out}.

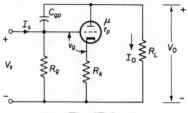

Fig. 2P-2

2-3. Write the differential equations for the mechanical systems of Fig. 2P-3.

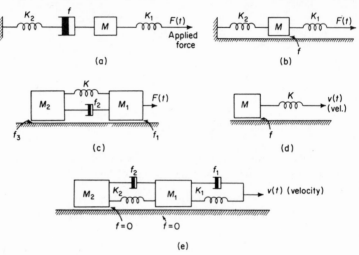

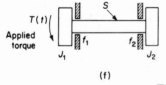

Fig. 2P-3

2-4. Write the differential equations of the gear train system in Fig. 2P-4. The moments of inertia of the gears and shafts are J_1, J_2, and J_3. $T(t)$ is the applied torque. N denotes the number of gear teeth. Assume $S = \infty$ for all shafts (rigid shafts).

2-5. Write the transfer functions $X_2(s)/F(s)$ for the mechanical systems of Fig. 2P-3a and b, where $X_2(s)$ is the Laplace transform of the displacement of M.

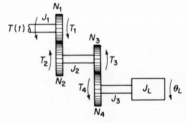

Fig. 2P-4

2-6. For the system of Fig. 2P-6, determine the transfer function $V_0(s)/T_m(s)$. The potentiometer rotates through 10 turns and the voltage applied across the potentiometer terminals is V volts.

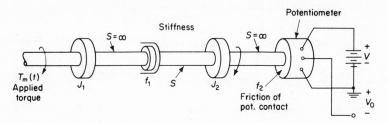

Fig. 2P-6

2-7. The spring of the mechanical system shown in Fig. 2P-7 is non-Hookean (nonlinear). The restoring force of the spring is described by

$$F_s = Kx^2$$

where K is a constant and x is linear displacement. Determine the displacement of the mass as a function of time when the applied force is a unit step function,

$$f(t) = u(t)$$

Assume zero initial conditions.

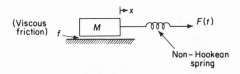

Fig. 2P-7

2-8. For the system of Fig. 2P-8, find the steady-state value of the output $c(t)$ when the input $r(t)$ is a unit step function.

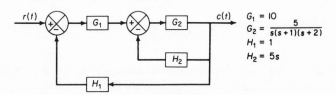

Fig. 2P-8

2-9. Verify Eq. (2-104).

2-10. The impulse response of a certain linear system is given by

$$g(t) = e^{-2t} \qquad t > 0$$

For an input $r(t) = 2t$ $(t > 0)$, show that Eqs. (2-98) and (2-103) give the same result for the output of the system.

2-11. Determine the relations C_2/R_1, C_2/R_2, C_1/R_1, and C_1/R_2 from the block diagram in Fig. 2P-11.

2-12. Construct a signal flow graph for the electrical circuit of Fig. 2P-1a. Evaluate the transfer function V_{out}/V_{in} from the flow graph (V_{out} is taken across R_2).

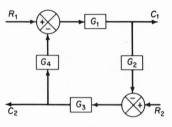

2-13. Construct a signal flow graph for the electrical circuit of Fig. 2P-1d. Evaluate the relation V_{out}/I from the flow graph (V_{out} is taken across L).

Fig. 2P-11

2-14. Construct a signal flow graph for the mechanical system of Fig. 2P-3a. Evaluate the relations $X_1(s)/F(s)$, $X_2(s)/F(s)$, $X_3(s)/F(s)$, and $X_3(s)/X_1(s)$ from the signal flow graph.

2-15. Construct a signal flow graph for the mechanical system of Fig. 2P-3b. Evaluate the relations $X_1(s)/F(s)$, $X_2(s)/F(s)$, and $X_2(s)/X_1(s)$ from the flow graph.

2-16. For the ladder network of Fig. 2-38a, determine the input impedance V_{in}/I and the transfer impedance V_{out}/I from the signal flow graph.

2-17. Derive the closed-loop transfer function C/R from the block diagram of Fig. 2P-17 by means of the block diagram reduction technique.

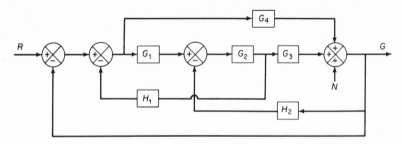

Fig. 2P-17

2-18. Construct the equivalent signal flow graph for the block diagram of Fig. 2P-17 and evaluate C/R by use of Mason's gain formula.

2-19. In the system of Fig. 2P-17, determine the relation between the transfer functions G_1, G_2, G_3, G_4, H_1, and H_2 so that the output c is not affected by the disturbance N. (The system is assumed to be stable.)

2-20. Draw a signal flow graph for the feedback amplifier in Fig. 2P-20 (assume midband linear incremental operation). Find the voltage gain E_0/E_s and the return difference F_{Rk}. $\mu_1 = \mu_2 = 20$, $r_{p1} = r_{p2} = 10K$, $R_{L2} = R = 400K$, and k is unspecified.

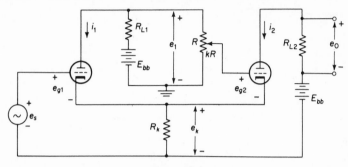

Fig. 2P-20

2-21. One of the problems associated with the operation of sensitive d-c amplifiers is the erratic drift in output voltage caused by random changes in cathode emission. The Miller compensation circuit shown in Fig. 2P-21 provides a means of overcoming cathode drift in the d-c amplifier. The drift is simulated here by an equivalent random-drift generator e_d in the common cathode lead of the two tubes. By means of the signal flow graph technique, determine the optimum value of R_2 necessary to render cathode drift ineffective. What is the voltage gain of the d-c amplifier under no-drift conditions?

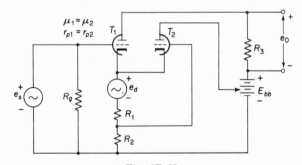

Fig. 2P-21

2-22. A certain network is represented by the following system of equations. Solve for I_1, using the Cramer rule and the signal flow graph methods.

$$\begin{bmatrix} 2 \\ 1 \\ 0 \\ 0 \end{bmatrix} = \begin{bmatrix} 1 & 1 & -1 & 0 \\ 4 & 1 & 0 & -1 \\ 1 & 0 & 1 & 0 \\ -4 & 0 & 2 & 1 \end{bmatrix} \begin{bmatrix} I_1 \\ I_2 \\ I_3 \\ I_4 \end{bmatrix}$$

3

General Feedback Theory

3.1 What Is Feedback?

The concept of feedback plays an important role in control system engineering. In order to understand and appreciate the significance of feedback, it is important to define the term. Although it appears to have a very simple meaning, and despite the fact that it is often used in our daily language, a precise definition is surprisingly difficult. The existence of feedback in physical systems is often obscure and difficult to demonstrate. In Chapter I, we gave several simple illustrations of feedback control systems: in each system, a specific variable is to be controlled; control is brought about by making a comparison of the actual value of this variable with its desired value and utilizing the difference to reduce the error observed. When feedback is deliberately introduced for the purpose of control, its existence and function are easily identified. The reduction of system error is merely one of the many effects that feedback may have upon a system. We shall show in the following sections that feedback also affects such system properties as stability, bandwidth, over-all gain, impedance level, nonlinearity and distortion effects, and transient response, etc. In order to understand the effect of feedback on all these parameters, it is essential that we examine this elusive and sometimes paradoxical phenomenon with a very broad mind. As a matter of fact, some of the physical systems which we identify as inherently non-feedback systems may turn out to have feedback if we look at them in a certain manner. An example is readily found by referring to the passive ladder network shown in Fig. 2-38a. Certainly we do not recognize that the network possesses any physical feedback; at least, there is no visual feedback path. But, referring to the signal flow graph of the network shown in Fig. 2-38b, we can identify three feedback loops, each representing a *closed sequence of cause-and-effect relation* between certain currents and voltages. From a general point of view, the last statement may be used to define adequately the existence of feedback in physical systems. We can state that whenever a closed sequence of cause-and-effect relationships exists among variables of a system, feedback is said to exist. This viewpoint will inevitably admit feedback in a large number of systems which we ordinarily would identify as non-feedback systems. But with the availability of signal flow graphs and the mathematics of feedback theory, this general definition of feedback enables numerous systems, with or without physical feedback, to be studied through the use of feedback theory once the existence of feedback in the above-mentioned sense is established.

3.2 The Effect of Feedback

This section and the following sections are devoted to a general analysis of feedback systems and the meaning of feedback. The principal object of

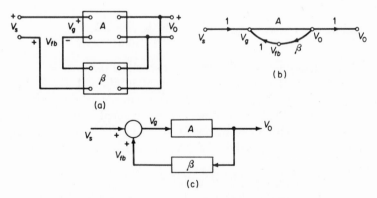

Fig. 3-1. Single-loop feedback system. (a) Simplified schematic diagram representation; (b) Signal flow graph representation; (c) Block diagram representation.

the analysis is the development of a general feedback theory through the use of familiar electronic amplifier circuits.

Three common ways of representing a single-loop feedback system are shown in Fig. 3-1. The over-all transfer function, or gain, of the system portrayed is given by

$$M = \frac{V_0}{V_s} = \frac{A}{1 - A\beta} \tag{3-1}$$

where A and β denote the transfer functions of the forward and feedback paths respectively, and are frequency dependent quantities in general.*

Effect of Feedback on Over-all Gain

As seen from Eq. (3-1) and Fig. 3-1, without the feedback path, the transfer function of the system would be given by $M = A$. Therefore:
Feedback reduces the gain of a feedback system by the factor $1 - A\beta$.
The statement just made is true when A and β are pure numbers. But A and β may be functions of frequency, so that the magnitude of $1 - A\beta$ may be greater than unity in one frequency range but less than one is another. Therefore, feedback could increase the gain of a feedback amplifier in one frequency range, but decrease the gain in another.

Effect of Feedback on Sensitivity

Sensitivity is normally used to express the ratio of the percentage variation in some specific system quantities such as gain, impedance, etc., to the percentage variation in one of the system parameters. The sensitivity function is defined as:

$$S_K^M = \frac{d \ln M}{d \ln k} = \frac{dM/M}{dk/k} = \frac{\text{Percentage change in } M \text{ (due to change in } k)}{\text{Percentage change in } k}$$

$$\tag{3-2}$$

where M is a transfer function and k is a specified parameter.

Let us consider the signal flow graph configuration of Fig. 3-1b. First, when the feedback path is open, the sensitivity of the over-all gain M to the variation of forward path gain A is apparently equal to unity. This result is expected, since without feedback $M = A$ and $S_A^M = 1$. With the feedback loop closed, the sensitivity of over-all gain with respect to $k = A$ is given by

$$S_A^M = \frac{d \ln M}{d \ln k} = \frac{dM}{dk} \frac{k}{M} = \frac{1}{1 - A\beta} \tag{3-3}$$

---

*It should be noted that the notations of feedback amplifiers are used here. If we let $A = G$ and $\beta = -H$, then Eq. (3-1) is identical with the notation used for single-loop feedback control systems. The difference in sign between H and β stems from the fact that negative feedback concept is assumed in control systems (feedback signal is subtracted from the input), while in feedback amplifiers, positive feedback is assumed, with the feedback signal being added to the input signal.

The sensitivity can be made arbitrarily small by increasing $A\beta$. In the ideal case, $A\beta \to \infty$, and $S_A^M \to 0$.

When the feedback element β is considered to be variable, $k = \beta$.

$$S_\beta^M = \frac{dM}{d\beta}\frac{\beta}{M} = \frac{A\beta}{1 - A\beta} \tag{3-4}$$

The possibility of reducing the sensitivity does not exist (unless $A = 0$); as $A\beta$ grows larger, sensitivity S approaches unity.

In view of the preceding discussion, we can make the following conclusions in regard to the effect of feedback on sensitivity:

(1) Feedback, when used properly, may reduce sensitivity with respect to change in system parameter.

(2) Feedback does not affect variations of parameters in the feedback path.

(3) Feedback does not affect variations of parameters in a path with no feedback path around it (open-loop system).

(4) Feedback reduces sensitivity with respect to a parameter located in the forward path of a loop. The larger the loop gain $A\beta$, the more effective feedback is in reducing sensitivity.

Effect of Feedback on Distortion

Feedback may be used to reduce the effects of certain types of extraneous signals which occur in amplifiers and control systems, but it has no effect on other types. "Extraneous signal" is intended here to include many types of unwanted effects either from external or internal sources of a system. Examples of extraneous signals are thermal noise voltage in amplifier circuits, synchro noise of servo systems, wind gust exerted on antenna of radar systems, or harmonic components resulting from nonlinear characteristics of system components.

The effect of feedback on extraneous signals depends greatly upon where the signal is introduced into the system. Let us refer to the signal flow graph shown in Fig. 3-2. In this graph, V_n represents a noise signal

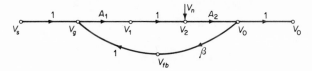

Fig. 3-2. Signal flow graph of feedback system with extraneous signal in the forward path.

which is considered to be introduced at an arbitrary point in the forward path. In the absence of feedback, that is, for β equals zero, the output signal is

$$V_o = A_1 A_2 V_s + A_2 V_n = V_{os} + V_{on} \tag{3-5}$$

where V_{os} represents the signal component of the output, and V_{on} is the noise component. The output signal-to-noise ratio with no feedback is

$$\frac{\text{Output due to signal}}{\text{Output due to noise}} = \left|\frac{V_{os}}{V_{on}}\right| = \left|\frac{A_1 A_2 V_s}{A_2 V_n}\right| = \left|\frac{A_1 V_s}{V_n}\right| \tag{3-6}$$

Evidently, in order to increase the signal-to-noise ratio, we should increase the magnitude of A_1 or V_s relative to that of V_n. Varying the magnitude of A_2 would have no effect whatsoever on the ratio.

With the presence of feedback, the system output signal is given by

$$V_{o\,\text{fb}} = \frac{A_1 A_2}{1 - A_1 A_2 \beta} V_s + \frac{A_2}{1 - A_1 A_2 \beta} V_n$$

$$= V_{os\,\text{fb}} + V_{on\,\text{fb}} \tag{3-7}$$

Comparing Eq. (3-7) with Eq. (3-5), we see that the noise component in the output signal, $V_{on\,\text{fb}}$, is reduced by the factor $(1 - A_1 A_2 \beta)$, but the signal component, $V_{os\,\text{fb}}$, is also reduced by the same amount.
Therefore, the signal-to-noise ratio is

$$\left|\frac{V_{os\,\text{fb}}}{V_{on\,\text{fb}}}\right| = \left|\frac{A_1 A_2 V_s/(1 - A_1 A_2 \beta)}{A_2/(1 - A_1 A_2 \beta)}\right| = \left|\frac{A_1 V_s}{V_n}\right| \tag{3-8}$$

and is the same as that without feedback. In this case, feedback has no direct effect on the output signal-to-noise ratio. However, the application of feedback suggests a possibility of improving the signal-noise ratio. Let us assume that with feedback incorporated, we increase the magnitude of A_1 to A_1', and V_s to V_s' with other factors unchanged, so that the output due to signal alone is at the same level as that when feedback is absent. In other words, we set

$$\left|V_{os\,\text{fb}}\right| = \left|\frac{A_1 A_2 V_s}{1 - A_1' A_2 \beta}\right| = |A_1 A_2 V_s| \tag{3-9}$$

But when A_1 becomes larger, the output due to noise becomes

$$\left|V_{on\,\text{fb}}\right| = \left|\frac{A_2 V_n}{1 - A_1' A_2 \beta}\right| \tag{3-10}$$

which is smaller than V_{on} when feedback is absent. The signal-to-noise ratio is now

$$\left|\frac{V_{os\,\text{fb}}}{V_{on\,\text{fb}}}\right| = \left|\frac{V_s A_1}{V_n}(1 - A_1' A_2 \beta)\right| \tag{3-11}$$

Through the comparison of this ratio with that of Eq. (3-6), it is apparent that the signal-to-noise ratio with feedback is increased by a factor of $(1 - A_1' A_2 \beta)$. If, however, V_s and A_1 could not be increased, then feedback would be of no avail in improving the output signal-noise ratio.

Let us now investigate the situation when the noise signal is originated at the output of a system. This may be due to ripples in the power supply voltage of the output stage of an amplifier, or disturbance exerted on the load of a servo system. A signal flow graph illustrating this situation is depicted in Fig. 3-3.

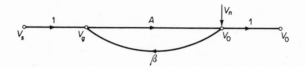

Fig. 3-3. Signal flow graph of feedback system with extraneous signal in the output.

It can be shown that, in this case, feedback does not affect the output signal-to-noise ratio. But, similar to the previous case, if V_s and A can be increased (to V_s' and A', respectively) with respect to V_n, the signal-noise ratio may be increased by a factor of $(1 - A'\beta)$.

When extraneous signal V_n appears at the same point as the input signal V_s, it is as if the input were $V_n + V_s$. It is easy to see that feedback will have no effect and will not provide improvement of the signal-to-noise ratio. The extraneous signal in the input may be due to synchro noise or transducer noise in servo systems, or to hum voltage in an input transformer of an electrical amplifier.

Effect of Feedback on Bandwidth

Bandwidth is the characteristic of the frequency response which is most often specified in the design of amplifiers and feedback control systems. The definition of bandwidth is depicted on typical frequency responses of amplifiers and servo systems in Fig. 3-4. The bandwidth is significant

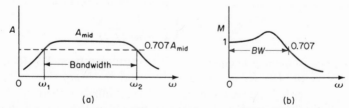

Fig. 3-4. (a) Typical frequency response of an RC-coupled amplifier; (b) Typical frequency response of a feedback control system.

because it measures the ability of the amplifier or servo system to reproduce the input signal, and the noise rejection characteristics. The effect of feedback on bandwidth is illustrated here by considering the single stage R-C coupled amplifier with potentiometer feedback, as shown in Fig. 3-5.

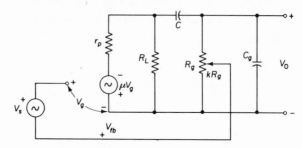

Fig. 3-5. Single-stage RC-coupled amplifier with negative feedback.

If R_g is much greater than R_L (this is usually true), for sinusoidal quantities, the gain of the amplifier without feedback ($k = 0$), is given by

$$A = \left(\frac{-\mu R_L}{r_p + R_L}\right)\left(\frac{j\omega R_g C}{1 + j\omega R_g C}\right)\left(\frac{1}{1 + j\omega R_e R_g}\right) \tag{3-12}$$

where

$$R_e = \frac{r_p R_L}{r_p + R_L} \tag{3-13}$$

If we assume that a middle frequency range exists, the reactance of the coupling capacitor C is so small that it virtually constitutes a short circuit, and the reactance of the shunt capacitance C_g is so large as to form an open circuit. The amplifier gains at mid-frequency, low frequency, and high frequency ranges are given, respectively, by

$$A_{\text{mid}} = -\frac{\mu R_L}{r_p + R_L} \tag{3-14}$$

$$A_{\text{low}} = A_{\text{mid}}\left(\frac{j\omega R_g C}{1 + j\omega R_g C}\right) \tag{3-15}$$

$$A_{\text{hi}} = A_{\text{mid}}\left(\frac{1}{1 + j\omega R_e C_g}\right) \tag{3-16}$$

When the frequency is equal to $1/R_g C$ (rad/sec), from Eq. (3-15), the magnitude of the low frequency gain is found to be equal to $0.707 A_{\text{mid}}$. Hence, the lower half power frequency of the amplifier without feedback is $1/R_g C$. Similarly, from Eq. (3-16), it is clear that the upper half power frequency is equal to $1/R_e C_g$.

Now consider that feedback is in effect, ($k \neq 0$). The gain at midband is given by

$$A_{\text{mid fb}} = \frac{A_{\text{mid}}}{1 - k A_{\text{mid}}} \tag{3-17}$$

since the feedback amplifier is of the single-loop configuration shown in Fig. 3-1. The gain at the low frequency range is obtained in the same manner:

$$A_{\text{low fb}} = \frac{A_{\text{low}}}{1 - kA_{\text{low}}} \tag{3-18}$$

Substituting Eq. (3-15) into Eq. (3-18) and simplifying, we have

$$A_{\text{low fb}} = \frac{A_{\text{mid}}j\omega R_g C}{1 + j\omega R_g C(1 - kA_{\text{mid}})} \tag{3-19}$$

By the use of Eq. (3-17), the last equation is written as

$$A_{\text{low fb}} = A_{\text{mid fb}} \frac{j\omega R_g C(1 - kA_{\text{mid}})}{1 + j\omega R_g C(1 - kA_{\text{mid}})} \tag{3-20}$$

Equation (3-20) is of the same form as Eq. (3-15); therefore, the lower half power frequency of the amplifier with feedback is $1/R_g C(1 - kA_{\text{mid}})$. Hence, the lower half power frequency of the feedback amplifier is reduced by the factor $(1 - kA_{\text{mid}})$.

The gain with feedback at the high frequency end is

$$A_{\text{hi fb}} = \frac{A_{\text{hi}}}{1 - kA_{\text{hi}}} \tag{3-21}$$

Substituting Eq. (3-16) into Eq. (3-21) and simplifying, we have

$$A_{\text{hi fb}} = A_{\text{mid fb}} \frac{1}{1 + \dfrac{j\omega R_e C_g}{1 - kA_{\text{mid}}}} \tag{3-22}$$

which is of the same form as Eq. (3-16). Therefore, the upper half power frequency of the feedback amplifier is equal to $(1 - kA_{\text{mid}})/R_e C_g$, and is increased by the factor $(1 - kA_{\text{mid}})$ over that of the amplifier without feedback. Typical frequency responses of the single-stage amplifier with and without feedback are depicted in Fig. 3-6. The bandwidth of the feed-

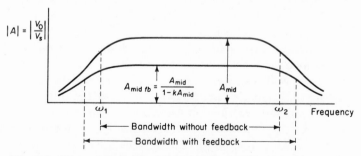

Fig. 3-6. Effect of feedback on bandwidth of single-stage RC-coupled amplifier.

back amplifier is increased by the factor $(1 - kA_{\text{mid}})^2$, while the midband gain is reduced by the factor $(1 - kA_{\text{mid}})$. In this case, the feedback is described as *degenerative** over the complete frequency range since the gain with feedback is always less than the gain without feedback. Figure 3-7

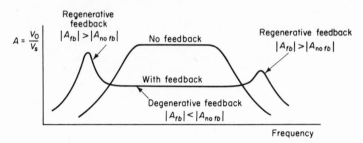

Fig. 3-7. Effect of feedback on bandwidth of three-stage RC-coupled amplifier (feedback around all three stages).

depicts the effect of feedback on the frequency response if feedback is applied across three stages of cascaded R-C coupled amplifiers. In the low and high frequency regions, the gain with feedback is greater than that of no feedback, and the feedback is described as *regenerative* at these frequencies.

Effect of Feedback on Impedance

One of the important effects of feedback is its influence on the impedance that the system presents to any external system or circuit connected to it. For instance, in electronic amplifiers, the input impedance faced by the source of signal voltage, or the output impedance faced by the load are important, since they affect the efficiency of power transfer from the source to the amplifier, and from the amplifier to the load. In servo systems, by analogy, we can regard the torque-to-velocity ratio of the system output as the output impedance faced by the load. In general, feedback may increase or decrease the impedance seen between any two open terminals of a system, depending on the type of feedback associated with the terminals. Generally speaking, shunt feedback will decrease impedance, and series feedback will increase impedance. First we shall define the meanings of series and shunt feedback. Let us consider the simple feedback amplifier circuit shown in Fig. 3-8. We are primarily interested in the types of feedback into the terminals a–a', b–b', and c–c', and the effect of feedback on the impedance into these terminals. With reference to any pair of terminals, if the feedback signal is in series with the terminals, feedback is described as

---

*Feedback is defined as degenerative if $|A_{\text{fb}}| < |A_{\text{no fb}}|$; otherwise, it is regenerative.

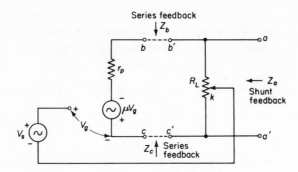

Fig. 3-8. Illustration of series and shunt feedback by means of a feedback amplifier.

series feedback. If the feedback signal is parallel with the terminals in question, shunt feedback is said to exist. In the present case, for terminals a–a', the feedback is of the shunt type, and for the terminals b–b' and c–c', we have series feedback. Therefore, the same circuit is said to have either shunt or series feedback depending upon the point at which feedback is measured.

The impedances into the three pairs of terminals are now to be evaluated for the amplifier with and without feedback. Let Z_a be the impedance into terminals a–a' with V_s replaced by a short circuit (this is also the output impedance) and without feedback ($k = 0$), and $Z_{a\,\text{fb}}$, with feedback. Then

$$Z_a = \frac{r_p R_L}{r_p + R_L} \tag{3-23}$$

The output impedance with feedback, obtained by the method illustrated in Sec. 2.3, is

$$Z_{a\,\text{fb}} = \frac{r_p R_L}{r_p + R_L + \mu k R_L} \tag{3-24}$$

Equation (3-24) can also be written as

$$Z_{a\,\text{fb}} = \frac{r_p R_L/(r_p + R_L)}{1 + k \dfrac{\mu R_L}{r_p + R_L}} = \frac{Z_a}{1 - Ak} \tag{3-25}$$

where A is the gain of the amplifier without feedback ($k = 0$) and is given by

$$A = -\frac{\mu R_L}{r_p + R_L} \tag{3-26}$$

Thus, the impedance into shunt feedback terminals is reduced by a factor $(1 - Ak)$.

The impedance at terminals b–b' is evaluated by considering that a voltage generator with voltage V is inserted between $b-b'$, and the impedance is equal to the ratio of V to the current I that flows through the generator (V_s is shorted). Without feedback ($k = 0$),

$$Z_b = r_p + R_L \tag{3-27}$$

When feedback is in effect, the following mesh equations are written for the circuit:

$$V = (r_p + R_L)I - \mu V_g \tag{3-28}$$

$$V_g = - kIR_L \tag{3-29}$$

From the last two equations, the impedance at terminals $b-b'$ is obtained as

$$Z_{b\text{ fb}} = V/I = r_p + R_L + k\mu R_L \tag{3-30}$$

or

$$Z_{b\text{ fb}} = (r_p + R_L)\left(1 + k\frac{\mu R_L}{r_p + R_L}\right) = Z_b(1 - kA) \tag{3-31}$$

Therefore, the impedance into series feedback terminals is increased by the factor $(1 - Ak)$.

In the same manner, we can show that the impedance at terminals $c-c'$ with no feedback is

$$Z_c = \frac{r_p + R_L}{(1 + \mu)} \tag{3-32}$$

and when feedback is incorporated,

$$
\begin{aligned}
Z_{c\text{ fb}} &= \frac{r_p + R_L + k\mu R_L}{(1 + \mu)} \\
&= \frac{(r_p + R_L)(1 - Ak)}{(1 + \mu)}
\end{aligned}
\tag{3-33}
$$

It should be mentioned that it may be difficult to determine the type of feedback in a complex system. Quite often, it may be a combination of both shunt and series feedback, and then the increase or decrease of impedance due to feedback may depend entirely upon the values of the system parameters used.

Effect of Feedback on Transient Response

The effect of feedback on the transient response of linear systems is investigated by means of two simple illustrations. Consider the single stage feedback amplifier shown in Fig. 3-9. When there is no feedback ($k = 0$), the transfer function or gain of the amplifier is of the form:

$$\frac{V_0}{V_s} = \frac{A}{1 + sT} \tag{3-34}$$

where

$$A = - \frac{\mu R_L}{r_p + R_L} \tag{3-35}$$

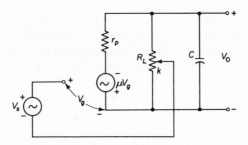

Fig. 3-9. Single-stage feedback amplifier.

and
$$T = \frac{r_p R_L C}{r_p + R_L} \tag{3-36}$$

The inverse Laplace transform of C/R is the impulse response of the system, hence

$$g(t) = \mathcal{L}^{-1}\left(\frac{V_0}{V_s}\right) = \frac{A}{T} e^{-t/T} \tag{3-37}$$

Since the time constant T is always positive, the impulse response of the amplifier without feedback is an exponential decay, and the amplifier is said to be always *stable*.

When $k \neq 0$, the closed-loop transfer function of the amplifier is

$$\frac{V_0}{V_s}(s) = \frac{A}{Ts + (1 - Ak)} = \frac{A}{T\left(s + \dfrac{1 - Ak}{T}\right)} \tag{3-38}$$

and the inverse Laplace transform is

$$g(t) = \frac{A}{T} e^{-(1-Ak)/T} = \frac{A}{T} e^{-t/T_0} \tag{3-39}$$

where
$$T_0 = \frac{T}{1 - Ak} \tag{3-40}$$

is the time constant of the closed-loop system. From Eq. (3-40), T_0 may be positive or negative, depending on the value of Ak. If Ak is negative (positive feedback), T_0 is positive, and the impulse response in Eq. (3-39) is

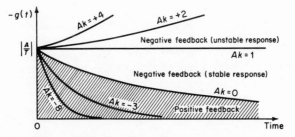

Fig. 3-10. Time responses showing the effect of feedback.

an exponential decay; but if Ak is positive (negative feedback), and greater than unity, T_0 becomes negative, the impulse response will increase without bound, and the response (or the system) is said to be *unstable*. Figure 3-10 shows how the impulse response varies with different values for Ak.

It is of interest to study the variation of the poles of $V_0(s)/V_s(s)$ when the value of Ak is varied. The denominator of $V_0(s)/V_s(s)$ when it is set equal to zero is called the *characteristic equation* of the system. Without feedback, the characteristic equation of the system is simply

$$1 + sT = 0 \tag{3-41}$$

which has a root at $s = -1/T$ in the s-plane. When feedback is applied, the characteristic equation of the feedback amplifier is given by

$$s + (1 - Ak)/T = 0 \tag{3-42}$$

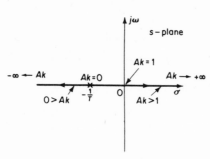

Fig. 3-11. Loci of roots of Eq. (3-42).

and the root is at $-(1-AK)/T$, which varies when Ak takes on different values. The locus of the root when Ak is varied is depicted in Fig. 3-11. When Ak is positive and greater than one, the root moves into the right half of the s-plane, the impulse response diverges, and the system is unstable. In general, the relation between the location of the characteristic equation roots and the system transient response is apparent, since the roots with positive real parts will give rise to exponential time functions which increase with time, and those in the left half of the s-plane correspond to exponential-decay time functions.

As a second example, consider that two stages of the amplifier shown in Fig. 3-9 are connected in cascade and feedback is applied across the over-all circuit. Without feedback ($k = 0$), the transfer function of the two-stage amplifier is simply

$$\frac{V_0}{V_s} = \frac{A^2}{(1 + sT)^2} \tag{3-43}$$

where A and T areas given in Eqs. (3-35) and (3-36). The inverse Laplace transform of $V_0(s)V/_s(s)$ is obtained from the Laplace transform table in Appendix A. Thus

$$g(t) = \mathcal{L}^{-1}\left(\frac{V_0}{V_s}\right) = \frac{A^2}{T^2} t e^{-t/T} \tag{3-44}$$

Without feedback, the amplifier is stable since, with $k = 0$, $g(t)$ approaches zero as time approaches infinity. A sketch of the impulse response $g(t)$ is shown in Fig. 3-12.

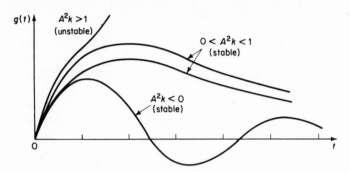

Fig. 3-12. Time responses showing the effect of feedback.

When feedback is applied, the overall transfer function of the amplifier is

$$\frac{V_0}{V_s}(s) = \frac{A^2/(1 + sT)^2}{1 - A^2k/(1 + sT)^2} = \frac{A^2}{T^2s^2 + 2Ts + (1 - A^2k)} \quad (3\text{-}45)$$

The characteristic equation of the amplifier with feedback, obtained by setting the denominator of Eq. (3-45) equal to zero, is

$$T^2s^2 + 2Ts + (1 - A^2k) = 0 \quad (3\text{-}46)$$

Since Eq. (3-46) is a quadratic equation of s, its two roots will be located in the left half of the s-plane so long as the coefficients of the equation are all of the same sign; otherwise, at least one of the roots will be found in the right half of the s-plane. The two roots of the characteristic equation are given by

$$s_{1,2} = -\frac{1}{T} \pm \frac{1}{2}\sqrt{\frac{4A^2k}{T^2}} \quad (3\text{-}47)$$

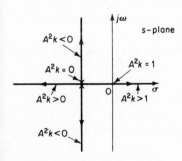

Figure 3-13 shows how the roots very with different values for A^2k. When A^2k is positive (negative feedback), the two roots are real; the over-all transfer function in Eq. (3-45) can be written as

$$\frac{V_0}{V_s}(s) = \frac{A^2}{T^2}\frac{1}{(s + a)(s + b)} \quad (3\text{-}48)$$

where

$$a = \frac{1}{T}(1 + A\sqrt{k}) \quad (3\text{-}49)$$

Fig. 3-13. Loci of roots of Eq. (3-46).

$$b = \frac{1}{T}(1 - A\sqrt{k}) \quad (3\text{-}50)$$

The impulse response of the system is the inverse Laplace transform of V_0/V_s in Eq. (3-48). Therefore

$$g(t) = \frac{A}{2T\sqrt{k}} (e^{-bt} - e^{-at}) \tag{3-51}$$

For $0 < A^2k < 1$, the impulse response is convergent, since a and b are all positive constants. For A^2k greater than unity, b is negative and the impulse response is divergent. The stable and unstable responses are depicted in Fig. 3-11.

When A^2k is negative, the roots s_1 and s_2 in Eq. (3-47) are complex. In this case, the inverse Laplace transform of Eq. (3-45) is obtained from the transform table:

$$g(t) = \frac{A}{T} \frac{1}{\sqrt{k}} e^{-t/T} \sin\left(\frac{A\sqrt{k}}{T}\right) t \tag{3-52}$$

which is of the form of a damped sinusoid. The frequency of the damped oscillation is $A\sqrt{k}/T$ rad/sec.

From the two illustrative examples just given, it is seen that the impulse responses of the amplifiers without feedback are always convergent (stable). But when negative feedback is applied, if the loop gain exceeds unity, the feedback amplifier will become unstable. Therefore, although negative feedback generally gives improved characteristics for sensitivity, distortion, and others mentioned previously, it does have an adverse effect on system stability.

3.3 Mathematical Definition of Feedback

The reason that the existence and effects of feedback have been so vividly illustrated by the examples in the preceding section is that we have considered only simple system configurations which can be represented by the single-loop diagram of Fig. 3-1. Since the forward path A and the feedback path β are readily identified in these simple systems, the effect of feedback on system characteristics is evaluated without much difficulty. However, not all systems have apparent feedback structures; the A and β paths are not apparent in systems with complex configurations (such as a multiple-loop system). Therefore, it is necessary to derive a set of mathematical definitions for feedback which will be general enough to be used on systems of any complexity.

In general, a qualitative measure of feedback with reference to a given element of a system is given by the quantities termed the "return ratio" and the "return difference." * The definitions of these terms can be made

---

*H. W. Bode, *Network Analysis and Feedback Amplifier Design*, D. Van Nostrand Co., Inc., New York, 1945, Chapter IV.

general enough by considering the signal flow graph shown in Fig. 3-14a. The signal flow graph is drawn in a very general sense; only the input and the output nodes are shown (of course, it may be extended to systems with

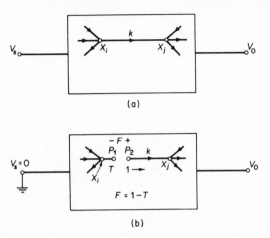

(a)

(b)

Fig. 3-14. (a) Signal flow graph for any arbitrary system; k is an element that appears a gain in only one branch; (b) Signal flow graph with the input end of the branch containing k opened.

several input and output nodes). We assume that the element k appears as the transmittance or gain of a branch between two nodes, for example, x_i and x_j (k does not appear anywhere else in the flow graph). The return ratio and return difference are defined as follows:

(1) The branch with transmittance k is broken at the beginning of the branch. Effectively, we have introduced two new nodes, P_1 and P_2, at either side of the break (see Fig. 3-14b).

(2) The input node is grounded; that is, $V_s = 0$.

(3) A signal of unity strength is transmitted from node P_2, and the signal returning to node P_1 is measured. The returned signal at P_1 is obtained by considering P_2 to be the input node and P_1 to be the output node and applying Mason's signal flow graph formula Eq. (2-128).

(4) The ratio of the returned to the transmitted signal is the return ratio for the element k, and is denoted by T_k.

(5) The return difference for the element k, denoted by F_k, is the difference between the transmitted and the returned signal, or

$$F_k = 1 - T_k \tag{3-53}$$

A general expression can be derived for the return difference by use of Mason's formula. Let Δ be the determinant of the flow graph shown in Fig. 3-14a, i.e., when the branch containing k is not broken. Since k is considered to appear as a gain factor only in one branch, we can factor out k and all the terms that are associated with k from Δ, so that Δ is written

$$\Delta = \Delta^0 + k \sum_q M_q \Delta_q^0 \tag{3-54}$$

where Δ^0 represents the terms in Δ that do not contain k, or simply

$$\Delta^0 = \Delta \mid_{k=0} \tag{3-55}$$

and M_q = gain of the qth forward path between node i and node j with the k-branch opened (Fig. 3-14b).

Δ_q^0 = determinant of the part of the flow graph not touching the qth forward path between node i and node j when the k-branch is opened (Fig. 3-14b).

It should be noted here that the requirement that k appear only in one branch is necessary only from the point of view of interpreting F physically. Mathematically, Eq. (3-54) is true if k appears in more than one branch provided that it appears as first-order gain factors. This condition also carries over to the validity of the formula of F which will be given in Eq. (3-58).

According to the definition of return ratio, T_k is obtained by applying Mason's formula to the signal flow graph of Fig. 3-14b between node P_2 (input) and node P_1 (output). We have

$$T_k = \frac{-k \sum_q M_q \Delta_q^0}{\Delta^0} \tag{3-56}$$

The return difference is obtained from Eq. (3-53):

$$F_k = 1 - \frac{-k \sum_q M_q \Delta_q^0}{\Delta^0} = \frac{\Delta^0 + k \sum_q M_q \Delta_q^0}{\Delta^0} \tag{3-57}$$

Hence

$$F_k = \frac{\Delta}{\Delta^0} \tag{3-58}$$

Therefore, the return difference for an element k in a system is equal to the ratio of the values assumed by the signal flow graph determinant when the specified element has its normal value and when the element vanishes. Equation (3-58) expresses F_k in terms of the determinant of the system flow graph, which can normally be evaluated by inspection. The formula for F thus represents one of the most convenient working formulas for the analytic treatment of feedback.

Let us now illustrate the usefulness of F_k by means of the single-loop structure shown in Fig. 3-15. In the system, A is considered to be the specific element for which feedback will be measured. The branch contain-

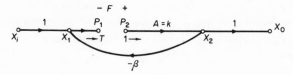

Fig. 3-15. Single loop feedback structure illustrating the return difference.

ing A is broken at the input end and a unit signal is sent into node P_2; the returned signal at node P_1 is $A\beta$. Hence

$$T_A = A\beta \qquad (3\text{-}59)$$

In this simple structure the return ratio is shown to be equal to the loop gain. The return difference for A is

$$F_A = 1 - T_A = 1 - A\beta \qquad (3\text{-}60)$$

This is the factor by which the sensitivity, impedance, bandwidth, and over-all gain are increased or decreased on account of the presence of feedback in the simple systems shown in the last section. Therefore, for simple cases at least, the return difference is a direct measure of feedback.

The calculation of the return difference for a practical system is given in the following examples.

EXAMPLE 3-1. Consider the simple amplifier circuit shown in Fig. 3-16a. The return difference for the amplification factor μ of the tube is to be

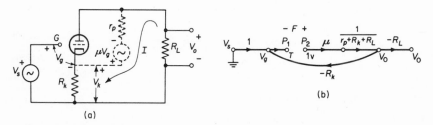

Fig. 3-16. (a) Amplifier circuit; (b) Signal flow graph for the evaluation of F_μ.

determined. The network equations for the construction of a signal flow graph are

$$V_g = V_s - IR_k \qquad (3\text{-}61)$$

$$I = \frac{\mu V_g}{r_p + R_k + R_L} \qquad (3\text{-}62)$$

$$V_0 = -IR_L \qquad (3\text{-}63)$$

The signal flow graph with the element μ appearing as a gain factor in only one branch is depicted in Fig. 3-16b. In this case, it appears that the easiest way to find F_k is to use Eq. (3-58). The determinant of the flow graph is obtained by inspection.

$$\Delta = 1 + \frac{\mu R_k}{r_p + R_k + R_L} \tag{3-64}$$

and

$$\Delta^0 = \Delta \mid_{\mu=0} = 1 \tag{3-65}$$

hence

$$F_\mu = \frac{\Delta}{\Delta^0} = \frac{r_p + R_L + (1 + \mu)R_k}{r_p + R_k + R_L} \tag{3-66}$$

The same solution can also be arrived at by following the definitions of T_μ and F_μ. As shown in Fig. 3-16b, the input node is grounded $(V_s = 0)$ and the input end of the μ branch is broken; a signal of unity strength is transmitted from node P_2. (In this case, since the input node of μ is V_g, the transmitted signal is 1 volt.) The returned signal at P_1, or the return ratio, is

$$T_\mu = - \frac{\mu R_k}{r_p + R_k + R_L} \tag{3-67}$$

which apparently will lead to the same result for F_μ as appeared in Eq. (3-66).

EXAMPLE 3-2. As a second example, the return difference for the cathode resistor R_k in the circuit used in the last example is to be determined. The signal flow graph depicted in Fig. 3-16b cannot be used in this case, since R_k does not appear as a gain factor in one branch. We may rewrite the system equations as

$$V_g = V_s - V_k \tag{3-68}$$

$$I = \frac{\mu V_g - V_k}{r_p + R_L} \tag{3-69}$$

$$V_k = I R_k \tag{3-70}$$

$$V_0 = - I R_L \tag{3-71}$$

The signal flow graph representing the last four equations is now drawn in Fig. 3-17, and R_k appears only in one branch. Hence

$$F_{R_k} = \frac{\Delta}{\Delta^0} = \frac{1 + \dfrac{R_k}{r_p + R_L} + \dfrac{\mu R_k}{r_p + R_L}}{1} = \frac{r_p + R_L + (1 + \mu)R_k}{r_p + R_L} \tag{3-72}$$

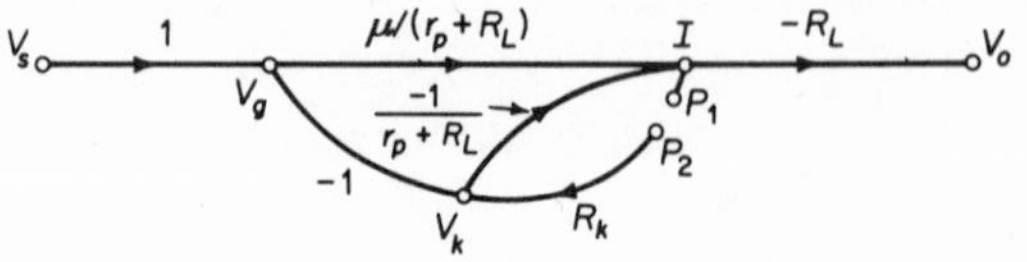

Fig. 3-17. A signal flow graph of the circuit in Fig. 3-16, with R_k isolated in one branch.

From the return ratio concept, a signal of one ampere is transmitted into node P_2 (since the node represents current I), and the return current I at node P_1 is measured. The return ratio is

$$T_{R_k} = -\frac{R_k}{r_p + R_L} - \frac{\mu R_k}{r_p + R_L} \qquad (3\text{-}73)$$

Physical Interpretation of Return Difference and Return Ratio

We have illustrated in the last two examples how the return differences for an active element (μ of a tube) and a passive element (cathode resistor) are determined. We may then ask the question: What is the physical meaning of "return difference of the μ of a tube" or "return difference of R_k"? The concept of return difference and return ratio in terms of the signal flow graph is clear, but it seems that an interpretation of F and T in terms of the physical elements is still desirable.

The physical interpretation of T_μ may be illustrated by referring to Fig. 3-18. The vacuum tube in which we are interested is isolated from the

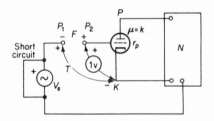

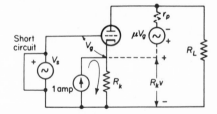

Fig. 3-18. Circuit for physical interpretation of $F\mu$.

Fig. 3-19. Circuit for physical interpretation of F_{R_k}.

rest of the network. The grid lead of the tube is broken at P_1 and P_2, and a voltage of one volt is applied across the grid-cathode terminals $P_2 K$. The voltage returning to P_1 and measured across $P_1 K$ is termed the return voltage. Since the transmitted signal is one volt, the return voltage is also equal to the return ratio T_μ. The return difference for μ is obtained readily by taking the difference between the transmitted and the returned voltages.

The return difference for a passive element has the following significance. With reference to Fig. 3-19, a current of one ampere is injected into R_k; this is equivalent to placing across R_k a generator of R_k volts with the polarities as shown. The return current I is measured and is numerically equal to T_{R_k}. In the circuit, V_s is zero; V_g equals $-R_k$ volts; the return current is

$$I = -\frac{(1+\mu)R_k}{r_p + R_L} = T_{R_k} \qquad (3\text{-}74)$$

which agrees with the result given by Eq. (3-73). Notice that, since the voltage across R_k is considered a source, R_k itself is not used in the loop impedance.

3.4 The Sensitivity Function

The simple illustrations given in Sec. 3.2 clearly indicate that system sensitivity is quantitatively measured by the return difference. A general relation between sensitivity and return difference can be established from the general signal flow graph of Fig. 3-14. The sensitivity of the over-all gain with respect to a given parameter k has been defined in Eq. (3-2):

$$S_k^M = \frac{d \ln M}{d \ln k} \qquad (3\text{-}75)$$

where

$$M = \frac{\sum_m M_m \Delta_m}{\Delta} \qquad \text{(Mason's formula)} \qquad (3\text{-}76)$$

is the over-all gain of the system. Substitution of Eq. (3-76) into Eq. (3-75) yields

$$S_k^M = \frac{d\left(\dfrac{\ln \sum_m M_m \Delta_m}{\Delta}\right)}{d \ln k} \qquad (3\text{-}77)$$

or

$$S_k^M = \frac{d \ln \left(\sum_m M_m \Delta_m\right)}{d \ln k} - \frac{d \ln \Delta}{d \ln k} \qquad (3\text{-}78)$$

Equation (3-78) can be written

$$S_k^M = \frac{d \sum_m M_m \Delta_m}{dk} \frac{k}{\sum_m M_m \Delta_m} - \frac{d \Delta}{dk} \frac{k}{\Delta} \qquad (3\text{-}79)$$

In this analysis we assume that the specific element k appears only as a first-order gain factor in a number of branches (again, as described in the last section, it is no tnecessary that k appear only in one branch), then $d \Delta/dk$ represents the value of Δ with only the terms containing k retained. Using the notation defined in Eq. (3-54), we have

$$\frac{d\Delta}{dk} = \sum_q M_q \Delta_q^0 \qquad (3\text{-}80)$$

where M_q and Δ_q^0 have been defined previously. Hence from Eq. (3-54)

$$k \frac{d\Delta}{dk} = k \sum_q M_q \Delta_q^0 = \Delta - \Delta^0 \qquad (3\text{-}81)$$

For similar reasons, we can write

$$k \frac{d\left(\sum\limits_{m} M_m \Delta_m\right)}{dk} = \sum_{m} M_m \Delta_m - \left(\sum_{m} M_m \Delta_m\right)^0 \tag{3-82}$$

where

$$\left(\sum_{m} M_m \Delta_m\right)^0 = \sum_{m} M_m \Delta_m \Big|_{k=0} \tag{3-83}$$

Substituting Eq. (3-31) and Eq. (3-82) into Eq. (3-79), we have

$$S_k^M = \frac{\sum\limits_{m} M_m \Delta_m - \left(\sum\limits_{m} M_m \Delta_m\right)^0}{\sum\limits_{m} M_m \Delta_m} - \frac{\Delta - \Delta^0}{\Delta} \tag{3-84}$$

simplifying,

$$S_k^M = \frac{\Delta^0}{\Delta} - \frac{\left(\sum\limits_{m} M_m \Delta_m\right)^0}{\sum\limits_{m} M_m \Delta_m} \tag{3-85}$$

or

$$S_k^M = \frac{\Delta^0}{\Delta}\left(1 - \frac{\left(\sum\limits_{m} M_m \Delta_m\right)^0 / \Delta^0}{\sum\limits_{m} M_m \Delta_m / \Delta}\right) \tag{3-86}$$

Therefore, the sensitivity for the over-all gain with respect to k is

$$S_k^M = \frac{1}{F_k}\left(1 - \frac{M^0}{M}\right) \tag{3-87}$$

and

$$M^0 = M \mid_{k=0} \tag{3-88}$$

is sometimes termed the *direct transmission* between the input and output of the system; M^0 is the over-all gain when all the branches containing k are broken. When the direct transmission is zero, Eq. (3-87) becomes

$$S_k^M = \frac{1}{F_k} \tag{3-89}$$

and the sensitivity is inversely proportional to the return difference.

As an example of the calculation of sensitivity, the sensitivity functions of the over-all gain, with respect to μ and R_k in the circuit of Fig. 3-16a, are determined as follows: Referring to the flow graph in Fig. 3-16b, when μ vanishes, the direct transmission M^0 is zero (there is no transmission between V_s and V_0 when P_1 and P_2 are broken). Therefore

$$S_\mu^M = \frac{1}{F_\mu} = \frac{r_p + R_k + R_L}{r_p + R_L + (1 + \mu)R_k} \tag{3-90}$$

In order to determine $S_{R_k}^M$, we refer to the flow graph in Fig. 3-17. The over-all gain of the flow graph is

$$M = \frac{-\mu R_L}{r_p + R_L + (1 + \mu)R_k} \tag{3-91}$$

In this case, the direct transmission is not zero; it is

$$M^0 = M \mid_{R_k=0} = \frac{-\mu R_L}{r_p + R_L} \tag{3-92}$$

Thus
$$S_{R_k}^M = \frac{1}{F_{R_k}}\left(1 - \frac{M^0}{M}\right) = \frac{-(1+\mu)R_k}{r_p + R_L + (1+\mu)R_k} \tag{3-93}$$

3.5 Impedance and Admittance Functions

It has been shown that feedback has definite effects on impedances seen by looking into a system at various points. For this reason, it is a common practice to introduce feedback into certain types of systems for the purpose of controlling impedances.

In a very general way, the impedance function (or the admittance function) can be regarded as a cause-and-effect relation between two specific variables. If we bear the cause-and-effect concept in mind, the understanding of the significance of impedance and admittance functions and the means of controlling them will be greatly enhanced. The definition

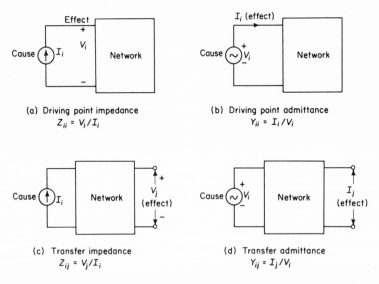

(a) Driving point impedance
$Z_{ii} = V_i/I_i$

(b) Driving point admittance
$Y_{ii} = I_i/V_i$

(c) Transfer impedance
$Z_{ij} = V_j/I_i$

(d) Transfer admittance
$Y_{ij} = I_j/V_i$

Fig. 3-20. Cause-and-effect concept of impedance and admittance functions.

of driving point and transfer impedances and admittances based on the cause-and-effect relation are illustrated in Fig. 3-20. For example, in Fig. 3-20a, the driving point impedance of the network between terminals

i-i' is defined as the cause-and-effect relation between the current source, which acts as the cause, and the voltage appearing across the terminals, which is regarded as the effect (with all other external sources replaced by their internal impedances). Thus

$$\text{Driving point impedance } Z_{ii} = \frac{V_i \text{ (effect)}}{I_i \text{ (cause)}} \tag{3-94}$$

The other impedance and admittance functions, depicted in Fig. 3-20b, c, and d, are defined in similar fashions.

It is important to note that the cause-and-effect view of impedance and admittance functions is exactly analogous to the foundation of signal flow graphs, a fact which suggests that the signal flow graph method can be used for the evaluation of impedance and admittance functions. For example, to determine the driving point impedance Z_{ii} of Fig. 3-20a, I_i is denoted as the input node and V_i as the output node of the network signal flow graph, and Z_{ii} is readily determined by applying Mason's formula.

One of the important considerations in the design of control systems is the minimization of the effect of the external disturbances which may occur at various points of a system. The term disturbance is used here to include any extraneous effect, such as the variation of load impedance of an amplifier, gusts of wind against a radar antenna, and others, which usually have harmful effects on the performance of a control system. In general, if the effect ratio-disturbance (cause) is dimensionally an impedance or an admittance, the minimization of the effect/cause ratio may be realized by controlling the impedance or admittance level at the point (or points) of interest. For example, changes in load impedance at the output of an electronic amplifier usually cause the amplifier output voltage to vary. In this case, the variation in the load current represents disturbance (cause), and the effect is the corresponding variation in the output voltage; thus, the output impedance of the amplifier is a direct measure of the disturbance effect and should be kept small. Gusts of wind against a radar antenna are disturbances in the forms of torques, and they can cause large oscillations in the antenna position. In such a case, the output velocity (effect) to disturbance (cause) ratio may be regarded as the mechanical output admittance of the system and should be kept small. In general, the effect of disturbance and noise signal in any signal system can be evaluated either as driving point or as transfer immittances,* depending upon the location of the cause and effects.

Consider that the impedance into a pair of terminals designated as i-i' of the system shown in Fig. 3-21a is desired (with all external signal sources

---

*The term immittance is used to represent impedance or admittance.

replaced by their internal impedances). A signal flow graph may be constructed for the system with I_i as the input node and V_i, the resultant

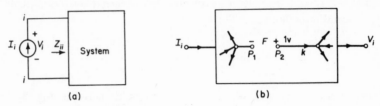

Fig. 3-21. (a) Driving point impedance of a system; (b) Signal flow graph for system in (a).

voltage between the two terminals, as the output node. A general flow graph configuration is shown in Fig. 3-21b.

The driving point impedance seen into terminals i-i' is readily obtained from the signal flow graph of Fig. 3-21b by means of Mason's formula; that is,

$$Z_{ii} = \frac{\sum\limits_{m} M_m \Delta_m}{\Delta} \tag{3-95}$$

where the equation represents the gain between nodes I_i and V_1. In general, the same method can be applied to the determination of transfer impedance or admittances. It is possible to express the impedance (or admittance) functions in terms of the feedback properties of the system; namely, the return difference. Equation (3-95) is written

$$Z_{ii} = \frac{\sum\limits_{m} M_m \Delta_m \, \Delta^0}{\Delta} \frac{\left(\sum\limits_{m} M_m \Delta_m\right)^0}{\Delta^0 \left(\sum\limits_{m} M_m \Delta_m\right)^0} \tag{3-96}$$

Rearranging, we have

$$Z_{ii} = \frac{\left(\sum\limits_{m} M_m \Delta_m\right)^0}{\Delta^0} \frac{\sum\limits_{m} M_m \Delta_m}{\left(\sum\limits_{m} M_m \Delta_m\right)^0} \frac{\Delta^0}{\Delta} \tag{3-97}$$

The first term in the last equation is identified as the direct transmission between I_i and V_i, that is, the transmission when the element k is equal to zero. Hence

$$Z_{ii}^0 \text{ (direct transmission)} = (Z_{ii})_{k=0} = \frac{\left(\sum\limits_{m} M_m \Delta_m\right)^0}{\Delta^0} \tag{3-98}$$

The last term of Eq. (3-97) is simply the inverse of the return difference for k, where k can be any element of the system, passive or active. Therefore, Eq. (3-97) can be written

$$Z_{ii} = Z_{ii}^0 \frac{1}{F_k} \frac{\sum\limits_{m} M_m \Delta_m}{\left(\sum\limits_{m} M_m \Delta_m\right)^0} \tag{3-99}$$

Equation (3-99) is similar to the following expression given by Bode:*

$$Z = Z(0) \frac{F_k(0)}{F_k(\infty)} \qquad (3\text{-}100)$$

where $F_k(\infty)$ denotes the return difference for k with the terminals i-i' open (the normal F_k in this case), and $F_k(0)$ denotes the return difference for k with the terminals i-i' shorted; $F_k(0)$ is given the name *null return differ-ence*.† The corresponding Z's in Eqs. (3-99) and (3-100) have the same meaning; therefore

$$F(0) = \frac{\underset{m}{\Sigma} M_m \Delta_m}{\left(\underset{m}{\Sigma} M_m \Delta_m\right)^0} \qquad (3\text{-}101)$$

To prove this equation, let us refer to the signal flow graph in Fig. 3-21b. The terminals at P_1 and P_2 are opened in front of the element k (again, there may be more than one branch having k as a multiplying factor as far as the validity of Eqs. (3-99) and (3-101) is concerned). The null return difference $F_k(0)$ is defined as the return difference for the element k when the terminals i-i' are shorted; that is, V_i is zero. It should be noted, however, that, unlike the process of evaluating F_k [or $F_k(\infty)$], the input I_i is not set to zero; it is, rather, set at a specific value, so that the zero V_i condition is realized. In terms of the signal flow graph shown in Fig. 3-21b, the desired value for I_i is determined as follows: A unit signal is transmitted from node P_2; this and the signal I_i should contribute to zero V_i. Therefore

$$\frac{\Sigma \, M_{P_2 V_i} \Delta_{P_2 V_i} + I_i (\Sigma \, M_m \Delta_m)^0}{\Delta^0} = 0 \qquad (3\text{-}102)$$

where the first term represents the unit signal times the transmission be-tween nodes P_2 and V_i, and the second term is the product of I_i and the direct transmission between I_i and V_i. From Eq. (3-102), we have

$$I_i = \frac{-\,\Sigma M_{P_2 V_i} \, \Delta_{P_2 V_i}}{(\Sigma \, M_m \Delta_m)^0} \qquad (3\text{-}103)$$

According to the definition of the null return difference, the null return ratio for k is equal to the signal which appears at node P_1 when a unit signal is transmitted from P_2 with the simultaneous application of I_i, whose value is given by Eq. (3-103). The null return ratio is

$$T_k(0) = \frac{I_i \, \Sigma \, M_{I_i P_1} \Delta_{I_i P_1} - k \, (d\Delta/dk)}{\Delta^0} \qquad (3\text{-}104)$$

---

*H. W. Bode, *Network Analysis and Feedback Amplifier Design*, D. Van Nostrand Co., Inc., New York, 1945, p. 68.

†J. G. Truxal, *Control System Synthesis*, McGraw-Hill Book Co., Inc., 1955, p. 128.

where the first term on the right side denotes the product of I_i and the transmission between I_i and P_1, and the second term is the transmission from node P_2 to P_1. Substituting Eqs. (3-81) and (3-103) into Eq. (3-104) and simplifying, we write the null return difference

$$F_k(0) = 1 - T_k(0) = \frac{\Sigma\, M_{I_i P_1}\, \Delta_{I_i P_1} \Sigma\, M_{P_2 V_i}\, \Delta_{P_2 V_i} + \Delta(\Sigma\, M_m\, \Delta_m)^0}{(M_m\, \Delta_m)^0\, \Delta^0}$$

$$(3\text{-}105)$$

But the over-all transmission of the signal flow graph of Fig. 3-21b can be written

$$\frac{\Sigma\, M_m\, \Delta_m}{\Delta} = \frac{\Sigma\, M_{I_i P_1}\, \Delta_{I_i P_1}}{\Delta} \times \frac{\Sigma\, M_{P_2 V_i}\, \Delta_{P_2 V_i}}{\Delta^0} + \frac{(\Sigma\, M_m\, \Delta_m)^0}{\Delta^0} \quad (3\text{-}106)$$

Hence, Eq. (3-105) reads

$$F_k(0) = \frac{\Sigma\, M_m\, \Delta_m}{(\Sigma\, M_m\, \Delta_m)^0} \tag{3-107}$$

Similarly, the admittance seen looking into any pair of terminals of a system (with all external sources replaced by their internal admittances) is calculated by using the voltage between the terminals as the input, and the current as the output. In terms of the admittance functions, Eq. (3-100) is written

$$Y = Y(0)\, \frac{F_k(0)}{F_k(\infty)} \tag{3-108}$$

where $Y(0)$ = admittance seen looking into the terminals when $k = 0$.

$F_k(0)$ = return difference for k when the terminals are open (zero admittance); equal to the normal F_k.

$F_k(\infty)$ = return difference for k when the terminals are shorted (infinite admittance); equal to the null return difference.

The feedback amplifier circuit shown in Fig. 3-8 is used here to illustrate the calculation of the impedance into terminals a–a' (output impedance). The amplification factor (μ) of the tube is taken as the reference element k. The signal flow graph of the system is drawn in Fig. 3-22; the current I_0

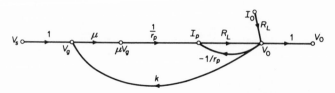

Fig. 3-22. Signal flow graph for feedback amplifier in Fig. 3-8.

is introduced for the purpose of computing the output impedance. Applying Mason's formula directly to the flow graph with I_0 as the input and V_0 as the output $(V_s$ is shorted), we find that the output impedance of the amplifier is

$$Z_a(Z_{out}) = \frac{r_p R_L}{r_p + R_L(1 + \mu k)} \tag{3-109}$$

This result can also be obtained by use of Eq. (3-100). The impedance seen between a–a' when μ is zero, is

$$Z(0) = \frac{r_p R_L}{r_p + R_L} \tag{3-110}$$

The return difference for μ when the terminals a–a' are open is

$$F(\infty) = \frac{\Delta}{\Delta^0} = \frac{r_p + R_L(1 + \mu k)}{r_p + R_L} \tag{3-111}$$

The return difference for μ when the terminals a–a' are shorted is

$$F(0) = 1 \tag{3-112}$$

since there is no feedback with output terminals shorted. Thus

$$Z_a(Z_{out}) = Z(0) \frac{F_k(0)}{F_k(\infty)} = \frac{r_p R_L}{r_p + R_L(1 + \mu k)} \tag{3-113}$$

which agrees with the result given by Eq. (3-109).

Problems

3-1. In Fig. 3P-1:
(a) Find the return difference F_k for $k = \mu$.
(b) Find the return difference F_k for $k = R_k$.
(c) Show that $F_\mu = F_{g_m}$.

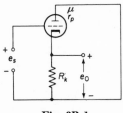

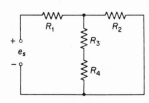

Fig. 3P-1   **Fig. 3P-3**

3-2. Determine the relationship between $F_{k\,mesh}$ and $F_{k\,node}$ for $k =$ bilateral passive element; $F_{k\,mesh}$ represents return difference for k, evaluated by mesh method, and $F_{k\,node}$ is F_k obtained by node method.

3-3. Determine the return difference for R_4 (F_{R_4}) in Fig. 3P-3 by use of the signal flow graph method. Check the result by means of the physical meaning of F_k.

3-4. For the amplifier circuit shown in Fig. 3P-1, determine

$$S^M_\mu, \quad S^M_{R_k} \quad \text{and} \quad S^M_{r_p}$$

where

$$M = E_0/E_s.$$

Use the signal flow graph technique.

3-5. For the circuit shown in Fig. 3P-5, determine the sensitivity function S^M_k, where $M = E_0/E_s$ and $k = X_c/R_2 = 1/\omega CR_2$. Give the significance of this sensitivity function.

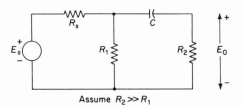

Assume $R_2 \gg R_1$

Fig. 3P-5

3-6. The network shown in Fig. 3P-6 has an external source at the kth node. Y_L is an admittance located at the nth node.

Prove that $\dfrac{V_n (Y_L = 0)}{V_n (Y_L = Y_L)} = F$ (return difference for Y_L)

Δ = determinant of network.

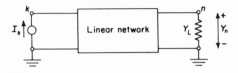

Fig. 3P-6

3-7. A feedback amplifier has several tubes and several feedback loops. The impedance seen in a given mesh is to be determined in terms of the passive impedance seen into the mesh. "Passive" means that there are no active elements in the entire circuit. Derive a relation similar to the relationship given by Eq. (3-100) in the text.

3-8. With reference to Fig. 3P-8:

(1) Draw the current source mid-band incremental equivalent circuit. Does the amplifier have positive or negative feedback?

(2) Construct a signal flow graph for the amplifier.

(3) Evaluate the following quantities:

$$M = e_0/e_s, \qquad F_{gm_1}, \qquad F_{gm_2}, \qquad S_{gm_2}^M \text{ (when } g_{m2} \text{ is very large.)}$$

Assume $R_g \gg R_1$ and R_2.

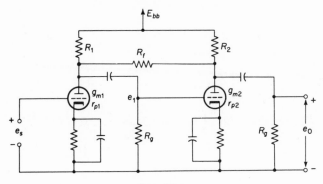

Fig. 3P-8

4

Components of Feedback Control Systems

4.1 Introduction

In this chapter, the characteristics and performances of some of the fundamental components of feedback control systems will be studied. The transfer functions and block diagrams of these elements will be derived so that mathematical analysis may be performed on the feedback control systems. Although the nature of the feedback control system may be arbitrary (that is, it may be composed of mechanical, hydraulic, or electrical elements), in general, it can be represented by the basic block diagram

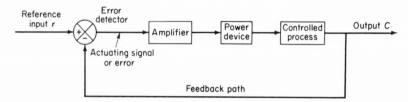

Fig. 4-1. Basic block diagram of a feedback control system.

shown in Fig. 4-1. The sensing device measures the difference between the output and the reference input and sends a signal to the amplifier. The amplification can also be mechanical, hydraulic, electrical, or a combination of these. The amplified signal, in turn, drives the power device which is the motivating power source of the servo system. Not included in Fig. 4-1 are auxiliary devices, which are necessary to convert the actuating signal into proper form for amplification. These elements may include modulators, demodulators, and various types of filters.

4.2 Transducers and Error-sensing Devices

A transducer is a device which converts energy from one form to another. For example, one of the most common transducers is the potentiometer, which converts mechanical shaft positions into proportional electrical signals. A tachometer generator is a typical transducer, since it generates a voltage at its output terminals proportional to the velocity of the shaft. Other examples of the electro-mechanical transducers are the galvanometer, the differential transformer, and many other familiar components.

An error-sensing device compares two signals simultaneously. In feedback control systems, the purpose of an error-sensing device is to produce a signal which is proportional to the difference between the reference input and the controlled output variable. Linear wire-wound potentiometers, properly connected, are frequently used as error detectors. Other error detectors are the E-transformers, synchros, etc., which operate on the principle of magnetic coupling.

Potentiometers as Error-sensing Devices

Figure 4-2 shows a single-turn wire-wound potentiometer. The schematic diagram of the potentiometer is shown in Fig. 4-3.

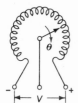

Fig. 4-2.
Single-turn
potentiometer.

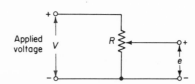

Fig. 4-3. Schematic diagram of potentiometer.

If the potentiometer is assumed to be linear, the transfer function relating the output voltage e and the angular shaft rotation θ is given by

$$\frac{e}{\theta} = \frac{\text{Applied voltage across fixed terminals}}{\text{Maximum possible shaft rotation}} = \frac{V}{\theta_{max}}\left(\frac{\text{volts}}{\text{rad}}\right) \quad (4\text{-}1)$$

Equation (4-1) implies that a single potentiometer can be used as an error detector simply by connecting the reference input shaft to the potentiometer case and the controlled shaft to the shaft of the potentiometer. However, this scheme is not commonly feasible because, in feedback control systems, the controlled shaft and the reference input shaft are almost always remotely located. A more practical application is to connect two potentiometers as shown in Fig. 4-4.

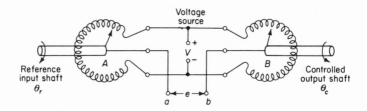

Fig. 4-4. Two potentiometers connected as an error detector.

The two potentiometers convert the input and output shaft positions into proportional electric signals. The two electric signals are, in turn, compared and the difference voltage e is produced at the two terminals a and b. From the electrical viewpoint, the diagram given in Fig. 4-5 repre-

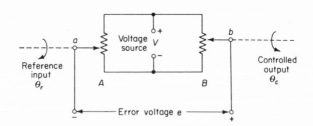

Fig. 4-5. Schematic diagram of a potentiometer sensing device.

sents a simple bridge circuit. When the two arms are in the same relative position, the potential difference between a and b is zero. If the position of the output shaft is above the input shaft (Fig. 4-5), the potential will be higher at point b than at a, and the polarity mark of the error e is that shown in Fig. 4-5. If the position of the input is above that of the output shaft, the polarity of e will be reversed. The applied voltage V can be either d-c or a-c. If a d-c voltage is applied, the polarity marks indicate the sign of e; for an a-c applied voltage, the polarity marks refer to the phase of

$e(t)$ with respect to that of $V(t)$. In either case, the transfer function of the potentiometric sensing device may be written as

$$e = K_s(\theta_r - \theta_c) \qquad (4\text{-}2)$$

where e = error voltage in volts

and K_s = sensitivity of the error detector in volts/rad or volts/deg

  θ_r = reference input shaft position in radians or degrees

  θ_c = controlled output shaft position

A typical application of the pair of potentiometers as an error detector in a servomechanism is shown in Fig. 4-6. In this system, an electric signal,

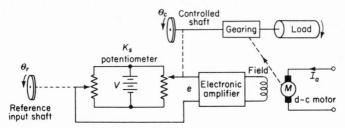

Fig. 4-6. Simple servomechanism with potentiometers as sensing device.

proportional to the misalignment between the reference input shaft and the controlled shaft, is generated at the output of the potentiometer. The amplifier amplifies the electric signal until it is of sufficient power to drive the d-c motor. The motor will then rotate in such a direction as to reduce the error voltage. Theoretically, when the error voltage is zero, the output shaft is in correspondence with the reference input shaft.

Resolution of Potentiometers

Most of the potentiometers used in servo applications are of the wire-wound type. As the potentiometer shaft is rotated, the sliding brush contacts only discrete points on the wire. Thus the output voltage of the potentiometer is not an exact continuous function of the shaft rotation. The actual relation between e and θ is shown in Fig. 4-7b.

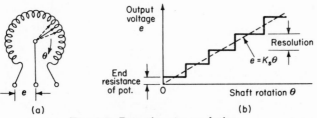

Fig. 4-7. Potentiometer resolution.

The resolution of a potentiometer is defined as the minimum change in output voltage V obtained by rotating the shaft, expressed as a percentage of the total applied voltage V. If we let the number of turns of resistance wire be n, we can write

$$\text{Resolution} = \frac{\Delta V}{V} = \frac{V/n}{V} = \frac{1}{n} \qquad (4\text{-}3)$$

The resolution of a potentiometer places an upper limit on the accuracy of a servo system. The resolution of precision wire-wound potentiometers ranges between 0.001–0.5 per cent. For a carbon potentiometer, the resolution is zero, since the slider moves along a continuous resistance path.

Although the principle of operation and construction of a potentiometer is quite simple, its application in feedback control system is seldom satisfactory for the following major reasons:

(1) Precision wire-wound potentiometers are very delicate devices. The sliding contact may be subject to damage if it is not handled carefully.

(2) The output voltage is discontinuous; thus it contributes to servo inaccuracy.

(3) For a single-turn potentiometer, the useable angle of rotation is less than 360 deg.

(4) Because of the limit on heat dissipation of the potentiometer, the voltage applied to the potentiometer cannot be too large. The sensitivity, therefore, seldom exceeds 0.1 v/deg; a higher-gain amplifier is required than if synchros are used.

A-C Synchros

Among the various types of error-sensing devices, perhaps the most widely used in feedback control systems is a pair of synchros. Basically, a synchro is a rotary device which is used to produce a correlation between an angular position and a voltage or set of voltages. Depending upon the manufacturers, synchros are identified by such trade names as "Selsyn," "Autosyn," "Diehlsyn," "Telesyn," etc. There are several different types and applications of synchros, but in this section only the synchro transmitter, the synchro control transformer, and the synchro differential transmitter will be discussed.

(1) Synchro Transmitter

A synchro transmitter has a Y-connected stator winding which resembles the stator of a three-phase induction motor. The rotor is a salient-pole, dumbbell-shaped magnet with a single winding. A single-phase excitation voltage is applied to the rotor through two slip rings. The voltage may be 115 v at 60 cycles, 115 v at 400 cycles, or some other voltage and fre-

quency depending upon the rating of the synchro. The schematic diagrams
of a synchro transmitter are shown in Fig. 4-8.

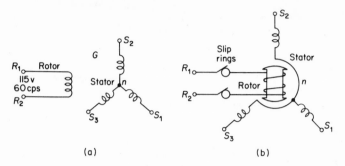

Fig. 4-8. Schematic diagrams of a synchro transmitter.

The symbol "G" is often used to designate a synchro transmitter, which
is sometimes known as a synchro generator.

Let the a-c voltage applied to the rotor be

$$v_R(t) = V_R \sin \omega t \qquad (4\text{-}4)$$

When the rotor is in the position shown in Fig. 4-8b,* the voltage induced
across the stator winding S_2 and the neutral is maximum and is written as

$$v_{S_2n}(t) = KV_R \sin \omega t \qquad (4\text{-}5)$$

where K is a proportional constant. The voltages appearing across the
terminals S_1n and S_3n are given by

$$v_{S_1n}(t) = KV_R \cos 240° \sin \omega t = -0.5KV_R \sin \omega t \qquad (4\text{-}6)$$

$$v_{S_3n}(t) = KV_R \cos 120° \sin \omega t = -0.5KV_R \sin \omega t \qquad (4\text{-}7)$$

The three terminal voltages of the stator are

$$v_{S_1S_2} = v_{S_1n} - v_{S_2n} = -1.5KV_R \sin \omega t \qquad (4\text{-}8)$$

$$v_{S_2S_3} = v_{S_2n} - v_{S_3n} = 1.5KV_R \sin \omega t \qquad (4\text{-}9)$$

$$v_{S_3S_1} = v_{S_3n} - v_{S_1n} = 0 \qquad (4\text{-}10)$$

The above equations show that, despite the similarity between the
construction of a synchro stator and that of a three-phase machine, there
are only single-phase voltages induced in the stator.

Consider now that the rotor is allowed to rotate in a counterclockwise
direction, as shown in Fig. 4-9. The voltages in each stator winding will

---

*This position of the rotor is normally defined as the electric zero of the synchro.

vary as the function of the cosine of the rotor displacement θ; that is, the voltage magnitudes are

$$V_{S_1 n} = K V_R \cos (\theta - 240°) \qquad (4\text{-}11)$$

$$V_{S_2 n} = K V_R \cos \theta \qquad (4\text{-}12)$$

$$V_{S_3 n} = K V_R \cos (\theta - 120°) \qquad (4\text{-}13)$$

The magnitudes of the stator terminal voltages become

$$V_{S_1 S_2} = V_{S_1 n} + V_{n S_2} = \sqrt{3} K V_R \sin (\theta + 240°) \qquad (4\text{-}14)$$

$$V_{S_2 S_3} = V_{S_2 n} + V_{n S_3} = \sqrt{3} K V_R \sin (\theta + 120°) \qquad (4\text{-}15)$$

$$V_{S_3 S_1} = V_{S_3 n} + V_{n S_1} = \sqrt{3} K V_R \sin \theta \qquad (4\text{-}16)$$

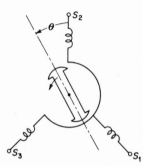

A plot of these terminal voltages as the rotor shaft rotates from 0 deg to 360 deg is given in Fig. 4-10. The voltage-shaft-position relation implies that the synchro transmitter can be used to identify an angular position by measuring and identifying the set of voltages at the stator terminals.

(2) *Synchro Control Transformer*

Fig. 4-9. Rotor position of synchro transmitter.

Since the function of an error detector is to convert the difference of two shaft positions into an electric signal, a single synchro transmitter is apparently inadequate. A typical arrangement of a synchro error detector in servo applications is to connect the stator leads of the trans-

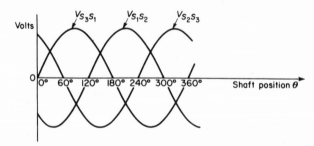

Fig. 4-10. Variation of the terminal voltages of a synchro transmitter as a function of the rotor shaft position (θ is measured counterclockwise from the electric zero).

mitter to the stator leads of a synchro control transformer, as shown in Fig. 4-11. For small deviations, the voltage at the rotor terminals of the control transformer is proportional to the deviation between the two rotor positions.

Basically, the construction of a synchro control transformer is very similar to that of the synchro transmitter, except that the rotor is cylindrically shaped so that the air gap flux is uniformly distributed around the

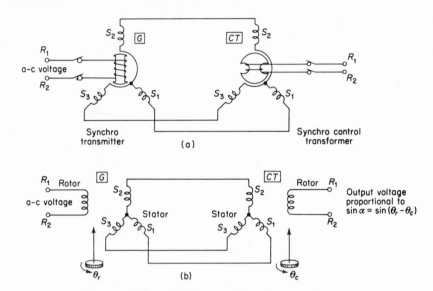

Fig. 4-11. Schematic diagrams of synchro error detector.

rotor. This is essential to a control transformer since its rotor terminals are usually connected to an amplifier; the change in the rotor impedance with rotation of the shaft should be minimized. The symbol "CT" is often used to designate a synchro control transformer.

The voltages given by Eqs. (4-14), (4-15), and (4-16) are now impressed across the corresponding stator leads of the control transformer. Because of the similarity in the magnetic construction, the flux patterns produced in the two synchros will be the same if all losses are neglected. For example, if the rotor of the transmitter is in its electric zero position, the fluxes produced in the transmitter and in the control transformer are all vertical, as shown in Fig. 4-12a, b.

When the rotor of the control transformer is in the position shown in Fig. 4-12b, the induced voltage at its rotor winding terminals is zero. The shafts of the two synchros are considered to be in alignment. However, when the rotor position of the control transformer is rotated 180° from the position shown in Fig. 4-12b, the terminal voltage is again zero. These are known as the two null positions of the control transformer. If the control transformer rotor is rotated an angle α from either of the null positions

(Fig. 4-12c), the magnitude of the rotor voltage is proportional to sin α. Similarly, it can be shown that when the transmitter shaft is in any position other than that shown in Fig. 4-12a, the flux pattern will change accord-

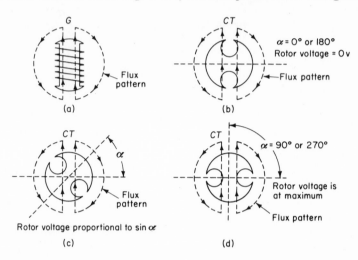

Fig. 4-12. Relations between flux patterns, rotor positions, and the rotor voltage of synchro error detector.

ingly, and the rotor voltage of the control transformer will be proportional to the sine of the difference of the rotor positions α. The rotor voltage of a control transformer versus the difference in positions of the rotors of the transmitter and the control transformer is given in Fig. 4-13.

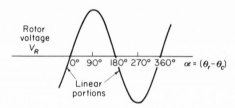

Fig. 4-13. Rotor voltage of control transformer as a function of the difference of rotor positions.

For small angular displacement (approximately, up to 15 deg) in the vicinity of the two null positions, the rotor voltage of the control transformer is approximately proportional to the difference between the positions of the rotors of the transmitter and the control transformer.

A typical a-c servo system employing a synchro error detector is shown in Fig. 4-14. The purpose is to make the controlled shaft follow the angular variations of the reference input shaft. The rotor of the control transformer is mechanically connected to the controlled shaft. The rotor of the synchro transmitter is connected to the reference input shaft. The error signal which appears at the rotor terminals of the control transformer is amplified, and the amplified signal eventually drives the two-phase induction motor.

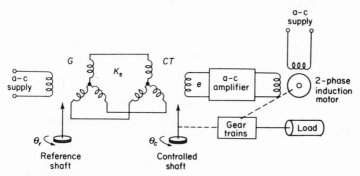

Fig. 4-14. An a-c servomechanism employing synchro error detector.

When the controlled shaft is aligned with the reference shaft, the error voltage is zero and the motor does not turn. When an angular misalignment exists, an error voltage of relative polarity appears at the amplifier input. The motor will turn in the corresponding direction to correct this discrepancy. For small discrepancies, of the controlled and reference shaft positions, the transfer function of the synchro error detector can be written as

$$\frac{E}{\theta_r - \theta} = K \tag{4-17}$$

where E = error voltage

θ_r = reference shaft position in degrees

θ_c = controlled shaft position in degrees

K_s = sensitivity of the error detector in volts per degree.

From the characteristics shown in Fig. 4-13, it is clear that K_s has opposite signs at the two null positions. However, in closed-loop systems only one of the two null positions is the true null; the other one corresponds to an unstable operating point. Suppose that, in the system given in Fig. 4-14, the synchros are operating close to the true null, and the controlled shaft lags behind the reference shaft; a positive error voltage will cause the motor to turn in the proper direction to correct the lag. But if the synchros are operating close to the false null, for the same lag between θ_r and θ_c, the error voltage is negative, which will cause the motor to turn in the direction to increase the lag.* A larger lag in the controlled shaft will increase the magnitude of the error voltage still further and cause the motor to turn further

---

*A two-phase servomotor rotates in opposite directions for opposite polarities of the voltage applied to its control phase winding.

in the same direction until K_s is reversed in sign and the true null position is reached.

In practice, the discrepancy between the controlled shaft and the reference shaft may be represented as a function of time $\theta_e(t)$, as shown in Fig. 4-15a. The error voltage is in a modulated form; i.e.,

$$e(t) = K_s \theta_e(t) \sin \omega_c t \qquad (4\text{-}18)$$

where ω_c, the carrier frequency, is the same as the frequency of the a-c supply voltage. The magnitude of the modulated carrier wave is propor-

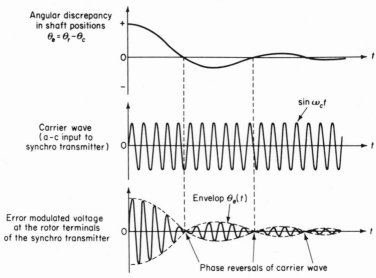

Fig. 4-15. Typical waveforms of a synchro error detector.

tional to the shaft discrepancy $\theta_e(t)$, and the instantaneous polarity depends on the sign of the error.

(3) Synchro Differential Transmitter

Both the stator and the rotor of a synchro differential transmitter have distributed windings similar to the winding on the stator of the synchro transmitter or the control transformer. The differential transmitter is often used to place a shaft in a position which is the sum of two shaft angles. For this purpose, the unit is connected between a synchro transmitter and control transformer as shown in Fig. 4-16.

A-C Tachometers

The a-c tachometer is an electromechanical device which is very similar to a two-phase induction motor. A schematic connection diagram for an a-c tachometer is shown in Fig. 4-17. A sinusoidal voltage of rated value is applied to the primary winding of the tachometer setting up a flux in the

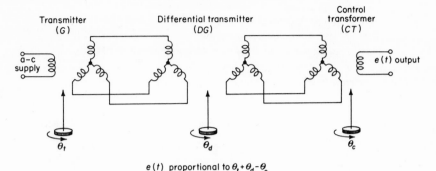

$e(t)$ proportional to $\theta_t + \theta_d - \theta_c$

Fig. 4-16. Synchro differential transmitter used in a summing system. The output voltage of the control transformer rotor is proportional to $(\theta_t + \theta_d) - \theta_c$.

tachometer. The secondary winding is placed at a 90 deg angle mechanically with respect to the primary winding, so that when the rotor shaft is stationary the output voltage at the secondary winding is zero.* When the rotor shaft is rotated, the output voltage is closely proportional to the rotor velocity. The polarity of the voltage is dependent on the direction of rotation. Thus, the characteristic equation of an a-c tachometer can be written as

$$e_t = K_t \frac{d\theta}{dt} \qquad (4\text{-}19)$$

where e_t is the output voltage, θ is the shaft position, and K_t is the sensitivity of the tachometer in v/rad/sec or v/rpm.

Taking the Laplace transform of Eq. (4-19), we have the transfer function of the a-c tachometer:

$$\frac{E_t(s)}{\theta(s)} = sK_t \qquad (4\text{-}20)$$

where s is the Laplace operator. The magnitude of K_t for some existing tachometers is in the range of 0.3 v/1000 rpm to 10 v/1000 rpm. The applications of the a-c tachometer are quite extensive. In servomechanisms, a system with tachometer feedback is known to have better stability in its response. A typical servo employing an a-c tachometer is shown in Fig. 4-18.

The equation which describes the synchro error detecting is written as

$$e = K_s(\theta_r - \theta_c) \qquad (4\text{-}21)$$

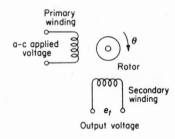

Fig. 4-17. Schematic diagram of an a-c tachometer.

*This is only theoretically true; actually there are residual voltages at the output of an a-c tachometer when the speed of the shaft is zero.

The signal at the input of the amplifier is

$$e_1 = e - e_t \qquad (4\text{-}22)$$

The block diagram of the system is given in Fig. 4-19.

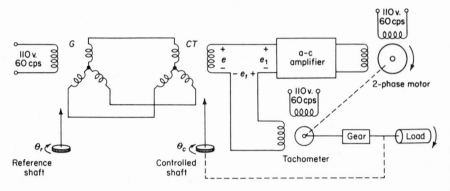

Fig. 4-18. Positional servomechanism employing a-c tachometer.

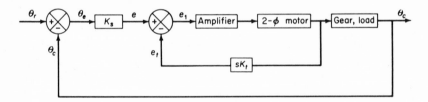

Fig. 4-19. Block diagram of the servo system in Fig. 4-18.

D-C Tachometer

D-c tachometers are applied to d-c servo systems because the tachometer output is a direct voltage. The magnetic field of the device is obtained by means of a permanent magnet; therefore no excitation voltage is required. The transfer function of the d-c tachometer is

$$\frac{E_t(s)}{\theta(s)} = sK_t \qquad (4\text{-}23)$$

---

*The terminals of the tachometer output should be connected in such a way that the instantaneous polarity of e_t, is as shown in Fig. 4-18; otherwise, the effect of the tachometer feedback is de-stabilizing rather than stabilizing.

A d-c tachometer can also be used in an a-c servo system if a modulator is used to convert its d-c output signal into an a-c voltage. Similarly, an a-c tachometer can also be used in a d-c servo system if a phase-sensitive demodulator is used to convert its a-c output signal into a d-c voltage.

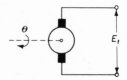

Fig. 4-20. Schematic diagram of a d-c tachometer.

4.3 Servo Motors

D-C Motors

(1) *Series Excitation and Shunt Excitation*

The characteristics of the series-excited and the shunt-excited motors are highly nonlinear; such motors are seldom used in servo systems. However, in systems where linearity is not so important but where high starting torque is required, a modified version of the series motor, called the split-field series motor,* is used.

(2) *Separate Excitation*

Most of the d-c motors in servo applications are of the separately excited type. The output of the d-c servo amplifier can be connected either to the field terminals or to the armature terminals of the motor. When the field is energized by the amplifier signal, the motor is said to be "field controlled"; if the armature is energized by the amplifier, the motor is "armature controlled."

Field-controlled D-C Motor. The schematic diagram of a field-controlled motor is shown in Fig. 4-21. The derivation of the transfer function is based on the following assumptions:

a) A constant current I_a is fed into the armature.

b) The air gap flux ϕ is proportional to the field current I_f; i.e.,

$$\phi = K_f I_f \qquad (4\text{-}24)$$

where K_f is a constant.

c) The torque developed by the motor T_m is proportional to the air gap flux and the armature current; i.e.,

$$T_m = K_m' \phi I_a = K_m' K_f I_f I_a = K_m K_f I_f \qquad (4\text{-}25a)$$

where $$K_m = K_m' I_a \qquad (4\text{-}25b)$$

---

*R. A. Bruns and R. M. Saunders, *Analysis of Feedback Control Systems*, McGraw-Hill, 1955, pp. 55–58.

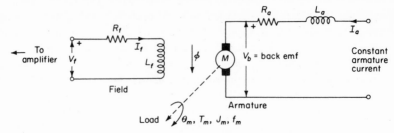

Fig. 4-21. Schematic diagram of field-controlled d-c motor.

The transformed equation of the field circuit is

$$V_f(s) = (R_f + sL_f)I_f(s) \tag{4-26}$$

where R_f is the resistance in ohms and L_f is the inductance* in henries of the field circuit. The motor torque T_m is related to the shaft position by

$$T_m(s) = (J_m s^2 + f_m s)\theta_m(s) \tag{4-27}$$

where J_m is the moment of inertia and f_m is the viscous friction coefficient of the motor.

Equating Eq. (4-25a) and Eq. (4-27):

$$T_m(s) = (J_m s^2 + f_m s)\,\theta_m(s) = K_m K_f I_f(s) \tag{4-28}$$

Solution of Eq. (4-26) for I_f and substituting it in Eq. (4-28) yields

$$T_m(s) = (J_m s^2 + f_m s)\,\theta_m(s) = K_m K_f I_f(s) = \frac{V_f(s)K_m K_f}{(R_f + sL_f)} \tag{4-29}$$

from which the transfer function of the field-controlled motor is derived.

$$\frac{\theta_m(s)}{V_f(s)} = \frac{\text{Output displacement}}{\text{Input voltage to field}} = \frac{K_m K_f}{s(J_m s + f_m)(R_f + sL_f)} \tag{4-30}$$

or

$$\frac{\theta_m(s)}{V_f(s)} = \frac{K_m K_f}{R_f f_m s(1 + s\tau_m)(1 + s\tau_f)} \tag{4-31a}$$

where $\tau_m = J_m/f_m$ = time constant of the motor. $\tag{4-31b}$

and $\tau_f = L_f/R_f$ = time constant of the field. $\tag{4-31c}$

The block diagram of the field-controlled motor is shown in Fig. 4-22.

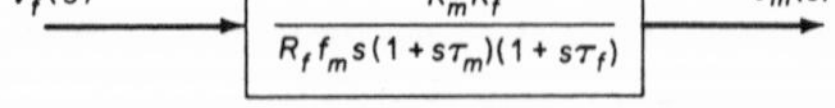

The assumption of constant armature current is important in leading to the linear equations

$$V_f(s) \longrightarrow \boxed{\dfrac{K_m K_f}{R_f f_m s(1 + s\tau_m)(1 + s\tau_f)}} \longrightarrow \theta_m(s)$$

Fig. 4-22. Block diagram representation of a field-controlled d-c motor.

*A question which is frequently raised by the student is: "Why must we consider inductance in a d-c motor?" The reason is that, in servo systems, the transient response is considered to be an important factor, and the inductance governs the transient behavior of the motor.

representing the operation of the motor. However, if instead, a constant voltage source is applied to the armature, the equation of the motor becomes nonlinear and cannot be handled by linear analysis methods.

Armature-controlled D-C Motor. The schematic diagram of an armature-controlled d-c motor is shown in Fig. 4-23. In this type of application, the

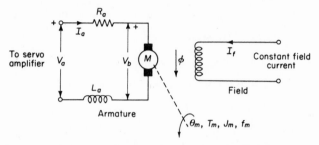

Fig. 4-23. Schematic diagram of armature-controlled d-c motor.

armature of the motor is energized by the signal from the amplifier; the field current is held constant.

The following assumptions are assumed in the derivation of the motor transfer function:

a) The air gap flux is proportional to the field current.

$$\phi = K_f I_f \tag{4-32}$$

b) The torque developed by the motor is proportional to the air gap flux and the armature current.

$$T_m = K_m' \phi I_a = K_m' K_f I_f I_a \tag{4-33}$$

c) The back electromotive-force voltage is proportional to the motor speed.

$$\text{Back emf } V_b = K_b s \theta_m \tag{4-34}$$

In the armature circuit, the transformed equation is

$$V_a(s) = (R_a + sL_a)I_a(s) + V_b(s)$$
$$= (R_a + sL_a)I_a(s) + K_b s \theta_m(s) \tag{4-35}$$

Solving for $I_a(s)$ in the last equation, we have

$$I_a(s) = \frac{V_a(s) - K_b s \theta_m(s)}{R_a + sL_a} \tag{4-36}$$

Substituting the last equation into Eq. (4-33) yields

$$T_m(s) = K_m' K_f I_f \frac{V_a - K_b s \theta_m(s)}{R_a + sL_a} \tag{4-37}$$

Also $$T_m(s) = (J_m s + f_m) s \theta_m(s) \tag{4-38}$$

When we equate Eq. (4-37) and Eq. (4-38), the transfer function of the armature-controlled motor is

$$\frac{\theta_m(s)}{V_a(s)} = \frac{K'_m K_f I_f}{s(R_a + sL_a)(J_m s + f_m) + K_b s K'_m K_f I_f} \tag{4-39}$$

or

$$\frac{\theta_m(s)}{V_a(s)} = \frac{K_i}{s R_a f_m (1 + s\tau_a)(1 + s\tau_m) + K_b K_i s} \tag{4-40}$$

where $K_i = K'_m K_f I_f = $ constant $\tag{4-41}$

$$\tau_a \Rightarrow L_a/R_a = \text{armature time constant} \tag{4-42}$$

$$\tau_m = J_m/f_m = \text{mechanical time constant of motor} \tag{4-43}$$

The significance of Eq. (4-40) is clarified if the equation is divided by the factor $s R_a f_m (1 + s\tau_a)(1 + s\tau_m)$ in the numerator and in the denominator:

$$\frac{\theta_m(s)}{V_a(s)} = \frac{\dfrac{K_i}{s R_a f_m (1 + s\tau_a)(1 + s\tau_m)}}{1 + sK_b \dfrac{K_i}{s R_a f_m (1 + s\tau_a)(1 + s\tau_m)}} \tag{4-44}$$

It is readily seen that the last equation is of the form

$$\frac{\theta_m(s)}{V_a(s)} = \frac{G(s)}{1 + G(s)H(s)} \tag{4-45}$$

if

$$H(s) = sK_b \tag{4-46}$$

and

$$G(s) = \frac{K_i}{s R_a f_m (1 + s\tau_a)(1 + s\tau_m)} \tag{4-47}$$

Thus the block diagram of the armature-controlled d-c motor can be represented by a feedback system, as shown in Fig. 4-24. The effect of the back

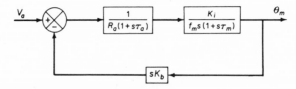

Fig. 4-24. Block diagram representation of the armature-controlled d-c motor.

emf is represented by the feedback of a signal proportional to the speed of the motor. It is easy to see that the back emf effect resembles the tachometer feedback control system given in the previous sections.

In the English unit system, K_i is given in lb-ft/amp and the unit of the back emf constant K_b is v/rad/sec. With these units, K_b and K_i differ only by a constant ratio. The mechanical power developed in the motor armature is

$$P = V_b I_a \quad \text{(w)} = V_b I_a / 746 \quad \text{hp} \tag{4-48}$$

Since

$$V_b = K_b \frac{d\theta_m}{dt} \tag{4-49}$$

and

$$I_a = K_i T_m \tag{4-50}$$

Equation (4-48) becomes the following with the substitution of the last two equations:

$$P = \frac{K_b T_m}{746 K_i} \frac{d\theta_m}{dt} \quad \text{hp} \tag{4-51}$$

Also

$$P = \frac{T_m}{550} \frac{d\theta_m}{dt} \quad \text{hp} \tag{4-52}$$

Hence

$$P = \frac{K_b T_m}{746 K_i} \frac{d\theta_m}{dt} = \frac{T_m}{550} \frac{d\theta_m}{dt} \tag{4-53}$$

from which

$$K_i = \frac{550}{746} K_b = 0.737 K_b \tag{4-54}$$

or

$$K_b = 1.36 K_i \tag{4-55}$$

Comparison Between the Armature- and Field-controlled Motor Operations

There are three important differences between the armature-controlled and the field-controlled types of operation of a d-c motor.

(a) The inductance in the armature circuit can usually be neglected; Eq. (4-40) is thereby reduced to a second-order equation in the armature-controlled operation. In the field-controlled operation, the field inductance is not negligible, and Eq. (4-29) remains a third-order equation.

(b) In the armature-controlled operation, in addition to the damping due to the armature resistance R_a and the motor friction f_m, an aquivalent damping due to the back emf effect is observed. The back emf effect, however, does not appear in the field-controlled case, so the entire damping must come from the motor and the load.

(c) The amplifier used to energize the armature circuit must be able to supply a greater amount of current than if it were to energize the field, circuit.

A-C Servo Motor

For low power applications, a-c motors are preferred, because they are lightweight, rugged, and there are no brush contacts to maintain. Most of the a-c motors used in feedback control systems are of the two-phase induction type. Unlike the motors used for other general purposes, the output power of the a-c servomotor usually varies from a fraction of a watt up to only a few hundred watts. The frequency is normally either 60 cycles or 400 cycles.

A schematic diagram of a two-phase induction motor is shown in Fig. 4-25. The motor consists of a stator with two distributed windings dis-

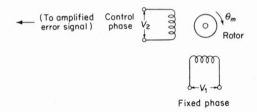

Fig. 4-25. Schematic diagram of a two-phase induction motor.

placed 90 electrical degrees apart. The voltages applied to the windings are not balanced. Under normal operating conditions, a fixed voltage from a constant-voltage source is applied to one phase; the other phase, which is called the *control phase*, is energized by a voltage, of variable magnitude and polarity, which is at 90 degrees out of phase with respect to the voltage of the fixed phase. The control phase voltage is usually supplied from the servo amplifier. The direction of rotation of the motor reverses if the control phase signal changes sign.

The rotor construction is usually of the squirrel-cage or the drag-cup type with no electrical access. The diameter of the rotor is made small in order to reduce the inertia, and thus to improve the acceleration characteristics.

The torque-speed characteristic of a conventional induction motor is shown in Fig. 4-26. It is well-known that the shape of the characteristic depends on the ratio of the rotor reactance to the rotor resistance. For a conventional induction motor, the X/R ratio is high in order to obtain a

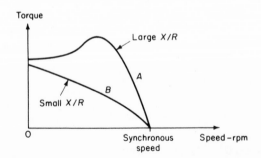

Fig. 4-26. Torque-speed characteristics of an induction motor.

high maximum torque (Curve A, Fig. 4-26). However, this type of characteristic curve is not suitable for feedback control systems, chiefly because of the positive slope on part of the curve. It will be shown later that a negative slope on the torque-speed curve is essential for stability. Thus, the rotor of the two-phase induction motor is built with high resistance.

The torque-speed curves of a typical 5-watt, 60 cycle, two-phase induction motor are shown in Fig. 4-27. It is seen that these curves are

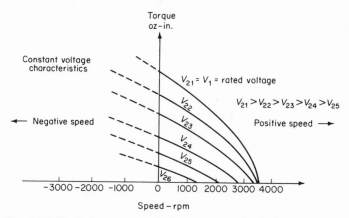

Fig. 4-27. Typical torque-speed characteristics of a two-phase induction motor.

nonlinear except at very low signals and in the region of low control voltages. In order to derive a transfer function for the motor, some linear assumptions and approximations are necessary. It is normally true that a servomotor seldom operates at high speeds; therefore, the linear portions of the torque-speed curves can be extended out to the high speed region, as shown in Fig. 4-28. But even with this approximation, the resultant curves

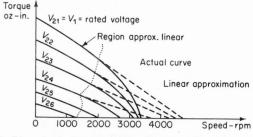

Fig. 4-28. Linearized torque-speed characteristics of a two-phase induction motor by extending the linear portion at low speeds.

are still not parallel to each other. This means that for constant speeds, except near-zero speed, the torque does not vary linearly with respect to the control voltage V_2. The curves given in Fig. 4-29 illustrate this effect. The next necessary assumption is to assume that all the curves are straight lines parallel to the chaarcteristic at rated control voltage ($V_1 = V_2 = $ rated

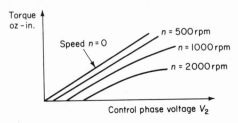

Fig. 4-29. Torque-control voltage curves of a two-phase induction motor indicating that torque is proportional to voltage only at very low speeds.

voltage), and that they are equally spaced for equal increments of the control voltage V_2 (Fig. 4-30).

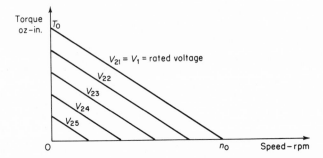

Fig. 4-30. Completely linearized torque-speed characteristics of a two-phase induction motor.

So far, the assumptions we have made on the linearization of the torque-speed curves have not really been proved to be justified, for we do not know how valid they are under actual operating conditions. It should be remembered that a linear analysis is considered to be valid only if experimental results and nonlinear studies corroborate closely the linear theoretical analysis. Thus, at present, we can only take the assumptions for granted and proceed to the derivation of the transfer function of the motor.

Let k be the blocked rotor torque at rated voltage per unit control voltage, i.e.,

$$k = \frac{\text{Blocked rotor torque at } V_2 = V_1}{\text{Rated control voltage } V_1} = \frac{T_0}{V_1} \qquad (4\text{-}56)^*$$

_____

*k is also known as the slope of the $n = 0$ curve in Fig. 4-29.

Let m be the slope of the linearized torque-speed curve* shown in Fig. 4-30.

$$m = -\frac{\text{Blocked rotor torque}}{\text{No load speed}} = \frac{-T_0}{n_0} \tag{4-57}$$

Then for any torque T_m, the family of straight lines in Fig. 4-30 are represented by the equation.

$$T_m = kV_2 + m\frac{d\theta_m}{dt} \tag{4-58}$$

If we consider that the moment of inertia of the motor rotor and shaft is J_m, and the viscous friction is f_m, we have

$$T_m = kV_2 + m\frac{d\theta_m}{dt} = J_m\frac{d^2\theta_m}{dt^2} + f_m\frac{d\theta_m}{dt} \tag{4-59}$$

Taking the Laplace transform on both sides of the last equation, assuming zero initial conditions, yields

$$kV_2(s) + ms\theta_m(s) = (J_m s^2 + f_m s)\theta_m(s) \tag{4-60}$$

from which the transfer function of the two-phase motor is obtained as

$$\frac{\text{Motor shaft displacement}}{\text{Control phase voltage}} = \frac{\theta_m(s)}{V_2(s)} = \frac{k}{(f_m - m)s\left(1 + s\dfrac{J_m}{f_m - m}\right)} \tag{4-61}$$

or

$$\frac{\theta_m(s)}{V_2(s)} = \frac{K_m}{s(1 + s\tau_m)} \tag{4-62}$$

where

$$K_m = \frac{k}{f_m - m} = \text{motor gain constant} \tag{4-63}$$

and

$$\tau_m = \frac{J_m}{f_m - m} = \text{motor time constant} \tag{4-64}$$

Since m is negative, the above equations show that the effect of the slope of the torque-speed curve is to add more friction to the motor, which does improve the damping of the motor. This added damping effect is sometimes called the "internal electric damping" of the two-phase motor. However, if m is a positive number, for $m > f_m$, negative damping occurs, and the motor becomes unstable. This verifies the statement made previously that the conventional induction motors are not suitable for servo applications.

---

*m is a negative number.

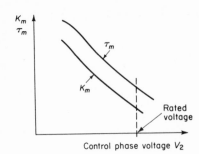

Control phase voltage V_2

Fig. 4-31. K_m and τ_m versus control phase voltage of a two-phase servomotor.

Since the value of m is not constant, judging from the actual torque-speed curves given in Fig. 4-27, K_m and τ_m are also variable with respect to the control voltage. Figure 4-31 shows the actual plot of K_m and τ_m (obtained experimentally)[*] as a function of V_2.

The torque-speed characteristics shown in Fig. 4-27 indicate that m is always negative (the slope of the curves is always negative); therefore, the damping is always positive. However, a familiar degeneration in the motor performance is that, under certain conditions, the motor is capable of running when only the fixed phase is excited but the control voltage is zero. This phenomenon is usually called the "single phasing" of the servomotor. The reason for this behavior is that the source impedance has a great effect on the internal damping of the motor. The characteristics shown in Fig. 4-27 are also known as the constant-voltage-source curves because they are obtained experimentally by exciting both phases of the motor from a zero impedance source. However, in the actual system application, the control phase of the motor is usually driven by an amplifier which has a finite output impedance. This finite source impedance will affect the torque-speed characteristics in such a way that the internal damping effect is often degenerated and thereby causes the motor to run as a single phase motor.

Figure 4-32 shows a set of typical torque-speed characteristics of the two-phase motor when the two phases of the motor are fed by constant current sources which correspond to infinite source impedance. Note that since the slope of the constant current curves is positive in the low speed region, the internal damping of the motor is negative. Thus, for some critical source impedance above which the internal damping will be negative in the low speed region the motor becomes unstable. It was shown[†] that a two-phase motor with zero control voltage does not develop a positive torque at any speed, provided that $|Z|$, the Thevenin's equivalent impedance which the rotor sees looking toward the source, is less than the effective rotor resistance r_2; otherwise, single phasing will occur. Also, when $|Z|$ is greater than r_2, but is of the order of r_2, poor damping qualities, especially near zero speed, will be exhibited.

---

[*]W. A. Stein, G. J. Thaler, "Effect of Nonlinearity in a 2-Phase Servomotor", *AIEE Trans.*, Vol. 73, Part II, 1954, pp. 518–521.

[†]S. S. L. Chang, "The Equivalent Circuit of the Capacitor Motor", *AIEE Trans.*, Vol. 66, 1947, pp. 631–640.

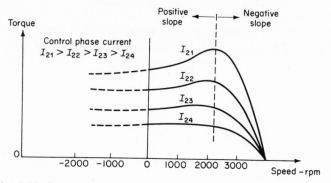

Fig. 4-32. Torque-speed characteristics of a two-phase motor when excited with constant current source.

When Eq. (4-62) is applied, it is important to check carefully the units in which each constant is expressed so that no inconsistency in units will ensue. Since the power output of the two-phase motor is usually small, the torque will usually be in units such as ounce-inches or gram-centimeters, and the friction f_m in oz-in.-sec/rad, and J_m in oz-in.^{2}, oz-in.-sec^2, or gram-cm^2.

As an example, consider a two-phase motor with the torque-speed curves similar to those shown in Fig. 4-27. The important data of the motor are given as follows:

Rated fixed phase and control phase voltage	115 v
Blocked rotor torque at rated V_2	7 oz-in.
Moment of inertia of rotor	0.1 oz-in.^{2}
Viscous friction of motor	0.01 oz-in.-sec/rad

Assume that the extension of the linear portion of the torque-speed curve for rated control voltage intersects the horizontal axis at 4000 rpm.

From Eq. (4-56)

$$k = \frac{T_0}{V_1} = \frac{7 \text{ oz-in.}}{115 \text{ v}} = 0.061 \text{ oz-in./v} \qquad (4\text{-}65)$$

and from Eq. (4-57)

$$m = \frac{-T_0}{n_0} = \frac{-7 \text{ oz-in.}}{4000 \text{ rpm}} = \frac{-7}{4000} \frac{60}{2\pi} \frac{\text{oz-in.-sec}}{\text{rad}} \qquad (4\text{-}66)$$

hence
$$m = -0.0167 \text{ oz-in.-sec/rad} \qquad (4\text{-}67)$$

The equation representing the linearized torque-speed curves is given by Eq. (4-58):

$$T_m = 0.061 V_2 - 0.0167 \frac{d\theta_m}{dt} \qquad (4\text{-}68)$$

The motor gain constant is

$$K_m = \frac{k}{f_m - m} = \frac{0.061 \text{ oz-in./v}}{0.01 + 0.0167 \text{ oz-in.-sec/rad}} \qquad (4\text{-}69)$$

hence

$$K_m = 2.28 \frac{1}{\text{v-sec}} \qquad (4\text{-}70)$$

The motor time constant is

$$\tau_m = \frac{J_m}{f_m - m} = \frac{0.1 \text{ oz-in.}^2}{0.01 + 0.0167 \text{ oz-in.-sec/rad}} \qquad (4\text{-}71)$$

Apparently, the unit of J_m must be converted to oz-in.-sec^2, so that the units in Eq. (4-71) may be consistent.

$$\text{Thus } J_m = \frac{0.1 \text{ oz-in.}^2}{32.2 \cdot 12 \text{ in./sec}} = 0.1 \cdot 2.59 \cdot 10^{-3} \qquad \text{oz-in.-sec}^2$$

$$= 2.59 \cdot 10^{-4} \qquad \text{oz-in.-sec}^2 \qquad (4\text{-}72)$$

Substituting J_m into Eq. (4-71) yields

$$\tau_m = \frac{2.59 \cdot 10^{-4} \text{ oz-in.-sec}^2}{0.0267 \text{ oz-in.-sec/rad}} = 0.97 \cdot 10^{-2} \text{ sec} \qquad (4\text{-}73)$$

Hence, from Eq. (4-62), the transfer function of the motor is

$$\frac{\theta_m(s)}{V_2(s)} = \frac{K_m}{s(1 + s\tau_m)} = \frac{2.28}{s(1 + 0.97 \cdot 10^{-2}s)} \qquad (4\text{-}74)$$

4.4 Modulators and Demodulators

The modulators used in servo systems are frequently called phase-sensitive detectors, because they convert d-c voltages into phase-sensitive a-c voltages. In other words, the a-c voltage from the modulator must be proportional to the d-c signals in magnitude, and its polarity must depend on that of the d-c voltage. D-c input signals with opposite polarity will yield a-c voltages which are 180 deg out of phase. Similarly, a demodulator converts an a-c voltage into a d-c voltage whose polarity depends on the sense of the a-c input. In feedback control systems, it is often desirable to convert d-c signals into a-c signals. For instance, some transducers, such as a thermocouple or a d-c tachometer, yield only d-c outputs; if it is desired to use a-c amplifiers to amplify these d-c voltages, modulators are needed. On the other hand, it is often necessary to convert a-c suppressed carrier signals into d-c signals. One example is in the application of compensation networks and components to improve servo performance. In general, d-c compensation networks are preferable to a-c networks. Thus, carrier modulated signals often have to be demodulated before being sent to the d-c networks.

Figure 4-33 shows the schematic diagram of a *chopper*, which is probably the most widely used phase-sensitive detector in servo systems.

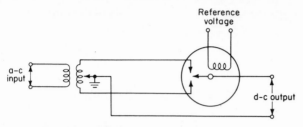

Fig. 4-33. Schematic diagram of a chopper.

Figure 4-34 illustrates a typical application of a chopper in a servo system. The function of the chopper is to rectify the synchro error detector output into a d-c signal, which is then used to drive a d-c motor after it is amplified by a d-c amplifier. The reference voltage of the chopper is supplied from the same source as the error-detector supply, which is usually of either 60 or 400 cycles.

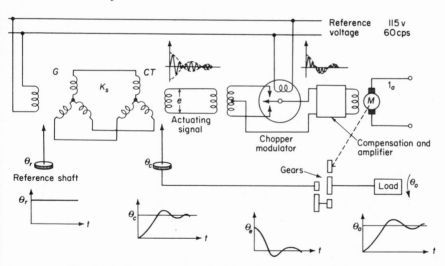

Fig. 4-34. Servo system employing a chopper as demodulator.

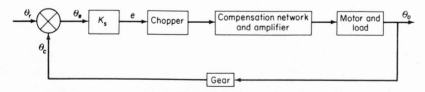

Fig. 4-35. Block diagram of the servo system shown in Fig. 4-34.

Consider that the reference shaft of the servo system is subjected to a sudden fixed angular rotation (step displacement input) at $t = 0$. The operation of the chopper is explained with the aid of Fig. 4-36. The actuating signal $e(t)$ is a suppressed-carrier modulated wave; its waveform is shown in Fig. 4-36a. Figure 4-36b shows the reference signal supplied to the chopper. Since the carrier of $e(t)$ and the reference signal are obtained from the same source, $e(t)$ either is exactly in phase or is exactly out of phase with respect to the reference signal. (In Fig. 4-36 they are shown to be in phase.) When the two signals are multiplied together, the waveform of Fig. 4-36c is obtained, which represents the output of the chopper. Typical signals at other points of the system corresponding to the step displacement input are illustrated in Fig. 4-34.

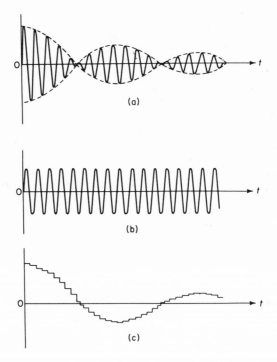

Fig. 4-36. Waveforms illustrating the operation of a chopper used as a demodulator.

In Fig. 4-35 is given the block diagram of the system shown in Fig. 4-34. The chopper shown in Fig. 4-33 can also be used as a modulator. Most demodulators can be reversed and used as modulators. Figure 4-37 illustrates a servo system in which a chopper is used to modulate the d-c output of a d-c tachometer. The modulated output of the chopper is fed into an a-c amplifier, whose output drives the two-phase motor. The operation of the chopper as a modulator can be explained with the aid of Fig. 4-15. The input d-c signal is modulated by the reference voltage to give the suppressed-carrier output voltage. When the reference shaft input is a step function, the output of the d-c tachometer is proportional to the speed of the motor. The typical signals at various points of the system are shown in Fig. 4-37.

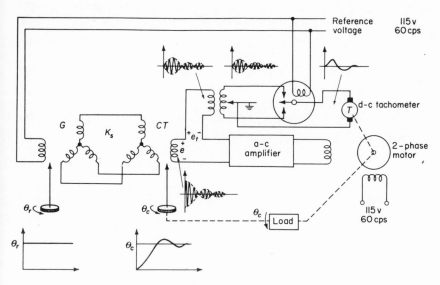

Fig. 4-37. Servo system employing a chopper as modulator.

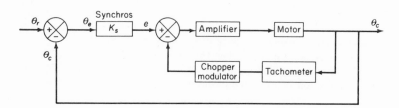

Fig. 4-38. Block diagram of servo system shown in Fig. 4-37.

4.5 Servo Amplifiers

The purpose of this section is to discuss the characteristics and features of the amplifiers used in servo systems. The reader is, presumably, familiar with the basic theory of audio-frequency amplifiers.

Although both a-c and d-c amplifiers are used in feedback control systems, the a-c amplifiers are by far the more common because of the disadvantages associated with d-c amplification. The main disadvantages of d-c amplifiers are, namely, drifts of the output voltage and power supply problems for cascaded stages. The desirable feature of an a-c servo amplifier are as follows:

(1) The frequency response (gain versus frequency) must be flat over the frequency range of $\omega_c - \omega_{sh}$ to $\omega_c + \omega_{sh}$, where ω_c is the carrier frequency, and ω_{sh} is the highest modulation frequency the servo will transmit. For example, if the carrier frequency of a servo system is 60 cps and the highest signal frequency to which the system is expected to respond is 20 cps, the servo amplifier gain should be flat from 40 cps to over 80 cps.

(2) There should be no change in phase shift with the level of input signal.

(3) The amplifier should have a low output impedance. It has been shown previously that when the servomotor is driven by an amplifier, the output impedance of the amplifier has a definite effect on the performance of the servomotor; if the output impedance is high, the servomotor may become unstable.

(4) Unlike conventional audio amplifiers used for the reproduction of speech, the servo amplifiers are used to amplify the output of the null detector; thus, linearity is not essential. However, the servo amplifier should have a low noise characteristic.

Problems

4-1. A simplified schematic diagram of a closed-loop voltage regulator used on a d-c generator is shown in Fig. 4P-1. A potentiometer is used at the output terminals of the generator to give a feedback voltage kV_0, where k is a constant ($k \leq 1$). The potentiometer resistance is high enough that it may be assumed to draw negligible current. The generator is rated at 100 kw, 250 v. The generator armature resistance R_a is 0.01 ohm, and the field resistance R_f is 20 ohms. When the generator is driven at a constant speed, it generates an internal voltage of $V_g = K_g I_f$, where $K_g = 20$ v/amp. The gain of the amplifier is 1000, and $V_i = 50$ v.

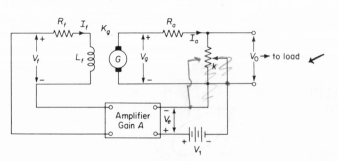

Fig. 4P-1

(a) Draw a block diagram of the system involving the amplifier, the field circuit, and the armature of the generator in separate blocks.

(b) Determine the value of k of the potentiometer setting in order to give a no-load generator terminal voltage V_0 of rated value. What is the value of the error voltage V_e under this condition?

(c) If a load is connected to the output terminals of the generator so that I_a = rated value, what is the steady-state value of the voltage V_0? (Use the value of k determined in part b.)

4-2. A simple positional servo system is shown in Fig. 4P-2. The air gap flux ϕ of the motor is assumed to be proportional to the field current by the constant K_f; the motor torque is proportional to the field flux and the armature current $(T_m = K_m'\phi I_a)$. The sensitivity of the potentiometer-error detector is K_s (v/rad).

(a) Construct a signal flow graph of the servo system using nodes to represent variables θ_r, V_e, V_f, T_m, θ_m, θ_L, and θ_c.

(b) Draw a block diagram of the system with blocks representing the error detector, the amplifier, the motor, and the gear trains.

(c) Evaluate expressions of the open-loop transfer function $\dfrac{\theta_L(s)}{V_e(s)}$ and the closed-loop transfer function $\dfrac{\theta_L(s)}{\theta_r(s)}$.

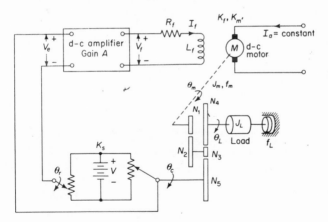

Fig. 4P-2

4-3. A simple positional servo system is shown in Fig. 4P-3. The transfer function of the demodulator is given as K_d a-c-v/d-c-v. The sensitivity of the synchro error detector is K_s in v/rad; V_b is the back electromotive force of the d-c motor.

(a) Construct a signal flow graph of the system, using nodes θ_r, V_e, V_d, V_a, I_a, T_m, θ_m, and θ_L.

(b) Draw a block diagram of the system with blocks representing the error detector, the demodulator and amplifier, the motor, and the gear train.

(Express the effect of the back electromotive force by an internal feedback path.)

(c) Evaluate the open-loop transfer function $\theta_L(s)/V_e(s)$ and the closed-loop transfer function $\theta_L(s)/\theta_r(s)$.

(d) Modify the block diagram constructed for part c to include the effect of an external torque disturbance T_L which is exerted on the load. Evaluate the transfer function $\theta_L(s)/T_L(s)$ when $\theta_r \equiv 0$.

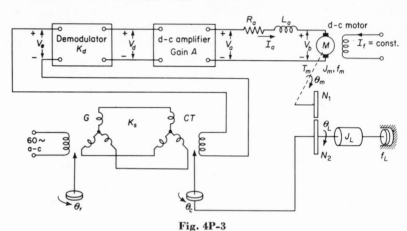

Fig. 4P-3

4-4. An a-c tachometer is used as a component in an integrator of a certain computer, as shown in Fig. 4P-4. The transfer function of the tachometer may be represented by K_t in v/rad/sec. The motor is assumed to be ideal with a torque constant of K_m (lb-ft/v). The total inertia of motor, load and tachometer is J, and the viscous friction is f.

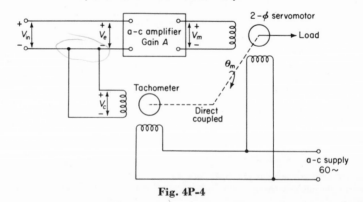

Fig. 4P-4

(a) Construct a signal flow graph for the system, using nodes to represent v_{in}, v_e, v_c, v_m, and θ_m. Evaluate $\theta_m(s)/V_{\text{in}}(s)$.

(b) Draw a block diagram of the system, using three blocks to represent the amplifier, the motor load, and the tachometer, respectively.

4-5.   A two-phase servomotor has the torque-speed characteristics shown in Fig. 4P-5. In the low-speed range, these characteristics may be closely approximated by a series of parallel straight lines whose intersections with the vertical axis are proportional to the magnitude of the control phase voltage V_2 when the voltage V_1 is held constant. The motor develops a blocked-rotor

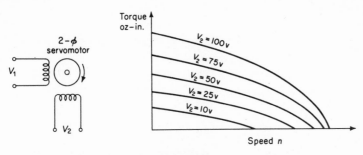

Fig. 4P-5

torque of 5 oz-in when V_2 is at rated 75 v. An extension of the linear portion of the torque-speed curve for $V_2 = 75$ v intersects the horizontal axis at 4500 rpm. The inertia of the motor is 0.1 oz-in². The viscous friction of the motor may be neglected.

(a) Draw the linearized torque-speed curves for the motor with values of V_2 equal to 10, 25, 50, 75, and 100 v.

(b) Write an algebraic equation for the motor developed torque in terms of V_2 and motor angular velocity.

(c) Determine the transfer function $\theta_m(s)/V_2(s)$ of the motor.

5

Time Response of Feedback Control Systems

5.1 Introduction

The solution of a differential equation of any physical system generally consists of two parts — the transient solution, and the steady-state solution. In a servomechanism, for instance, the steady-state response, when it is compared with the reference input signal, gives an indication of the accuracy of the system. If the output steady-state response does not exactly agree with the input, the system is said to have a steady-state error. Also, since all systems contain inertia and friction, the output response before the steady state is reached does not follow the reference input at all times. The transient solution furnishes information on such system behaviors as the extent to which the output deviates from the input, and the time interval during the transient state.

In this chapter, performance criteria and specifications of the feedback control systems will be given in the time domain. From these simple criteria, the performance of linear feedback control systems when some typical test signals are applied is analyzed.

5.2 Typical Test Input Signals for the Transient Analysis of Feedback Control Systems

In practice, the input excitation to a feedback control system is not known ahead of time. In most cases, the actual inputs vary in random fashions with respect to time. For instance, in a radar tracking system, the position and speed of the target to be tracked may vary in any unpredictable manner, so they cannot be expressed mathematically by any simple equation. However, for the purpose of analysis and design, it is necessary to assume some basic types of input functions so that the performance of a system can be analyzed with at least these test signals. In a design problem, performance criteria are derived with respect to these test signals, and linear systems are designed to meet the criteria. In general, the following three types of input are used:

(1) *Step Displacement Input*

This is the instantaneous change in the reference input variable; e.g., a sudden rotation of an input shaft. The mathematical representation of a step function is

$$r(t) = R \qquad\qquad t > 0$$
$$r(t) = 0 \qquad\qquad t < 0 \qquad (5\text{-}1)$$

and at $t = 0$, the function is not defined. The step function is shown in Fig. 5-1a.

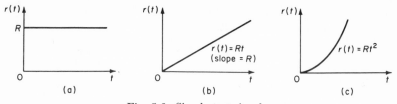

Fig. 5-1. Simple test signals.

(2) *Step Velocity Input (Ramp Function)*

In this case, the reference input variable is considered to have a constant change in position with respect to time. Mathematically, a ramp function is represented by

$$r(t) = Rt \qquad\qquad t > 0$$
$$r(t) = 0 \qquad\qquad t < 0 \qquad (5\text{-}2)$$

The ramp function is shown in Fig. 5-1b.

(3) *Acceleration Input (Parabolic Function)*

The mathematical representation of an acceleration input is

$$r(t) = Rt^2 \qquad\qquad t > 0$$
$$r(t) = 0 \qquad\qquad t < 0 \qquad (5\text{-}3)$$

The graphical representation of an acceleration function is shown in Fig. 5-1c.

5.3 Time Domain Performance Characteristics of Feedback Control Systems

(1) Steady-State Performance

It was mentioned previously that the steady-state error is a measure of the system accuracy when a specific type of input is applied to a feedback control system. In a physical system, because of friction and other related factors, the steady-state output response of a system seldom agrees exactly with the reference input. The steady-state performance of a feedback control system is generally judged by evaluating the steady-state error due to the three typical test signals given above. A detailed study of the steady-state error of feedback control systems will be given in Sec. 5.8.

(2) Transient Performance

The transient performance of a feedback control system is normally analyzed by using a unit-step function as the reference input. A typical step response is shown in Fig. 5-2. The response is usually characterized by the following quantities:

(a) *Overshoot*. The overshoot is an indication of the largest error between input and output during the transient state. It is also recognized as a measure of the relative stability of a system. The overshoot is often represented as a percentage of the final value; that is,

$$\text{Per cent overshoot} = \frac{\text{Maximum overshoot}}{\text{Final desired value}} 100 \qquad (5\text{-}4)$$

(b) *Time delay*. The time delay T_d is normally defined as the time required for the response to reach 50 per cent of the final value.

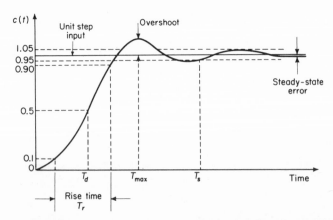

Fig. 5-2. Response to unit step input showing time-domain specifications of feedback control systems.

(c) *Rise time*. The rise time T_r is defined as the time required for the response to rise from 10 per cent to 90 per cent of its final value. Sometimes an equivalent measure is to represent the rise time as the reciprocal of the slope of the response at the instant the response is equal to 50 per cent of its final value.

(d) *Settling time*. The settling time T_s is defined as the time required for the response to decrease to and stay within a specified percentage of its final value. A frequently used figure is 5 per cent.

There are other important quantities, such as the damping ratio, the damping factor, and the undamped natural frequency, which cannot be represented on the time response shown in Fig. 5-2. The significance of these quantities will be discussed in the next section.

5.4 Transient Response of Feedback Control Systems

The Characteristic Equation

Consider the block diagram of a feedback control system which is shown in Fig. 5-3. The closed-loop transfer function of the system is

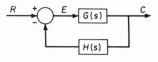

Fig. 5-3. Feedback control system.

$$\frac{C(s)}{R(s)} = \frac{G(s)}{1 + G(s)H(s)} \qquad (5\text{-}5)$$

The denominator of the closed-loop transfer function, when it is set equal to zero, reads

$$1 + G(s)H(s) = 0 \qquad (5\text{-}6)$$

The last equation is called the "characteristic equation" of the linear feedback control system. Normally Eq. (5-6) is a rational function with constant coefficients, so its roots must be either real numbers or pairs of complex conjugate numbers.

Equation (5-5) can be written

$$\frac{C(s)}{R(s)} = \frac{K \prod\limits_{j=1}^{\nu} (s + z_j)}{\prod\limits_{i=1}^{n+2m} (s + p_i)} = \frac{K \prod\limits_{j=1}^{\nu} (s + z_j)}{\prod\limits_{i=1}^{n} (s + \sigma_i) \prod\limits_{k=1}^{m} [s + (\alpha_k + j\omega_k)][s + (\alpha_k - j\omega_k)]}$$

$$(5\text{-}7)$$

where $-\sigma_i$ denotes the real roots, and $-\alpha_k \pm j\omega_k$ denotes the complex conjugate roots of the characteristic equation. The response of the system to an input signal $r(t)$ is

$$c(t) = \mathcal{L}^{-1}[C(s)] = \mathcal{L}^{-1}\left\{ R(s) \frac{K \prod\limits_{j=1}^{\nu} (s + z_j)}{\prod\limits_{i=1}^{n} (s + \sigma_i) \prod\limits_{k=1}^{m} [s + (\alpha_k + j\omega_k)][s + (\alpha_k - j\omega_k)]} \right\}$$

$$(5\text{-}8)$$

If the input $r(t)$ is a unit step function, the output is

$$c(t) = \mathcal{L}^{-1}\left\{ \frac{K \prod\limits_{j=1}^{\nu}(s + z_j)}{s \prod\limits_{i=1}^{n}(s + \sigma_i) \prod\limits_{k=1}^{m}[s^2 + 2\alpha_k s + (\alpha_k^2 + \omega_k^2)]} \right\} \tag{5-9}$$

When the last equation is expanded by the partial fraction expansion, the output response becomes

$$c(t) = \mathcal{L}^{-1}\left[\frac{1}{s} + \sum_{i=1}^{n} \frac{A_i}{(s + \sigma_i)} + \sum_{k=1}^{m} \frac{B_k}{s^2 + 2\alpha_k s + (\alpha_k^2 + \omega_k^2)} \right] \tag{5-10}$$

where A_i and B_k are constants which depend on the poles and the zeros of Eq. (5-7).

From the Laplace transform table, the following transform pairs are identified:

$$\mathcal{L}^{-1}\left(\frac{1}{s + \sigma_i}\right) = e^{-\sigma_i t} \tag{5-11}$$

and

$$\mathcal{L}^{-1}\left[\frac{1}{s^2 + 2\alpha_k s + (\alpha_k^2 + \omega_k^2)} \right] = \frac{1}{\omega_k} e^{-\alpha_k t} \sin(\omega_k t) \tag{5-12}$$

If there are no repeated roots in the characteristic equation, the expression for $c(t)$ is

$$c(t) = 1 + \sum_{i=1}^{n} A_i e^{-\sigma_i t} + \sum_{k=1}^{m} B_k \frac{1}{\omega_k} e^{-\alpha_k t} \sin(\omega_k t) \tag{5-13}$$

It is clear that, in the last equation, all terms appearing under the summation symbol represent the transient response, and that the first term, 1, is the steady-state response. Furthermore, the transient response is characterized by either the exponential terms, the damped sinusoids, or both. An important fact is that the location of the roots of the characteristic equation in the s-plane uniquely defines the form of the transient response. The real roots σ_i and the real parts of the complex roots α_k appear as exponents; thus, they control the damping of the time response. The imaginary parts of the roots ω_k appear as the frequencies of sinusoidal oscillations of the response.

Location of the Roots of the Characteristic Equation

It is apparent that if any one of the real roots is positive, i.e., located in the right half of the s-plane, its corresponding exponential term in the transient response will increase monotonically with time; the system is said to be unstable. Similarly, a pair of complex conjugate roots with positive real parts will correspond to a sinusoidal oscillation with increasing amplitude. Hence, we can conclude that for a stable response, the roots of the characteristic equation should not be found in the right half of the s-plane. Roots which are on the imaginary axis correspond to systems with sustained constant amplitude oscillations. The effect on the shape of the exponential and damped sinusoidal responses by various root locations in the s-plane is shown in Fig. 5-4.

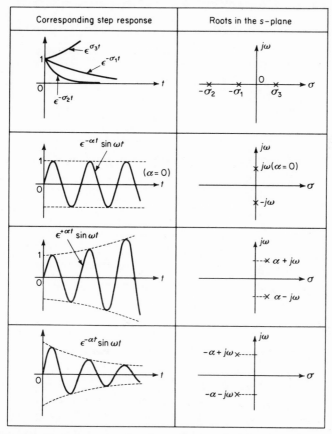

Fig. 5-4. Response comparison for various root locations in the s-plane.

From the responses given in Fig. 5-4, it is seen that stable responses which correspond to roots close to the imaginary axis die out more slowly than do those which correspond to roots that are far away from the imaginary axis. The time required for the decay of the transient response is measured by the horizontal distance from the root to the $j\omega$ axis. The smaller the distance, the more slowly the transient dies out. The roots which are closest to the $j\omega$ axis are sometimes called the dominant roots of the characteristic equation, because all other roots will cause transients to decay more rapidly. In feedback control systems, usually the dominant roots are in complex conjugate pairs.

Consider the equation:

$$s^2 + 2\alpha s + (\alpha^2 + \omega^2) = 0 \tag{5-14}$$

Normally, it is convenient to write the last equation in the form:

$$s^2 + 2\delta\omega_n s + \omega_n^2 = 0 \tag{5-15}$$

The two roots of Eq. (5-15) are

$$s_1, s_2 = -\delta\omega_n \pm j\omega_n\sqrt{1 - \delta^2} = -\alpha \pm j\omega \tag{5-16}$$

where δ = damping ratio

ω_n = undamped natural frequency = frequency of oscillation when damping is zero ($\delta = 0$), $\omega_n = \sqrt{\alpha^2 + \omega^2}$

$\alpha = \delta\omega_n$ = damping constant (actual damping)

$\omega = \omega_n\sqrt{1 - \delta^2}$ = conditional frequency*

In terms of the damping ratio, the roots of the characteristic equation are real if $\delta \geq 1$.

For

$\delta < 1$	$s_1, s_2 = -\delta\omega_n \pm j\omega_n\sqrt{1 - \delta^2}$	(underdamped case)
$\delta = 1$	$s_1, s_2 = -\omega_n$	(critical damped case)
$\delta > 1$	$s_1, s_2 = -\delta\omega_n \pm \omega_n\sqrt{\delta^2 - 1}$	(overdamped case)
$\delta = 0$	$s_1, s_2 = \pm j\omega_n$	(undamped case)

If ω_n is held constant and δ is varied from 0 to ∞, the location of the roots of the characteristic equation will move away from the imaginary axis along a circular path of radius ω_n; the roots will meet at the point $s = -\alpha = -\omega_n$ when $\delta = 1$, and then separate and travel along the real axis toward zero and infinity. This is illustrated in Fig. 5-5.

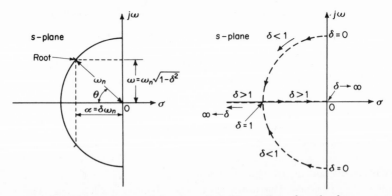

Fig. 5-5. Locus of roots of the characteristic equation when the damping ratio is varied from 0 to ∞ (ω_n is held constant).

---

*Although ω is frequently called the actual frequency of the damped sinusoid, strictly speaking, it is not a true frequency, since a damped sinusoid is not a periodic function.

For complex roots, ω_n is the radial distance from the roots to the origin $(\omega_n = \sqrt{(\alpha^2 + \omega^2)})$. The damping ratio δ is equal to the cosine of the angle between the radial line to the roots and the negative real axis; i.e.,

$$\delta = \cos \theta \tag{5-17}$$

5.5 Transient Response of a Second-Order System

Consider a feedback control system with the closed-loop transfer function

$$\frac{C(s)}{R(s)} = \frac{\omega_n^2}{s^2 + 2\delta\omega_n s + \omega_n^2} \tag{5-18}$$

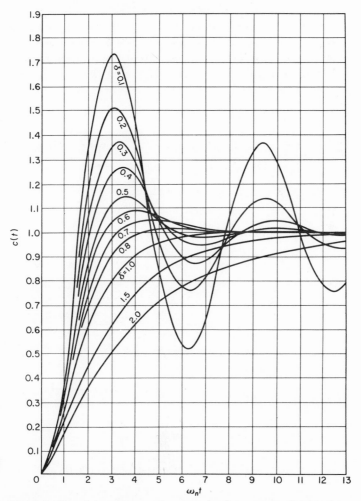

Fig. 5-6. Transient response of a second-order servomechanism to a unit step displacement input.

For a unit step-function input, the output response of the system is

$$c(t) = \mathcal{L}^{-1}\left[\frac{\omega_n^2}{s(s^2 + 2\delta\omega_n s + \omega_n^2)}\right] \tag{5-19}$$

The inverse transform of the last equation is found in the Laplace transform table.

$$c(t) = 1 - \frac{e^{-\delta\omega_n t}}{\sqrt{1 - \delta^2}}\sin\left[\omega_n\sqrt{1 - \delta^2}\,t + \tan^{-1}\frac{\sqrt{1 - \delta^2}}{\delta}\right] \tag{5-20}$$

In Fig. 5-6 is plotted the variation of the output response for various values of damping ratio δ as a function of the normalized time $\omega_n t$. It is seen that the response becomes more oscillatory as δ decreases in value. When $\delta \geq 1$, there is no overshoot in the response; the output response never exceeds the reference input. The exact relation between the damping ratio and the amount of overshoot can be obtained by taking the derivative of Eq. (5-20) and setting it equal to zero. Thus

$$\frac{dc(t)}{dt} = \frac{-e^{-\delta\omega_n t}}{\sqrt{1 - \delta^2}}\omega_n\sqrt{1 - \delta^2}\cos(\omega t + \phi) + \frac{\delta\omega_n e^{-\delta\omega_n t}}{\sqrt{1 - \delta^2}}\sin(\omega t + \phi)$$
$$\tag{5-21}$$

where
$$\phi = \tan^{-1}\frac{\sqrt{1 - \delta^2}}{\delta} \tag{5-22}$$

Setting Eq. (5-21) equal to zero and simplifying, we have

$$-\omega_n\sqrt{1 - \delta^2}\cos(\omega t + \phi) + \delta\omega_n\sin(\omega t + \phi) = 0 \tag{5-23}$$

from which
$$\tan(\omega t + \phi) = \frac{\omega_n\sqrt{1 - \delta^2}}{\delta\omega_n} = \frac{\sqrt{1 - \delta^2}}{\delta} \tag{5-24}$$

or
$$\tan\left(\omega t + \tan^{-1}\frac{\sqrt{1 - \delta^2}}{\delta}\right) = \frac{\sqrt{1 - \delta^2}}{\delta} \tag{5-25}$$

Thus
$$\omega t = n\pi \qquad (\text{for } n = 0, 1, 2, \ldots)$$

which gives
$$t = \frac{n\pi}{\omega_n\sqrt{1 - \delta^2}} \tag{5-26}$$

The first maximum value of the output response $c(t)$ occurs at $n = 1$; hence

$$t_{\max} = \frac{\pi}{\omega_n\sqrt{1 - \delta^2}} \tag{5-27}$$

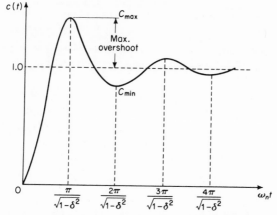

Fig. 5-7. Step response illustrating that the maxima and minima occur at periodic intervals.

In general, for all odd values of n (that is, $n = 1, 3, 5, \ldots$), Eq. (5-26) gives the times at which the overshoots occur; for all even values of n, it gives the times at which the undershoots occur (Fig. 5-7). It is interesting to note that, although the maxima and the minima of the response occur at periodic intervals, the damped sinusoid is not a periodic function. The magnitudes of the overshoots and the undershoots can be obtained by substituting Eq. (5-26) into Eq. (5-20). Hence

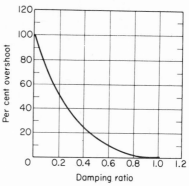

Fig. 5-8. Per cent overshoot as a function of damping ratio for the step displacement response of a second-order system.

$$c(t)\Big|_{\substack{\text{max or} \\ \text{min}}} = 1 - \frac{e^{-n\pi\delta/\sqrt{1-\delta^2}}}{\sqrt{1-\delta^2}} \sin\left(n\pi + \tan^{-1}\frac{\sqrt{1-\delta^2}}{\delta}\right) \qquad (5\text{-}28)$$

$$(\text{for } n = 1, 2, 3, 4, \ldots)$$

or

$$c(t)\Big|_{\substack{\text{max or} \\ \text{min}}} = 1 - (-1)^n e^{-n\pi\delta/\sqrt{1-\delta^2}} \qquad (5\text{-}29)$$

The maximum overshoot is obtained by letting $n = 1$ in the last equation.

$$\text{Maximum overshoot} = c_{\text{max}} - 1 = e^{-\pi\delta/\sqrt{1-\delta^2}} \qquad (5\text{-}30)$$

and

$$\text{Per cent overshoot} = 100\, e^{-\pi\delta/\sqrt{1-\delta^2}} \qquad (5\text{-}31)$$

Therefore, for a second-order system, the overshoot of the step response is only a function of the damping ratio. The relationship between per cent overshoot and damping ratio for a second-order system is depicted in Fig. 5-8.

5.6 Transient Response of a Positional Servomechanism

Consider the simple servomechanism shown in Fig. 5-9. The system is to position a mechanical load with viscous friction and inertia. A potentiometric error-detector with sensitivity K_s is used to measure the discrepancy between the reference and the controlled shaft. The actuating signal is amplified by a d-c amplifier, whose output is connected across the armature of a d-c motor.

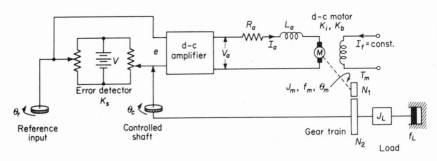

Fig. 5-9. Simple d-c positional servomechanism.

The constants of the system are given as follows:

Sensitivity of error detector $\qquad K_s = 1/57.3$ v/deg. $= 1$ v/rad

Gain of the d-c amplifier $\qquad A$

Resistance in the armature of motor $\quad R_a = 5$ ohms

Inductance in the armature of motor $\quad L_a =$ Negligible

Inertia of motor $\qquad J_m = 10^{-3}$ lb-ft-sec^2

Friction of motor $\qquad f_m =$ Negligible

Friction of load $\qquad f_L = 0.1$ lb-ft/rad/sec

Inertia of load $\qquad J_L = 0.1$ lb-ft/rad/sec^2

Gear ratio $\qquad n = N_1/N_2 = 1/10$

Motor constant $\qquad K_i = 0.5$ lb-ft/amp

If the initial conditions of the system are zero, the first step in the analysis is to write the transfer functions of each component of the system.

(1) For the error-detector:

$$\frac{E(s)}{\theta_r(s) - \theta_c(s)} = \frac{E(s)}{\theta_e(s)} = K_s = 1 \text{ v/rad} \tag{5-32}$$

(2) For the amplifier:

$$\frac{V_a(s)}{E(s)} = A = \text{gain} \tag{5-33}$$

(3) For the d-c motor: The motor is armature controlled; the transfer function of the motor is given by Eq. (4-40):

$$\frac{\theta_m(s)}{V_a(s)} = \frac{K_i}{sR_af_m(1 + sT_a)(1 + sT_m) + K_bK_is} \tag{5-34}$$

However, in this case, in addition to the viscous friction and inertia of the motor, the friction and inertia of the load have to be considered when the transfer function is derived, as in Eq. (5-34). The equivalent friction and inertia on the motor side can be written:

$$J = J_m + n^2J_L = 10^{-3} + \frac{1}{100}\,0.1 = 2 \cdot 10^{-3} \text{ lb-ft/rad/sec}^2 \tag{5-35}$$

and $$f = f_m + n^2f_L = 10^{-3} \text{ lb-ft/rad/sec} \tag{5-36}$$

Hence, Eq. (5-34) becomes

$$\frac{\theta_m(s)}{V_a(s)} = \frac{K_i}{sR_af(1 + sT_a)(1 + sT) + K_bK_is} \tag{5-37}$$

where $T_a = L_a/R_a$ = negligible, and $T = J/f = 2$ sec.

The back electromotive force constant K_b is not given originally, but the relation between K_b and K_i was given by Eq. (4-55). Hence,

$$K_b = 1.36K_i = 1.36 \times 0.5 = 0.68 \text{ v/rad/sec} \tag{5-38}$$

The block diagram of the entire system is now constructed by connecting together the block diagram representation of each individual component, as shown in Fig. 5-10.

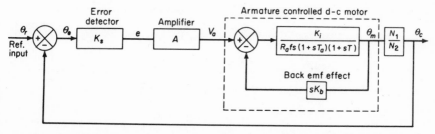

Fig. 5-10. Block diagram representation of the servo system shown in Fig. 5-9.

The open-loop transfer function of the servo system can readily be shown to be

$$G(s) = \frac{\theta_c(s)}{\theta_e(s)} = \frac{K_s A K_i n}{s R_a f(1 + sT_a)(1 + sT) + K_b K_i s} \tag{5-39}$$

The closed-loop transfer function of the system is

$$\frac{\theta_c(s)}{\theta_r(s)} = \frac{K_s A K_i n}{s R_a f(1 + sT_a)(1 + sT) + K_b K_i s + K_s A K_i n} \tag{5-40}$$

Since $T_a \approx 0$, the last equation becomes

$$\frac{\theta_c(s)}{\theta_r(s)} = \frac{K_s A K_i n}{R_a J s^2 + (K_b K_i + R_a f)s + K_s A K_i n} \tag{5-41}$$

or

$$\frac{\theta_c(s)}{\theta_r(s)} = \frac{K_s A K_i n / R_a J}{s^2 + \dfrac{K_b K_i + R_a f}{R_a J} s + \dfrac{K_s A K_i n}{R_a J}} \tag{5-42}$$

The last equation is of the second order; thus, it can be written in the standard form given by Eq. (5-18). The undamped natural frequency of the system is

$$\omega_n = \pm \sqrt{\frac{K_s A K_i n}{R_a J}} \tag{5-43}$$

The damping ratio is

$$\delta = \frac{K_b K_i + R_a f}{2 R_a J \omega_n} = \frac{K_b K_i + R_a f}{2\sqrt{K_s A K_i n R_a J}} \tag{5-44}$$

When the values of the system parameters are substituted into Eq. (5-42), we have

$$\frac{\theta_c(s)}{\theta_r(s)} = \frac{5A}{s^2 + 34.5s + 5A} \tag{5-45}$$

Let us suppose that the gain of the d-c amplifier is, arbitrarily, 200. The natural undamped frequency and the damping ratio are, respectively,

$$\omega_n = \pm \sqrt{1000} = \pm 31.6 \text{ rad/sec} \tag{5-46}$$

$$\delta = 0.546 \tag{5-47}$$

The characteristic equation of the system is

$$s^2 + 34.5s + 1000 = 0 \tag{5-48}$$

whose roots are

$$s_1, s_2 = -17.25 \pm j26.5 \tag{5-49}$$

For a unit step displacement input, $\theta_r(t) = 1$ rad, the output response of the system is

$$\theta_c(t) = \mathcal{L}^{-1}\left[\frac{1000}{s(s^2 + 34.5s + 1000)}\right] \tag{5-50}$$

Or $\theta_c(t) = 1 + 1.2e^{-0.546\omega_n t} \sin (0.837\omega_n t + \pi + \tan^{-1} 1.53)$

$$= 1 + 1.2e^{-17.25t} \sin (26.4t + 236.8°) \tag{5-51}$$

The output response of the system is plotted in Fig. 5-11 as a function of the normalized time $\omega_n t$.

It is interesting to see how the time response changes when the gain A is varied. Note that in Eq. (5-43) and in Eq. (5-44), an increase in the gain A will increase the undamped natural frequency ω_n but will decrease the damping ratio. For $A = 1500$, the damping ratio δ is 0.2, and $\omega_n = 86.2$ rad/sec. The output response to a unit step displacement input in this case is shown in Fig. 5-11. The response oscillates violently back and forth about the final steady-state value. The overshoot is very large, although the rise time T_r is apparently reduced. The settling time T_s is also shortened by increasing the gain.* On the other hand, for low values of gain, for example, $A = 13.5$, the damping ratio and the natural undamped frequency are $\delta = 2.0$ and $\omega_n = 8.62$ rad/sec respectively. The output step response corresponding to $A = 13.5$ is overdamped. Table 5-1 gives the comparison of the transient behavior of the servo system for the three different values of gain A.

Table 5-1.

COMPARISON OF TRANSIENT RESPONSE OF A SECOND-ORDER SERVO SYSTEM WHEN THE GAIN VARIES.

Gain A	Damping ratio δ	Undamped frequency ω_n	Maximum overshoot	Per cent Overshoot	Delay time T_d	Rise time T_r	Settling time T_s	Time at max. overshoot t_{max}
13.5	2.0	8.62	0	0	0.348	1.043	1.51	—
200	0.546	31.6	0.141	14.1	0.041	0.057	0.168	0.119
1500	0.2	86.2	0.52	52	0.012	0.014	0.15	0.037

The velocity of the controlled shaft is obtained by taking the first derivative of $\theta_c(t)$ with respect to $\omega_n t$.

$$\frac{d\theta_c(t)}{d\omega_n t} = \frac{\delta}{\sqrt{1 - \delta^2}} e^{-\delta\omega_n t} \sin (\omega_n\sqrt{1 - \delta^2}\, t + \phi)$$
$$- e^{-\delta\omega_n t} \cos (\omega_n\sqrt{1 - \delta^2}\, t + \phi) \tag{5-52}$$

which is simplified to

$$\frac{d\theta_c(t)}{d\omega_n t} = \frac{1}{\sqrt{1 - \delta^2}} e^{-\delta\omega_n t} \sin \omega_n\sqrt{1 - \delta^2}\, t \tag{5-53}$$

---

*In Fig. 5-11, the response for $A = 1500$ seems to take a longer time to reach the steady state than that for $A = 200$. This is not true, however, since the responses are plotted as a function of the normalized time $\omega_n t$; for $A = 1500$, $\omega_n = 86.2$ rad/sec, as compared to $\omega_n = 31.6$ rad/sec for $A = 200$.

The output velocity of the system for $A = 13.6$, 200, and 1500 are plotted in Fig. 5-12 as functions of $\omega_n t$.

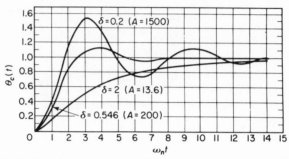

Fig. 5-11. Transient response of the servo system given in Fig. 5-9 when the input is a unit-step displacement.

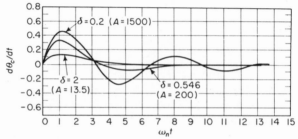

Fig. 5-12. Output velocity of servo system given in Fig. 5-9 when the input is a unit-step displacement.

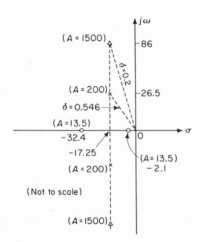

Fig. 5-13. Roots of the characteristic equation of the servo system given in Fig. 5-9 for $A = 13.5$, 200, 1500 respectively.

In Fig. 5-13 is shown the variation of the location of the roots of the system characteristic equation as a function of amplifier gain A. For values of A between zero and 59.5, the two roots of the characteristic equation are real and lie on the negative real axis in the s-plane, and the system response is over-damped. For values of A greater than 59.5, the roots are complex conjugate; the real parts of the roots are equal to $- 17.25$ and are not affected by the change in values of A. Thus, as the value of A approaches infinity, the damping factor α is always equal to 17.25 sec^{-1}. It is also apparent that a second-order system is always stable for all finite positive values of gain.

Response to Ramp Input

When a unit ramp function input $\theta_r(t) = t$ is applied to the servo system shown in Fig. 5-9, the output response becomes

$$\theta_c(t) = \mathcal{L}^{-1}\left[\frac{\omega_n^2}{s^2(s^2 + 2\delta\omega_n s + \omega_n^2)}\right] \tag{5-54}$$

and from the Laplace transform table, we have

$$\theta_c(t) = t - \frac{2\delta}{\omega_n} + \frac{1}{\omega_n\sqrt{1 - \delta^2}}\, e^{-\delta\omega_n t} \sin(\omega_n\sqrt{1 - \delta^2}\, t - \phi) \tag{5-55}$$

where

$$\phi = 2\tan^{-1}\frac{\sqrt{1 - \delta^2}}{-\delta} \tag{5-56}$$

When $A = 200$, Eq. (5-55) becomes

$$\theta_c(t) = t - \frac{1.092}{\omega_n} + \frac{1.2}{\omega_n}\, e^{-0.546\omega_n t} \sin(0.837\omega_n t + 113.6°) \tag{5-57}$$

In the last equation, note that when t approaches infinity, the steady-state response of the system is

$$\lim_{t\to\infty} \theta_c(t) = \theta_{c_{ss}} = t - \frac{1.092}{\omega_n}\bigg|_{t\to\infty} \tag{5-58}$$

It is apparent that the output response at steady state does not agree with the unit ramp input. The steady-state error, which is defined as

$$\theta_r(t) - \theta_{c_{ss}} \tag{5-59}$$

is a displacement lag of $1.092/\omega_n$ rad in this case. Figure 5-14 shows the output responses $\theta_c(t)$ when the input is a unit ramp function for A equals 13.5, 200, and 1500. The steady-state error is decreased as the gain is increased. However, if we choose to improve the steady-state accuracy of the servo system by increasing the forward gain, the transient response of the

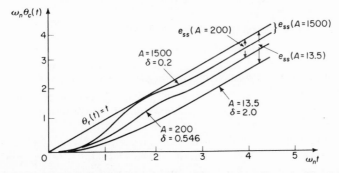

Fig. 5-14. Output displacement of the servo system shown in Fig. 5-9 when the input is a unit-ramp function.

system will, in general, become more oscillatory, or it may sometimes even become unstable. This phenomenon is rather characteristic of all servo systems.

Transient Response of a Third-Order System

It was shown in the last section that if the motor armature inductance L_a is neglected, the control system is of the second order; it can be shown that a second-order system is always stable for all positive values of A. Suppose we now let $L_a = 0.1$ henry in the system in Fig. 5-9 and keep the other parameters unchanged. The armature constant T_a is now 0.02 sec. The closed-loop transfer function given by Eq. (5-40) is now

$$\frac{\theta_c(s)}{\theta_r(s)} = \frac{0.05A}{5 \cdot 10^{-3}s(1 + 0.02s)(1 + 2s) + 0.34s + 0.05A} \tag{5-60}$$

or

$$\frac{\theta_c(s)}{\theta_r(s)} = \frac{250A}{s^3 + 50.5s^2 + 172.5s + 250A} \tag{5-61}$$

The characteristic equation of the system is

$$s^3 + 50.5s^2 + 172.5s + 250A = 0 \tag{5-62}$$

The system is now of the third order, and we are confronted with the task of solving a third-order equation.

If we let $A = 13.5$, the characteristic equation has a real root at $s = -48.4$ and two complex roots at $-1.05 \pm j8.33$. The closed-loop transfer function can now be written as

$$\frac{\theta_c(s)}{\theta_r(s)} = \frac{1}{(1 + 0.0206s)(1 + 0.0298s + 0.0142s^2)} \tag{5-63}$$

For a unit-step displacement input, the transform of the output is

$$\theta_c(s) = \frac{1}{s(1 + 0.0206s)(1 + 0.0298s + 0.0142s^2)} \tag{5-64}$$

The inverse transform of the last equation is

$$\theta_c(t) = 1 - 0.0304\, e^{-48.4t} + 1.015\, e^{-1.05t} \sin(8.33t + 253°) \tag{5-65}$$

The damping ratio δ and the undamped natural frequency ω_n of the quadratic term in Eq. (5-64) are 12.5 per cent and 8.4 rad/sec respectively. In the general case, the transient behavior of a third-order system is also governed by the first-order term $(1 + 0.0206s)$. However, in this case, the transient response of the system is predominantly controlled by the oscillatory mode, since the real root of the characteristic equation is at $s = -48.4$, and the transient term due to this root will decay very rapidly (time constant is 0.0206 sec).

The maximum overshoot of the step response is 67.3 per cent, compared to no overshoot when the armature inductance L_a is neglected. Obviously, we should expect this result, since adding inductance is the same as adding electric inertia, which makes the system response more oscillatory.

If the gain A is increased to 200, the characteristic equation becomes

$$s^3 + 50.5s^2 + 172.5s + 50,000 = 0 \qquad (5\text{-}66)$$

The roots of the characteristic equation are at -61.1, $5.34 + j410$, and $5.35 - j410$ in the s-plane. Since the two complex roots have positive real parts, the output step response will oscillate with increasing amplitude; the system is said to be unstable.

The loci of the three characteristic equation roots when A is varied from zero to infinity are depicted in Fig. 5-15. When A is equal to 13.5, the real root is at -48.4 on the real axis, and the complex roots are quite close to the imaginary axis $(-1.05 \pm j8.33)$ of the s-plane. It can be verified that, when A equals 34.8, the two complex roots are located on the imaginary axis, and the system is on the verge of becoming unstable. For all values of

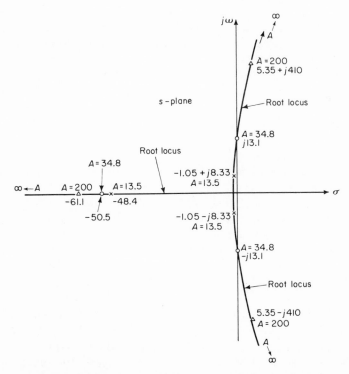

Fig. 5-15. Roots of the characteristic equation of Eq. 5-62 when $A = 13.5$, 34.8, and 200.

A greater than 34.8, the system is unstable, since the two complex roots are located in the right half of the s-plane.

We have learned from the preceding two examples that a second-order system is always stable so long as the open-loop gain is finite and positive, but a third- (or higher-) order system will become unstable if the open-loop gain exceeds a certain marginal value.

5.7 Effects of Derivative and Integral Controls on the Transient Performance of Feedback Control Systems

The discussions of the transient response of servomechanisms given so far in this chapter cover only systems of the proportional type; a proportional type feedback control system is one which develops a correcting effort proportional to the magnitude of the actuating signal. The example given in the previous section shows one limitation, or disadvantage, of a proportional type system: a compromise is often necessary in selecting a proper forward gain A so that the size of the steady-state error and the maximum overshoot of the output response are within acceptable tolerances. A compromise, however, cannot always be reached, since, in most practical cases, the system corresponding to the gain selected to realize a maximum acceptable steady-state error may have excessive overshoot in its time response, or may even be unstable.

It is logical, then, to consider some other types of control which may improve the transient or steady-state behavior of an ordinary proportional type system. In general, the following three basic principles are adapted to modify the performance of feedback control systems:

(1) Derivative control.

(2) Integral control.

(3) Rate-feedback control.

It will be shown that it is impossible to improve both the transient and the steady-state performances by means of one of the above schemes. The derivative control, for instance, will improve the overshoot of a given system, but will not effect a constant steady-state error. On the other hand, a servomechanism with integral control will have better steady-state accuracy than will the proportional type, but it will be less stable in general.

(1) *The Effect of Derivative Control on Transient Response*

Figure 5-17(a) shows the typical step response of a proportional type servomechanism; the corresponding error signal $e(t)$ and the time rate of change of $e(t)$ are shown in Figs. 5-17(b) and 5-17(c), respectively. Let us consider first that the system has only a proportional type control and that high overshoot in the step response is observed. The large overshoot is entirely due to the excessive amount of positive torque developed by the motor in the time interval $0^+ < t < t_1$, during which the error signal is positive. For the time interval $t_1 < t < t_3$, the error signal is negative, and the motor torque is reversed in direction; this negative torque acts as a retarding torque, bringing the overshooting output back. When $t = t_3$, the torque is positive again, tending to reduce the undershoot in the response caused by the negative torque in the interval $t_2 < t < t_3$. The process is repeated, and for a stable system, a steady-state is finally reached.

Considering the explanation given above, we can say that the contributing factors to a high overshoot are as follows: (1) The positive correcting torque in the interval $0 < t < t_1$ is too large, and (2) the retarding torque in the interval $t_1 < t < t_2$ is inadequate. A logical approach to the reduction of the high overshoot in the output response is to decrease the amount of positive correcting torque and to increase the retarding torque. Similarly, in the time interval $t_2 < t < t_4$, the negative corrective torque would be reduced and the retarding torque, which is now in the positive direction, should be increased in order to improve the undershoot. The derivative control is a scheme designed to give precisely this kind of effect. Now consider that the proportional type servomechanism is modified so that the torque developed by the motor is proportional to the signal $e(t) + \tau_d \dfrac{de}{dt}$, where τ_d is a constant. In other words, in addition to the error signal, a signal which is proportional to the time rate of change of the error is also applied to the motor. The block diagram of a basic second-order system with derivative control is shown in Fig. 5-16. In Fig. 5-17, it is seen that for

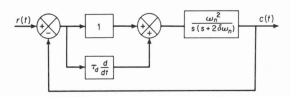

Fig. 5-16. Feedback control system with derivative control.

$0 < t < t_1$, the time derivative of $e(t)$ is negative; this will reduce the original positive torque due to $e(t)$ alone. For $t_1 < t < t_2$, both $e(t)$ and de/dt are negative, which means that the negative retarding torque developed will be greater than that of the proportional case. Therefore, all these effects will result in a smaller overshoot (however, usually at the expense of a longer delay time). It is easy to see that $e(t)$ and de/dt have opposite signs in the time interval $t_2 < t < t_3$; therefore, the negative torque which originally contributes to the undershoot is also reduced.

The derivative control is essentially an anticipatory type of control. Normally, if the slope of $e(t)$ or $c(t)$ is large in linear systems, a high overshoot will occur in the very near future. The derivative control measures the instantaneous slope of $e(t)$, predicts the large overshoot ahead of time, and makes proper correcting effort before the overshoot occurs.

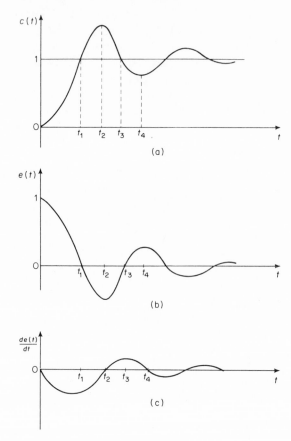

Fig. 5-17. Wave forms of $c(t)$, $e(t)$ and de/dt showing the effect of derivative control. (a) Step response; (b) Error signal; (c) Time rate of change of error signal.

It is apparent that the derivative control affects the steady-state error of a system only if the steady-state error varies with time. If the steady-state error of a system is constant with respect to time, the derivative control has no effect. But if the steady-state error increases with time, a torque is again developed proportional to de/dt, which reduces the magnitude of the error. Steady-state error of a feedback control system will be discussed in more detail in the following sections.

The effect of derivative control on time response of a feedback control system can also be evaluated by analytical means. The open-loop transfer function of the system with derivative control shown in Fig. 5-16 is

$$G(s) = \frac{C(s)}{E(s)} = \frac{(1 + sT_d)\omega_n^2}{s(s + 2\delta\omega_n)} \tag{5-67}$$

from which the closed-loop transfer function is determined as

$$\frac{C(s)}{R(s)} = \frac{(1 + sT_d)\omega_n^2}{s^2 + (2\delta\omega_n + T_d\omega_n^2)s + \omega_n^2} \tag{5-68}$$

The characteristic equation of the system is

$$s^2 + (2\delta\omega_n + T_d\omega_n^2)s + \omega_n^2 = 0 \tag{5-69}$$

The form of the last equation is similar to that of the characteristic equation of the proportional type system, except that the coefficient of the s term is increased by the quantity $T_d\omega_n^2$. This actually means that the damping of the system is increased. For instance, in the system given in the previous section, if the derivative control is applied, the open-loop transfer function is

$$G(s) = \frac{C(s)}{E(s)} = \frac{5A(1 + sT_d)}{s^2 + 34.5s} \tag{5-70}$$

Let us take the case in which $A = 1500$, and arbitrarily choose a T_d of 0.01 sec. The characteristic equation of the system with derivative control is now

$$s^2 + 109.5s + 7500 = 0 \tag{5-71}$$

from which the damping ratio of the system is obtained as 0.634, and $\omega_n = 86.2$ rad/sec; the maximum overshoot is 7.6 per cent. It is apparent that the transient performance of the system is vastly improved by the derivative control, since the original system has a damping ratio of 0.2 and the overshoot is 52 per cent. Therefore, this illustration verifies that this type of derivative control improves the damping of the time response.

Effect of Integral Control on the Transient Response

In order to eliminate a positional error completely, a logical approach is to introduce a signal to the servomotor which is proportional to the time

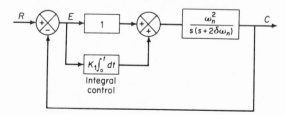

Fig. 5-18. Feedback control system with integral control.

integral of the error. As long as there is an error signal, there will always be a torque developed by the motor in a direction to correct this error. Figure 5-18 shows the block diagram of a feedback control system with integral control.

The signal supplied to the motor consists of two components: one proportional to the instantaneous error, the other, to the time integral of the error. The open-loop transfer function of the system is

$$\frac{C(s)}{E(s)} = \frac{\omega_n^2(1 + K_1/s)}{s(s + 2\delta\omega_n)} = \frac{\omega_n^2(s + K_1)}{s^2(s + 2\delta\omega_n)} \tag{5-72}$$

It is clear that the integral control has converted the second-order system into a third-order system. For reasons which will become apparent in future discussions, the higher the system order, the more the system tends to become unstable. An inherent property of a second-order system is that it is always stable for finite positive values of open-loop gain. We have shown that for a third-order system, the roots of the characteristic equation may be found in the right half of the s-plane if the gain is high.

Consider the servo system shown in Fig. 5-9; the open-loop transfer function of the system when the integral control is applied is

$$\frac{C(s)}{E(s)} = \frac{5A(s + K_1)}{s^2(s + 34.5)} \tag{5-73}$$

The closed-loop transfer function is

$$\frac{C(s)}{R(s)} = \frac{5A(s + K_1)}{s^3 + 34.5s^2 + 5As + 5AK_1} \tag{5-74}$$

For $A = 1500$, the characteristic equation is

$$s^3 + 34.5s^2 + 7500s + 7500K_1 = 0 \tag{5-75}$$

The roots of the characteristic equation depend on the value of K_1; if K_1 is very small, the transient behavior is very close to that of the original system; if the value of K_1 is large, for example, $K_1 = 47$, the roots of the characteristic equation are at -44.5, $+5 + j89$, and $+5 - j89$ in the s-plane. Since the complex roots have positive real parts, for $K_1 = 47$ the system is unstable for all values of A greater than zero.

It will be shown that the integral control does give improved steady-state performance to a servo system. From Eqs. (5-73) and (5-74), the transform of the error is written

$$E(s) = \frac{s^2(s + 34.5)}{s^3 + 34.5s^2 + 5As + 5AK_1} R(s) \tag{5-76}$$

The steady-state error of the system is obtained by applying the final-value theorem of the Laplace transform to Eq. (5-76):

$$e_{ss}(t) = \lim_{t \to \infty} e(t) = \lim_{s \to 0} sE(s) \tag{5-77}$$

Substituting Eq. (5-76) into Eq. (5-77), we see that when the reference input is either a step or a ramp function, the steady-state error of the system is zero; for a parabolic function input, the e_{ss} is a constant. Recall that, in the original system, the steady state error is a constant (see Eq. 5-58) when the input is a ramp function, and will increase with time if the input is proportional to t^2.

The effect of the derivative and the integral control on the transient response of a servomechanism can also be studied by plotting the root loci of the characteristic equation when the open-loop gain is varied from zero to infinity. When the derivative control is applied to a second-order system, the open-loop transfer function is given by Eq. (5-70). We see that the derivative control has added a zero at $s = -1/T_d$ to the open-loop transfer function. The characteristic equation is now

$$s^2 + (34.5 + 5AT_d)s + 5A = 0 \qquad (5\text{-}78)$$

The loci of the two roots of Eq. (5-78), when A is varied from zero to infinity, are depicted in Fig. 5-19 for two different values of T_d ($T_d < 34.5$ and $T_d > 34.5$). From these locus diagrams, the effect of the derivative control on the damping of the transient response is apparent. In Fig. 5-19a, the effect of adding the zero at $-1/T_d$ is to cause the original loci to bend toward the left, and for large values of A the output response is overdamped. It can be verified that the loci of the complex roots in Fig. 5-19a form a circle with the center at $-1/T_d{}^*$. In Fig. 5-19b, when a more derivative signal is applied ($T_d > 34.5$), the loci lie only on the negative real

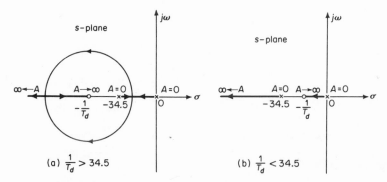

Fig. 5-19. Root locus diagrams of characteristic equation of servo system with derivative control, $s^2 + (34.5 + 5AT_d)s + 5A = 0$.

axis of the s-plane, and the system output response does not oscillate for all positive values of A.

---

*Detailed studies of the root locus diagrams are covered in Chapter 8.

From the open-loop transfer function given by Eq. (5-73), the effect of the integral control is to add a zero at $- K_1$ and a pole at the origin in the s-plane. The characteristic equation of the system is now

$$s^3 + 34.5s^2 + 5As + 5AK_1 = 0 \qquad (5\text{-}79)$$

It can be shown that the last equation will have roots in only the left half of the s-plane if the following condition is met:

$$0 < K_1 < 34.5 \qquad (5\text{-}80)$$

In other words, if the value of K_1 exceeds 34.5, the closed-loop system with integral control will be unstable for all positive values of A, since two of the three roots will have positive real parts. The root loci of Eq. (5-79) as a function of A are sketched in Fig. 5-20 for two different values of K_1. It is clear that the addition of the integral dipole (pole-zero combination) moves the loci toward the right in the s-plane.

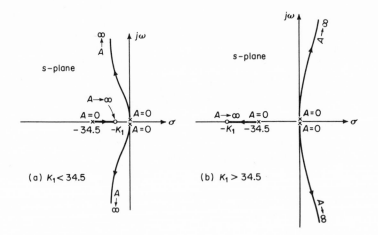

Fig. 5-20. Root locus diagrams of characteristic equation of servo system with integral control, $s^3 + 34.5s^2 + 5As + 5AK_1 = 0$.

Rate-Feedback (Tachometer) Control

The philosophy of using the derivative of the actuating signal to improve the damping of a system can also be extended to the output signal. The same effect can be obtained by feeding back the derivative of the output signal and comparing it with the reference input. Figure 5-21 shows the block diagram of a simple second-order system with a secondary path feeding back the output velocity of the system. The closed-loop transfer function of the system is given by

$$\frac{C(s)}{R(s)} = \frac{\omega_n^2}{s^2 + (2\delta\omega_n + K_t\omega_n^2)s + \omega_n^2} \tag{5-81}$$

and the characteristic equation is

$$s^2 + (2\delta\omega_n + K_t\omega_n^2)s + \omega_n^2 = 0 \tag{5-82}$$

Comparing this equation with Eq. (5-69), we see that they are of the same form. As a matter of fact, if T_d in Eq. (5-69) were replaced by K_t, they would be exactly identical. Therefore, we can conclude that the rate-feedback (or tachometer feedback) also improves the damping of the time response of a servo system.

Although, for the same damping ratio, the amount of overshoot for a second-order system will be the same for derivative control and rate-feedback, the two step responses are not the same. In general, because of the added zero in the open-loop transfer function, the rise time of the derivative controlled system will be faster.

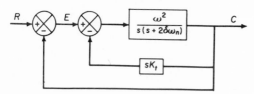

Fig. 5-21. Feedback control system with tachometer feedback.

5.8 Steady-State Response of Feedback Control Systems — Steady-State Error

In the previous section, only the transient response of feedback control systems was discussed. In the analysis and design of feedback systems, the steady-state response is also of great importance. For instance, for a positional servomechanism, it is desirable to have the final position of the output shaft in exact correspondence with the reference position; in a velocity control system, it is essential that the controlled velocity be as close as possible to the reference value. But in actual practice, because of physical imperfections of system components, friction, and other inherent properties of feedback, there is usually a deviation between the actual output variable and the desired quantity.

If the reference input $r(t)$ and the controlled output $c(t)$ are dimensionally the same (a voltage controlling a voltage, a position controlling a position, etc.) and are at the same level or of the same magnitude (unity-feedback systems), the error function is simply

$$e(t) = r(t) - c(t) \tag{5-83}$$

However, sometimes it may be impossible or inconvenient to provide a reference input which is at the same level or even of the same dimension as the controlled variable. For instance, it may be necessary to use a low voltage source for the control of the output of a high voltage power source; in a velocity servomechanism (perfect integrator), a voltage source or position input may be used to control the velocity of the output shaft. In such cases, a non-unity element, H, is usually incorporated in the feedback path, and the error defined in Eq. (5-83) becomes meaningless. In other words, error cannot be defined simply as the difference between reference input and controlled output; the input and the output signals must be of the same dimension and at the same level before subtraction. For a non-unity feedback system, the error of the system is measured by use of the actuating signal ϵ (see Fig. 5-22); that is,

$$\epsilon(t) = r(t) - b(t) \qquad (5\text{-}84)$$

or, in terms of the Laplace transformed variables,

$$\mathcal{E}(s) = R(s) - B(s) = R(s) - H(s)C(s) \qquad (5\text{-}85)$$

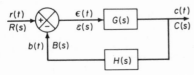

Fig. 5-22. Non-unity-feedback control system.

For example, if a 10-v reference is used to regulate a 100-v voltage supply, H is a constant and is equal to 0.1. When the output voltage is exactly 100 v, the actuating signal is

$$\epsilon(t) = 10 - 0.1 \times 100 = 0 \qquad (5\text{-}86)$$

The steady-state error of a feedback control system is defined as the error (or actuating signal in general) when the steady state is reached; that is,

$$\text{steady-state error} = e_{ss} = \lim_{t \to \infty} e(t) \qquad (5\text{-}87)$$

or

$$\epsilon_{ss} = \lim_{t \to \infty} \epsilon(t) \qquad (5\text{-}88)$$

Before proceeding, it is necessary to investigate the factors which have direct influence on the steady-state error of a feedback control system. In the simple servomechanism analyzed in Sec. 5.6, for $L_a = 0$, the system is of the second-order; when a unit step-displacement input is applied to the system, the output response given by Eq. (5-51) shows that it is in exact correspondence with the reference input when the steady state is reached. In other words, there is no steady-state error in the system response. However, for the same system, if a unit ramp function is applied as reference input, Eq. (5-57) and Eq. (5-58) show that the output displacement will lag behind the input by $1.092/\omega_n$ ($1.092/5A$) rad. It can also be shown that if a parabolic function is applied as input, the steady-state error will increase linearly with time. Therefore, from this simple example, we have learned that the steady-state error of a given system depends upon the type of input applied. Furthermore, the steady-state error also depends to a great extent, upon the nature and characteristics of the system itself. Since we have little or no control over the input signal of a control system, we could reduce the steady-state error by increasing the forward path gain or by altering the characteristic of the system, but the system may become less stable or even unstable.

For the sake of simplicity, the following discussion is given with reference to systems with unity feedback, but the extension to non-unity feedback systems is quite straightforward. Consider the feedback control system shown in Fig. 5-23. The Laplace transformed error function is given by

$$E(s) = \frac{R(s)}{1 + G(s)} \qquad (5\text{-}89)$$

By the use of the final-value theorem, the steady-state error of the system is written

$$e_{ss} = \lim_{t \to \infty} e(t) = \lim_{s \to 0} sE(s) \qquad (5\text{-}90)*$$

where $sE(s)$ is to have no poles which lie on the imaginary axis and in the right half of the s-plane. Substituting Eq. (5-89) into Eq. (5-90), we have

$$e_{ss} = \lim_{s \to 0} \frac{sR(s)}{1 + G(s)} \qquad (5\text{-}91)$$

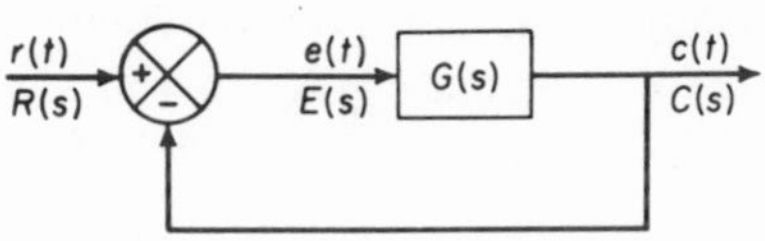

Fig. 5-23. Unity-feedback control system.

which shows that the steady-state error depends on the reference input $R(s)$ and the system transfer function $G(s)$.

The computation of the steady-state error is simplified if some basic facts and relationships among the types of inputs, systems, and the steady-state error are established. We shall consider only the three basic types of test inputs (step, ramp, acceleration) at present.

(1) *Steady-State Error of Systems with Step Displacement Input (The Positional Error Constant K_p)*

If the reference input to the feedback system of Fig. 5-23 is a step dis-

---

*For a non-unity feedback system, the actuating signal is given by

$$\varepsilon(s) = \frac{R(s)}{1 + G(s)H(s)}$$

and then simply by replacing $\varepsilon(s)$ by $E(s)$ in Eq. (5-90).

placement of magnitude R, the Laplace transform of $r(t)$ is R/s. Equation (5-91) now becomes

$$e_{ss} = \lim_{s \to 0} \frac{sR(s)}{1 + G(s)} = \lim_{s \to 0} \frac{R}{1 + G(s)} = \frac{R}{1 + \lim_{s \to 0} G(s)} \qquad (5\text{-}92)$$

If we let
$$K_p = \lim_{s \to 0} G(s) \qquad (5\text{-}93)$$

where K_p is defined as the "positional error constant," Eq. (5-92) is written

$$e_{ss} = \frac{R}{1 + K_p} \qquad (5\text{-}94)$$

Since R is the amplitude of the step displacement input, and also is the desired magnitude of the steady-state output response, we can write Eq. (5-94) as

$$K_p = \frac{R - e_{ss}}{e_{ss}} \qquad (5\text{-}95)$$

or, positional error constant

$$K_p = \frac{\text{Desired output} - \text{Allowable } e_{ss}}{\text{Allowable steady-state error}} \qquad (5\text{-}96)$$

Equation (5-96) indicates that, whenever the desired output positional response and its allowable steady-state error are specified for a servo system, the corresponding K_p of the system is determined; with the use of Eq. (5-93), the desired behavior of $G(s)$ at $s = 0$ is fixed.

(2) *Steady-State Error of Systems with Step Velocity Input (Velocity Error Constant K_v)*

In the input to the feedback control system of Fig. 5-23 is

$$r(t) = Rt \qquad (5\text{-}97)$$

where R is in displacement/sec, the Laplace transform of $r(t)$ is $R(s) = R/s^2$. Substituting $R(s)$ into Eq. (5-91), we have

$$e_{ss} = \lim_{s \to 0} \frac{R}{s + sG(s)} = \frac{R}{\lim_{s \to 0} sG(s)} \qquad (5\text{-}98)$$

If we let $K_v = \lim_{s \to 0} sG(s) = \text{Velocity error constant} \qquad (5\text{-}99)$

Eq. (5-98) reads $e_{ss} = R/K_v \qquad (5\text{-}100)$

or $K_v = \dfrac{R}{e_{ss}} = \dfrac{\text{Desired output velocity}}{\text{Steady-state error}} \ (\text{sec}^{-1}) \qquad (5\text{-}101)$

The steady-state error represented by Eq. (5-100) is usually called the *velocity error*. It should be kept in mind that the velocity error is not an error in velocity; it is, rather, the error in displacement due to a ramp type input $r(t) = Rt$. Figure 5-24 further clarifies this point by showing a typical ramp input with the output response lagging behind it by an error in displacement when the system has reached its steady state.

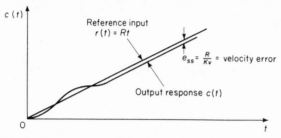

Fig. 5-24. Output response of feedback control system with ramp input.

(3) *Steady-State Error of Systems with Acceleration Input (The Acceleration Error Constant, K_a)*

If an acceleration input $r(t) = Rt^2/2$ is applied to the system of Fig. 5-23, the Laplace transform of $r(t)$ is R/s^3, where R is in displacement/sec²; Eq. (5-91) now becomes

$$e_{ss} = \lim_{s \to 0} \frac{R}{s^2 + s^2 G(s)} = \frac{R}{\lim_{s \to 0} s^2 G(s)} = \frac{R}{K_a} \tag{5-102}$$

where

$$K_a = \lim_{s \to 0} s^2 G(s) = \text{Acceleration error constant} \tag{5-103}$$

or

$$K_a = \frac{R}{e_{ss}} = \frac{\text{Desired output acceleration}}{\text{Steady-state error}} \ (\text{sec}^{-2}) \tag{5-104}$$

Similar to the two previous cases, the steady-state error given by Eq. (5-102) is called the *acceleration error*, which is the error in displacement due to an acceleration type input. Figure 5-25 illustrates a typical acceleration error in the steady-state output reponse when the input is of the acceleration type.

From the foregoing discussions, it is clear that when the reference input to a unity-feedback control system is of the step displacement, ramp, or acceleration type, the steady-state error due to each input depends upon the

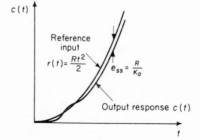

Fig. 5-25. Output response of feedback control system with acceleration input.

error constants K_p, K_v, and K_a respectively. The error constants are summarized as follows:

(1) Positional Error Constant $\qquad K_p = \lim_{s \to 0} G(s)$ $\qquad\qquad$ (5-105)

(2) Velocity Error Constant $\qquad\quad K_v = \lim_{s \to 0} sG(s)$ $\qquad\qquad$ (5-106)

(3) Acceleration Error Constant $\quad\; K_a = \lim_{s \to 0} s^2 G(s)$ $\qquad\quad$ (5-107)

The Classification of G(s)

The values of the error constants for a given system with unity-feedback apparently depend upon the type of $G(s)$. In order to classify the open-loop transfer function $G(s)$, in general, we may write

$$G(s) = \frac{K(1 + sT_1)(1 + sT_2) \ldots (1 + sT_m)}{s^j(1 + sT_a)(1 + sT_b) \ldots (1 + sT_n)} \qquad (5\text{-}108)$$

where K is the forward gain and the T's are constants of the system. The poles at the origin s^j, where $j = 0, 1, 2, 3, \ldots$, may be used to determine the type of the system, since, in Eq. (5-105) through Eq. (5-107), the behavior of $G(s)$ at $s = 0$ determines the error constants, and at $s = 0$, $G(s)$ approaches K/s^j. Thus a type 0 system is one for which $j = 0$; a type 1 system, $j = 1$; etc. For instance,

$$G(s) = \frac{K(1 + 0.5s)}{s^2(1 + s)(1 + 2s)} \qquad (5\text{-}109)$$

represents a type 2 system, since $j = 2$. In simple words, the value of j in Eq. (5-108) completely determines the type of the feedback control system. The values of m, n and T bear no importance in the system type and do not affect the values of the error constants.

Once the type of a system is determined by inspection, the error constants of the system are determined readily from Eqs. (5-105) through (5-107). The error constants are then used to calculate the steady-state error when the reference input is specified as one of the three basic types mentioned earlier.

For a specific type of feedback control system, the error constants can be infinite, zero, or finite in value. For instance, for a type 0 system, $G(s)$ is of the form

$$G(s) = \frac{K(1 + sT_1)(1 + sT_2) \ldots (1 + sT_m)}{(1 + sT_a)(1 + sT_b) \ldots (1 + sT_n)} \qquad (5\text{-}110)$$

Hence $K_p = K$, $K_v = 0$, and $K_a = 0$. This means that the steady-state error of the system due to a step displacement input of $r(t) = R$ will be $R/(K+l)$; the steady-state error due to a ramp input $r(t) = Rt$ will be equal to $R/K_v = \infty$; the steady-state error due to an acceleration input is also infinite. A steady-state error of infinite magnitude simply means that the error increases with time. It can be shown by actually solving the system differential equation that the steady-state error of the above system with ramp input increases as the first order of t, and that the steady-state error with an acceleration input will increase as the second order of t; i.e., t^2.

The error constants for other types of feedback control systems are computed in the same manner. The relations among the error constants, types of system, and the input types are summarized in Table 5-2. The

Table 5-2.

THE STEADY-STATE ERROR

Type of system	K_p	K_v	K_a	Step displacement input $e_{ss} = \dfrac{R}{1 + K_p}$	Velocity input $e_{ss} = \dfrac{R}{K_v}$	Acceleration input $e_{ss} = \dfrac{R}{K_a}$
				Position error $e_{ss} = \dfrac{R}{1 + K}$	Velocity error $e_{ss}(t) = A + Bt$ $= \infty$	Acceleration error $e_{ss}(t) = C + Dt + Et^2$ $= \infty$
0	K	0	0			
1	∞	K	0	$e_{ss} = 0$	$e_{ss} = R/K$	$e_{ss}(t) = D + Et$ $e_{ss} = \infty$
2	∞	∞	K	$e_{ss} = 0$	$e_{ss} = 0$	$e_{ss} = R/K$
3	∞	∞	∞	$e_{ss} = 0$	$e_{ss} = 0$	$e_{ss} = 0$

(A, B, C, D, and E are constants.)

chief disadvantage of the definition of the error constants is that only one of the constants has a finite value which is not zero for a particular system. Another drawback is that, in cases in which the steady-state error is a function of time, the error constants give only an answer of infinity and do not provide any indication of how the error varies with time.

However, the applications of the error constants are not limited only to systems with inputs classified as one of the three basic types of test signals. For linear systems, the concept can easily be extended to systems with inputs that can be represented by a polynomial, for example, $r(t) = 1 + 2t + t^2/2$. The steady-state error in this case is simply $e_{ss} = 1/K_p + 2/K_v + 1/K_a$ — a superposition of the errors due to each input signal component acting alone.

5.9 The Generalized Definition of Error Coefficients (The Error Series)

In this section, the error constant concept is generalized to include inputs of almost any arbitrary function of time. Equation (5-89) states that

$$E(s) = \frac{R(s)}{1 + G(s)}$$

where $E(s)$ represents the error of a unity-feedback control system. From the theory of the convolution integral discussed in Sec. 2.7, the error $e(t)$ may be written as

$$e(t) = \int_{-\infty}^{t} w_e(\tau) r(t - \tau) d\tau \qquad (5\text{-}111)$$

where $w_e(\tau)$ is the inverse Laplace transform of $\left[W_e(s) = \dfrac{1}{1 + G(s)} \right]$, and τ is a dummy time variable. If the first n derivatives of $r(t)$ exist for all values of τ, the function, $r(t - \tau)$, can be expanded into a Taylor series, that is,

$$r(t - \tau) = r(t) - \tau r'(t) + \frac{\tau^2}{2!} r''(t) - \frac{\tau^3}{3!} r'''(t) + \cdots \qquad (5\text{-}112)$$

Since $r(t)$ is zero for negative time, the limit of the convolution integral may be taken from 0 to t; substituting Eq. (5-112) into Eq. (5-111), we have

$$e(t) = \int_{0}^{t} w_e(\tau) \left[r(t) - \tau r'(t) + \frac{\tau^2}{2!} r''(t) - \frac{\tau^3}{3!} r'''(t) + \cdots \right] d\tau$$

$$= r(t) \int_{0}^{t} w_e(\tau) d\tau - r'(t) \int_{0}^{t} \tau w_e(\tau) d\tau + r''(t) \int_{0}^{t} \frac{\tau^2}{2!} w_e(\tau) d\tau + \cdots$$
$$(5\text{-}113)$$

The steady-state error is obtained by taking the limit of $e(t)$ as t approaches infinity; that is,

$$e_{ss} = \lim_{t \to \infty} e(t) = \lim_{t \to \infty} \int_{0}^{t} w_e(\tau) r(t - \tau) d\tau = \int_{0}^{\infty} w_e(\tau) r(t - \tau) d\tau$$

$$= r(t) \int_{0}^{\infty} w_e(\tau) d\tau - r'(t) \int_{0}^{\infty} \tau w_e(\tau) d\tau + r''(\tau) \int_{0}^{\infty} \frac{\tau^2}{2!} w_e(\tau) d\tau - \cdots$$
$$(5\text{-}114)$$

If we define

$$C_0 = \int_{0}^{\infty} w_e(\tau) d\tau \qquad (5\text{-}115)$$

$$C_1 = - \int_{0}^{\infty} \tau w_e(\tau) d\tau \qquad (5\text{-}116)$$

$$C_2 = \int_{0}^{\infty} \tau^2 w_e(\tau) d\tau \qquad (5\text{-}117)$$

$$\cdot$$
$$\cdot$$

$$C_n = (-1)^n \int_{0}^{\infty} \tau^n w_e(\tau) d\tau \qquad (5\text{-}118)$$

Equation (5-114) can be written

$$e_{ss} = \lim_{t \to \infty} e(t) = C_0 r(t) + C_1 r'(t) + \frac{C_2}{2!} r''(t) + \cdots + \frac{C_n}{n!} r^{(n)}(t) + \cdots$$
$$(5\text{-}119)$$

where the coefficients, $C_0, C_1, C_2, \ldots, C_n, \ldots$ are defined as the generalized error coefficients. In Eq. (5-119), the steady-state error is shown to be dependent on the generalized error coefficients, the input $r(t)$, and all the higher derivatives of $r(t)$. The error coefficients may readily be evaluated from the system transfer function $G(s)$ for a unity feedback system; for a non-unity feedback system, $G(s)H(s)$ should be used.

Consider the equation:

$$W_e(s) = \int_0^\infty w_e(\tau)e^{-s\tau}\,d\tau \tag{5-120}$$

which is the Laplace transform of $w_e(\tau)$. Taking the limit of Eq. (5-120) as s approaches zero, we have

$$\lim_{s \to 0} C_0 e^{-s\tau} = C_0 = \lim_{s \to 0} W_e(s) \tag{5-121}$$

Taking the derivative of $W_e(s)$ with respect to s yields

$$\frac{dW_e(s)}{ds} = -\int_0^\infty \tau w_e(\tau)e^{-s\tau}\,d\tau = C_1 e^{-s\tau} \tag{5-122}$$

from which we have

$$C_1 = \lim_{s \to 0} \frac{dW_e(s)}{ds} \tag{5-123}$$

The rest of the error coefficients are obtained by successive differentiation of Eq. (5-122); therefore,

$$C_2 = \lim_{s \to 0} \frac{d^2 W_e(s)}{ds^2} \tag{5-124}$$

$$C_3 = \lim_{s \to 0} \frac{d^3 W_e(s)}{ds^3} \tag{5-125}$$

$$\cdot$$
$$\cdot$$

$$C_n = \lim_{s \to 0} \frac{d^n W_e(s)}{ds^n} \tag{5-126}$$

The advantages of using the generalized error coefficients are summarized as follows:

(1) The generalized error coefficients provide a simple way of determining the nature of the response of a feedback control system to almost any arbitrary input.

(2) The generalized error coefficients lead to the calculation of the complete steady-state response without actually solving the system differential equation.

EXAMPLE 5-1.   In this example, the steady-state error of a unity-feedback control system will be computed by use of the generalized error coefficients. Consider a unity-feedback control system with the open-loop transfer function given as

$$G(s) = K/(s+1) \qquad (5\text{-}127)$$

The classic error constants are

$$K_p = K, \quad K_v = 0, \quad \text{and} \quad K_a = 0.$$

Therefore, when the reference input to the system is a unit step displacement, the steady-state error in the output is $1/(1 + K)$; when the input is either a velocity or an acceleration function, the steady-state error is infinite in magnitude, since it increases with time. It is clear that the classic error constants fail to indicate the manner in which the error function increases with time. Ordinarily, if the steady-state response of this system due to a velocity or an acceleration input is desired, the system differential equation must be solved. We shall show in the following that the steady-state output response can actually be obtained from the error series.

For this system,

$$W_e(s) = \frac{1}{1 + G(s)} = \frac{s+1}{s+K+1} \qquad (5\text{-}128)$$

Thus

$$C_0 = \lim_{s \to 0} W_e(s) = \frac{1}{1+K} \qquad (5\text{-}129)$$

$$C_1 = \frac{K}{(1+K)^2} \qquad (5\text{-}130)$$

$$C_2 = \frac{-2K}{(1+K)^3} \qquad (5\text{-}131)$$

With the substitution of the error coefficients into Eq. (5-119), the error series is

$$e_{ss}(t) = \frac{1}{1+K} r(t) + \frac{K}{(1+K)^2} r'(t) + \frac{-K}{(1+K)^3} r''(t) + \cdots \qquad (5\text{-}132)$$

(1) When the input signal is a unit step displacement, the steady-state error given by Eq. (5-132) is

$$e_{ss} = \frac{1}{1+K} \qquad (5\text{-}133)$$

which agrees with the result given by the classical error constant.

(2) When the input signal is a unit step velocity, $r(t) = t$. Then, $r'(t) = 1, r''(t) = 0, r'''(t)$, and all higher derivatives are zero. The system steady-state error is given by

$$e_{ss}(t) = \frac{1}{1+K} t + \frac{K}{(1+K)^2} \qquad (5\text{-}134)$$

which consists of $K/(1 + K)^2$ units of positional error, and $1/(1 + K)$ units of error which increases linearly with time.

(3) For an acceleration input, $r(t) = t^2/2$, $r'(t) = t$, $r''(t) = 1$, and all other higher derivatives are zero. The steady-state error is

$$e_{ss}(t) = \left(\frac{1}{1 + K}\right)\frac{t^2}{2} + \frac{K}{(1 + K)^2}\,t - \frac{K}{(1 + K)^3} \tag{5-135}$$

Now the error is proportional to t and t^2.

(4) When the input signal is represented by a polynomial of t, for example,

$$r(t) = a_0 + a_1 t + \frac{a_2 t^2}{2} \tag{5-136}$$

where a_0, a_1, and a_2 are constants,

$$r'(t) = a_1 + a_2 t \tag{5-137}$$

$$r''(t) = a_2 \tag{5-138}$$

The error series is written

$$e_{ss}(t) = \frac{1}{1 + K}\,r(t) + \frac{1}{(1 + K)^2}\,r'(t) + \frac{-K}{(1 + K)^3}\,r''(t) \tag{5-139}$$

Substituting Eqs. (5-136), (5-137), and (5-138) into the last equation, we have

$$e_{ss}(t) = \left[\frac{1}{1 + K}\,a_0 + \frac{K}{(1 + K)^2}\,a_1 - \frac{K}{(1 + K)^3}\,a_2\right]$$
$$+ \left[\frac{a_1}{1 + K} + \frac{a_2 K}{(1 + K)^2}\right]t + \frac{a_2}{2(1 + K)}\,t^2 \tag{5-140}$$

5.10 Stability of Linear Feedback Control Systems

It has been shown previously that the transient response of a feedback control system is uniquely determined by the locations of the roots of the characteristic equation in the s-plane. Figure 5-4 shows some of the typical transient responses corresponding to various locations of a pair of dominant roots. Basically, the design of feedback control systems can be regarded as a problem of arranging the location of the characteristic equation roots in such a way that the corresponding system will perform according to the prescribed specifications. However, among the many usual performance specifications, the most important requirement is that the system must be stable at all times. In simple words, a system is defined as stable if the output response to any bounded input disturbance is finite. This implies that all the roots of the characteristic equation must be located in the left half of the s-plane. Roots that are in the right half of the plane give rise to transients which tend to diverge from the steady state, and the system is said to be unstable. Thus the stability of a linear feedback control system is also uniquely determined by the location of the roots of its characteristic equation. In Fig. 5-26 the complex s-plane is divided into two regions: the stable region, which is the left half of the plane, and the unstable region, which is the right half of the s-plane.

The Routh-Hurwitz Criterion

It is established that the problem of determining the stability of a linear system is one of finding the roots of the characteristic equation. However, for polynomials of the third order or higher, the task of finding the roots is very tedious and time consuming. Hence, it is desirable that an alternate method be used, so that the system stability can be determined without actually solving for the roots of the characteirstic equation.

Suppose that the characteristic equation of linear systems is written in the general form:

$$F(s) = 1 + G(s)H(s) = a_0 s^n + a_1 s^{n-1} + a_2 s^{n-2} + \cdots + a_{n-1} s + a_n = 0 \tag{5-141}$$

In order that there be no roots of the last equation with positive real parts, it is necessary but not sufficient that*
(1) all the coefficients of the polynomial have the same sign.
(2) none of the coefficients vanish.

---

*From the basic laws of algebra, the following relations are true for the polynomial given in Eq. (5-141):

$$\frac{a_1}{a_0} = -\Sigma \text{ all roots}$$

$$\frac{a_2}{a_0} = \Sigma \text{ products of the roots taken two at a time}$$

$$\frac{a_3}{a_0} = -\Sigma \text{ products of the roots taken three at a time}$$

.

.

$$\frac{a_n}{a_0} = (-1)^n \text{ products of all roots}$$

All the ratios must be positive and nonzero unless at least one of the roots has a positive real part.

The two necessary conditions given above can be checked by inspection. However, they are not sufficient; it is quite likely that a polynomial with all its coefficients positive and nonzero will have roots in the right half of the plane. The necessary and sufficient condition that all the roots of an nth order polynomial lie in the left half of the s-plane is that the polynomial's Hurwitz determinants D_k ($k = 1, 2, 3, \ldots, n$) must be all positive.

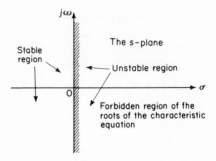

Fig. 5-26. The stable and the unstable regions in the s-plane.

The Hurwitz determinants of Eq. (5-141) are given by

$$D_1 = a_1 \qquad D_2 = \begin{vmatrix} a_1 & a_3 \\ a_0 & a_2 \end{vmatrix} \qquad D_3 = \begin{vmatrix} a_1 & a_3 & a_5 \\ a_0 & a_2 & a_4 \\ 0 & a_1 & a_3 \end{vmatrix}$$

$$\cdots \qquad D_n = \begin{vmatrix} a_1 & a_3 & a_5 & \cdots & a_{2n-1} \\ a_0 & a_2 & a_4 & \cdots & a_{2n-2} \\ 0 & a_1 & a_3 & \cdots & a_{2n-3} \\ 0 & a_0 & a_2 & \cdots & a_{2n-4} \\ 0 & 0 & a_1 & \cdots & a_{2n-5} \\ \cdot & & & & \\ \cdot & & & & \\ 0 & 0 & 0 & \cdots & a_n \end{vmatrix} \qquad (5\text{-}142)$$

where the coefficients with indexes larger than n or with negative indexes are replaced by zeros.

Routh-Hurwitz's criterion is stated as follows: *The necessary and sufficient condition that all the roots of the polynomial $F(s) = 0$ of Eq. (5-141) lie in the left half of the s-plane is that $a_0 > 0$, $D_1 > 0$, $D_2 > 0$, $\ldots$, $D_n > 0$, where $D_1, D_2, D_3, \ldots D_n$ are defined in Eq. (5-142).*

At first glance, the application of the criterion may seem to be formidable for high-order polynomials because of the labor involved in evaluating the Hurwitz determinants. However, the rule can be applied without actually working with the high-order determinants given in Eq. (5-142) by following the steps given below.

The first step in the simplification of the Routh-Hurwitz criterion is to arrange the polynomial coefficients into two rows: the first row consists of the first, third, fifth coefficients, etc., and the second row consists of the second, fourth, sixth coefficients, etc., as shown in the following tabulation:

$$a_0 \quad a_2 \quad a_4 \quad a_6 \quad a_8 \quad \cdots$$
$$a_1 \quad a_3 \quad a_5 \quad a_7 \quad a_9 \quad \cdots$$

The next step is to form the following array of numbers obtained by the indicated operations. The example is shown for a sixth-order system.

$$
\begin{array}{c|cccc}
s^6 & a_0 & a_2 & a_4 & a_6 \\
s^5 & a_1 & a_3 & a_5 & 0 \\
s^4 & \dfrac{a_1 a_2 - a_3 a_0}{a_1} = A & \dfrac{a_1 a_4 - a_0 a_5}{a_1} = B & \dfrac{a_1 a_6 - a_0 \times 0}{a_1} = a_6 & 0 \\
s^3 & \dfrac{A a_3 - a_1 B}{A} = C & \dfrac{A a_5 - a_1 a_6}{A} = D & \dfrac{A \times 0 - a_1 \times 0}{A} = 0 & 0 \\
s^2 & \dfrac{CB - AD}{C} = E & \dfrac{C a_6 - A \times 0}{C} = a_6 & \dfrac{C \times 0 - A \times 0}{C} = 0 & 0 \\
s^1 & \dfrac{ED - C a_6}{E} = F & 0 & 0 & 0 \\
s^0 & \dfrac{F a_6 - E \times 0}{F} = a_6 & 0 & 0 & 0
\end{array}
$$

The last step is to investigate the signs of the numbers in the first column in the last tabulation. The roots of the polynomial are all in the left half of the s-plane if all the elements of the first column are positive. If there are negative signs in the elements of the first column, the number of sign changes indicates the number of roots with positive real parts. The reason for this statement is apparent since the relations between the elements in the first column and the Hurwitz determinants are given as follows:

$$
\begin{array}{ccc}
s^6 & a_0 = & a_0 \\
s^5 & a_1 = & D_1 \\
s^4 & A = & D_2/D_1 \\
s^3 & C = & D_3/D_2 \\
s^2 & E = & D_4/D_3 \\
s^1 & F = & D_5/D_4 \\
s^0 & a_6 = & D_6/D_5
\end{array}
$$

EXAMPLE 5-2. Consider the polynomial:

$$(s + 1)(s - 2)(s - 3) = s^3 - 4s^2 - 5s + 6 = 0 \tag{5-143}$$

The polynomial given in the last equation has negative coefficients; thus, from the necessary condition, we know without applying Routh's test that there are roots with positive real parts. But for the purpose of illustrating Routh-Hurwitz's criterion, the Routh's tabulation is formed as follows:

$$
\begin{array}{cc|cc}
\text{Change in sign} & s^3 & 1 & -5 \\
& s^2 & -4 & 6 \\
\text{} & s^1 & \dfrac{(-4)(-5) - 6}{-4} = -3.5 & 0 \\
\text{Change in sign} & s^0 & \dfrac{(-3.5)(6) - (-4)(0)}{-3.5} = 6 &
\end{array}
$$

Since there are two sign changes in the first column, the polynomial has two roots located in the right half of the s-plane. This checks with the given problem, since it is known that the two unstable roots are $s = 2$ and $s = 3$.

EXAMPLE 5-3. Consider the polynomial

$$2s^4 + s^3 + 3s^2 + 5s + 10 = 0 \qquad (5\text{-}144)$$

The Routh's tabulation is

$$
\begin{array}{c|ccc}
s^4 & 2 & 3 & 10 \\
s^3 & 1 & 5 & 0 \\
s^2 & \dfrac{(1)(3) - (2)(5)}{1} = -7 & 10 & 0 \\
s^1 & \dfrac{(-7)(5) - (1)(10)}{-7} = 6.43 & 0 & 0 \\
s^0 & 10 & &
\end{array}
$$

Change in sign

Change in sign

Since there are two changes in sign in the first column, the polynomial has two roots with positive real parts.

Special Cases

Occasionally, in applying Routh-Hurwitz's criterion, the following kinds of difficulties may occur:

(1) The first element in any one row of the Routh's tabulation is zero, while the other elements are not.

(2) The elements in one row of the Routh's tabulation are all zero.

These two cases will be discussed separately as follows:

(1) When the first element in any row of the Routh's tabulation is zero, while the other elements are not: If a zero appears in the first position of a row, the elements in the next row become infinite, and Routh's test breaks down. To restore the missing power of s, simply multiply the polynomial by the factor $(s + a)$ where a is any positive real number, and carry on the usual Routh's test.

EXAMPLE 5-4. Consider the polynomial:

$$(s - 1)^2(s + 2) = s^3 - 3s + 2 = 0 \qquad (5\text{-}145)$$

Since the coefficient of the s^2 term is zero, we know from the necessary condition that there must be at least one root of the polynomial which is located in the right half of the s-plane. The Routh's tabulation of the coefficients is

$$
\begin{array}{c|cc}
s^3 & 1 & -3 \\
s^2 & 0 & 2 \\
s^1 & \infty & \\
s^0 & &
\end{array}
$$

Because of the zero in the first element of the second row, the first element of the third row is infinite. To correct this situation, simply multiply the polynomial in Eq. (5-145) by the factor $(s + a)$. If the constant a is arbitrarily chosen as 3 (for reasons which will become apparent later, the value of a is not chosen as 1 or 2), we have

$$(s - 1)^2(s + 2)(s + 3) = s^4 + 3s^3 - 3s^2 - 7s + 6 = 0 \qquad (5\text{-}146)$$

The Routh's tabulation of the last equation is

s^4	1	-3	6
s^3	3	-7	0
s^2	$\dfrac{-9+7}{3} = \dfrac{-2}{3}$	6	
s^1	$\dfrac{(-2/3)(-7) - 18}{(-2/3)} = +20$	0	
s^0	6		

Change in sign (at s^3 to s^2)

Change in sign (at s^2 to s^1)

Since there are two changes in sign in the first column of the Routh's tabulation, two roots of the polynomial are in the right half of the s-plane.

(2) When all the elements in one row of the Routh's tabulation are zero: This condition indicates that there are pairs of real roots with opposite signs, pairs of conjugate roots on the imaginary axis, or both; or conjugate roots forming a quadrate in the s-plane. The equation corresponding to the coefficients just above the row of zeros is called the *auxiliary equation*. The order of the auxiliary equation is always even, and it indicates the number of root pairs that are equal in magnitude but opposite in sign. For example, if the auxiliary equation is of the second order, there are two equal and opposite roots. For a fourth-order auxiliary equation, there must be two pairs of equal and opposite roots. All these roots with equal magnitude can be obtained by solving the auxiliary equation. Again, Routh's test breaks down; in this case, because of the row of zeros. To correct this situation, simply take the first derivative of the auxiliary equation with respect to s, replace the row of zeros with the coefficients of the resultant equation obtained by taking the derivative of the auxiliary equation, and carry on with Routh's test.

EXAMPLE 5-5. Consider the same polynomial used in the last example: $s^3 - 3s + 2 = 0$. In multiplying this polynomial by the factor $(s + a)$, logically, the first number to come into one's mind would be $a = 1$. Thus,

$$(s - 1)^2(s + 2)(s + 1) = s^4 + s^3 - 3s^2 - s + 2 = 0 \qquad (5\text{-}147)$$

The Routh's tabulation is

s^4	1	-3	2
s^3	1	-1	
s^2	$\dfrac{-3+1}{1} = -2$	2 auxiliary equation	
s^1	$\dfrac{2-2}{-2} = 0$	0	

Since the s^1 row contains all zeros, Routh's test breaks down. The multiplication of the factor $(s + 1)$ to the original polynomial, which has a root at $s = 1$, has made the new polynomial fit the special case (2). The auxiliary equation is obtained by using the elements contained in the s^2 row as the coefficients of the equation. Thus,

$$A(s) = -2s^2 + 2 = 0 \qquad (5\text{-}148)$$

and
$$\frac{dA(s)}{ds} = -4s \qquad (5\text{-}149)$$

Now the row of zeros in the Routh's tabulation are replaced by the coefficients of the last equation; the Routh's tabulation reads as follows:

s^4	1	-3	2
change in sign $\quad s^3$	1	-1	
s^2	-2	2	
change in sign $\quad s^1$	-4	0	coefficients of $\dfrac{dA(s)}{ds}$
s^0	2	0	

Since there are two changes in sign in the elements in the first row of the new Routh's tabulation, two roots of the polynomial have positive real parts. By solving the roots of the auxiliary equation in Eq. (5-148) we have

$$s^2 = 1, \quad \text{or} \quad s = \pm 1.$$

EXAMPLE 5-6. Consider the polynomal:

$$(s + 2)(s - 2)(s + j)(s - j)(s^2 + s + 1) = s^6 + s^5 - 2s^4 - 3s^3 - 7s^2$$
$$- 4s - 4 = 0 \quad (5\text{-}150)$$

It is known that the polynomial in the last equation has two pairs of equal roots with opposite signs at $s = \pm 2$ and $s = \pm j$. The Routh's tabulation is

s^6	1	-2	-7	-4
s^5	1	-3	-4	
s^4	$\dfrac{-2+3}{1} = 1$	$\dfrac{-7+4}{1} = -3$	-4	
s^3	0	0	0	

The auxiliary equation is

$$A(s) = s^4 - 3s^2 - 4 = 0 \qquad (5\text{-}151)$$

which indicates that there are two pairs of equal roots with opposite signs. The first derivative of the auxiliary equation with respect to s is

$$\frac{dA(s)}{ds} = 4s^3 - 6s \qquad (5\text{-}152)$$

from which the coefficients 4 and -6 are substituted into the row of zeros in the Routh's tabulation. The new Routh's tabulation is

$$
\begin{array}{llll}
s^6 & 1 & -2 \quad -7 & -4 \\
s^5 & 1 & -3 \quad -4 \\
s^4 & 1 & -3 \quad -4 \\
s^3 & 4 & -6 \quad\;\; 0 & \leftarrow \text{Coefficients of } \dfrac{dA(s)}{ds} \\
s^2 & \dfrac{-12+6}{4} = -1.5 & -4 \quad\;\; 0 \\
s^1 & \dfrac{-9+16}{-1.5} = -16.7 & 0 \\
s^0 & -4 & 0
\end{array}
$$

change in sign

Since there is only one change in sign in the first column of the new Routh's tabulation, the polynomial has one root with a positive real part. This result obviously checks with the given polynomial roots. The two pairs of equal roots are obtained by solving the auxiliary equation given in Eq. (5-151). The roots are $s = \pm 2$ and $s = \pm j$.

A frequent use of Routh's criterion is to determine the condition of stability of a linear feedback control system. For instance, the servo system with integral control shown in Fig. 5-18 has the characteristic equation

$$s^3 + 34.5s^2 + 7500s + 7500K_1 = 0 \tag{5-153}$$

The Routh's criterion is to be applied to the last equation to determine the range of value of K_1 for which the closed-loop system is stable. The Routh's tabulation of Eq. (5-153) is

$$
\begin{array}{lcc}
s^3 & 1 & 7500 \\
s^2 & 34.5 & 7500K_1 \\
s^1 & (258{,}750 - 7500K_1)/34.5 & 0 \\
s^0 & 7500K_1
\end{array}
$$

For the system to be stable, all the coefficients in the first column of the Routh's tabulation must be positive. The conditions are

$$(258{,}750 - 7500K_1)/34.5 > 0 \tag{5-154}$$

and
$$7500K_1 > 0 \tag{5-155}$$

From the condition in Eq. (5-154) we have
$$K_1 < 34.5 \tag{5-156}$$

and from the condition in Eq. (5-155) we have
$$K_1 > 0 \tag{5-157}$$

Hence, the condition for stability is that K_1 must satisfy the relation
$$0 < K_1 < 34.5 \tag{5-158}$$

EXAMPLE 5-7. Consider the characteristic equation of a certain closed-loop system,

$$s^3 + 3Ks^2 + (K + 2)s + 4 = 0 \qquad (5\text{-}159)$$

The Routh's tabulation is

$$
\begin{array}{ccc}
s^3 & 1 & (K + 2) \\
s^2 & 3K & 4 \\
s^1 & \dfrac{3K(K + 2) - 4}{3K} & 0 \\
s^0 & 4 &
\end{array}
$$

From the s^2 row, the condition of stability is

$$K > 0 \qquad (5\text{-}160)$$

and from the s^1 row, we have

$$3K^2 + 6K - 4 > 0 \qquad (5\text{-}161)$$

from which $\qquad\qquad K < -2.528 \quad \text{or} \quad K > 0.528 \qquad (5\text{-}162)$

Comparing the conditions, $K > 0$ and $K > 0.528$, apparently the latter limitation is the most stringent one. Hence, for the closed-loop system to be stable the value of K must be greater than 0.528.

Problems

5-1. A pair of complex conjugate poles in the s-plane is required to meet the various specifications given below. For each specification, sketch the region in the s-plane in which the poles may be located.
   (a) $\delta \geq 0.707 \quad \omega_n \geq 2 \text{ rad/sec}$ (positive damping, stable)
   (b) $0 \leq \delta \leq 0.707$ conditional frequency $\omega \leq 2 \text{ rad/sec}$ (positive damping)
   (c) $\delta \leq 0.5 \quad 2 \leq \omega_n \leq 4 \text{ rad/sec}$ (positive damping)
   (d) $0.5 \leq \delta \leq 0.707 \quad \omega_n \leq 2 \text{ rad/sec}$ (positive and negative damping)

5-2. The following loop-transfer functions are given for a single-loop servo system configuration. Plot in the s-plane the roots of the characteristic equation of the system. Indicate the stability of each of the systems.

   (a) $G(s)H(s) = \dfrac{100}{s(1 + 2s)}$

   (b) $G(s)H(s) = \dfrac{1050}{s(1 + s)(1 + 0.1s)}$

   (c) $G(s)H(s) = \dfrac{(1 + 3s)}{s^2 + 2s + 50}$

   (d) $G(s)H(s) = \dfrac{9}{s^2(s + 2)}$

5-3. The open-loop transfer function of a servo system with unity-feedback is given by

$$G(s) = \frac{C(s)}{E(s)} = \frac{1}{s(s^2 + 5s + 6)}$$

(a) When the input to the system is a unit step function, find the time required for the output response to settle down to 1 per cent of its final value.
(b) With the input still a unit step function, calculate the initial value of $c(t)$, and the first three initial derivatives of $c(t)$; i.e., $c'(0^+)$, $c''(0^+)$, $c'''(0^+)$.

5-4. The open-loop transfer function of a unity-feedback control system is given by

$$C(s) = \frac{A}{s(1 + sT)}$$

(a) By what factor should the amplifier gain A be multiplied so that the damping ratio is increased from a value of 0.2 to 0.6?
(b) By what factor should the amplifier gain A be multiplied so that the overshoot of the unit step response is reduced from 80 per cent to 20 per cent?

5-5. The open-loop transfer function of a servo system with unity-feedback is given by

$$G(s) = \frac{C(s)}{E(s)} = \frac{10}{s(1 + 0.5s)(1 + 0.2s)}$$

Determine the damping ratio and undamped natural frequency of the oscillatory roots. What is the per cent overshoot of the response to a unit step function input?

5-6. The block diagram of a simple servo system is shown in Fig. 5P-6.
(a) For $K = 10$, determine values of a and b to give an overshoot of 16 per cent, and a time constant of 0.1 sec of the system response to a unit step input.
(b) If the value of K is decreased slightly, how does it affect the damping ratio of the system?
(c) Plot several points on the loci of roots of the system characteristic equation as K is varied from 0 to ∞.

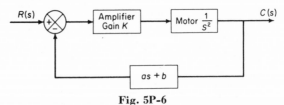

Fig. 5P-6

5-7. The parameters of the positioning servo system shown in Fig. 5P-7 are given below:

J_L = Load inertia	1 ft-lb/rad/sec²
f_L = Load viscous friction	0.00143 ft-lb/rad/sec
J_m = Motor inertia	$8 \cdot 10^{-4}$ ft-lb/rad/sec²
f_m = Motor viscous friction	negligible

R_f = Generator field resistance   50 ohms
L_f = Generator field inductance   5 henries
R_a = Total armature resistance of generator & motor   48.8 ohms
K_i = Motor torque constant   0.812 ft-lb/amp
K_g = Generator constant   200 v/amp
L_a = Total armature inductance of generator & motor   negligible

(a) For an amplifier gain of gain $K = 100$, find the roots of the characteristic equation of the system. Locate these roots in the s-plane.

(b) For $K = 100$, evaluate the output response $\theta_L(t)$ when $\theta_r(t)$ is a unit step displacement input. Sketch the waveform of $\theta_L(t)$.

(c) Repeat parts (a) and (b) for $K = 60.7$.

(d) Repeat parts (a) and (b) for $K = 50$. How does the steady-state response of $\theta_L(t)$ compare with the reference input $\theta_r(t)$?

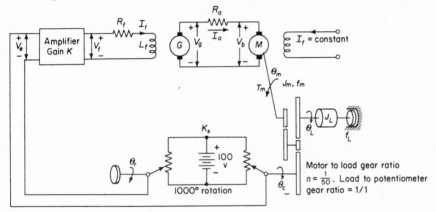

Fig. 5P-7

5-8. The following parameters are given for the servo system shown in Fig. 4P-3.

K_s = Sensitivity of error detector   1 volt/rad
J_L = Load inertia   0.05 ft-lb/rad/sec²
f_L = Load viscous friction   0.005 ft-lb/rad/sec
J_m = Motor inertia   0.05 ft-lb/rad/sec²
f_m = Motor viscous friction   negligible
K_i = Motor torque constant   1 ft-lb/amp
L_a = Motor armature inductance   negligible
R_a = Motor armature resistance   10 ohms
K_d = Gain of demodulator   1 v/v
Gear ratio $n = N_1/N_2$ 1 : 1

(a) Write the characteristic equation of the system and determine the value of the d-c amplifier gain A for a critically damped system.

(b) What is the limiting value of A so that the system becomes unstable?

(c) For a unit ramp function input $\theta_r(t) = t$, what should be the minimum value of A so that the steady-state value of the response $\theta_L(t)$ will follow the reference input with a positional error not exceeding 0.0186 radian? With this gain setting, evaluate the output response $\theta_L(t)$.

5-9. In the feedback control system shown in Fig. 5P-9, the sensitivity of the synchro error detector is 1 v/deg. After the entire system is set up, the transfer function of the two-phase motor is determined experimentally as

$$\frac{\theta_m(s)}{V_2(s)} = \frac{K_m}{s(1 + sT_m)}$$

where $K_m = 10$ v/sec, and $T_m = 0.1$ sec.

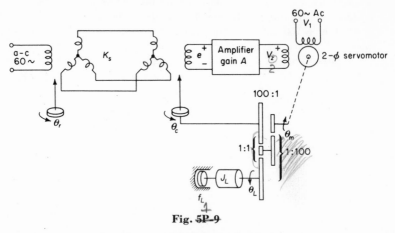

Fig. 5P-9

(a) If the load on the output shaft is to be driven in its steady state at a constant speed of 30 rpm, what is the minimum value of gain A of the amplifier in order that the deviation between output and input positions will not exceed 3 deg when the steady state is reached?

(b) The gain of the amplifier is given by $A = 35$; determine the damping ratio δ and the undamped natural frequency of the system.

(c) The amplifier is modified to differentiate the error signal so that the output of the amplifier is written as

$$V_2 = A\,e(t) + A\,T_d\,\frac{de(t)}{dt} \qquad (A = 35)$$

Determine the value of T_d so that the damping ratio is 40 per cent. Repeat part (a) with this modified amplifier.

5-10. Determine the position, velocity, and acceleration error coefficients for the following feedback control systems (with unity feedback); the open-loop transfer functions are given by:

(a) $G(s) = \dfrac{50}{(1 + 0.1s)(1 + 2s)}$

(b) $G(s) = \dfrac{K}{s(1 + 0.1s)(1 + 0.5s)}$

(c) $G(s) = \dfrac{K}{s^2(s^2 + 4s + 200)}$

(d) $G(s) = \dfrac{K(1 + 2s)(1 + 4s)}{s^2(s^2 + 2s + 10)}$

5-11. For the systems of Problem 5-10, determine the steady-state errors for a unit step input, a unit ramp input t, and an acceleration input $t^2/2$.

5-12. A servomechanism is being designed to keep the antenna of a tracking radar pointed at a flying target. The servo system must be able to follow a target traveling a straight-line course with speed up to 600 mph with a maximum permissible error of 0.01 deg. The shortest distance from antenna to target is 1000 ft. Determine the value of the velocity error coefficient K_v in order to satisfy these specifications.

5-13. Determine the error coefficients K_p, K_v, and K_a of the system in Problem 5-8 when $A = 186$. Evaluate the steady-state error between the output and the reference input when $\theta_r(t) = u(t)$, t, and $t^2/2$, respectively. Repeat the problem when the amplifier is introduced with a 180 deg phase shift ($A = -186$).

5-14. The open-loop transfer function of a servo system with unity-feedback is given by

$$G(s) = \frac{500}{s(1 + 0.1s)}$$

Evaluate the error series for the system. Determine the steady-state error of the system when the following inputs are applied:
(a) $r(t) = t^2/2$
(b) $r(t) = 1 + 2t + t^2$
Show that the steady-state error obtained from the error series is equal to the inverse Laplace transform of $E(s)$ with the terms generated by the poles of $E(s)/R(s)$ discarded.

5-15. In Problem 5-14, if a sinusoidal input $r(t) = \sin \omega t$ is applied to the servo system, determine the steady-state error of the system by using the error series for $\omega = 5$ rad/sec. What are the limitations in the error series when $r(t)$ is sinusoidal?

5-16. In the servo system of Fig. 5P-6, write the error series for the system. Determine the steady-state error when the input is $r(t) = 1 + 2t + t^2$.

5-17. Assume that the servo system being designed in Problem 5-12 has an open-loop transfer function

$$G(s) = \frac{K}{s(1 + sT)} \quad \text{and} \quad H(s) = 1$$

The specifications are the same as those given in Problem 5-12. By use of the error series, determine the values of K and T which will satisfy the specifications.

5-18. A servo system with disturbance input T_L is shown in Fig. 5P-18. Evaluate the steady-state error due to T_L alone.

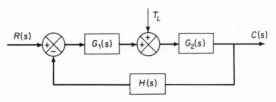

Fig. 5P-18

5-19. By means of the Routh-Hurwitz stability criterion, determine the stability of the systems which have the following characteristic equations. In each case, determine the number of roots of the equation which are in the right half of the s-plane.
(a) $s^3 + 20s^2 + 9s + 100 = 0$
(b) $s^3 + 20s^2 + 9s + 200 = 0$
(c) $3s^4 + 10s^3 + 5s^2 + s + 2 = 0$
(d) $s^4 + 2s^3 + 6s^2 + 8s + 8 = 0$
(e) $s^6 + 2s^5 + 8s^4 + 12s^3 + 20s^2 + 16s + 16 = 0$

5-20. The characteristic equations for certain feedback control systems are given below. In each case, determine the values of K which correspond to a stable system.
(a) $s^4 + 22s^3 + 10s^2 + 2s + K = 0$
(b) $s^4 + 20Ks^3 + 5s^2 + (10 + K)s + 15 = 0$
(c) $s^3 + (K + 0.5)s^2 + 4Ks + 50 = 0$

5-21. The conventional Routh-Hurwitz criterion gives only the location of the roots of a polynomial with respect to the right half and the left half of the s-plane. The open-loop transfer function of a unity-feedback control system is given as

$$G(s) = \frac{K}{s(1 + sT)}$$

It is desired that all the roots of the system's characteristic equation lie in the region to the left of the line $s = -a$. This will assure that not only is a stable system obtained, but also that the system has a minimum amount of damping. Extend the Routh-Hurwitz criterion to this case, and determine the values of K and T required so that there are no roots to the right of the line $s = -a$.

5-22. For the servo system represented by Eq. (5-61), determine the magnitudes of the amplifier gain A which will give a stable system.

5-23. The loop transfer function of a feedback control system is given by

$$G(s)H(s) = \frac{K(s + 1)}{s(1 + Ts)(1 + 2s)}$$

The parameters K and T may be represented in a plane with K as the horizontal axis and T as the vertical axis. Determine the region in which the closed-loop system is stable.

5-24. The open-loop transfer function of a unity-feedback control system is given by

$$G(s) = \frac{K(s + 5)(s + 40)}{s^3(s + 200)(s + 1000)}$$

Discuss the stability of the closed-loop system as a function of K. Determine the values of K which will cause sustained oscillations in the closed-loop system. What are the frequencies of oscillations?

6

The Frequency Response Method

6.1 Introduction

In the previous chapter, the analysis of feedback control systems was carried out mainly in terms of the transient and the steady-state responses in the time domain. On the other hand, the frequency response method of analysis and design has been quite popular, chiefly because it is easy to apply. The frequency response method is also regarded as a graphical method, as compared with the time response method, which is involved directly with the differential equation and is essentially an analytical approach. The essential feature of the frequency response method is that the description of the system is given in terms of its response to a sinusoidally varying input signal. If the system is linear, the output will also be a sine wave of the same frequency as the input; if the system is nonlinear, the output will, in addition, contain higher harmonics, and sometimes subharmonics. A second important feature of the frequency response method is that the transfer function describing the sinusoidal steady-state behavior of the system can be obtained from the transfer function simply by replacing the Laplace operator s with $j\omega$. The sinusoidal transfer function is thus a complex function of complex variables, and, in general, can be represented by a magnitude and a phase angle. For example, let $G(s)$ be the open-loop transfer function of a certain feedback control system. The sinusoidal transfer function is simply

$$G(j\omega) = [G(s)]_{s=j\omega} = |G|\underline{/\phi_0} \tag{6-1}$$

where $|G|$ denotes the magnitude of $G(j\omega)$, and $\underline{/\phi_0}$ is the angle of $G(j\omega)$.

The following methods of plotting the transfer function $G(j\omega)$ are particularly useful in the analysis and design of feedback control systems:

(1) *Polar Plot.* A plot of magnitude versus phase shift on polar coordinates as ω is varied from zero to infinity.

(2) *Bode Plot (corner plot).* A plot of magnitude in decibel versus log ω (or ω) and phase angle versus log ω (or ω) in rectangular coordinates.

(3) *Magnitude versus Phase Shift Plot.* A plot of magnitude in decibel versus phase shift on rectangular coordinates with frequency as a varying parameter on the curve.

6.2 The Polar Plot

The polar plot is primarily used for the analysis and design of systems by means of the Nyquist criterion. To illustrate the plotting of the transfer function $G(j\omega)$ curve on polar coordinates, consider the function

$$G(s) = \frac{C(s)}{E(s)} = \frac{1}{1 + sT} \tag{6-2}$$

where T is the time constant.
Putting $s = j\omega$, we have

$$G(j\omega) = \frac{C(j\omega)}{E(j\omega)} = \frac{1}{1 + j\omega T} \tag{6-3}$$

In terms of magnitude and phase shift, the last equation can be written as

$$G(j\omega) = \frac{1}{\sqrt{1 + \omega^2 T^2}} \underline{/- \tan^{-1} \omega T} \tag{6-4}$$

When ω is zero, the magnitude of $G(j\omega)$ is unity, and the phase shift of $G(j\omega)$ is zero degree. Thus, at $\omega = 0$, $G(j\omega)$ is represented by a phasor of unit length on the real axis. As ω increases, the magnitude of $G(j\omega)$ decreases and the phase angle also increases. When ω approaches infinity, the magnitude of $G(j\omega)$ becomes zero, and the phase shift is $- 90$ deg. This is represented by a phasor of zero length directed along the $- 90$-degree axis in the $G(j\omega)$ plane. By

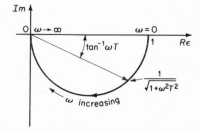

Fig. 6-1. The polar plot of $G(j\omega) = 1/(1 + j\omega T)$

substituting other finite values of ω into Eq. (6-4), the locus of $G(j\omega)$ is depicted in Fig. 6-1 as a semicircle.

As a second example, consider the transfer function

$$G(j\omega) = \frac{1 + j\omega T_a}{1 + j\omega T_1} \tag{6-5}$$

where T_a and T_1 are time constants. Equation (6-5) can also be written

$$G(j\omega) = \sqrt{\frac{1 + \omega^2 T_a^2}{1 + \omega^2 T_1^2}} \; \underline{/\tan^{-1} \omega T_a - \tan^{-1} \omega T_1} \tag{6-6}$$

The polar plot of $G(j\omega)$, in this case, apparently depends upon the relative magnitudes of T_a and T_1. If $T_a > T_1$, the magnitude of $G(j\omega)$ is always greater than unity as ω is varied from zero to infinity, and the phase shift of $G(j\omega)$ is always positive. If $T_a < T_1$, the magnitude of $G(j\omega)$ is always less than unity, and the phase shift is always negative. The transfer function loci of $G(j\omega)$ corresponding to the two different situations are plotted in Fig. 6-2 and Fig. 6-3 respectively.

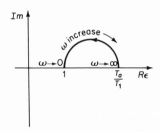

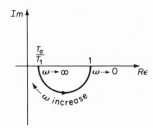

Fig. 6-2. Polar plot of
$$G(s) = \frac{1 + j\omega T_a}{1 + j\omega T_1} \quad (T_a > T_1)$$

Fig. 6-3. Polar plot of
$$G(s) = \frac{1 + j\omega T_a}{1 + j\omega T_1} \quad (T_a < T_1)$$

6.3 The Bode Plot (Corner Plot)

Another useful form of the transfer function plot is to use two graphs — one with the magnitude of $G(j\omega)$ plotted in decibel versus log ω(or ω), and the other with the phase shift of $G(j\omega)$ in degrees as a function of log ω (or ω). These graphs are often referred to as the Bode plot, the corner plot, or the logarithmic plot of $G(s)$.

The Bode plot has the following advantages:

(1) The product factors in the expression of $G(j\omega)$ become additive terms, since logarithms are used.

(2) The shape of the corner plot for the most commonly encountered

functions in servo systems makes it possible to represent approximately the exact function plot by straight line asymptotes.

(3) Since the corner plots are easy to construct, the data necessary for the construction of the polar plot and the magnitude in decibels versus phase shift plot can be obtained directly from the corner plot.

In general, we can represent the open-loop transfer function of a feedback control system (if the system does not have pure time lag in the forward path) by the following equation:

$$G(s) = \frac{K'(s + z_1)(s + z_2) \cdots (s + z_m)}{(s + p_1)(s + p_2) \cdots (s + p_n)} \tag{6-7}$$

where K' is a constant. The z's and the p's may be zero, real, or complex conjugate numbers. Hence, Eq. (6-7) can also be written

$$G(s) = \frac{K' \overset{\mu}{\underset{i=1}{\Pi}} (s + \sigma_i) \overset{m}{\underset{k=1+\mu}{\Pi}} \left(\frac{s^2}{\omega_{nk}^2} + \frac{2\delta_k}{\omega_{nk}} s + 1 \right)}{\overset{\nu}{\underset{q=1}{\Pi}} (s + \sigma_q) \overset{n}{\underset{r=1+\nu}{\Pi}} \left(\frac{s^2}{\omega_{nr}^2} + \frac{2\delta_r}{\omega_{nr}} s + 1 \right)} \tag{6-8}$$

where σ_i and σ_q are real numbers. Under sinusoidal steady-state conditions, $s = j\omega$, Eq. (6-8) becomes

$$G(j\omega) = \frac{K' \overset{\mu}{\underset{i=1}{\Pi}} (j\omega + \sigma_i) \overset{m}{\underset{k=1+\mu}{\Pi}} \left[\left(\frac{j\omega}{\omega_{nk}} \right)^2 + \left(\frac{2\delta_k}{\omega_{nk}} \right) j\omega + 1 \right]}{\overset{\nu}{\underset{q=1}{\Pi}} (j\omega + \sigma_q) \overset{n}{\underset{r=1+\nu}{\Pi}} \left[\left(\frac{j\omega}{\omega_{nr}} \right)^2 + \left(\frac{2\delta_r}{\omega_{nr}} \right) j\omega + 1 \right]} \tag{6-9}$$

which can also be written

$$G(j\omega) = \frac{K \overset{\mu}{\underset{i=1}{\Pi}} (1 + j\omega T_i) \overset{m}{\underset{k=1+\mu}{\Pi}} (- \mu_k^2 + j2\delta_k \mu_k + 1)}{\overset{\nu}{\underset{q=1}{\Pi}} (1 + j\omega T_q) \overset{n}{\underset{r=1+v}{\Pi}} (- \mu_r^2 + j2\delta_r \mu_r + 1)} \tag{6-10}$$

where
$$K = \frac{K' \overset{\mu}{\underset{i=1}{\Pi}} \sigma_i}{\overset{\nu}{\underset{q=1}{\Pi}} \sigma_q}$$

$$T_i = \frac{1}{\sigma_i}$$

$$T_q = \frac{1}{\sigma_q}$$

$$\mu_k = \omega / \omega_{nk}$$

and
$$\mu_r = \omega / \omega_{nr}$$

The magnitude of $G(j\omega)$ in decibels is obtained by multiplying the logarithm to the base 10 of $G(j\omega)$ by 20; we have

$$20 \log_{10} |G(j\omega)| = 20 \log_{10} K + 20 \sum_{i=1}^{\mu} \log_{10} |1 + j\omega T_i| + 20 \sum_{k=1+\mu}^{m} \log |1 + j2\delta_k\mu_k$$

$$- \mu_k^2| - 20 \log \sum_{q=1}^{\nu} \log_{10} |1 + j\omega T_q| - 20 \sum_{r=1+v}^{n} \log_{10} |1 + j2\delta_r\mu_r - \mu_r^2|$$

(6-11)

The phase of $G(j\omega)$ is

$$\text{Arg}G(j\omega) = \text{Arg } K + \sum_{i=1}^{\mu} \text{Arg}(1 + j\omega T_i) + \sum_{k=1+\mu}^{m} \text{Arg}(1 + j2\delta\mu_k - \mu_k^2)$$

$$- \sum_{q=1}^{\nu} \text{Arg}(1 + j\omega T_q) - \sum_{r=1+v}^{n} \text{Arg}(1 + j2\delta\mu_r - \mu_r^2) \quad (6-12)$$

where Arg $K = 0$.

The last two equations show that the magnitude and phase of an open-loop transfer function $G(j\omega)$ are composed of four simple types of factors, which are as follows:

(1) Constant $\qquad\qquad\qquad\qquad\qquad$ K

(2) Poles or zeros at the origin (σ_i or $\sigma_q = 0$) $\quad (j\omega)^{\pm n}$ $(n = 1, 2, \ldots)$

(3) Simple pole or zero $\qquad\qquad\qquad$ $(1 + j\omega T)^{\pm 1}$

(4) Quadratic pole or zero $\qquad\qquad$ $(1 + 2j\delta\mu - \mu^2)^{\pm 1}$

The advantage of the logarithmic plot is quite apparent since each of the four kinds of factors may be considered as a separate plot. The plots are then added or subtracted accordingly to yield the magnitude and phase of $G(j\omega)$. The curves may be plotted on either semilog paper or linear rectangular coordinate paper.

With semilog paper: $\qquad\qquad$ linear scale — decibel gain $|G|$ db
$\qquad\qquad\qquad\qquad\qquad\quad$ logarithmic scale — frequency ω
With linear rectangular paper: $\quad$ vertical scale — decibel gain $|G|$ db
$\qquad\qquad\qquad\qquad\qquad\quad$ horizontal scale — $\log_{10} \omega$
The four different kinds of factors are now to be investigated separately.

(1) *The Constant Term K*

Since $\qquad\qquad\qquad K_{db} = 20 \log_{10} K = \text{constant}$ $\qquad\qquad\qquad$ (6-13)

and $\qquad\qquad\qquad\qquad \text{Arg } K = 0 \text{ deg}$ $\qquad\qquad\qquad\qquad\qquad$ (6-14)

the gain in decibels and the zero phase shift are plotted in Fig. 6-4 on semilog paper.

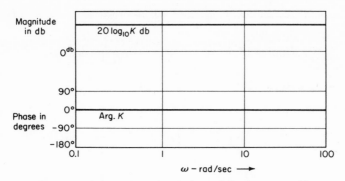

Fig. 6-4. Gain in decibel and phase shift of constant K.

(2) *Poles or Zeros at the Origin* $(j\omega)^{\pm n}$

The magnitude of $(j\omega)^{\pm n}$ in decibels is

$$20 \log_{10} |(j\omega)^{\pm n}| = \pm 20n \log_{10} \omega \text{ db} \tag{6-15}$$

which is the equation of a straight line in either semi-logarithmic coordinates or rectangular coordinates. The slopes of these straight lines may be obtained by taking the derivative of Eq. (6-15) with respect to $\log_{10} \omega$; that is,

$$\frac{d\, 20 \log |(j\omega)^{\pm n}|}{d \log_{10} \omega} = \pm 20n \text{ db} \tag{6-16}$$

Hence, in the rectangular coordinates a unit change in $\log_{10} \omega$ will correspond to a change of $\pm 20n$ db. Furthermore, a unit change in $\log_{10} \omega$ is equivalent to a change of 1 to 10, 10 to 100, etc., in the logarithmic scale. Thus the slopes of these straight lines are described by

$$20n \text{ decibel per decade of frequency} \tag{6-17}$$

Sometimes the unit *octave* is used to represent the separation of two frequencies. The frequencies ω_1 and ω_2 are separated by an octave if $\omega_2/\omega_1 = 2$. The number of octaves between any two frequencies is defined by

$$\text{Number of octaves} = \frac{\log_{10} \dfrac{\omega_2}{\omega_1}}{\log_{10} 2} \tag{6-18}$$

The number of decades between any two frequencies is defined by

$$\text{Number of decades} = \frac{\log_{10} \dfrac{\omega_2}{\omega_1}}{\log_{10} 10} \tag{6-19}$$

176 THE FREQUENCY RESPONSE METHOD

For one decade of frequency, $\omega_2/\omega_1 = 10$; the relation between *octaves* and *decades* is

$$\text{Number of octaves} = \frac{1}{\log_{10} 2} = \frac{1}{0.301} \text{ decade} \qquad (6\text{-}20)$$

Hence $\quad \pm 20n$ db/decade $= \pm 20n \times 0.301 \approx \pm 6n$ db/octave $\qquad (6\text{-}21)$

For a single pole at the origin ($s = 0$), the slope of the magnitude curve is -20 db/decade of frequency or -6 db/octave of frequency. The phase shift of $(j\omega)^{\pm n}$ is

$$\text{Arg } (j\omega)^{\pm n} = \pm n \times 90 \text{ deg} \qquad (6\text{-}22)$$

The magnitude and phase shift curves of the term $(j\omega)^{\pm n}$ are shown in Fig. 6-5 for several values of n.

(3) *Simple Pole or Zero* $(1 + j\omega T)^{\pm 1}$

(a) *Simple zero:* Let
$$G(j\omega) = 1 + j\omega T \qquad (6\text{-}23)$$

Taking the logarithm of the last equation, we have

$$20 \log_{10} |G(j\omega)| = 20 \log_{10} \sqrt{1 + T^2\omega^2} \qquad (6\text{-}24)$$

Also $\qquad\qquad\qquad \text{Arg } G(j\omega) = \tan^{-1} \omega T \qquad (6\text{-}25)$

A linear asymptotic approximation is normally used in plotting the magnitude curve. At very low frequencies, $\omega T \ll 1$.

$$20 \log_{10} |G(j\omega)| = 20 \log_{10} \sqrt{1 + \omega^2 T^2} \cong 20 \log_{10} 1 = 0 \text{ db} \qquad (6\text{-}26)$$

At very high frequencies, $\omega T \gg 1$.

$$20 \log_{10} |G(j\omega)| = 20 \log_{10} \sqrt{\omega^2 T^2} = 20_{10} \log \omega T = 20 \log_{10} \omega + 20 \log_{10} T \qquad (6\text{-}27)$$

Equation (6-27) represents a straight line with a slope of $+20$ decibels per decade of frequency (or 6 db/octave). The intersection of the low frequency and the high frequency asymptotes is found by equating Eq. (6-26) to Eq. (6-27); that is,

$$20 \log_{10} \omega T = 0 \text{ db} \qquad (6\text{-}28)$$

from which $\qquad\qquad\qquad \omega = 1/T \qquad (6\text{-}29)$

The frequency ω obtained in Eq. (6-29) is sometimes known as the "positive corner frequency" of the plot. The actual magnitude curve, however, is a smooth curve, but deviates only slightly from the straight line asymptotes. The magnitude and phase shift of the factor $(1 + j\omega T)$ are given in Table 6-1 for various values of ωT. In Table 6-2 is a comparison of

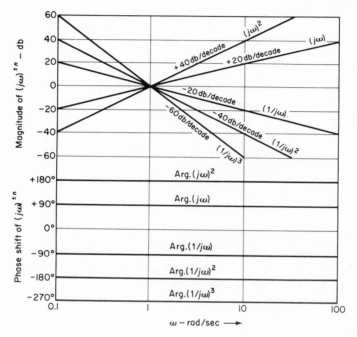

Fig. 6-5. Bode plot of magnitude and phase of the factor $(j\omega)^{\pm n}$.

the actual magnitude and the straight line asymptotes at some significant frequencies.

Table 6-1.

ωT	$\log_{10} \omega T$	$\mid 1 + j\omega T \mid$	$\mid 1 + j\omega T \mid$ db	Arg $(1 + j\omega T)$
0.01	-2	1	0	$0.5°$
0.1	-1	1.04	0.043	$5.7°$
0.5	-0.3	1.12	1	$26.6°$
0.76	-0.12	1.26	2	$37.4°$
1.0	0	1.41	3	$45.0°$
1.31	0.117	1.65	4.3	$52.7°$
1.73	0.238	2.0	6.0	$60.0°$
2.0	0.3	2.23	7.0	$63.4°$
5.0	0.7	5.1	14.2	$78.7°$
10.0	1.0	10.4	20.3	$84.3°$

Table 6-2.

ωT		Magnitude of $(1 + j\omega T)$ in db	Asymptotic values of magnitude (db)	Error (db)
0.1	One decade below corner freq.	0.3	0	+0.3
0.5	One octave below corner freq.	1.0	0	+1
0.76	At the corner freq.	2	0	+2
1.0	At the corner freq.	3	0	+3
1.31		4.3	2.3	+2
2.0	One octave above corner freq.	7	6	+1
10	One decade above corner freq.	20.3	20	+0.3

(b) *Simple pole:* When

$$G(j\omega) = \frac{1}{1 + j\omega T} \tag{6-30}$$

it is easy to see that negative signs are added to Eq. (6-26) and Eq. (6-27). The low frequency asymptote of the magnitude curve is still a straight line of zero slope and the high frequency asymptote is a straight line which has a slope of -20 db/decade. The intersection of these two straight lines is still the same as in the simple zero case; i.e., $\omega = 1/T$. This corner frequency, however, is usually called the "negative corner frequency." The phase shift is the negative of all the values given in Table 6-1.

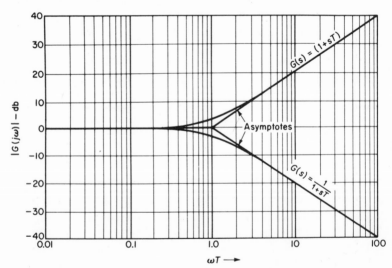

Fig. 6-6. Magnitude versus frequency
$G(s) = 1 + sT$ and $G(s) = 1/1 + sT$

The magnitude curves and the error between the actual and the asymptotic curves are plotted in Fig. 6-6 and Fig. 6-7 respectively. The

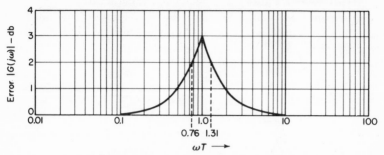

Fig. 6-7. Error in magnitude versus frequency

$$G(s) = 1 + sT \quad \text{and} \quad \frac{1}{1 + sT}$$

phase shift curves for the simple pole and zero are plotted in Fig. 6-8 in semilogarithmic coordinates.

It is interesting to note that the error between the actual magnitude curve and the asymptotic plot is symmetrical with respect to the corner

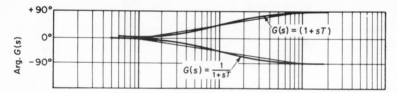

Fig. 6-8. Phase angle versus frequency

$$G(s) = \frac{1}{1 + sT} \quad \text{and} \quad G(s) = 1 + sT$$

frequency $1/T$. Furthermore, the error is 3 db at the corner frequency, and 1 db at one octave above and below the corner frequency. At one decade above and below the corner frequency, the error is about 0.3 db. From these known facts, the procedure in plotting the corner plot for the linear factor $(1 + j\omega T)^{\pm 1}$ may be outlined as follows:

(1) Locate the corner frequency $\omega = 1/T$.

(2) Draw the 6 db/octave straight line asymptotes through the corner frequency ($+ 6$ db/octave for positive corner, and $- 6$ db/octave for negative corner).

(3) The actual curve is obtained by locating the points given in Table 6-2. Usually a smooth curve can be sketched by locating the 3 db point at the corner frequency and the 1 db points at one octave above and below the corner frequency.

Similarly, a straight line can be used to approximate the phase shift curve. The line is drawn from 0 deg at one decade below the corner frequency to ± 90 deg at one decade above the corner frequency. It is seen that the maximum deviation of the straight line approximation from the actual curve is about 6 deg. Table 6-3 gives the error between the actual phase shift curve and the straight line approximation.

Table 6-3.

ωT	Actual $Arg\ (1 + j\omega T)$	Straight line approximation	Error
0.1	5.7°	0°	+5.7°
0.3	16.7°	21.7°	−5°
0.5	26.6°	31.6°	−5°
1.0	45°	45°	0°
2.0	63.4°	58.4°	+5°
3.0	71.6°	66.6°	+5°
10.0	84.3°	90.0°	−5.7°

(4) *Quadratic Poles and Zeros*

Consider the second-order transfer function:

$$G(s) = \frac{\omega_n^2}{s^2 + 2\delta\omega_n s + \omega_n^2} = \frac{1}{\dfrac{s^2}{\omega_{n:}^2} + \dfrac{2\delta}{\omega_n} s + 1} \qquad (6\text{-}31)$$

If we let $s = j\omega$, the last equation becomes

$$G(j\omega) = \frac{1}{\left[1 - \left(\dfrac{\omega}{\omega_n}\right)^2\right] + j\omega \dfrac{2\delta}{\omega_n}} \qquad (6\text{-}32)$$

The magnitude of $G(j\omega)$ in decibels is

$$20 \log_{10} |\,G(j\omega)\,| = -20 \log_{10} \sqrt{\left[1 - \left(\dfrac{\omega}{\omega_n}\right)^2\right]^2 + \left(\dfrac{2\delta\omega}{\omega_n}\right)^2} \qquad (6\text{-}33)$$

The phase shift of $G(j\omega)$ is

$$\text{Arg } G(j\omega) = -\tan^{-1} \left(\frac{\dfrac{2\delta\omega}{\omega_n}}{1 - \left(\dfrac{\omega}{\omega_n}\right)^2}\right) \qquad (6\text{-}34)$$

At very low frequencies, $\dfrac{\omega}{\omega_n} \ll 1$; Eq. (6-33) may be written as

$$20 \log |\,G(j\omega)\,| \cong -20 \log_{10} 1 = 0 \text{ db} \qquad (6\text{-}35)$$

Hence, the low frequency asymptote for the second-order factor plot is, again, a straight line with zero slope.

At very high frequencies, $\dfrac{\omega}{\omega_n} \gg 1$; the magnitude of $G(j\omega)$ in decibels becomes

$$20 \log_{10} | G(j\omega) | = - 20 \log_{10} \sqrt{\left[1 - \left(\frac{\omega}{\omega_n} \right)^2 \right]^2 + \left(2\delta \frac{\omega}{\omega_n} \right)^2}$$

$$\cong - 20 \log_{10} \sqrt{\left(\frac{\omega}{\omega_n} \right)^4} = - 40 \log \left(\frac{\omega}{\omega_n} \right) db \qquad (6\text{-}36)$$

The last equation represents the equation of a straight line with slope of $- 40$ db/decade in the semi-logarithmic coordinates.

The intersection of the two asymptotes is found by equating

$$- 40 \log_{10} \left(\frac{\omega}{\omega_n} \right) = 0 \text{ db} \qquad (6\text{-}37)$$

from which $\qquad\qquad\qquad \omega = \omega_n \qquad\qquad\qquad\qquad (6\text{-}38)$

Hence the frequency $\omega = \omega_n$ is considered to be the corner frequency of the second-order factor. The actual magnitude plot in this case, however, differs strikingly from the asymptotic lines. The reason for this is that the amplitude and phase curves depend not only on the corner frequency ω_n (same as the natural undamped frequency), but also on the damping ratio δ. The actual magnitude plot and the phase shift plot are plotted in Fig. 6-9 and Fig. 6-10 respectively. The error between the curves shown in Fig. 6-9 and the asymptotic straight lines are plotted in Fig. 6-11. Usually, if a transfer function of the quadratic form is given, first, the values of δ and ω_n are determined; then, by using the sets of curves shown in Fig. 6-11, the magnitude and phase shift versus frequency curve may be plotted.

6.4 The Magnitude Versus Phase Shift Plot

As mentioned in the introduction of this chapter, the magnitude versus phase shift plot is a plot of the magnitude of the transfer function $G(s)$ in decibels versus its phase shift in degrees with frequency as a parameter on the curves. The chief advantage of using this set of coordinates is that the plot can be superposed on the Nichols chart (see Chapter 7) to determine the relative stability of the closed-loop system. When the gain constant K of the transfer function $G(j\omega)$ is varied, the plot is simply raised or lowered vertically according to the logarithmic scale. However, the unique property of adding the individual plot for cascaded terms in the corner plot does not carry over to this case. The magnitude versus phase shift plots are usually obtained by first plotting the corner plot and then transferring the data to the decibel versus phase coordinates. As an example, the corner plots of the second order factor shown in Fig. 6-9 and Fig. 6-10 are transferred to the magnitude versus phase shift plot, as shown in Fig. 6-12. It is seen that the normalized frequency ω/ω_n is used as a parameter on the curves.

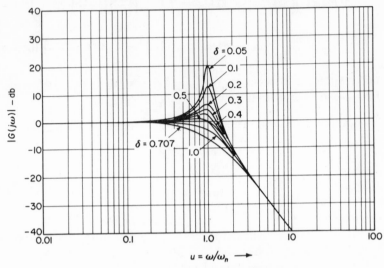

Fig. 6-9. Magnitude versus frequency

$$G(s) = \frac{1}{1 + 2\delta(s/\omega_n) + (s/\omega_n)^2}$$

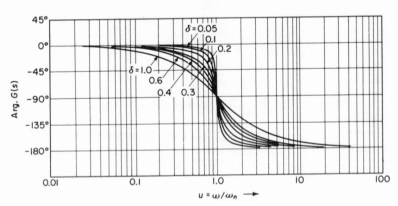

Fig. 6-10. Phase angle versus frequency

$$G(s) = \frac{1}{1 + 2\delta(s/\omega_n) + (s/\omega_n)^2}$$

6.5 Frequency Response of Feedback Control Systems

A feedback control system may also be regarded as a filtering device. The obvious question concerning the performance of a filter is: What is the

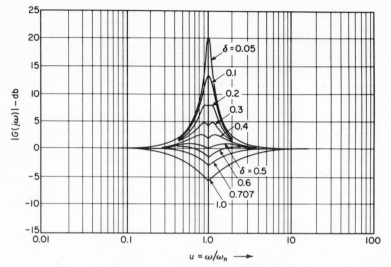

Fig. 6-11. Error in magnitude versus frequency

$$G(s) = \frac{1}{1 + 2\delta(s/\omega_n) + (s/\omega_n)^2}$$

frequency response of the filter? Or simply, if the reference input to the system is a sine wave, what is the output response? In terms of a control system, we can ask: If the synchro transmitter shaft (reference input) is driven to oscillate sinusoidally, what will be the behavior of the output shaft? It is, of course, very unlikely that the input to the system will be sinusoidal in practice, but by working with the frequency response, we shall show that interpretation may be made also on the transient behavior of the system.

Consider the closed-loop transfer function of a unity-feedback control system:

$$\frac{C(s)}{R(s)} = \frac{G(s)}{1 + G(s)} \tag{6-39}$$

Under sinusoidal steady-state conditions, the last equation becomes

$$M = \frac{C(j\omega)}{R(j\omega)} = \frac{G(j\omega)}{1 + G(j\omega)} \tag{6-40}$$

where

$$M = M\underline{/\phi_m} \tag{6-41}$$

is called the "magnification" of the feedback control system. The significance of M to a feedback control system is similar to the gain or amplification A to an electronic amplifier. In an audio amplifier, for instance, an ideal design criterion is that the amplifier must have a flat gain response in the audio frequency range. In servo systems, however, the ideal situation

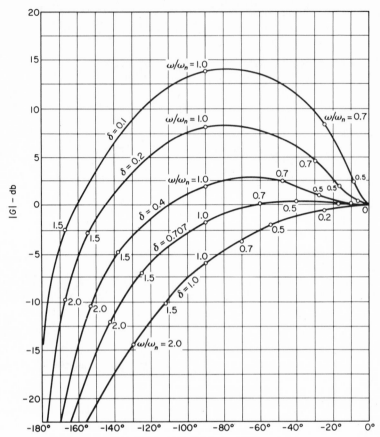

Fig. 6-12. Magnitude versus phase shift curve for

$$G(s) = \frac{\omega_n^2}{s^2 + 2\delta\omega_n s + \omega_n^2}$$

is that the output must follow the input signal at all times, or, simply, M must equal unity for all frequencies. But from the expression of Eq. (6-40), M can be unity only when G is infinite. Or, in other words, the forward path gain must be infinite at all frequencies. This, is of course, impossible to achieve in practice, nor would it be desirable, since most systems become unstable for high values of gain. Furthermore, all servo systems are subjected to noise. Thus, in addition to responding to the input signal, the servo systems must be able to reject noise and unwanted signals. This means that the frequency response of a servo system must have a cut-off characteristic in general, and sometimes even characteristics of band-pass or band-eliminate filters. The phase characteristic of the frequency response is also important. The ideal situation is that the phase shift must be a linear function of frequency within the frequency band of the input signal. Figure 6-13a shows the gain and phase characteristics of an ideal low-pass filter, which is impossible to realize physically.

The gain and phase characteristics of a typical servo system are shown in Fig. 6-13b. It is seen that the gain decreases gradually as the frequency is

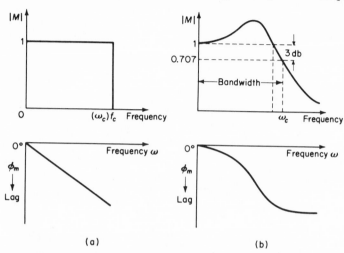

(a)   (b)

Fig. 6-13. Comparison of gain-phase characteristics of an ideal low-pass filter and a typical servo system. (a) Ideal filter; (b) Servo system.

increased. This is due to the effect of inertia and inductance in a physical system; all responses must cease as the frequency approaches infinity.

6.6 Frequency Domain Specifications

The specifications for the performance of a servo system in the frequency domain are commonly given in the following terms:

(1) *Bandwidth*: The bandwidth is defined with the conventional definition; it is shown in Fig. 6-14. The bandwidth roughly indicates the filtering characteristics of the system.

(2) *Resonance peak*: M_p: This is the maximum value of M, which indicates the relative stability of the system. It will be shown that a large

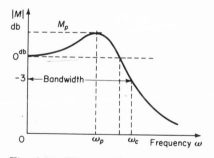

Fig. 6-14. The magnification curve of a servo system.

resonance peak M_p corresponds to a large overshoot in the transient response. An optimum value of M_p is usually somewhere between 1.1 and 1.5.

(3) *Resonant frequency: ω_p:* This is the frequency at which the resonance peak M_p occurs.

(4) *Cutoff rate:* In some cases, the rate of cutoff of the frequency response at high frequencies is important, since it indicates the characteristics of the system in distinguishing the signal from noise. However, in general, sharp cutoff characteristics are accompanied by large M_p, which means a less stable system.

Other important factors in measuring the relative stability of a servo system are the "gain margin," and the "phase margin." These terms will be discussed in detail in the next chapter.

6.7 M_p and ω_p for a Second-Order System

For a second-order feedback control system, the maximum resonance peak M_p and the resonant frequency ω_p are uniquely related to the damping ratio δ and the natural undamped frequency ω_n of the system.

Consider the second-order transfer function:

$$\overline{M} = \frac{C(j\omega)}{R(j\omega)} = \frac{1}{1 + j2\delta \dfrac{\omega}{\omega_n} - \left(\dfrac{\omega}{\omega_n}\right)^2} \tag{6-42}$$

If we let $u = \dfrac{\omega}{\omega_n}$, the magnitude of M is

$$|M| = \frac{1}{[(1 - u^2)^2 + (2\delta u)^2]^{1/2}} \tag{6-43}$$

and the phase of M is

$$\phi_m = -\tan^{-1} \frac{2\delta u}{1 - u^2} \tag{6-44}$$

The resonant frequency ω_p is determined first by taking the derivative of M with respect to u and setting it equal to zero.

Thus $\dfrac{d\,|M|}{du} = -\dfrac{1}{2}(u^4 - 2u^2 + 1 + 4\delta^2 u^2)^{-3/2}(4u^3 - 4u + 8u\delta^2) = 0$ (6-45)

from which $\qquad\qquad 4u^3 - 4u + 8u\delta^2 = 0 \tag{6-46}$

hence $\qquad\qquad u_p = \sqrt{1 - 2\delta^2} = \dfrac{\omega_p}{\omega_n}$

The resonant frequency $\qquad \omega_p = \omega_n\sqrt{1 - 2\delta^2} \tag{6-47}$

Evidently, the last equation is valid only for $1 \geq 2\delta^2$ or for $\delta \leq 0.707$, since otherwise, ω_p will become imaginary. However, this means simply that, for all values of $\delta > 0.707$, there is no peak (no M_p) in the M versus ω curve. The M curve is less than one for all values of $\omega > 0$ if the damping ratio δ is greater than 0.707.

Substituting Eq. (6-47) into the expression for M given by Eq. (6-43) we have

$$M_p = \frac{1}{\{[1 - (1 - 2\delta^2)]^2 + 4\delta^2(1 - 2\delta^2)\}^{1/2}} = \frac{1}{2\delta\sqrt{1 - \delta^2}} \quad (6\text{-}48)$$

It is important to note that the frequency domain characteristics M_p and ω_p of the second-order system are related to the time domain quantities δ and ω_n. The plots of M_p versus δ and u versus δ are given in Fig. 6-15 and Fig. 6-16 respectively.

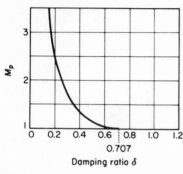

Fig. 6-15. M_p vs. δ plot for a second-order system,

$$M_p = \frac{1}{2\delta\sqrt{1 - \delta^2}}$$

Fig. 6-16. u vs. δ plot for a second-order system, $u = \sqrt{1 - 2\delta^2}$.

As an example, consider the servo system given in Sec. 5-6 (Fig. 5-9). The closed-loop transfer function of the system, which was already obtained in Eq. (5-40), is repeated as follows:

$$\frac{\theta_c(s)}{\theta_r(s)} = \frac{K_s A K_i n}{sR_a f(1 + sT_a)(1 + sT) + K_b K_i s + K_s A K_i n} \quad (6\text{-}49)$$

For a sinusoidal input,

$$\theta_r(t) = R \sin \omega t \quad (6\text{-}50)$$

where R is a constant; the closed-loop transfer function becomes

$$\overline{M} = \frac{\theta_c(j\omega)}{\theta_r(j\omega)} = \frac{K_s A K_i n}{j\omega R_a f(1 + j\omega T_a)(1 + j\omega T) + K_b K_i j\omega + K_s A K_i n} \quad (6\text{-}51)$$

Rearranging terms in the last equation, we have the magnitude of $\overline{M}$:

$$| M | = \left| \frac{\theta_c(j\omega)}{\theta_r(j\omega)} \right|$$

$$= \frac{K_s A K_i n}{\{[K_s A K_i n - \omega^2(T + T_a)R_a f]^2 + \omega^2[K_b K_i + R_a f - \omega^2 R_a f T T_a]^2\}^{1/2}} \quad (6\text{-}52)$$

The phase shift of $\overline{M}$ is

$$\phi_m = - \tan^{-1} \frac{\omega(K_b K_i + R_a f - \omega^2 R_a f T T_a)}{K_s A K_i n - \omega^2(T + T_a)R_a f} \quad (6\text{-}53)$$

From Eq. (6-52) it is seen that the magnitude of M can be greater than unity. Furthermore, if the denominator of Eq. (6-52) becomes zero, the magnitude of M is infinite. Hence, $M = \infty$ if

$$\omega^2 = \frac{K_s A K_i n}{(T + T_a) R_a f} = \frac{K_b K_i + R_c f}{R_a f T T_a} \tag{6-54}$$

By means of the Routh's criterion it is easy to show that two of the roots of the characteristic equation will lie on the $j\omega$ axis when

$$(R_a f T T_a)(K_s A K_i n) - (K_b K_i + R_a f)(T + T_a) R_a f = 0 \tag{6-55}$$

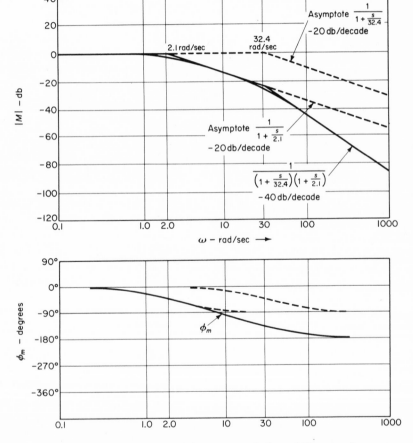

Fig. 6-17. The magnification curve and phase shift curve of

$$\overline{M} = \frac{1}{\left(1 + \dfrac{s}{32.4}\right)\left(1 + \dfrac{s}{2.1}\right)}$$

which is identical to Eq. (6-54). Thus, when the servo system goes into sustained oscillation, the magnification M of the system is infinite.

Now assume that the motor inductance L_a is zero while all other system parameters are kept unchanged. The closed-loop transfer function becomes

$$\frac{\theta_c(s)}{\theta_r(s)} = \frac{5A}{s^2 + 34.5s + 5A} \tag{6-56}$$

which is of the second order. For the three different values of A used in Sec. 5-6, the corresponding M_p and ω_p are calculated by means of Eq. (6-48) and Eq. (6-47) respectively and are tabulated in Table 6-3.

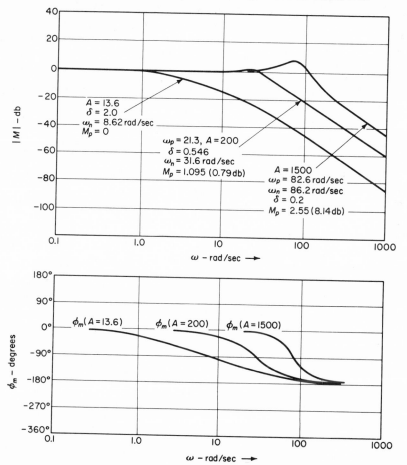

Fig. 6-18. The magnification and phase shift curves for

$$\overline{M} = \frac{5A}{s^2 + 34.5s + 5A}$$

Table 6-4.

Gain A	Damping ratio δ	Undamped nat. Freq. ω_n rad/sec	Peak M_p	Resonant Freq. ω_p rad/sec
13.5	2.0	8.62	0	—
200	0.546	31.6	1.095	21.3
1500	0.2	86.2	2.55	82.6

For $\delta = 0.546$ and $\delta = 0.2$, the $|M|$ versus ω and the phase shift ϕ_m versus ω curves may be obtained directly from the normalized plot of the second-order factor given in Fig. 6-9 and Fig. 6-10. For a damping ratio of $\delta = 2.0$, the system is overdamped and there is no resonance peak; the closed-loop system response may be obtained from the expression

$$\overline{M} = \frac{\theta_c(j\omega)}{\theta_r(j\omega)} = \frac{1}{(1 + s/32.4)(1 + s/2.1)} \tag{6-57}$$

which has two negative corner frequencies — one at $\omega = 32.4$ rad/sec, and the other at $\omega = 2.1$ rad/sec. The $|M|$ versus ω curve is the sum of the two plots for the simple first-order factors. Figure 6-17 illustrates the construction of the $|M|$ versus ω and phase ϕ_m versus ω curves. The magnitude of M and phase shift versus ω curves for the three different values of gain A used are plotted in Fig. 6-18. It is seen that the effect of increasing the amplifier gain is to increase M_p and ω_p.

Problems

6-1. Sketch polar plots for the following transfer functions.

(a) $G(s) = \dfrac{s}{1 + sT}$

(b) $G(s) = \dfrac{K}{s(1 + sT)}$

(c) $G(s) = \dfrac{K}{(1 + sT_1)(1 + sT_2)}$

(d) $G(s) = \dfrac{K}{s^2(1 + sT)}$

(e) $G(s) = \dfrac{K}{s(1 + sT_1)(1 + sT_2)}$

(f) $G(s) = \dfrac{K(1 + s)}{s(1 + 0.2s)(1 + 0.5s)}$

(g) $G(s) = \dfrac{K(1 + 0.1s)}{s(1 + 0.2s)(1 + 0.5s)}$

6-2. Sketch the Bode plots in magnitude and phase shift versus frequency for the following transfer functions.

(a) $G(s) = \dfrac{1 + sT_1}{1 + sT_2}$

(b) $G(s) = \dfrac{K}{s(1 + sT)}$

(c) $G(s) = \dfrac{K(1 + 3s)}{s^2(1 + 2s)}$

(d) $G(s) = \dfrac{10(1 + 0.5s)}{s(1 + 0.1s)(1 + 0.2s)}$

6-3. The magnitude curves of the open-loop transfer function $G(s)$ of certain feedback control systems are given in Fig. 6P-3a and b. In each case, determine the transfer function $G(s)$, and sketch the corresponding phase shift versus frequency curve. Sketch the corresponding polar plots.

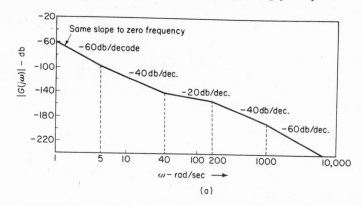

(a)

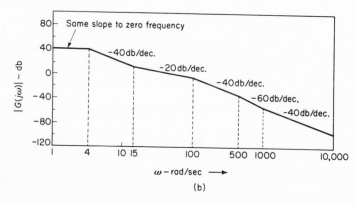

(b)

Fig. 6P-3

6-4. The low-frequency characteristics of the magnitude curves of the open-loop transfer function $G(s)$ of certain unity-feedback systems are given in Fig. 6P-4. Determine the error constants K_p, K_v, and K_a for each system.

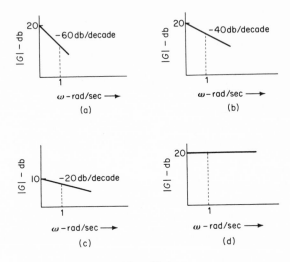

Fig. 6P-4

6-5. The pole-zero configuration of a closed-loop transfer function is shown in Fig. 6P-5a.
(a) Compute the bandwidth of the system.
(b) A zero is added to the closed-loop system, as shown in Fig. 6P-5b; how is the band width affected?
(c) Another pole is inserted on the negative real axis in Fig. 6P-5b, but at a distance ten times further from the origin than the zero; how is the band width affected?

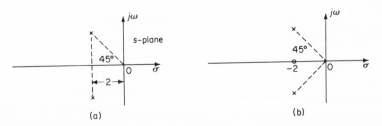

Fig. 6P-5

6-6. Sketch the polar plots for the open-loop transfer function $\theta_L(s)/\theta_e(s)$ in Problem 5-7 for $K = 50$, 60.7, and 100. On each plot, determine the point at which the locus intersects the negative real axis in the G-plane.

6-7. The specification given on a certain second-order feedback control system is that the overshoot of the step response should not exceed 25 per cent.
(a) What are the corresponding limiting values of the damping ratio δ and peak resonance M_p?
(b) Determine the corresponding values for ω_p and t_{max}.

6-8. For the servo system described in Problem 4-3 and Problem 5-8, plot the frequency response ($|M|$ versus ω) curves for $A = 10$, 100, and 1000. Determine the resonance peak M_p and the resonant frequency for each case.

6-9. The closed-loop transfer function of a feedback control system is given by

$$M(s) = \frac{C(s)}{R(s)} = \frac{1}{(1 + 0.01s)(1 + 0.05s + 0.01s^2)}$$

(a) Plot the frequency response curve of the closed-loop system.
(b) Determine the peak resonance M_p and the resonant frequency ω_p of the system.
(c) Determine the damping ratio δ and natural undamped frequency ω_n of the second-order system which will produce the same M_p and ω_p determined for the original system.

7

The Nyquist Criterion

7.1 Introduction

Thus far, two methods have been used to determine the location of the roots of the characteristic equation:

(1) The roots are actually determined by solving the characteristic equation, which is a polynomial of s.

(2) The location of the roots with respect to the right half or the left half of the s-plane is determined by means of the Routh criterion. Although the application of the Routh criterion is quite straightforward, the only information that the criterion can furnish is the absolute stability of the system. If the system is stable, the Routh test does not tell how stable it is; it is quite possible that the damping is so small that the system is still undesirable. Moreover, the Routh criterion does not give any information concerning methods of improving a system.

The Nyquist criterion possesses the following features which make it particularly desirable for the stability analysis of feedback control systems:

(1) It provides the same amount of information on the absolute stability of a feedback system as the Routh criterion.

(2) In addition to the absolute system stability, the Nyquist criterion also indicates the degree of stability of a stable system, and gives information about how the system stability may be improved, if necessary.

(3) The Nyquist locus gives information concerning the frequency response
of the system.

Consider the feedback control system
shown in Fig. 7-1. The closed-loop transfer function of the system is

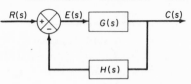

Fig. 7-1. Feedback control system.

$$\frac{C(s)}{R(s)} = \frac{G(s)}{1 + G(s)H(s)} \qquad (7\text{-}1)$$

Let the denominator of Eq. (7-1) be represented by $F(s)$; that is,

$$F(s) = 1 + G(s)H(s) \qquad (7\text{-}2)$$

The zeros of $F(s)$ are the roots of the characteristic equation of the system.
In this chapter the functions $G(s)$ and $H(s)$ are assumed to be rational
functions. In other words, $G(s)H(s)$ is a quotient of two polynomials with
constant coefficients. Thus, in general, $F(s)$ can be written as follows:

$$F(s) = 1 + G(s)H(s) = \frac{(s + z_1)(s + z_2) \cdots (s + z_m)}{s^j(s + p_1)(s + p_2) \cdots (s + p_n)} \qquad (7\text{-}3)$$

The zeros of $F(s)$ at $-z_1, -z_2, -z_3, \ldots, -z_m$ are the roots of the characteristic equation; they are either real, imaginary, or in complex conjugate
pairs. For a stable closed-loop system, it is required that none of these
roots has a positive real part; there is no particular restriction on the
location of the poles of $F(s)$, which are at $s = 0, -p_1, -p_2, \ldots, -p_n$.
It is important to note that the poles of $F(s)$ are the same as those of
$G(s)H(s)$. If any one of the poles of $G(s)H(s)$ lies in the right half of the
s-plane, the open-loop system* is said to be unstable; however, the closed-
loop system can still be stable if all the zeros of $F(s)$ are found in the left
half of the s-plane. This is a very important feature of a feedback control
system. In previous chapters, it was made clear that a high forward gain K
generally reduces the steady-state error of a system; consequently, it is a
common practice to use high gain in multiple-loop systems. While this
practice may result in an unstable inner-loop system, the entire closed-loop
system can be made stable by proper design.

This section can be summarized as follows:

(1) Identification of the poles and zeros:

(a) The loop-gain zeros = The zeros of $G(s)H(s)$

(b) The loop-gain poles = The poles of $G(s)H(s)$

(c) The closed-loop poles = The poles of $C(s)/R(s)$

= The zeros of $F(s) = 1 + G(s)H(s)$

= The roots of the characteristic
equation

*The open-loop system here refers to the loop transfer function $G(s)H(s)$.

(2) The poles of $F(s)$ are the same as the loop-gain poles.

(3) For a stable feedback control system, there is no restriction on the location of the loop-gain zeros and the loop-gain poles, but the closed-loop poles must all be located in the left half of the s-plane.

7.2 "Encircled" and "Enclosed"

Before starting on the discussion of the Nyquist criterion, it is important to distinguish between the two terms — "encircled" and "enclosed" — which will be used frequently in this chapter.

(1) *"Encircled"*

The point A shown in Fig. 7-2a is said to be encircled by the closed path Γ, since A is found inside the closed path. The direction of encirclement is indicated by the arrow on the path. The point A shown in Fig. 7-2b is

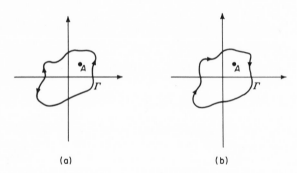

(a)   (b)

Fig. 7-2. An "encircled" point. (a) Point A is encircled by Γ in the counterclockwise direction; (b) Point A is encircled by Γ in the clockwise direction.

encircled by the locus Γ in a clockwise direction, while that of Fig. 7-2a is encircled by Γ in a counterclockwise direction.

(2) *"Enclosed"*

(a)   (b)

Fig. 7-3. "Enclosed" points and regions. (a) Point A is enclosed by the locus Γ; (b) Point A is *not* enclosed by the locus Γ.

The region enclosed by a closed path Γ is defined as the region to the left of the path when the path is traced in a prescribed direction. The shaded regions shown in Figs. 7-3a and 7-3b are considered to be enclosed by the Γ locus. In other words, the point A in Fig. 7-3a is enclosed by Γ, but the point A in Fig. 7-3b is not enclosed by Γ.

7.3 The Principle of the Argument

The Nyquist criterion was originated from the principle of the argument* in complex variable theories. Let $F(s)$ be a single-valued rational function which is analytic everywhere in a specified region except at a finite number of points in the s-plane. For each point of analyticity in the specified region in the s-plane, there is a corresponding point in the $F(s)$-plane. Suppose that a continuous closed path Γ_s is arbitrarily chosen in the s-plane, as shown in Fig. 7-4; if all the points on Γ_s are in the specified region in which $F(s)$ is analytic, the curve Γ_F mapped by the function $F(s)$ into the F-plane is also a closed one. If, corresponding to the point s_1 in the s-plane, a point $F(s_1)$ is located in the F-plane, as the Γ_s locus is traced starting from the point s_1 in a clockwise direction (arbitrarily chosen) and then returning to s_1 after going through all the points on the Γ_s locus, the corresponding Γ_F locus will start from the point $F(s_1)$ and go through the points $F(s_2)$, $F(s_3)$, . . ., and back to the starting point $F(s_1)$. The direction of traverse of Γ_F may be either clockwise or counterclockwise, depending on the particular function $F(s)$.†

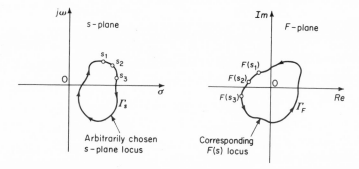

Fig. 7-4. The arbitrarily chosen s-plane locus Γ_s, and the corresponding $F(s)$-plane locus Γ_F.

---

*C. R. Wylie, Jr., *Advanced Engineering Mathematics*, McGraw-Hill Book Company, Inc., New York, 1951.

†It is important to note that, although the mapping from the s-plane to the $F(s)$-plane is one-to-one, the reversed process is not a one-to-one correspondence. For example, let

$$F(s) = \frac{K}{(s+a)(s+b)(s+c)}$$

The function $F(s)$ is analytic in the finite s-plane except at the points $s = -a$, $-b$, and $-c$. For each value of s in the finite s-plane other than the three points $-a$, $-b$, and $-c$, there is only one corresponding point in the F-plane. But for a given point in the F-plane, there is more than one corresponding point in the s-plane. For $F(s) = $ constant, we can write

$$(s+a)(s+b)(s+c) = K/F(s)$$

The last equation is a cubic equation, which has three roots for each F.

The principle of the argument states:

Let $F(s)$ be a single-valued rational function which is analytic in a specified region in the s-plane except at a finite number of points. Suppose that an arbitrary closed path Γ_s is chosen in the s-plane so that at every point on the Γ_s path $F(s)$ is analytic; the corresponding $F(s)$ locus mapped in the F-plane will *encircle* the origin as many times as the difference between the number of the zeros and the number of the poles of $F(s)$ that are encircled by the s-plane locus Γ_s. In other words,

$$N = Z - P \qquad (7\text{-}4)$$

where N = number of encirclement of the origin made by the $F(s)$ locus Γ_F in the F-plane

and Z = number of zeros of $F(s)$ encircled by the s-plane locus Γ_s in the s-plane

P = number of poles of $F(s)$ encircled by the s-plane locus. Γ_s in the s-plane

In general, N can be positive $(Z > P)$, zero $(Z = P)$, or negative $(Z < P)$. These three different situations are discussed as follows:

(1) $N > 0 \ (Z > P)$

If the s-plane locus encircles more zeros than poles of $F(s)$ in a certain direction (clockwise or counterclockwise), N is a positive integer; the $F(s)$-plane locus will encircle the origin* N times in the *same* direction as that of Γ_s.

(2) $N = 0 \ (Z = P)$

If the s-plane locus encircles as many poles as zeros, or encircles no poles and zeros of $F(s)$, the F-plane locus Γ_F will not encircle the origin.

(3) $N < 0 \ (Z < P)$

If the s-plane locus encircles more poles than zeros of $F(s)$ in a certain direction, N is a negative number; the $F(s)$-plane locus Γ_F will encircle the origin N times in the *opposite* direction from that of Γ_s.

The principle of the argument will become apparent if we consider, for instance, $F(s)$, which is given as

$$F(s) = \frac{(s + z_1)(s + z_2)}{(s + p_1)(s + p_2)(s + p_3)} \qquad (7\text{-}5)$$

$$F(s) = \frac{\prod_{m=1}^{2} |s + z_m|}{\prod_{n=1}^{3} |s + p_n|} \ [\ \sum_{m=1}^{2} \underline{/s + z_m} - \sum_{n=1}^{3} \underline{/s + p_n}] \qquad (7\text{-}6)$$

or $$F(s) = |F(s)| \ \underline{/F(s)} \qquad (7\text{-}7)$$

*In the stability studies, the origin in the F-plane is referred to as the "critical point," where $F(s) = 1 + G(s)H(s)$.

Let us assume that the pole-zero configuration of $F(s)$ is as shown in Fig. 7-5; Γ_s is the s-plane locus, and s_1 is an arbitrary point on the closed path Γ_s. The factor $(s_1 + z_1)$ can be represented graphically by the vector drawn from z_1 to s_1. Thus, Eq. (7-5) is represented by vectors drawn from the given poles and zeros to the point s_1. Now, the point s_1 is moved along the locus Γ_s in the counterclockwise direction (arbitrarily chosen) until it returns to the starting point; the angles generated by the vectors drawn from the poles and zeros not encircled by Γ_s when s_1 completes one round trip are zero, while the vector $(s_1 + z_2)$ drawn from the zero $-z_2$, which is encircled by the s-plane locus, generates a positive angle (counterclockwise sense) of 2π rad. Then, in Eq. (7-7) the angle of $F(s)$ is

$$\underline{/F(s)} = +2\pi \qquad (7\text{-}8)$$

which means that the corresponding $F(s)$ locus must go around the origin 2π radians in a counterclockwise direction, such as that which is shown in Fig. 7-6.

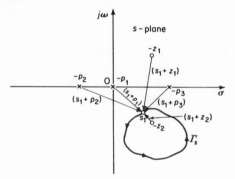

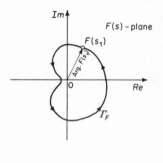

Fig. 7-5. Pole-zero configuration of $F(s)$ and the s-plane locus Γ_s.

Fig. 7-6. The $F(s)$-plane locus Γ_F corresponding to Γ_s given in Fig. 7-5. Γ_F encircles the origin once in the counterclockwise direction.

In general, if there are N more zeros than poles of $F(s)$ which are encircled by the s-plane locus in a counterclockwise direction,

$$\underline{/F(s)} = 2\pi(Z - P) = 2\pi N \qquad (7\text{-}9)$$

The last equation implies that the F-plane locus will encircle the origin N times in the counterclockwise direction. Conversely, if N more poles than zeros are encircled by the s-plane locus in the counterclockwise direction, the F-plane locus must encircle the origin N times in the clockwise direction, since, in Eq. (7-7),

$$\underline{/F(s)} = 2\pi(Z - P) = 2\pi N$$

$$= \text{negative number} \qquad (7\text{-}10)$$

The application of the argument principle is summarized in Table 7-1.

Table 7-1

SUMMARY OF THE ARGUMENT PRINCIPLE

$N = Z - P$	Sense of the s-plane locus	F-plane locus	
		No. of encirclements of the origin	Direction of encirclement
$N > 0$	clockwise	N times	clockwise
	counterclockwise		counterclockwise
$N < 0$	clockwise	N times	counterclockwise
	counterclockwise		clockwise
$N = 0$	clockwise	0 times	no encirclement
	counterclockwise		no encirclement

7.4 The Nyquist Path

The main objective in the stability studies of feedback control systems is to determine if any of the roots of the characteristic equation ($F(s) = 0$) lies in the right half of the s-plane. It is easy to see that the principle of the argument can be used for this purpose, provided that the s-plane locus is defined as shown in Fig. 7-7. The locus Γ_s is described in a counterclockwise direction so that it *encloses* the entire finite right half of the s-plane; this path is called the *Nyquist path*. For the convenience of analysis, the Nyquist path is divided into four separate sections:

(1) Section I: From $s = +j\infty$ to $+j0^+$ along the $j\omega$ axis.

(2) Section II: From $+j0^+$ to $-j0^+$ along the small semicircle around the origin.

(3) Section III: From $s = -j0^+$ to $s = -j\infty$ along the $-j\omega$ axis.

(4) Section IV: From $-j\infty$ to $+j\infty$ along the semicircle of infinite radius in the right half of the s-plane.

Since the Nyquist path must not pass through any singularity of $F(s)$, the small semicircles along the imaginary axis and at the origin are necessary if $F(s)$ has poles on the $j\omega$ axis and at the origin.

It is apparent that if any pole or zero of $F(s)$ lies in the right half plane in the s-plane, it must be enclosed by the Nyquist path. It is for this reason that the specific path is chosen. Small semicircles on the $j\omega$ axis are necessary to represent cases where poles of $G(s)H(s)$ are found on the $j\omega$ axis, so that a persistent but bounded oscillation exists in the system.

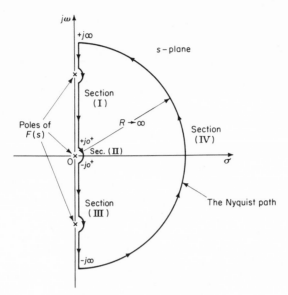

Fig. 7-7. The Nyquist path.

7.5 The Nyquist Criterion and the GH-Plot

The Nyquist criterion is a direct application of the principle of the argument when the s-plane locus is the Nyquist path. Once the Nyquist path is specified, the stability of a closed-loop system can be determined by plotting the $F(s) = 1 + G(s)H(s)$ locus when s takes on values along the Nyquist path, and investigating the behavior of the $F(s)$ plot with respect to the origin in the F-plane.

In general, $F(s)$ can be written as

$$F(s) = 1 + G(s)H(s) = \frac{(s + z_1)(s + z_2) \cdots (s + z_m)}{s^j(s + p_1)(s + p_2) \cdots (s + p_n)} \qquad (7\text{-}11)$$

It is important to remember that the poles of $F(s)$ are the same as the poles of $G(s)H(s)$, and the zeros of $F(s)$ are the roots of the characteristic equation, whose location is our main concern in the stability study. Thus, given a feedback control system, if $F(s)$ is of the form given by Eq. (7-11), we can apply the argument principle to determine its stability; the procedure is described as follows:

(1) The Nyquist path is defined as shown in Fig. 7-7.

(2) The $F(s) = 1 + G(s)H(s)$ locus is plotted in the F-plane corresponding to the Nyquist path.

(3) If the poles of $G(s)H(s)$ are all located in the left half of the s-plane, or on the $j\omega$ axis, the closed-loop system is stable, provided the Nyquist plot

of $F(s)$ does not encircle the origin. Since, in this case, given that $P = 0$, Eq. (7-4) gives

$$N = Z - P = Z \qquad (7\text{-}12)$$

Therefore, for a stable system, there will be no zero of $F(s)$ for the Nyquist path to enclose. Thus, in Eq. (7-12),

$$N = Z = 0$$

We can also say that, in this case, for stability, the Nyquist plot of $F(s)$ must not enclose the origin in the F-plane, for if $Z \neq 0$, $N = Z$ must be a positive integer and the origin in the F-plane will be encircled in a positive direction (enclosed). However, if some of the poles of $G(s)H(s)$ are in the right half of the s-plane, $P \neq 0$, and then

$$N = Z - P \qquad (7\text{-}13)$$

Since for a stable system Z always must be zero, the condition for a stable system is

$$N = -P \qquad (7\text{-}14)$$

which implies that the Nyquist plot of $F(s)$ must encircle the origin as many times as the number of P. The encirclement, if any, must be made in a negative (clockwise) direction.

Since, in general, the functions $G(s)$ and $H(s)$ are given, rather than $F(s)$, it is easier to plot or sketch the Nyquist plot of $G(s)H(s)$ than the plot of $F(s)$. The difference between the $F(s)$ plot and the $G(s)H(s)$ plot is simply a shift of the imaginary axis. The $(-1, +j0)$ point in the GH-plane corresponds to the origin in the F-plane. Given a certain $F(s)$ plot, as shown in Fig. 7-9, the corresponding GH-plot in the GH-plane will take the form shown in Fig. 7-8.

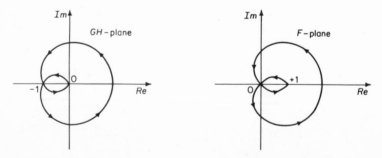

Fig. 7-8. The GH-plane plot.   **Fig. 7-9.** The F-plot.

The Nyquist criterion is normally defined with respect to the GH-plot as:

For a stable closed-loop system, the Nyquist plot of $G(s)H(s)$ should encircle the $(-1, j0)$ point as many times as there are poles of $G(s)H(s)$ in the right half of the s-plane; the encirclements, if there are any, must be made in the clockwise direction.

Furthermore, if N = Number of encirclement of the critical point $(-1, j0)$ in the GH-plane made by the Nyquist plot of $G(s)H(s)$, with $-N$ for clockwise encirclement, and $+N$ for counterclockwise encirclement,

Z = number of zeros of $1 + G(s)H(s)$ that are in the right half of the s-plane, and

P = number of poles of $1 + G(s)H(s)$ (also the same as for GH) that are in the right half of the s-plane;

$$N = Z - P \qquad (7\text{-}15)$$

For a stable system, Z must be zero, consequently,

$$N = -P \qquad (7\text{-}16)$$

In the majority cases, $G(s)$ and $H(s)$ are stable functions, so that $P = 0$. Eq. (7-16) becomes

$$N = 0 \qquad (7\text{-}17)$$

The last equation implies that the Nyquist plot of $G(s)H(s)$ must not encircle the $(-1, j0)$ point in the GH-plane for a system to be stable. However, if, in cases where the GH-plot encircles the critical point $(-1, j0)$, $(N = Z \neq 0)$, the encirclement would be made in the counterclockwise direction. For this reason, we can define a Nyquist criterion for a special case which occurs quite frequently; that is, when $P = 0$. The criterion states:

If the loop gain function $G(s)H(s)$ is a stable function, $P = 0$, for a stable closed-loop system, the Nyquist plot of $G(s)H(s)$ must not enclose the critical point $(-1, j0)$.

Also, if $P = 0$, it is necessary only to plot the Nyquist plot of $G(s)H(s)$ corresponding to section (I) on the Nyquist path; that is, from $s = +j\infty$ to $+j0$. For example, the GH-plot given in Fig. 7-11 is plotted only for the frequency range of $\omega = \infty$ to $\omega = 0$, which corresponds to section (I) on the Nyquist path. The region that is enclosed by the GH-plot is the area to the left of the path when the path is described from $\omega = \infty$ to $\omega = 0$. Thus, unless it is necessary to know how many zeros of $F(s)$ are located in the right half of the s-plane, the complete Nyquist plot for GH is not required; it is necessary only to investigate whether the $(-1, j0)$ point is to the left or to the right of the GH-curve, going from infinite to zero frequency along the GH locus.

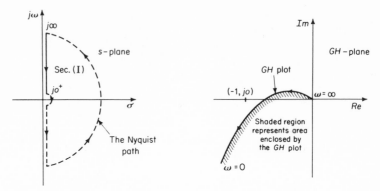

Fig. 7-10. The Nyquist path.   **Fig. 7-11.** The Nyquist plot.

7.6 The Application of the Nyquist Criterion

The following examples serve to illustrate the practical application of the Nyquist criterion on the stability of feedback systems.

EXAMPLE 7-1. Consider a simple feedback control system with $G(s)H(s)$ given as

$$G(s)H(s) = \frac{K}{s(s + a)} \tag{7-18}$$

where K and a are constants. It is apparent that $G(s)H(s)$ does not have a pole in the right half of the s-plane; thus, $P = 0$. In this case, to determine the stability of the closed-loop system, it is necessary only to sketch the Nyquist plot of $G(s)H(s)$ that corresponds to $\omega = \infty$ to $\omega = 0^+$ (section I) on the Nyquist path and see if it encloses the -1 point of the GH-plane. To construct the Nyquist plot of $G(s)H(s)$, we shall first determine the behavior of $G(s)H(s)$ at zero and infinite frequencies.

When $s = +j\infty$

$$\lim_{s \to j\infty} G(s)H(s) = \lim_{s \to j\infty} \frac{K}{s(s + a)} = \lim_{s \to j\infty} \frac{K}{s^2} = 0\underline{/-180 \deg} \tag{7-19}$$

When $s = +j0$

$$\lim_{s = j0} G(s)H(s) = \lim_{s = j0} \frac{K}{s(s + a)} = \lim_{s = j0} \frac{K}{sa} = \infty \underline{\,/-90 \deg} \tag{7-20}$$

The points on the GH plot between zero and infinite frequencies can be obtained by direct computation; for instance, when $\omega = 1$ rad/sec,

$$G(j1)H(j1) = \frac{K}{j1(j1 + a)} = \frac{K}{\sqrt{1 + a^2}} \underline{\left/ -90 \deg - \tan^{-1}\left(\frac{1}{a}\right)\right.}$$

$$\tag{7-21}$$

In general, the application of the Nyquist criterion does not require the exact plot of the GH curve. From Eqs. (7-19) and (7-20), it is known that when the frequency is varied from 0 to ∞, the GH plot varies from -90 deg to -180 deg; a sketch of GH, as shown in Fig. 7-12, is quite sufficient for the application of the Nyquist criterion.

In Fig. 7-12, since the critical point $(-1, j0)$ is not enclosed by the Nyquist GH-plot, the closed-loop system is stable. Furthermore, the critical point can never be enclosed by the GH-plot of this second-order system as long as K is a positive finite number.

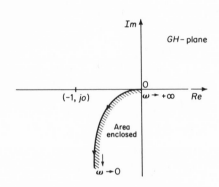

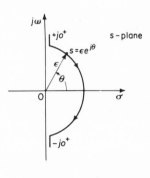

Fig. 7-12. The $G(s)H(s)$ plot for
$$G(s)H(s) = \frac{K}{s(s+a)}$$

Fig. 7-13. Section II of the Nyquist path.

It is of interest to sketch the entire Nyquist plot of $G(s)H(s)$ and interpret its significance in the investigation of open- and closed-loop system stability. In order to construct the portion of the GH-plot which corresponds to section II on the Nyquist path, the small semicircle of the Nyquist path is magnified as shown in Fig. 7-13. The points on this semi-circle of infinitesimal radius may be represented by a phasor

$$s = \epsilon e^{j\theta} \tag{7-22}$$

where $\epsilon(\epsilon \to 0)$ and θ denote the magnitude and phase of the phasor respectively. As the Nyquist path is described from $+j0^+$ to $-j0^+$ along section II of the Nyquist path, the phase rotates in the clockwise direction through 180 deg. Also, in going from $+j0^+$ to $-j0^+$, θ is varied from 90 deg to -90 deg through 0 deg. The corresponding plot of $G(s)H(s)$ can be determined simply by substituting Eq. (7-22) into the $G(s)H(s)$ function. Therefore, Eq. (7-18) becomes

$$G(s)H(s)|_{s=\epsilon e^{j\theta}} = \frac{K}{\epsilon e^{j\theta}(\epsilon e^{j\theta} + a)} \tag{7-23}$$

Since ϵ approaches zero, Eq. (7-23) may be simplified to read

$$G(s)H(s)|_{s=\epsilon e^{j\theta}} = \frac{K}{\epsilon a e^{j\theta}} = \infty \, e^{-j\theta} \qquad (7\text{-}24)$$

Therefore, we have established that the magnitude of $G(s)H(s)$ on section II of the Nyquist path is infinite, and the corresponding phase of $G(s)H(s)$ is opposite to that of s. The phase shift relationships are tabulated in the following as θ is varied from $+ 90$ deg to $- 90$ deg. It is seen that the phase shift of GH goes from $- 90$ deg to $+ 90$ deg through a total of 180 deg in

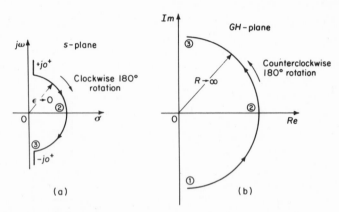

Fig. 7-14. Section II of the Nyquist path and the corresponding GH-plot for the system in Example 7-1. (a) Section II of the Nyquist path; (b) the GH-plot.

the counterclockwise direction. The correspondence of the s-plane locus (section II) and the GH-plane locus is shown in Fig. 7-14.

θ	$90°$	$60°$	$30°$	$0°$	$- 30°$	$- 60°$	$- 90°$
$\underline{/GH}$	$- 90°$	$- 60°$	$- 30°$	$0°$	$+ 30°$	$+ 60°$	$+ 90°$

In general, the GH-plot of section II on the Nyquist path may be determined without going through the detailed steps illustrated above. For instance, in this problem, it is necessary only to investigate the following equation:

$$\lim_{s \to 0} G(s)H(s) = \lim_{s \to 0} \frac{K}{s(s + a)} = \lim_{s \to 0} \frac{K}{sa} \qquad (7\text{-}25)$$

From the last equation, it is clear that the behavior of GH at $s = 0$ is inversely proportional to s. Therefore, as the Nyquist path is described from $+ j0^{+}$ to $- j0^{+}$ through a clockwise rotation of 180 deg (considered to be $- 180$-deg rotation), the GH plot must go around the origin of the

GH-plane 180 deg in the counterclockwise direction with infinite magnitude. It can be concluded that, in general, if the limit of $G(s)H(s)$ as s approaches 0 takes the form of

$$\lim_{s \to 0} G(s)H(s) = \lim_{s \to 0} K s^n \qquad (7\text{-}26)$$

the GH-plot from $s = +j0^+$ to $s = -j0^+$ will go around the origin of the GH-plane $n \times 180$ deg in the clockwise direction (same direction as that of section II of the Nyquist path) with zero magnitude if n is a positive integer; if n is a negative number, the GH-plot will go around the origin of the GH-plane $n \times 180$ deg in the counterclockwise direction with infinite magnitude.

Exactly the same technique may be used to sketch the GH-plot which corresponds to section IV of the Nyquist path. At infinite frequency, the large semicircle (section IV) in the s-plane is described in the counterclockwise direction from $s = -j\infty$ to $s = +j\infty$. The behavior of $G(s)H(s)$ at infinite frequency is described by

$$\lim_{s \to \infty} G(s)H(s) = \lim_{s \to \infty} \frac{K}{s(s+a)} = \lim_{s \to \infty} \frac{K}{s^2} \qquad (7\text{-}27)$$

Thus, the behavior of the GH-plot at infinite frequency is proportional to $1/s^2$. When s takes on values along the large semicircle in the s-plane, the corresponding GH-plot must rotate around the origin 2×180 degrees clockwise (opposite to the direction of the s-plane trajectory) with zero magnitude in the GH-plane. Thus, the GH-plot of the second-order system which corresponds to section IV of the Nyquist path (Fig. 7-15) is given in Fig. 7-16. The complete Nyquist plot of $G(s)H(s)$ is shown in Fig. 7-17.

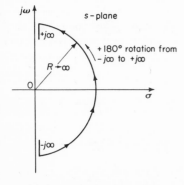

Fig. 7-15. Section IV of the Nyquist path.

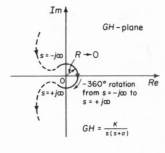

Fig. 7-16. The GH-plot corresponding to section IV of the Nyquist path.

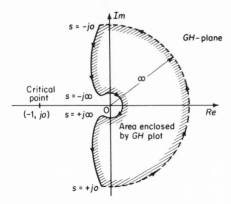

Fig. 7-17. The complete Nyquist plot of

$$G(s)H(s) = \frac{K}{s(s + a)}$$

It is apparent that the complete GH-plot does not encircle the -1 point, which means either that the number of poles and the number of zeros of $F(s) = 1 + G(s)H(s)$ which are located in the right half of the s-plane are both zero, or that the number of poles equals the number of zeros. This is merely an interesting check of the result obtained from Fig. 7-12.

Since $G(s)H(s)$ does not have a finite zero, and since all the poles of $G(s)H(s)$ are located in the left half of the s-plane, by inspection, the complete Nyquist plot of GH given in Fig. 7-17 does not enclose the critical point $(-1, j0)$; thus, the closed-loop system is stable.

EXAMPLE 7-2. Consider a feedback control system with the loop transfer function given as

$$G(s)H(s) = \frac{K}{1 - sT} \qquad (7\text{-}28)$$

where K and T are positive constants. It is apparent that GH has one pole in the right half of the s-plane. The characteristic equation of the closed-loop system is the numerator of

$$1 + G(s)H(s) = \frac{1 + K - sT}{1 - sT} \qquad (7\text{-}29)$$

Thus, the closed loop system is also unstable, since the closed-loop pole is at $s = (1 + K)/T$. The following conclusions can be reached regarding the behavior of the Nyquist plot of $G(s)H(s)$ based on what we already know about the system.

	Z	P	$N = Z - P$	Interpretation
$G(s)H(s)$	0	1	-1	The $G(s)H(s)$-plot encircles the origin in a clockwise direction.

	Z	P	$N = Z - P$	Interpretation
$1 + G(s)H(s)$	1	1	0	The $G(s)H(s)$-plot does not encircle the $(-1, j0)$ point at all.

The construction of the complete Nyquist plot of GH is summarized as follows:

s	∞	$j\infty$	$-j\infty$	s-plane Nyquist path, Section IV. $+180°$ rotation
GH	0	$\dfrac{K}{-sT}$	$0\underline{/90°}$	GH-plane Nyquist plot, $GH = \dfrac{K}{-sT}\Big\|_{s\to\infty}$ $-180°$ rotation $0\underline{/-90°}$

s	0	$j0$	$-j0$	s-plane Nyquist path, section II $-180°$ rotation
GH	K	$K\underline{/0°}$	$K\underline{/0°}$	GH-plane Nyquist plot, $GH = K\underline{/0°}$

The complete Nyquist plot of $G(s)H(s)$ is shown in Fig. 7-18; the locus encircles the origin once in the clockwise direction, but never encircles the $(-1, j0)$ point, which checks with the facts predicted.

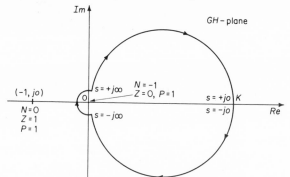

Fig. 7-18. The complete Nyquist plot of
$$G(s)H(s) = \frac{K}{1 - sT}$$

This example also points out the important fact that the critical point $(-1, j0)$ does not have to be encircled at all by the GH-plot for a closed-loop system to be unstable, if the function $G(s)H(s)$ has poles in the right half of the s-plane. Furthermore, in this case, the critical point must be encircled once in the clockwise direction by the GH-plot if a stable closed-loop system is desired.

EXAMPLE 7-3. Consider a feedback control system with the loop transfer function $G(s)H(s)$ given as

$$G(s)H(s) = \frac{5}{s(1 - s)} \tag{7-30}$$

Thus
$$1 + G(s)H(s) = \frac{-s^2 + s + 5}{s(1 - s)} \tag{7-31}$$

The characteristic equation has one root in the right half of the s-plane and one root in the left half of the s-plane ($s = 0.5 \pm 0.5\sqrt{21}$). The following conclusions can be drawn concerning the characteristics of the Nyquist plot of $G(s)H(s)$, based on what we already know about the system.

	Z	P	$N = Z - P$	*Interpretation*
$G(s)H(s)$	0	1	-1	The $G(s)H(s)$-plot encircles the origin once in a clockwise direction.

	Z	P	$N = Z - P$	*Interpretation*
$1 + G(s)H(s)$	1	1	0	The $G(s)H(s)$-plot does not encircle the $(-1, j0)$ point at all.

The construction of the complete Nyquist plot of $G(s)H(s)$ is summarized as follows:

s	∞	$j\infty$	$-j\infty$	s-plane Nyquist path, section IV. 180° rotation
GH	$\dfrac{5}{-s^2}$	$0/0°$	$0/0°$	GH-plane Nyquist plot, $GH = \left.\dfrac{5}{-s^2}\right\|_{s \to \infty}$ $-360°$ rotation

s	0	$j0$	$-j0$	s-plane Nyquist path, section II $-180°$ rotation
GH	$\dfrac{5}{s}$	$\infty/-90°$	$\infty/-90°$	GH-plane Nyquist plot, $GH = \left.\dfrac{5}{s}\right\|_{s \to 0}$ $+180°$ rotation

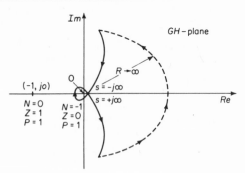

Fig. 7-19. The complete Nyquist plot of
$$G(s)H(s) = \frac{5}{s(1 - s)}$$

EXAMPLE 7-4. Consider a feedback control system with the loop transfer function $G(s)H(s)$ given as
$$G(s)H(s) = \frac{K}{s(1 + s)(1 + 2s)(1 + 3s)} \tag{7-32}$$

By inspection, the properties of the $G(s)H(s)$ plot in the GH plane are given as follows:

$G(s)H(s)$	Z	P	$N = Z - P$	*Interpretation*
	0	0	0	The GH-plot does not encircle the origin in the GH-plane.

However, the roots of the characteristic equation are unknown. The poles of $1 + G(s)H(s)$ are known to be located in the left half of the s-plane. The Nyquist criterion will be used to determine the stability of the closed-loop system by determining whether any of the zeros of the function $1 + G(s)H(s)$ is in the right half of the s-plane.

The Nyquist Plot of $G(s)H(s)$

By means of the procedure illustrated in Example 7-1, the construction of the Nyquist plot of $G(s)H(s)$ is summarized as follows:

s	∞	$j\infty$	$-j\infty$	s-plane Nyquist path, section IV.
GH	$\dfrac{K}{s^4}$	$0/\underline{-360°}$	$0/\underline{360°}$	$+180°$ rotation GH-plane Nyquist plot, $GH = K/s^4\big|_{s \to \infty}$ $-720°$ rotation

s	0	$j0$	$-j0$	s-plane Nyquist path, section II.
GH		$\dfrac{K}{s}$	$\infty\ \underline{/90°}$	$\infty\ \underline{/90°}$

(section II continued)
$-180°$ rotation
GH-plane Nyquist plot $GH = K/s\big|_{s \to 0}$
$+180°$ rotation

The details of the GH-plot at zero and infinite frequencies are given in Fig. 7-20. The complete GH-plot is shown in Fig. 7-21.

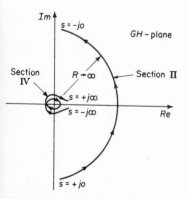

Fig. 7-20. The Nyquist plot of
$$G(s)H(s) = \frac{K}{s(1+s)(1+2s)(1+3s)}$$
at zero and infinite frequencies.

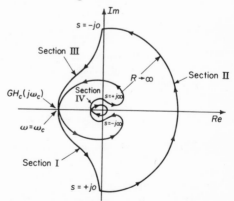

Fig. 7-21. The complete Nyquist plot of
$$G(s)H(s) = \frac{K}{s(1+s)(1+2s)(1+3s)}$$

From Fig. 7-21, it is clear that the Nyquist plot of $G(s)H(s)$ will enclose the $(-1, j0)$ point twice if the value of K is sufficiently large. For a stable closed-loop system, the critical point $(-1, j0)$ must not be enclosed. Substituting $s = j\omega$ into $G(s)H(s)$, we have

$$G(j\omega)H(j\omega) = \frac{K}{j\omega(1 + j\omega)(1 + j2\omega)(1 + j3\omega)}$$

$$= \frac{K}{6\omega^2(\omega^2 - 1) + j\omega(1 - 11\omega^2)} \qquad (7\text{-}33)$$

When the GH plot crosses the negative real axis in the GH-plane, the frequency at the crossing is designated as $\omega = \omega_c$, and the imaginary part of $G(j\omega)H(j\omega)$ is zero, thus,

$$1 - 11\omega^2 = 0 \qquad (7\text{-}34)$$

or

$$\omega = \omega_c = \pm 1/\sqrt{11} \qquad (7\text{-}35)$$

The frequency ω_c is sometimes called the critical frequency of the system. Substitution of Eq. (7-35) into Eq. (7-33) gives

$$GH_c(j\omega_c) = 121K/60 \qquad (7\text{-}36)$$

For the closed-loop system to be stable, the magnitude of $GH_c(j\omega_c)$ should be less than one, thus,

$$|GH_c| = 121K/60 < 1 \qquad (7\text{-}37)$$

or

$$K < 0.495 \qquad (7\text{-}38)$$

The critical value of K can also be obtained easily by means of the Routh-Hurwitz criterion. The characteristic equation of the system is

$$6s^4 + 11s^3 + 6s^2 + s + K = 0 \qquad (7\text{-}39)$$

The Routh tabulation is given as follows:

$$
\begin{array}{cccc}
s^4 & 6 & 6 & K \\
s^3 & 11 & 1 & \\
s^2 & \frac{60}{11} & K & \\
s^1 & \dfrac{\frac{60}{11} - 11K}{\frac{60}{11}} & 0 & \\
s^0 & K & 0 &
\end{array}
$$

The conditions of stability are

$$K > 0 \qquad (7\text{-}40)$$

and

$$\tfrac{60}{11} - 11K > 0 \qquad (7\text{-}41)$$

The critical frequency ω_c is obtained by solving for the roots of the auxiliary equation; that is,

$$-\tfrac{60}{11}\,\omega^2 + K = 0 \qquad\qquad (7\text{-}42)$$

hence

$$\omega_c = \pm\sqrt{\frac{11K}{60}} = \pm\frac{1}{\sqrt{11}}\text{rad/sec} \qquad\qquad (7\text{-}43)$$

It was pointed out earlier that if $G(s)H(s)$ does not have any poles in the right half of the s-plane, only the positive frequency locus of GH need be sketched. In this example, all the poles of $G(s)H(s)$ are located in the left half of the s-plane, so it is necessary to sketch only the portion of the Nyquist plot of GH which corresponds to section (I) on the Nyquist path; the Nyquist plot of GH is shown in Fig. 7-22. The region that is enclosed by the Nyquist plot of GH is indicated in Fig. 7-22 as the shaded area. For a stable system, the critical point $(-1, j0)$ must not be found inside this shaded region.

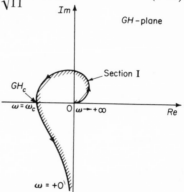

Fig. 7-22. Nyquist plot of

$$G(s)H(s) = \frac{K}{s(1 + s)(1 + 2s)(1 + 3s)}$$

corresponding to section I of the Nyquist path.

7.7 The Effects of Additional Poles and Zeros of $G(s)H(s)$ on the Shape of the Nyquist Locus

In this section, we shall investigate the effects on the Nyquist locus when poles and zeros are added to the loop transfer function $G(s)H(s)$. Assume that the loop transfer function of a certain feedback control system is of the form:

$$G(s)H(s) = \frac{K}{1 + sT_1} \qquad\qquad (7\text{-}44)$$

The Nyquist locus for positive frequencies of the loop transfer function given in the last equation is shown in Fig. 7-23.

(1) *Addition of Finite Poles*

Suppose that a pole at $s = -1/T_2$ is added to the $G(s)H(s)$ function given in Eq. (7-44); we then have

$$G(s)H(s) = \frac{K}{(1 + sT_1)(1 + sT_2)} \qquad\qquad (7\text{-}45)$$

The Nyquist plot of GH at zero frequency is not affected, since

$$\lim_{s \to 0} G(s)H(s) = K \qquad\qquad (7\text{-}46)$$

However, the locus at infinite frequency is

$$\lim_{s \to \infty} G(s)H(s) = \lim_{s \to \infty} \frac{K}{s^2 T_1 T_2} = 0 \underline{/-180} \text{ deg} \tag{7-47}$$

The Nyquist plot of GH for positive frequencies is sketched in Fig. 7-24.

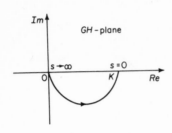

Fig. 7-23. The Nyquist plot of

$$G(s)H(s) = \frac{K}{(1 + sT_1)}$$

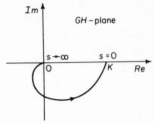

Fig. 7-24. The Nyquist plot of

$$G(s)H(s) = \frac{K}{(1 + sT_1)(1 + sT_2)}$$

Similarly, by adding one more term $(1 + sT_3)$ in the denominator of Eq. (7-45), the Nyquist locus at infinite frequency is at zero magnitude and an angle of $- 270$ deg.

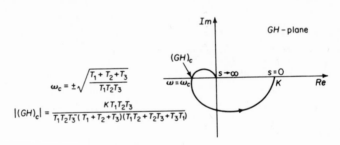

Fig. 7-25. The Nyquist locus of

$$G(s)H(s) = \frac{K}{(1 + sT_1)(1 + sT_2)(1 + sT_3)}$$

In general, we can conclude that the addition of n finite poles, each with a negative real part, to the $G(s)H(s)$ in Eq. (7-44), will result in the GH-plot to go around $(n + 1)\pi/2$ rad in the clockwise direction as ω is varied from zero to infinite frequency (Fig. 7-26).

In this case, the Nyquist locus of GH goes through a total of $(n + 1)$ quadrants, or as many quadrants as the number of time constants as the frequency is varied from 0 to ∞.

In general, the effect of adding more finite poles to GH is to make the closed-loop system less stable. The loci shown in Fig. 7-23 and Fig. 7-24 represent systems that are always stable. The closed-loop systems which

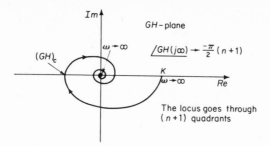

Fig. 7-26. The Nyquist locus of

$$G(s)H(s) = \frac{K}{(1 + sT_1)(1 + sT_2) \cdots (1 + sT_{n+1})}$$

correspond to the GH plots of Fig. 7-25 and Fig. 7-26 may be unstable, however, if $(GH)_c > 1$.

(2) Addition of Poles at the Origin

The addition of poles at the origin to the loop transfer function $G(s)H(s)$ also has the effect of making the closed-loop system less stable. If the factor $1/s^n$ is multiplied to the $G(s)H(s)$ of Eq. (7-44), the Nyquist locus at infinite and zero frequencies is rotated by an angle of $n\pi/2$ in the clockwise direction. It was pointed out that the GH plot will go through as many quadrants in the GH-plane as there are time constants T in the denominator of GH, regardless of the order of the poles at the origin. This fact is helpful in the sketching of the Nyquist locus of the type described in this section. The rule, however, does not apply if there is any term of the form $(1 + sT)$ found in the numerator of $G(s)H(s)$.

Some of the typical Nyquist plots of $G(s)H(s)$ are illustrated in Fig. 7-27.

(3) Addition of Zeros

It was pointed out in Chapter 5 that the effect of the derivative control on a closed-loop system is to make the system more stable. In terms of the Nyquist plot, this stabilizing effect is easily shown, since the multiplication of the factor $(1 + sT_d)$ to a $G(s)H(s)$ simply rotates the GH plot in the counterclockwise direction by 90 deg. For instance, consider the loop transfer function:

$$G(s)H(s) = \frac{K}{s(1 + sT_1)(1 + sT_2)} \qquad (7\text{-}48)$$

It is easy to show that the system is stable for all values of $K > 0$ and

$K < (T_1 + T_2)/T_1T_2$. Suppose that a zero at $s = -1/T_d$ is added to the loop transfer function in Eq. (7-48) so that

$$G(s)H(s) = \frac{K(1 + sT_d)}{s(1 + sT_1)(1 + sT_2)} \qquad (7\text{-}49)$$

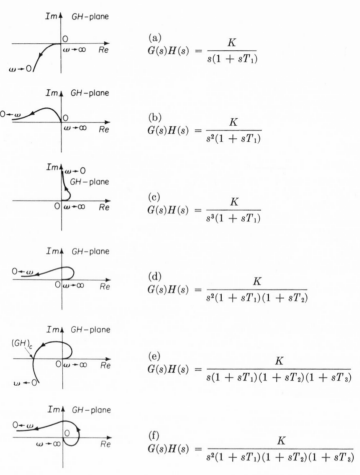

(a)
$$G(s)H(s) = \frac{K}{s(1 + sT_1)}$$

(b)
$$G(s)H(s) = \frac{K}{s^2(1 + sT_1)}$$

(c)
$$G(s)H(s) = \frac{K}{s^3(1 + sT_1)}$$

(d)
$$G(s)H(s) = \frac{K}{s^2(1 + sT_1)(1 + sT_2)}$$

(e)
$$G(s)H(s) = \frac{K}{s(1 + sT_1)(1 + sT_2)(1 + sT_3)}$$

(f)
$$G(s)H(s) = \frac{K}{s^2(1 + sT_1)(1 + sT_2)(1 + sT_3)}$$

Fig. 7-27. Nyquist loci for several loop transfer functions showing the effect of adding poles to GH.

The Nyquist loci for the two $G(s)H(s)$ functions with and without derivative control are shown in Fig. 7-28. It is seen that for the same values of K, T_1, and T_2, the system with derivative control is more stable, because the Nyquist locus is on the right side of the GH plot of the system without derivative control.

A system that is inherently unstable can be stabilized by adding zeros to the loop transfer function. The system corresponding to the Nyquist plot of Fig. 7-27b is unstable for all positive values of K. With the addition of the derivative control, the loop transfer function of the system is

$$G(s)H(s) = \frac{K(1 + sT_d)}{s^2(1 + sT_1)} \qquad (7\text{-}50)$$

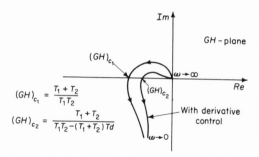

Fig. 7-28. Comparison of Nyquist loci of systems with and without derivative control.

$$G(s)H(s) = \frac{K}{s(1 + sT_1)(1 + sT_2)}$$

It can readily be shown that the closed-loop system is made stable if the time constant T_d is greater than T_1.

Some other Nyquist loci illustrating the effects of adding of zeros to the loop transfer function GH are shown in Fig. 7-30.

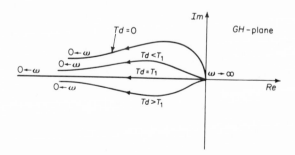

Fig. 7-29. Comparison of Nyquist loci of systems with and without derivative control.

$$G(s)H(s) = \frac{K}{s^2(1 + sT_1)}$$

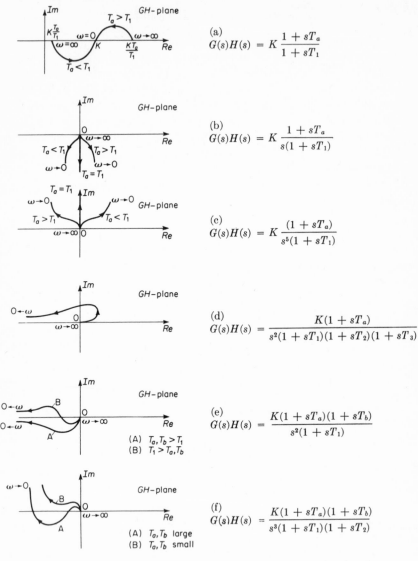

$$(a)\quad G(s)H(s) = K\frac{1 + sT_a}{1 + sT_1}$$

$$(b)\quad G(s)H(s) = K\frac{1 + sT_a}{s(1 + sT_1)}$$

$$(c)\quad G(s)H(s) = K\frac{(1 + sT_a)}{s^5(1 + sT_1)}$$

$$(d)\quad G(s)H(s) = \frac{K(1 + sT_a)}{s^2(1 + sT_1)(1 + sT_2)(1 + sT_3)}$$

$$(e)\quad G(s)H(s) = \frac{K(1 + sT_a)(1 + sT_b)}{s^2(1 + sT_1)}$$

$$(f)\quad G(s)H(s) = \frac{K(1 + sT_a)(1 + sT_b)}{s^3(1 + sT_1)(1 + sT_2)}$$

Fig. 7-30. Nyquist loci for several loop transfer functions showing the effect of adding zeros to $G(s)H(s)$.

7.8 Systems with Transportation Lags

Thus far we have considered only systems whose transfer functions are quotients of algebraic polynomials. These systems are characterized by the fact that the output starts to respond immediately after the application of the input. In some control systems, especially in systems with hydraulic, pneumatic, or mechanical transmissions, pure time lags may be encountered so that the output will not begin to respond to a transient input until after a given time interval. Because of the time lag effect, the transfer functions of these systems are no longer quotients of polynomials; they usually consist of the term e^{-Ts}, where T denotes the time lag or transportation lag. Figure 7-31 depicts examples in which transportation lags are observed. Figure 7-31a outlines an arrangement in which two different fluids are to be mixed in appropriate proportions. In order to make sure that a homogeneous solution is measured, the metering point is located at some distance from the mixing point. Thus, transportation lag exists between the mixing point and the place where the change in concentration is detected. If the rate of flow of the mixed solution is v inches per second, and d is the distance between the mixing and the metering points, the time lag is given by

$$T = d/v \quad (\text{sec}) \qquad (7\text{-}51)$$

Assuming that the concentration at the mixing point is $c(t)$ and that it is reproduced without change T seconds later at the metering point, the measured quantity is

$$b(t) = c(t - T) \qquad (7\text{-}52)$$

The Laplace transform of Eq. (7-52) is

$$B(s) = e^{-Ts}C(s) \qquad (7\text{-}53)$$

or

$$\frac{B(s)}{C(s)} = e^{-Ts} \qquad (7\text{-}54)$$

The arrangement shown in Fig. 7-31b may be thought of as a thickness control of the rolling of steel plates. Similar to the above case, the transfer function between the thickness at the roller and the measuring point is also given by Eq. (7-54).

Other examples of transportation lags are found in human beings as control systems where action and reaction are always accompanied by time delays. The operation of the sampler and hold device of a sampled-data system (Chap. 9) closely resembles a pure time delay; it sometimes can be approximated by a single time lag term, e^{-sT}.

The block diagram of a typical system which has a transportation lag is shown in Fig. 7-32 (the transportation lag could just as well be located in the feedback path). The loop-transfer-function of the system is given by

$$G(s)H(s) = e^{-sT}G_1(s) \qquad (7\text{-}55)$$

where $G_1(s)$ represents an algebraic rational function.

Since Eq. (7-55) is a transcendental function, an analytical analysis of the system with transportation lag is usually difficult. Normally, the transcendental transfer function is first converted into a rational function by approximating the exponential term by a polynomial of s, and then the usual technique of analysis can be applied.*

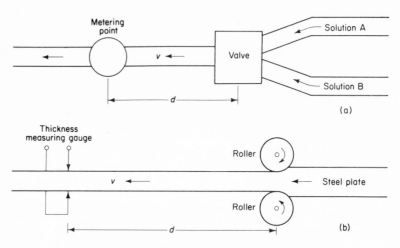

Fig. 7-31. Physical systems with transportation lags.

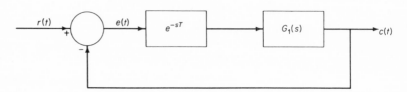

Fig. 7-32. Block diagram of feedback control system with transportation lag.

Since the term $e^{-j\omega T}$ merely represents a phase shift varying linearly with frequency, and since its magnitude is unity at all frequencies, a graphical analysis of systems with transportation lags by means of the Nyquist plots or Bode plots is quite straightforward. For example, in the system of Fig. 7-32, if the transfer function $G_1(s)$ is given by

$$G_1(s) = \frac{1}{s(s+1)} \qquad (7\text{-}56)$$

the Nyquist plots for the loop transfer function of the system for various values of time lag ($T = 0$, 0.5, 1.0, 1.5 sec) are constructed in Fig. 7-33. From this plot, it is seen that the closed-loop system is always stable when the time lag is zero, but the stability condition deteriorates as the time lag

---

*J. G. Truxal, *Automatic Feedback Control System Synthesis*, McGraw-Hill Book Company, Inc., New York, 1955, pp. 546–51.

is increased, and for large values of lag the system is unstable. The multiplication of $G_1(j\omega)$ by $e^{-j\omega T}$ simply rotates each point on the G_1 curve by an angle of ωT radians in the clockwise direction. Therefore, in this case, the Nyquist plots of the system with transportation lag spiral toward the origin as the frequency ω approaches infinity.

From the plots in Fig. 7-33 it appears that the marginal value of T for stability lies somewhere between 1.0 and 1.5 sec. The exact value of T which will make the Nyquist plot go through the -1 point can be determined by trial and error. The Routh-Hurwitz criterion breaks down in this case, since it cannot be applied to transcendental equations. However, a more elegant method is possible in the Nyquist analysis which does not involve trial and error. The roots of the characteristic equation of the system shown in Fig. 7-32 are given by the zeros of the following equation:

$$1 + G(s)H(s) = 1 + \frac{e^{-sT}}{s(s+1)} = 0 \qquad (7\text{-}57)$$

Ordinarily, the last equation is written as

$$G(s)H(s) = \frac{e^{-sT}}{s(s+1)} = -1 \qquad (7\text{-}58)$$

so that the zeros of Eq. (7-57) are also interpreted as the -1 *points* of $G(s)H(s)$; that is, the values of s that will make $G(s)H(s)$ equal to -1. Correspondingly, the -1 point has been used as the critical point in the GH-plane. From a different point of view, we can also write Eq. (7-58) as

$$G_1(s) = \frac{1}{s(s+1)} = -e^{+sT} \qquad (7\text{-}59)$$

and the zeros of Eq. (7-57) become the $-e^{+sT}$ *points* of $G_1(s)$. This means that a *critical locus*, corresponding to the -1 point in the GH-plane, is now described by $-e^{+j\omega T}$ in the G_1-plane. We can regard this critical locus as a locus of critical points, each corresponding to a given value of ωT. As the frequency is varied from zero to infinity, the critical points trace out a set of overlapping unit circles in the G_1-plane. In Fig. 7-34, the critical locus of $-e^{+j\omega T}$ and the $G_1(j\omega)$ plot are drawn in the G_1-plane. The intersection of the two loci corresponds to the intersection of the $G(j\omega)H(j\omega)$ plot with the -1 point in the GH-plane, provided that the frequencies on the two loci at the intersection point are the same. Figure 7-34 shows that the two loci intersect at $\omega T = 0.907$ rad; since the frequency at the intersection point on the G_1 locus is 0.79 rad/sec, T is 1.15 sec. For a value of T greater than this marginal value of 1.15, for example, 1.5, the critical point on the unit circle is shown to be enclosed by the $G_1(j\omega)$ locus and the system is unstable. The system is stable for all values of T less than 1.15 sec.

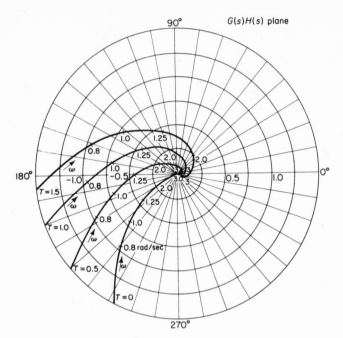

Fig. 7-33. Nyquist diagrams of

$$G(s)H(s) = \frac{e^{-sT}}{s(s+1)}$$

$T = 0, 0.5, 1.0,$ and 1.5 sec.

7.9 Relative Stability from the Nyquist Diagram — Gain Margin and Phase Margin

Some of the important questions that may be asked about the stability of a feedback control system are:

(1) If the system is stable, how stable is it?

(2) If the system is not stable enough, or if it is unstable, how can the stability of the system be improved?

It was pointed out earlier that the Nyquist plot of the loop transfer function $G(s)H(s)$ gives answers to these questions. Figure 7-35 shows the Nyquist plots of a third-order system for four different values of gain K. The GH-plot described in Fig. 7-35a encloses the $(-1, j0)$ point, so the system is unstable and the output response of the system increases with time. The GH-plot described in Fig. 7-35b goes through the critical point $(-1, j0)$; this is a borderline case, and the system is said to be on the verge of instability. Under this condition, the output response of the system is a sinusoidal oscillation. The GH-plots shown in Fig. 7-35c and d do not

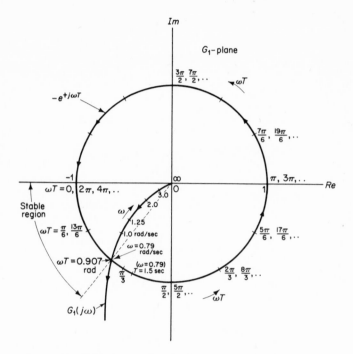

Fig. 7-34. Critical locus and the $G_1(j\omega)$ locus in the G_1-plane.

$$G(s)H(s) = e^{-sT}G_1(s), \qquad G_1(s) = \frac{1}{s(s+1)}$$

enclose the critical point. However, the GH-plot in Fig. 7-35c is closer to the critical point, and the output step-response is more oscillatory, with higher overshoot. The term "relative stability" is used to indicate the degree of stability of a system, or, in simple words, how close the Nyquist plot is to the critical point. To be more specific, the gain margin and the phase margin have been generally used to define the amount of relative stability of a closed-loop system.

(1) The Gain Margin

Consider the $G(s)H(s)$ plot shown in Fig. 7-36. The magnitude of $G(j\omega)H(j\omega)$ when it crosses the negative real axis is called $(GH)_c$, and the corresponding frequency on the locus is ω_c. The gain margin of the system is defined as

$$\text{Gain Margin (G.M.)} = 20 \log_{10} \frac{1}{|(GH)_c|} \text{ db} \qquad (7\text{-}60)$$

If, in the Nyquist plot of Fig. 7-36, the gain K is increased to the extent that the GH locus goes through the critical point so that $|(GH)_c|$ equals unity, from Eq. (7-60), the gain margin is zero db. On the other hand, for a second-order system, the GH locus does not intersect the negative real axis; therefore, $|(GH)_c|$ equals zero, and the gain margin given by Eq. (7-60) is

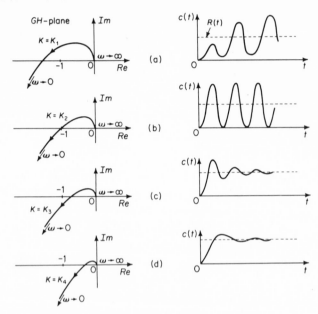

Fig. 7-35. Correspondence of Nyquist plots and transient responses.

infinite in decibels. Based on the above facts, the physical significance of gain margin can be written as follows: *Gain margin is the amount of gain K in decibels that can be allowed to increase before the system reaches instability.* When the GH locus goes through the $(-1, j0)$ point, the gain margin is

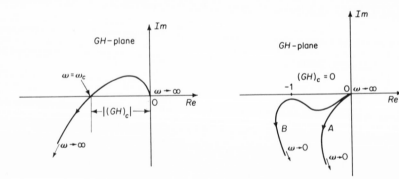

Fig. 7-36. Definition of gain margin.

Fig. 7-37. Nyquist plots showing systems with same gain margin but different amount of relative stability.

zero db, which implies that the gain K can no longer be increased without causing instability. For a second-order system, the crossover $(GH)_c$ on the negative real axis is zero, and the gain margin is infinite decibels; this means that, theoretically, the value of K can be increased to infinity before instability occurs. When the critical point is enclosed by the GH-plot, the magnitude of $(GH)_c$ is greater than unity, and the gain margin in decibels becomes negative. The following example illustrates how the gain margin of a given system is determined by the analytical method.

EXAMPLE 7-5. *Computation of the Gain Margin.* Consider that the loop gain transfer function of a feedback control system is given by

$$G(s)H(s) = \frac{K}{(1 + s)(1 + 2s)(1 + 3s)} \qquad (7\text{-}61)$$

Let us assume that the value of K is to be determined so that the gain margin of the system is equal to 20 db. From Eq. (7-60),

$$G.M. = 20 \log_{10} \frac{1}{|(GH)_c|} = 20 \text{ db} \qquad (7\text{-}62)$$

from which

$$\log_{10} \frac{1}{|(GH)_c|} = 1 \qquad (7\text{-}63)$$

hence

$$|(GH)_c| = 0.1 \qquad (7\text{-}64)$$

Substituting $s = j\omega$ into Eq. (7-61), we have

$$G(j\omega)H(j\omega) = \frac{K}{(1 - 11\omega^2) + j6\omega(1 - \omega^2)} \qquad (7\text{-}65)$$

Setting the imaginary part of the last equation equal to zero, we have

$$\omega_c = \pm 1 \text{ rad/sec} \qquad (7\text{-}66)$$

Substitution of this value of ω_c into Eq. (7-65) gives

$$(GH)_c = \frac{K}{-10} \qquad (7\text{-}67)$$

from which
$$|(GH)_c| = K/10 \qquad (7\text{-}68)$$

hence
$$K = 1 \qquad (7\text{-}69)$$

In general, the gain margin is merely one of the several essential terms used to indicate the relative stability of a feedback control system. Theoretically, a system with a large gain margin should be more stable than a system with a smaller gain margin. However, the statement just made is not true in general. For all practical purposes, gain margin alone does not sufficiently indicate the relative stability of a system. For instance, the two GH plots shown in Fig. 7-37 obviously have the same gain margin; that is, they all represent systems with infinite decibels of gain margin. However, locus A actually corresponds to a much more stable system than locus B, since, with any slight change in some system parameter (or parameters), it is entirely possible for locus B to pass through or even enclose the $(-1, j0)$ point. The two GH plots given in Fig. 7-38 also have the same gain margin, but the system corresponding to curve A certainly represents a more stable system.

In order to define adequately the relative stability of a system, the *phase margin* is used to distinguish the degree of stability of cases like those shown in Figs. 7-37 and 7-38.

(2) *The Phase Margin*

Phase margin is defined as the angle through which the Nyquist locus must be rotated in order that the unity magnitude point on the locus passes through the critical point $(-1, j0)$. In other words, the phase margin is the

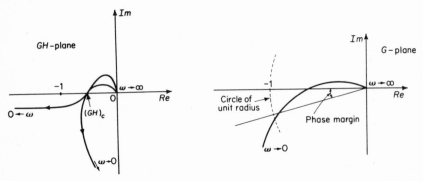

Fig. 7-38. Nyquist plots showing systems with same gain margin but different amount of relative stability.

Fig. 7-39. The phase margin measured in the G-plane.

angle that the unit radius phasor makes with the negative real axis in the GH-plane, as shown in Fig. 7-39. The phase margin has the significance of estimating the stability effect of changes of the parameters of the system which affect the phase of $G(s)H(s)$.

(3) *Gain Margin and Phase Margin from the Bode Plot*

It is usually preferable to evaluate the gain margin and the phase margin of a control system from its Bode plot. The reason is simply that the Bode plot is very easy to construct, and the gain margin and the phase margin are obtained directly from the plot by inspection. As an example, consider the open-loop transfer function

$$G(s) = \frac{K}{s(1 + 0.2s)(1 + 0.02s)} \qquad (7\text{-}70)$$

of a unity-feedback control system. The following steps are followed in constructing the Bode plot of $G(s)$ on semi-log coordinates:

(1) The corner frequencies of $G(s)$ are at $\omega = 0$, $\omega = 5$ rad/sec, and $\omega = 50$ rad/sec.

(2) Straight-line asymptotes are drawn for the magnitude curve and the phase shift curve corresponding to these corners.

(3) The straight-line asymptotes for the magnitude curve are added, and a smooth curve is sketched representing the actual magnitude curve (Fig. 7-40).

(4) The actual phase shift curves at the two corner frequencies $\omega = 5$ rad/sec, and $\omega = 50$ rad/sec are sketched approximately, based on the

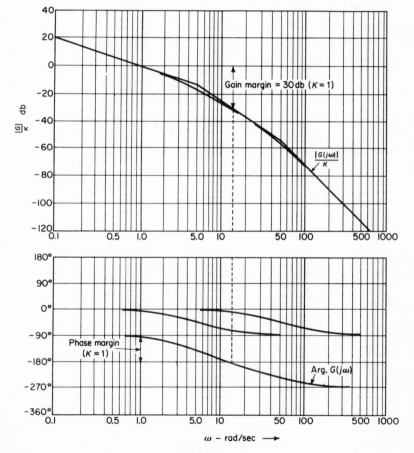

Fig. 7-40. Bode plot of
$$G(s) = \frac{K}{s(1 + 0.2s)(1 + 0.02s)}$$

straight-line asymptotes. The sum of the three phase shift curves gives the total phase characteristics of $G(j\omega)$.

It is seen from Fig. 7-40 that the phase shift curve passes through the -180 deg axis at approximately 15 rad/sec. The magnitude of $|G|/K$ corresponding to this point is -30 db. This means that if the gain K is increased to 30 db, the magnitude curve will cross the 0 db axis, which corresponds to the Nyquist plot of $G(j\omega)$ passing through the critical -1 point; the system is on the verge of becoming unstable. From the definition of the gain margin, the gain margin in this case is 30 db. Suppose that the next step is to determine the phase margin when K is 1. Remember that the phase margin is defined as the phase difference between Arg. $G(j\omega)$ and -180 deg when the magnitude of $G(j\omega)$ is unity. We simply locate the point where the magnitude curve $|G|/K$ crosses the 0 db axis ($\log_{10} 1 = 0$) and the corresponding phase shift of $G(j\omega)$ is approximately -100 deg. Thus, the phase margin when K is unity is 180 deg -100 deg $= 80$ deg.

The procedure in obtaining the gain margin and the phase margin from the Bode plot may be outlined as follows:

(1) Construct the Bode plot of $|G(j\omega)|/K$ versus ω and Arg. G versus ω.

(2) To obtain the gain margin, first locate the point at which the phase shift curve crosses the -180 deg axis. This point is usually called the "phase crossover," and the corresponding frequency is called the "phase crossover frequency." The magnitude of $|G|/K$ curve in decibels at the phase crossover frequency is the gain margin for $K = 1$. For any other values of K, the gain margin is simply equal to the difference between the gain at the phase crossover and the value of K in decibels. For example, in the previous example, if K is set at 10 db, the gain margin is 30 db $-$ 10 db $= 20$ db. Sometimes, the gain margin corresponding to $K = 1$ is called the "gain limit" G_1.* Then the gain margin in decibels for any gain K is simply

$$\text{Gain Margin (G.M.) in db} = \text{Gain Limit } G_1 \text{ db} - \text{Gain } K \text{ db} \qquad (7\text{-}71)$$

In terms of absolute values, the last equation is written as

$$\text{G.M.} = G_1/K \qquad (7\text{-}72)$$

Furthermore, if the phase shift curve never crosses the -180 deg axis from above, the system is always stable; e.g., in a second-order system, the phase shift only approaches -180 deg asymptotically as the frequency is increased to infinity.

(3) To obtain the phase margin, first locate the point where the magnitude curve $|G|/K$ crosses the zero decibels axis. This point is usually called the "gain crossover," and the corresponding frequency is called the "gain

---

*Y. Chu, "Correlation between Frequency and Transient Response of Feedback Control Systems," *AIEE Trans. Application and Industry*, Part II, Vol. 72, 1953, p. 82.

crossover frequency." The phase angle between the phase shift curve and
the -180 deg axis is the phase margin for $K = 1$. If the phase shift curve
is above the -180 deg axis, the phase margin is positive; otherwise, it is
negative. For any other value of K, the phase margin is obtained by
shifting the zero decibels axis to $-K$ in decibels and following the same
procedure. For instance, in the last example, if $K = 10$ db, the magnitude
curve is shifted up by 10 db. This is as if the zero decibels axis were shifted
down by 10 db. The new gain crossover frequency is about 3 rad/sec; the
phase margin for $K = 10$ db is about 60 deg.

7.10 Conditionally Stable System

Thus far, we have shown that if the gain of a control system is increased
sufficiently, the system will become unstable. Another class of systems has
the property that, in addition to the instability at high gain, if the gain is
reduced to a certain extent, the system again becomes unstable. In other
words, the system can be stable only for a finite range (or ranges) of K;
beyond these values of K, the system becomes unstable. The Nyquist locus
of a typical conditionally stable system is shown in Fig. 7-41, where regions

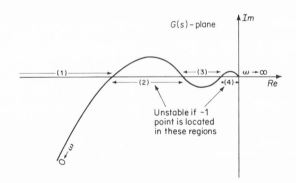

Fig. 7-41. Nyquist plot of a conditionally stable system.

(2) and (4) on the negative real axis apparently correspond to unstable
regions. The critical -1 point must not be found in these regions, or the
system will be unstable.

As an example, suppose that a certain unity-feedback control system
has the open-loop transfer function

$$G(s) = \frac{K(1 + 0.2s)(1 + 0.025s)}{s^3(1 + 0.001s)(1 + 0.005s)} \qquad (7\text{-}73)$$

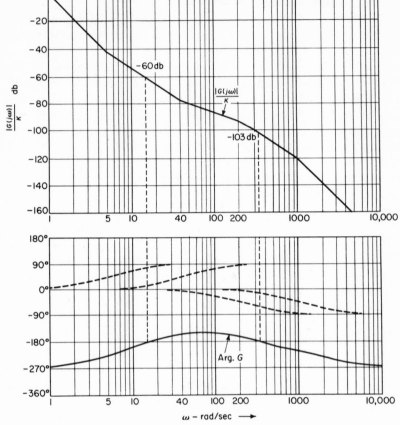

Fig. 7-42. Bode plot of

$$G(s) = \frac{K(1 + 0.2s)(1 + 0.025s)}{s^3(1 + 0.001s)(1 + 0.005s)}$$

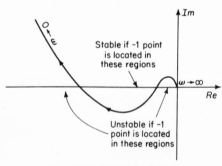

Fig. 7-43. Nyquist plot of

$$G(s) = \frac{K(1 + 0.2s)(1 + 0.025s)}{s^3(1 + 0.001s)(1 + 0.005s)}$$

The corner plot of $G(s)$ is given in Fig. 7-42 on semi-log coordinates. The gain crossover frequency is approximately 1 rad/sec, and the phase margin is negative. This means that the closed-loop system is unstable even for very small values of K. There are two phase crossover points: one at $\omega = 15$ rad/sec, and the other at $\omega = 350$ rad/sec. The phase characteristics between these two frequencies indicate that if the gain crossover lies in this range, the system is stable. From the corner plot, the range of K for stable operation is between 60 db and 103 db. For values of K above or below this range, the phase shift exceeds -180 deg, and the system is unstable. The conditional stable condition of the system is better illustrated if the Nyquist plot of $G(s)$ is sketched (Fig. 7-43).

One important feature of the Bode plot which is useful in the design of control systems is that a definite relation exists between the slope of the magnitude curve at the gain crossover and the relative stability of the system. To be specific, if the slope of the magnitude curve at the gain crossover is -60 db/decade or more, the system is unstable. The smaller the slope, the more stable is the system. Figure 7-42 serves as a good example in clarifying this point. At both very low and high frequencies, the slope of the gain curve is -60 db/decade; if the gain crossover falls in either of these two regions, the phase margins are negative and the system is unstable. In the two -40 db/decade sections, the system can be stable only in about half of these regions, but even then the phase margin is small. If the gain crossover falls within the -20 db/decade section, the phase margin is positive, and the system is rather stable.

7.11 The Constant M Loci in the G-Plane

In the previous sections, it has been shown that the maximum resonance peak M_p of the closed-loop frequency response curve is directly related to the maximum overshoot of the transient response. Normally, the magnification curve of M versus ω may be constructed by means of the corner plot technique if the closed-loop transfer function $C(j\omega)/R(j\omega)$ is given, and if its numerator and denominator are factored in the standard form of Eq.(6-8). It is not always easy to plot the M versus ω curve, for if the system order is high, the amount of work involved in solving for the roots of the characteristic equation may be quite extensive. However, it will be shown now that the information concerning M_p and the data necessary for plotting the M versus ω curve can be obtained from the Nyquist plot of the open-loop transfer function $G(j\omega)$.

Consider a feedback control system with unity feedback. The closed-loop transfer function is

$$\frac{C(s)}{R(s)} = \frac{G(s)}{1 + G(s)} \tag{7-74}$$

Let the coordinates of the Nyquist plot of $G(s)$ be represented by.

$$G = x + jy \tag{7-75}$$

Then

$$M = \left| \frac{C(j\omega)}{R(j\omega)} \right| = \left| \frac{G(j\omega)}{1 + G(j\omega)} \right| = \left| \frac{x + jy}{1 + x + jy} \right| = \frac{\sqrt{x^2 + y^2}}{\sqrt{(1 + x)^2 + y^2}}$$

(7-76)

which gives $\qquad M\sqrt{(1 + x)^2 + y^2} = \sqrt{x^2 + y^2}$ (7-77)

or $\qquad M^2[(1 + x)^2 + y^2] = x^2 + y^2$ (7-78)

Rearranging the last equation yields

$$(1 - M^2)x^2 + (1 - M^2)y^2 - 2M^2x = M^2$$

(7-79)

Dividing through Eq. (7-79) by $(1 - M^2)$, and adding the term $\left(\dfrac{M^2}{1 - M^2} \right)^2$

on both sides of the equation, we have

$$x^2 + y^2 - \frac{2M^2}{1 - M^2} x + \left(\frac{M^2}{1 - M^2} \right)^2 = \frac{M^2}{1 - M^2} + \left(\frac{M^2}{1 - M^2} \right)^2$$

(7-80)

which is simplified to

$$\left(x - \frac{M^2}{1 - M^2} \right)^2 + y^2 = \left(\frac{M}{1 - M^2} \right)^2$$

(7-81)

Equation (7-81) represents a circle with the center at $x = M^2/(1 - M^2)$; $y = 0$. The radius of the circle is $r = |M/(1 - M^2)|$. When $M = 1$, we have from Eq. (7-79) $x = -\frac{1}{2}$, which is the equation of a straight line parallel to the y-axis and passing through the point $(-\frac{1}{2}, 0)$ in the G-plane. Therefore, Eq. (7-81) represents the so-called "constant M loci" in the G-plane. The constant M circles for various values of M are defined in Table 7-2 and are constructed in Fig. 7-44. When the value of M becomes infi-

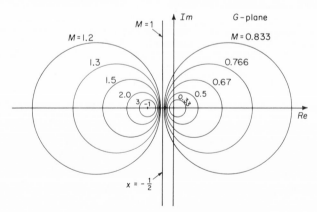

Fig. 7-44. The constant M circles.

nite, the circles degenerate into a point at $(-1, j0)$. This checks with the well-known fact that when the Nyquist plot of $G(j\omega)$ goes through the $(-1, j0)$ point in the G-plane, the system is on the verge of becoming unstable.

The constant M loci plot is symmetrical with respect to the $M = 1$ straight line and the real axis. The constant M circles to the left of the $M = 1$ line correspond to values of $M > 1$, and those to the right of the $M = 1$ line are for $M < 1$.

The intersections of the $G(j\omega)$ plot and the constant M loci give the value of M at the frequency denoted on the G-locus. If it is desired to keep the resonance peak M_p of a system less than a certain value, the open-loop

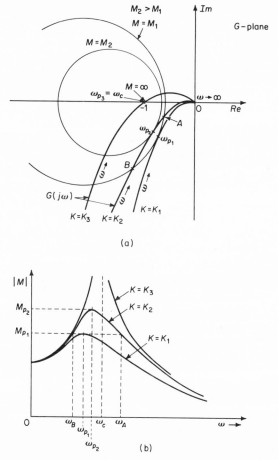

(a)

(b)

Fig. 7-45. (a) Polar plots of $G(s)$ and constant M loci showing method of determining the resonance peak M_p and the closed-loop frequency response in the G plane; (b) Closed-loop frequency responses.

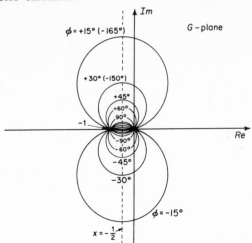

Fig. 7-46. The constant phase angle loci.

locus $G(j\omega)$ must not intersect the corresponding M circle at any point, and at the same time must not enclose the -1 point. The M circle with the smallest radius that is tangent to the $G(j\omega)$ locus gives the value of M_p, and the resonance frequency ω_p is read off at the tangent point on the $G(j\omega)$ locus.

Figure 7-45a shows the Nyquist plot of $G(j\omega)$ for a hypothetical system, together with several of the constant M loci. The resonance peak M_p in the closed-loop gain response for a certain chosen forward gain K_1 is found by locating the smallest circle that is tangent to the G-plot. The resonant frequency is designated as ω_{p1}. If the forward gain is increased to K_2, a constant M circle with a smaller radius, hence with a larger value of M_p, is found in tangent to the G-plot. The resonant frequency is shown to be ω_{p2}, which is closer to the phase-crossover frequency ω_c than ω_{p1}. If the value of K is still increased, so that eventually the G-plot passes through the $(-1, j0)$ point which corresponds to $M_p = \infty$ and $\omega_p = \omega_c$, the system is on the verge of becoming unstable. The corresponding values of M_p of the closed-loop frequency response found in the three cases above are sketched in Fig. 7-45b.

The entire closed-loop frequency response curve can also be obtained from the constant M and $G(j\omega)$ loci. The magnitude of M at any frequency is determined by reading the corresponding value of M on the constant M circle which intersects the $G(j\omega)$ locus at that frequency. For instance, when $K = K_2$, the $G(j\omega)$ locus shown in Fig. 7-45b intersects the $M = M_1$ circle at two points, A and B, with frequencies ω_a and ω_b respectively. This means that at these two frequencies of ω_a and ω_b, the magnitude of the closed-loop frequency response has the same value M_1; these are shown in Fig. 7-45b.

Table 7-2.

THE CONSTANT M CIRCLES

M	Center $x = \dfrac{M^2}{1 - M^2}, \; y = 0$	Radius $r = \dfrac{M}{1 - M^2}$
0.3	0.01	0.33
0.5	0.33	0.67
0.7	0.96	1.37
1.0	∞	∞
1.1	-5.76	5.24
1.2	-3.27	2.73
1.3	-2.45	1.88
1.4	-2.04	1.46
1.5	-1.80	1.20
1.6	-1.64	1.03
1.7	-1.53	0.90
1.8	-1.46	0.80
1.9	-1.38	0.73
2.0	-1.33	0.67
2.5	-1.19	0.48
3.0	-1.13	0.38
4.0	-1.07	0.27
5.0	-1.04	0.21
6.0	-1.03	0.17

7.12 The Constant Phase Shift Loci in the G-Plane

The loci of constant phase shift of the closed-loop system may also be located in the G-plane by means of a method similar to that used for the constant M loci. With reference to Eqs. (7-74) and (7-75), the phase shift of the closed-loop system may be written as

$$\phi = \text{Arg.} \; \overline{M} = \text{Arg.} \left(\frac{x + jy}{1 + x + jy} \right) \tag{7-82}$$

hence

$$\phi = \tan^{-1}(y/x) - \tan^{-1}(y/1 + x) \tag{7-83}$$

Taking the tangent of both sides of the last equation and simplifying, we have

$$\tan \phi = \frac{y}{x^2 + x + y^2} \tag{7-84}$$

Let $N = \tan \phi$; then Eq. (7-84) reads

$$x^2 + x + y^2 - \frac{y}{N} = 0 \tag{7-85}$$

Adding the term $\left(\dfrac{1}{4} + \dfrac{1}{4N^2} \right)$ to both sides of the last equation yields

$$x^2 + x + \frac{1}{4} + y^2 - \frac{y}{N} + \frac{1}{4N^2} = \frac{1}{4} + \frac{1}{4N^2}$$

or

$$\left(x + \frac{1}{2} \right)^2 + \left(y - \frac{1}{2N} \right)^2 = \left(\frac{1}{4} + \frac{1}{4N^2} \right) \tag{7-86}$$

which represents a family of circles with centers at $\left(x = -\dfrac{1}{2}, \; y = \dfrac{1}{2N} \right)$.

The radius of any circle corresponding to a given N is represented by

$$r = \sqrt{\frac{N^2 + 1}{4N^2}} \tag{7-87}$$

The constant phase shift loci for various values of ϕ are constructed in Fig. 7-46; their results are tabulated in Table 7-3.

Table 7-3.

THE CONSTANT N CIRCLES

$\begin{array}{c}\phi \pm 180°n \\ n = 0,1,2 \ldots\end{array}$	$N = \tan \phi$	Center $x = -\dfrac{1}{2},\ y = \dfrac{1}{2N}$		Radius $r = \sqrt{\dfrac{N^2 + 1}{4N^2}}$
-90	$-\infty$	0		0.500
-60	-1.732	-0.289		0.577
-45	-1.000	-0.500		0.707
-30	-0.577	-0.866		1.000
-15	-0.268	-1.866		1.931
0	0	∞		∞
15	0.268	1.866		1.931
30	0.577	0.866		1.000
45	1.000	0.500		0.707
60	1.732	0.289		0.577
90	∞	0		0.500

7.13 The Constant M and N Loci in Gain-Phase Plane (The Nichols Chart)

The constant M and N loci in the polar plane may be used for both the analysis and design of servo systems; however, in general, it is more convenient, especially in design problems, to have the M and N loci constructed in the gain-phase plane (decibel versus phase-shift). A point on a constant M locus in the gain-phase plane may be obtained by drawing a vector directed from the origin of the G-plane to a particular point on a constant M circle; the vector length measured in decibels and its phase angle determine the corresponding point in gain-phase plane. Figure 7-47 illustrates the process of locating three corresponding points on the constant M loci in the gain-phase plane. The critical point $(-1, j0)$ in the G-plane corresponds to the point of zero decibels and -180 deg in the gain-phase plane. By the same method, the constant N loci may also be located in the gain-phase plane. These constant M and N loci were first originated by N. B. Nichols,* and are called the "Nichols Chart." A typical Nichols

---

*H. M. James, N. B. Nichols, and R. S. Phillips, *Theory of Servomechanisms*, McGraw-Hill Book Company, Inc., New York, 1947.

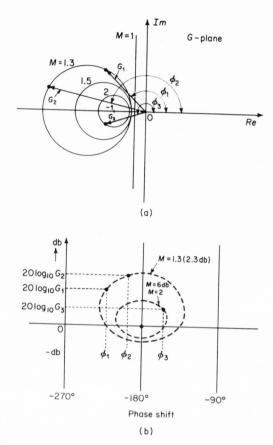

(a)

(b)

Fig. 7-47. (a) Constant M circles in the G-plane; (b) Constant M loci (Nichols Chart) for $M = 1.3$ and $M = 2$ in the gain-phase plane.

chart is constructed in Fig. 7-48 for the phase shift from -180 deg to 0 deg. The chart which corresponds to the phase from -360 deg to -180 deg is a mirror image of that shown in Fig. 7-48 with the mirror placed on the $\phi = -180$ deg axis. In Fig. 7-49 the Nichols chart is shown for -270 deg $< \phi < -90$ deg. It should be reiterated here that the Nichols chart consists simply of the same constant M and N loci originally developed in the polar plot, but now they are drawn in a different set of coordinates, namely magnitude (decibels) versus phase shift.

The following example will illustrate the relationship among the methods of the Bode plot, the Nyquist plot, and the Nichols chart with gain-phase plot.

EXAMPLE 7-6. The open-loop transfer function $G(s)$ given by Eq. 7-70

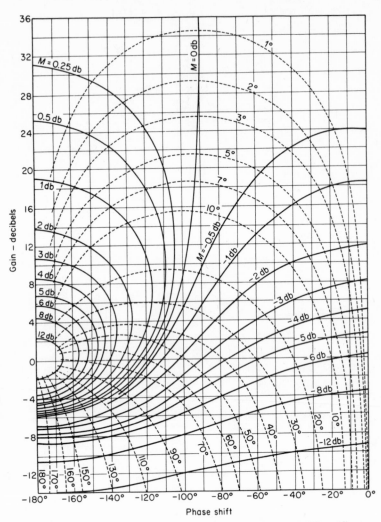

Fig. 7-48. The Nichols chart (for phase shift from $-180°$ to $0°$).

is used again in this example. The Bode diagram for $G(s)$ is originally constructed in Fig. 7-40 for $K = 1$. From this Bode plot, it is seen that the following values for gain margin and phase margin are determined for the system when K assumes the values of 1.0, 3.16, and 10.

K	Gain margin (decibels)	Phase margin (degrees)
1 (0 db)	30	82
3.16 (10 db)	20	57
10 (20 db)	10	25

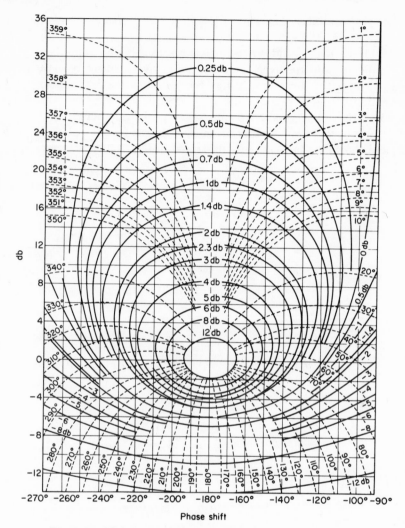

Fig. 7-49. Nichols chart (for phase shift from $-270°$ to $-90°$).

In order to evaluate the closed-loop frequency response, the transfer function $G(s)$ is now constructed in the gain-phase plot by use of the data taken from the Bode diagram of Fig. 7-40. In Fig. 7-51 the gain-phase plots for $G(s)$ are plotted for $K = 1, 3.16$, and 10 respectively. It is important to notice that the three loci have identical forms except for the shift in vertical positions. Thus, it is necessary only to plot $G(s)$ in the gain-phase plane for $K = 1$, for example, and the plot for any other K is obtained simply by shifting the $K = 1$ curve up or down along the vertical axis. For instance, for $K = 10$ db, the $K = 1$ (0 db) curve is shifted up by 10 db.

The gain and phase margins of the closed-loop system are also readily determined from the gain-phase plot by mere inspection. Since the intersection of the G-plot and the zero decibels axis in the gain-phase plane represents the gain-crossover, the phase margin is read directly as the phase angle between this intersection and the -180 deg axis. Similarly, the intersection of the $G(s)$ locus and the -180 deg axis in the gain-phase diagram is the phase crossover point, and gives the gain margin in decibels. The measurement of gain and phase margins in the Nyquist plot, the Bode plot, and the gain-phase plot are illustrated in Fig. 7-50.

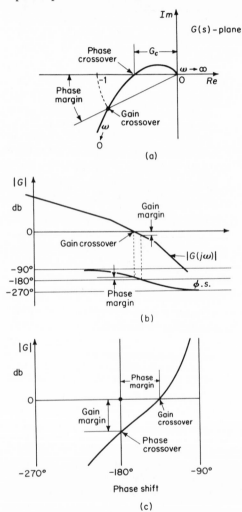

Fig. 7-50. (a) The Nyquist plot of $G(s)$ of Ex. 7-6; (b) Bode diagram of $G(s)$ of Ex. 7-6; (c) Gain phase plot of $G(s)$ of Ex. 7-6 (not to scale).

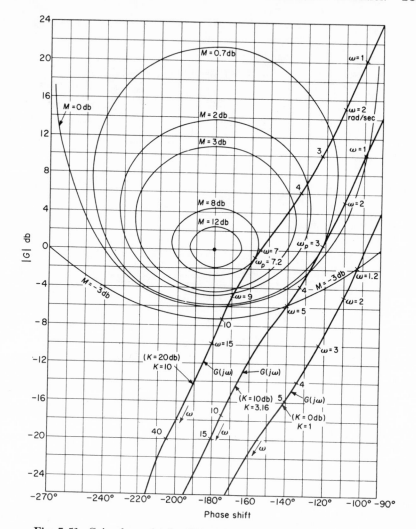

Fig. 7-51. Gain-phase plot for $G(s)$ and the Nichols chart for Ex. 7-6.

The constant M loci in the Nichols chart, superposed on the gain-phase diagram, enables the determination of the closed-loop frequency response of the system. The intersections of the constant M loci give the values of M at the corresponding frequencies ω, read on the $G(s)$ curve. The constant M locus that is tangent only to the G-locus gives the resonance peak M_p; the corresponding frequency is ω_p. For $K = 10$ (20 db), the $G(s)$ plot is tangent to the $M = 8$ db locus at $\omega = 7.2$ rad/sec; hence, the resonance peak of the system is $M_p = 8$ db (2.51), and the resonant frequency is 7.2 rad/sec. Similarly, for $K = 3.16$ (10 db), $M_p = 0.7$ db (1.084), and

$\omega_p = 3$ rad/sec. For $K = 1$ (0 db), the $G(s)$ locus is not in tangent to any constant M locus and there is no resonance.

The *bandwidth* of the closed-loop system can also be determined from the gain-phase diagram and the Nichols chart. It is easy to see that the frequency at the intersection of the $M = 0.707$ (-3 db) locus and the $G(s)$ plot is the bandwidth in rad/sec. Hence, from Fig. 7-51, the following values for the bandwidth are obtained:

K	*Bandwidth* (rad/sec)
1	1.2
3.16	5.0
10	10

Problems

7-1. For the following loop gain functions, sketch the Nyquist diagrams which correspond to the entire Nyquist path. In each case, check the values of N, P, and Z with respect to the origin in the GH-plane. Determine the values of N, P, and Z with respect to the -1 point, and specify if the closed-loop system is stable. Specify in which case it is necessary to sketch only the Nyquist plot for $\omega = 0$ to ∞ (section I) on the Nyquist path to investigate the stability of the closed-loop system.

(a) $G(s)H(s) = \dfrac{50}{s(1 + 0.1s)(1 + 0.2s)}$

(b) $G(s)H(s) = \dfrac{10}{s^2(1 + 0.25s)(1 + 0.5s)}$

(c) $G(s)H(s) = \dfrac{100(1 + s)}{s(1 + 0.1s)(1 + 0.5s)(1 + 0.8s)}$

(d) $G(s)H(s) = \dfrac{5(1 - 0.5s)}{s(1 + 0.1s)(1 - 0.25s)}$

(e) $G(s)H(s) = \dfrac{10}{s(1 + 0.2s)(s - 1)}$

(f) $G(s)H(s) = \dfrac{2.5(1 + 0.2s)}{1 + 2s + s^3}$

7-2. Sketch Nyquist diagrams for the following loop transfer functions. Sketch only the portion which is necessary to determine the stability of the closed-loop system. Determine the stability of the systems.

(a) $G(s)H(s) = \dfrac{100}{s(s^2 + 2s + 2)(s + 1)}$

(b) $G(s)H(s) = \dfrac{50}{s(s + 2)(s^2 + 4)}$

(c) $G(s)H(s) = \dfrac{s}{1 - 0.2s}$

7-3. Figure 7P-3 shows the entire Nyquist plots of the loop gains $G(s)H(s)$ of some feedback control systems. It is known that in each case, the zeros of

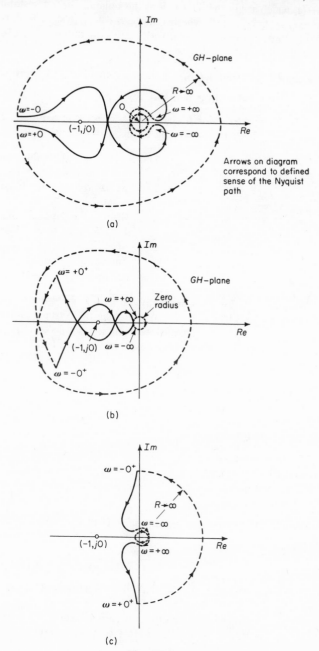

(a)

(b)

(c)

Fig. 7P-3.

$G(s)H(s)$ are all located in the left half of the s-plane; i.e., $Z = 0$ with respect to the origin in the GH-plane. Determine the number of poles of $G(s)H(s)$ which are in the right half of the s-plane. State the stability of the open-loop systems. State whether the closed-loop system is stable; if not, give the number of roots of the characteristic equation which are in the right half of the s-plane.

7-4. The characteristic equation of a feedback control system is given as

$$s^3 + 5Ks^2 + (2K + 3)s + 10 = 0$$

Apply the Nyquist criterion to determine the values of K for a stable closed-loop system. Check the answer by means of the Routh-Hurwitz criterion.

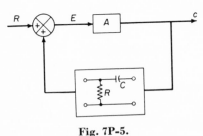

Fig. 7P-5.

7-5. Determine the value of A so that the system shown in Fig. 7P-5 will realize the transfer function of an ideal derivative control $(1 + Ts)$. Sketch the Nyquist diagrams for $C(s)/R(s)$ for three different values of $A (A > 1,\ A = 1,$ and $A < 1)$. Investigate the stability of the system in each case.

7-6. The Nyquist criterion was originally devised to investigate the absolute stability of a closed-loop system. By sketching the Nyquist plot of $G(s)H(s)$ which corresponds to the Nyquist path, it is possible to tell whether the system's characteristic equation has roots in the right half of the s-plane.
(a) Define a new Nyquist path in the s-plane which may be used to ensure that all the complex roots of the characteristic equation have damping ratios greater than some value δ_1.
(b) Define a new Nyquist path in the s-plane which may be used to ensure that all the characteristic equation roots are in the left half of the s-plane with real parts greater than α_1.

7-7. For the servo system given in Problem 5-24, sketch the Nyquist plot of $G(s)$ and discuss stability of the closed-loop system as a function of K. Determine the points where the Nyquist plot intersects the negative real axis.

7-8. The open-loop transfer function of a unity-feedback control system is given by

$$G(s) = \frac{K}{s(1 + 0.1s)(1 + s)}$$

(a) Determine the value of K so that the resonance peak M_p of the system is equal to 1.4.
(b) Determine the value of K so that the gain margin of the system is 20 db.
(c) Determine the value of K so that the phase margin of the system is 60 deg.

7-9. The open-loop transfer function of a unity-feedback control system is given by

$$G(s) = \frac{K(1 + Ts)}{s(1 + 0.1s)(1 + s)}$$

Determine the smallest possible value of T for the system to have an infinite gain margin.

7-10. The open-loop transfer function of a unity-feedback control system is given by

$$G(s) = \frac{K}{s(1 + 0.1s)(1 + 0.001s)}$$

Determine the value of K if the steady-state error of the output position must be less than or equal to 0.1 per cent for a ramp function input. With this value of K, what are the gain margin and the phase margin of the system? Plot $G(s)$ in the gain-phase plot and determine the resonance peak M_p and the resonant frequency ω_p.

7-11. A tandem compensation network is added in the forward path of the system in Problem 7-10 so that now the open-loop transfer function reads

$$G(s) = \frac{K(1 + 0.0167s)}{s(1 + 0.00222s)(1 + 0.1s)(1 + 0.001s)}$$

where K is determined in part (a) of Problem 7-10. Plot the gain-phase diagram of $G(s)$; evaluate M_p, ω_p, the gain margin, the phase margin, and the band width of the compensated system.

7-12. Each of the following loop transfer functions involves a transportation lag, as indicated by the exponential terms. By use of the Nyquist criterion, determine the values of K in order for the closed-loop systems to be stable.

(a) $G(s)H(s) = \dfrac{K\,e^{-2s}}{s(s + 5)}$

(b) $G(s)H(s) = \dfrac{K\,e^{-s}}{s^2 + 5s + 10}$

7-13. Each of the following loop transfer functions involves a transportation lag, as indicated by the exponential terms. By use of the Nyquist criterion determine the values of T in order for the closed-loop systems to be stable.

(a) $G(s)H(s) = \dfrac{10\,e^{-Ts}}{s^2 + 4s + 25}$

(b) $G(s)H(s) = \dfrac{2\,e^{-Ts}}{s(s + 10)}$

8

The Root Locus Technique

8.1 Introduction

In the frequency domain study of linear feedback control systems, the Nyquist criterion, the Bode plot, and the Nichols chart were shown to be very useful tools of analysis. The above-mentioned techniques will lead to the design of a feedback control system from the frequency response viewpoint if the specifications on system performance are given in terms of the gain margin, phase margin, peak of resonance M_p, band width, etc. However, in the study of linear systems, it is equally important to consider the time domain specifications, such as the overshoot, damping ratio, settling time, etc. Although, theoretically, there is a definite correlation between the frequency response and the transient response, unfortunately, simple relationships can be obtained only for systems of the order of two or less.

The root locus technique was introduced by Evans* in 1948, and the art has been greatly developed in the past few years. The technique can be regarded as a graphical method of determining the roots of the characteristic equation of a single feedback loop system.†

---

*W. R. Evans, "Graphical Analysis of Control Systems," *Trans.*, *AIEE*, Vol. 67, pp. 547–551, 1948; and W. R. Evans, "Control System Synthesis by Root Locus Method," *Trans.*, *AIEE*, Vol. 69, pp. 66–69, 1950.

†It will be shown later that the root locus technique can be extended to systems with multiple feedback loops.

The advantage of working in the s-plane is that the roots of the characteristic equation not only give information concerning the transient response directly, but also indicate, to a certain extent, the sinusoidal frequency behavior of the system.

Consider a unity-feedback control system with the open-loop transfer function

$$G(s) = \frac{K}{s(s+2)} \tag{8-1}$$

The characteristic equation of the system is

$$s^2 + 2s + K = 0 \tag{8-2}$$

The two roots of Eq. (8-2) are

$$s_1, s_2 = -1 \pm \sqrt{1 - K} \tag{8-3}$$

The variation of the roots when K is varied from $-\infty$ to $+\infty$ is considered in the following:

(1) For $-\infty < K < 0$: The two roots are both real, one being positive, the other negative.

(2) For $K = 0$: $s_1 = 0$, $s_2 = -2$; these roots are the same as the poles of $G(s)$.

(3) For $0 < K < 1$: The two roots are both negative real numbers.

(4) For $K = 1$: There is a double root at $s_1 = s_2 = -1$.

(5) For $1 < K < \infty$: The two roots are complex conjugate pairs with negative real parts equal to -1.

The loci of the two roots when K varies from $-\infty$ to ∞ are given in Fig. 8-1.

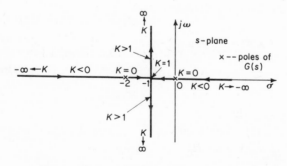

Fig. 8-1. Loci of the roots of $s^2 + 2s + K = 0$ as a function of K.

From the root loci given in Fig. 8-1, the following information on the system behavior is obtained.

(1) *Stability*

The system is unstable for negative values of K, but is stable for all positive values of K.

(2) *Transient Response*

(a) For all values of $0 < K < 1$, the system is over-damped ($\delta > 1$); for $1 < K < \infty$, the system is under-damped ($\delta < 1$). Critical damping ($\delta = 1$) occurs when $K = 1$.

(b) The undamped natural frequency ω_n increases with an increase in K.

(c) For all values of $K \geq 1$, the settling time of the step response is constant, since the real parts of the two roots are fixed.

(3) *Frequency Response*

(a) The band width of the system increases with an increase in K.

(b) For any given value of K, the roots s_1 and s_2 are determined from the root loci; the magnification M becomes

$$M = \frac{C(s)}{R(s)} = \frac{K}{(s - s_1)(s - s_2)} \tag{8-4}$$

The frequency response of the closed-loop system can be plotted by means of the Bode plot of the last equation.

8.2 The Root Loci (Definition)

Consider a feedback control system whose closed-loop transfer function is described by

$$\frac{C(s)}{R(s)} = \frac{G(s)}{1 + G(s)H(s)} \tag{8-5}$$

The characteristic equation of the system is simply

$$1 + G(s)H(s) = 0 \tag{8-6}$$

The conventional root locus plot includes the loci or the roots of Eq. (8-6) — the characteristic equation, when the gain K is varied from 0 to $+\infty$.* In other words, for a given value of K between 0 and $+\infty$, any point s_1 in the s-plane which satisfies Eq. (8-6) is a point on the root locus plot.

Equation (8-6) can also be written in a more convenient form as

$$G(s)H(s) = -1 \tag{8-7}$$

In order to satisfy the last equation, the following conditions must be met:

(1) $|G(s)H(s)| = 1$ \hfill (8-8)

(2) $\underline{/G(s)H(s)} = 180 \text{ deg} + k \times 360 \text{ deg}$ \hfill (8-9)

where $k = 0, \pm 1, \pm 2, \ldots$, all integers.

---

*If the system has unity feedback, the root locus plot is just the loci of the roots of $1 + G(s) = 0$ when K is varied from 0 to $+\infty$. When parameters other than K are varied (one at a time), the corresponding root locus plot is later defined as the generalized root loci — the root contours.

In feedback control systems without transportation lag, $G(s)H(s)$ is a rational algebraic function, so it can be written in a standard form:

$$G(s)H(s) = \frac{K(s + z_1)(s + z_2) \cdots (s + z_m)}{(s + p_1)(s + p_2) \cdots (s + p_{m+n})} \tag{8-10}$$

The two conditions given in Eqs. (8-8) and (8-9) then become

$$|G(s)H(s)| = \frac{K \prod\limits_{i=1}^{m} |s + z_i|}{\prod\limits_{j=1}^{m+n} |s + p_j|} = 1 \tag{8-11}$$

and $$\underline{/G(s)H(s)} = \sum_{i=1}^{m} \underline{/s + z_i} - \sum_{j=1}^{m+n} \underline{/s + p_j} = (2k + 1)\pi \tag{8-12}$$

Now consider an arbitrary point s_1 in the s-plane; if s_1 is a point on the root locus diagram, it must satisfy both Eq. (8-11) and Eq. (8-12); i.e.,

$$\frac{K \prod\limits_{i=1}^{m} |s_1 + z_i|}{\prod\limits_{j=1}^{m+n} |s_1 + p_j|} = 1 \tag{8-13}$$

and $$\sum_{i=1}^{m} \underline{/s_1 + z_i} - \sum_{j=1}^{m+n} \underline{/s_1 + p_j} = (2k + 1)\pi \tag{8-14}$$

As an illustration, let

$$G(s)H(s) = \frac{K(s + z_1)}{s(s + p_2)(s + p_3)} \tag{8-15}$$

The poles and zeros of $G(s)H(s)$ are assumed to have the location shown in Fig. 8-2.

Next, we assume an arbitrary point s_1 in the s-plane and draw vectors directed from the poles and zeros of $G(s)H(s)$ to the point s_1. If s_1 is a point on the root loci of the system, it must satisfy the following two conditions:

$$\frac{K|s_1 + z_1|}{|s_1|\,|s_1 + p_2|\,|s_1 + p_3|} = 1 \quad (8\text{-}16)$$

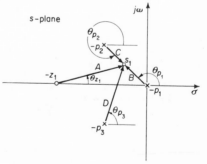

Fig. 8-2. Pole-zero configuration of

$$G(s)H(s) = \frac{K(s + z_1)}{s(s + p_2)(s + p_3)}$$

and $$\underline{/s_1 + z_1} - (\underline{/s_1} + \underline{/s_1 + p_2} + \underline{/s_1 + p_3}) = (2k + 1)\pi \tag{8-17}$$

for $k = 0, \pm 1, \pm 2, \ldots$.

The factor $|s_1 + z_1|$ is recognized as the length of the vector drawn from the zero z_1 to the point s_1, and the factor $|s_1 + p_2|$ is the length of the vector drawn from the pole p_2 to s_1. If, in Fig. 8-2, the vector lengths are represented by A, B, C, and D, Eq. (8-16) becomes

$$\frac{A}{BCD} = \frac{1}{K} \tag{8-18}$$

The angles θ_{z_1}, θ_{p_1}, θ_{p_2}, and θ_{p_3} are the arguments of the vectors measured with the positive real axis as zero reference. From Eq. (8-17), it is required that

$$\theta_{z_1} - (\theta_{p_1} + \theta_{p_2} + \theta_{p_3}) = (2k + 1)\pi \tag{8-19}$$

Consequently, given the pole-zero configuration of $G(s)H(s)$, the construction of the root locus diagram involves the following two steps:

(1) A search for the s_1 points in the s-plane which satisfy the condition given by Eq. (8-14).

(2) The determination of the value of K at a particular s_1 point on the root loci from the relation given by Eq. (8-13).

Although it seems that the search for all the s_1 points in the s-plane which satisfy Eq. (8-14) is an almost impossible task, the actual procedure of the root loci construction is not so formidably complex. Normally, the root loci can be sketched in most cases by following through the rules of construction which will be described in the next section. A special tool called the "Spirule"* can also be used to aid in plotting the root locus diagram.

8.3 The Construction of the Root Loci

The following rules of construction are developed from the relation between the poles and zeros of $G(s)H(s)$ and the roots of the characteristic equation. These rules should be regarded only as aids to the construction of the root loci; they do not give the exact plot.

(1) *The Starting Points of the Root Loci* $(K = 0)$

The root loci start at the poles of $G(s)H(s)$.

Proof: The root loci are considered to start at the points at which the gain K is zero. Equation (8-11) can be written as

$$\frac{\prod\limits_{i=1}^{m} |(s + z_i)|}{\prod\limits_{j=1}^{m+n} |(s + p_j)|} = \frac{1}{K} \tag{8-20}$$

As K approaches zero, the value of Eq. (8-20) approaches infinity, and correspondingly, s approaches the poles of $G(s)H(s)$; i.e., $s \rightarrow -p_j$.

---

*Available from the Spirule Company, 9728 El Venado, Whittier, California.

EXAMPLE 8-1. Consider the pole-zero configuration of

$$G(s)H(s) = \frac{K(s+1)}{s(s+2)(s+3)} \qquad (8\text{-}21)$$

given in Fig. 8-3. The poles of $G(s)H(s)$ are at $s = 0$, $s = -2$, and $s = -3$; the root loci must start at these poles.

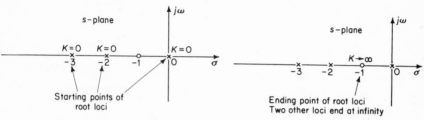

Fig. 8-3. Pole-zero configurations of
$$G(s)H(s) = \frac{K(s+1)}{s(s+2)(s+3)}$$

Fig. 8-4. Pole-zero configuration of
$$G(s)H(s) = \frac{K(s+1)}{s(s+2)(s+3)}$$

(2) *The Ending Points of the Root Loci* $(K = \infty)$

The root loci end at the zeros of $G(s)H(s)$.

Proof: The root loci are considered to end at the points at which K becomes infinite. With reference again to Eq. (8-20), as K approaches infinity, the equation approaches zero in value, which requires that s must approach the zeros of $G(s)H(s)$.

EXAMPLE 8-2. Figure 8-4 shows the pole-zero configuration of Eq. (8-21). The root loci, according to the rule, must end at the zeros of $G(s)H(s)$. There is only one finite zero of $G(s)H(s)$ at $s = -1$, but two zeros are located at infinity;* thus, two of the root loci must end at infinity.

(3) *Number of Separate Loci*

Let N = Number of separate loci

Z = Number of finite zeros of $G(s)H(s)$

P = Number of finite poles of $G(s)H(s)$

Then, $N = Z$ if $Z > P$

and $N = P$ if $P > Z$

It is apparent that, since the root loci must start at the poles and end at the zeros of $G(s)H(s)$, there must be as many loci as the larger value of Z and P.

---

*For a rational function, the total number of poles and zeros must equal if the poles and zeros at infinity are counted.

EXAMPLE 8-3. The number of separate root loci (of $1 + GH = 0$) is obtained by inspection for the following $G(s)H(s)$ functions:

$$G(s)H(s) = \frac{K(s + 1)}{s(s + 2)(s + 3)}$$

$P = 3$, $Z = 1$, hence $N = 3$.

$$G(s)H(s) = \frac{K}{s^2(s + 2)(s + 3)}$$

$P = 4$, $Z = 0$, hence $N = 4$.

(4) *Symmetry of the Root Loci*

The root loci are symmetrical with respect to the real axis. The proof to this rule is self-evident, since, for rational functions, the complex roots must appear in complex conjugate pairs.

(5) *Asymptotes of Root Loci*

For large values of s, the root loci are asymptotic to straight lines with angles given by

$$\frac{(2k + 1)\pi}{P - Z}$$

where $k = 0, 1, 2, \ldots$, up to $k = P - Z$. $\qquad$ (8-22)

Proof: The general form òf the open-loop transfer function can be written as

$$G(s)H(s) = \frac{K(s^m + a_1 s^{m-1} + \cdots + a_m)}{(s^{m+n} + b_1 s^{m+n-1} + \cdots + b_{m+n})} \qquad (8\text{-}23)$$

$$= \frac{K}{\left(\dfrac{s^{m+n} + b_1 s^{m+n-1} + \cdots + b_{m+n}}{s^m + a_1 s^{m-1} + \cdots + a_m}\right)} \qquad (8\text{-}24)$$

Hence, $G(s)H(s) = \dfrac{K}{s^n + (b_1 - a_1)s^{n-1} + \cdots + R(s)/P(s)} \qquad (8\text{-}25)$

where $R(s)$ is a polynomial of degree less than m, and

$$P(s) = s^m + a_1 s^{m-1} + \cdots + a_m \qquad (8\text{-}26)$$

The characteristic equation of the system is

$$s^n + (b_1 - a_1)s^{n-1} + \cdots + R(s)/P(s) = -K \qquad (8\text{-}27)$$

As s becomes very large, the term $R(s)/P(s)$ approaches zero, and only the first two terms of Eq. (8-27) are considered significant; Eq. (8-27) becomes

$$s^n + (b_1 - a_1)s^{n-1} = -K \qquad (8\text{-}28)$$

or $\qquad s\left(1 + \dfrac{b_1 - a_1}{s}\right)^{1/n} = (-K)^{1/n} \qquad (8\text{-}29)$

The factor $\left(1 + \dfrac{b_1 - a_1}{s}\right)^{1/n}$ in Eq. (8-29) is expanded into an infinite series, with the result

$$s\left(1 + \frac{b_1 - a_1}{ns} + \cdots\right) = (-K)^{1/n} \tag{8-30}$$

Again, if the terms higher than the second are neglected, we have

$$s + \frac{b_1 - a_1}{n} = (-K)^{1/n} \tag{8-31}$$

Now substitute $s = \sigma + j\omega$ into Eq. (8-31), which yields

$$\sigma + j\omega + \frac{b_1 - a_1}{n} = |K^{1/n}| \left[\cos\frac{(2k+1)\pi}{n} + j\sin\frac{(2k+1)\pi}{n}\right] \tag{8-32}$$

Equating the real and imaginary parts of Eq. (8-32), we have

$$\sigma + \frac{b_1 - a_1}{n} = |K^{1/n}|\cos\frac{(2k+1)\pi}{n} \tag{8-33}$$

and

$$\omega = |K^{1/n}|\sin\frac{(2k+1)\pi}{n} \tag{8-34}$$

Solving for $|K^{1/n}|$ from the last two equations, we have

$$|K^{1/n}| = \frac{\omega}{\sin\left(\dfrac{2k+1}{n}\right)\pi} = \frac{\sigma + \dfrac{b_1 - a_1}{n}}{\cos\left(\dfrac{2k+1}{n}\right)\pi} \tag{8-35}$$

and solving for ω, we have

$$\omega = \tan\left(\frac{2k+1}{n}\right)\pi\left[\left(\sigma + \frac{b_1 - a_1}{n}\right)\right] \tag{8-36}$$

Equation (8-36) represents a straight line in the s-plane; the equation is of the form

$$\omega = m(\sigma - \sigma_1) \tag{8-37}$$

where m is the slope and σ_1 is the interception on the σ-axis.

Thus,

$$m = \tan\frac{(2k+1)\pi}{n} = \tan\frac{(2k+1)\pi}{P - Z} \tag{8-38}$$

and

$$\sigma_1 = -\left(\frac{b_1 - a_1}{n}\right) \tag{8-39}$$

where $k = 0, 1, 2, \ldots$, up to $k = P - Z$

(6) *Intersection of the Asymptotes*

(a) The intersection of the $n = P - Z$ number of asymptotes lies on the real axis only.

(b) The intersection of the asymptotes on the real axis is given by

$$\sigma_1 = -\left(\frac{b_1 - a_1}{n}\right) = \frac{\Sigma \text{ Poles of } G(s)H(s) - \Sigma \text{ Zeros of } G(s)H(s)}{P - Z} \tag{8-40}$$

Proof: The proof of rule (a) is straightforward, since the root loci are symmetrical with respect to the real axis. The proof of Eq. (8-40) follows directly from Eq. (8-39), since, from the laws of algebra,

$$b_1 = -\Sigma \text{ Roots of the denominator of } G(s)H(s) = -\Sigma \text{ Poles of } G(s)H(s)$$

and

$$a_1 = -\Sigma \text{ Roots of the numerator of } G(s)H(s) = -\Sigma \text{ Zeros of } G(s)H(s)$$

EXAMPLE 8-4. Consider a feedback control system with the loop transfer function

$$G(s)H(s) = \frac{K(s + 1)}{s(s + 4)(s^2 + 2s + 2)} \tag{8-41}$$

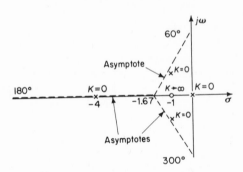

Fig. 8-5. Pole-zero configurations of

$$G(s)H(s) = \frac{K(s + 1)}{s(s + 4)(s^2 + 2s + 2)}$$

and the asymptotes of the root loci.

The pole-zero configuration of $G(s)H(s)$ is shown in Fig. 8-5. From the six rules described so far, the following information concerning the root loci is obtained:

(1) The root loci start at the poles of $G(s)H(s)$; $s = 0$, $s = -4$, $s = -1 + j1$, and $s = -1 - j1$.

(2) The root loci end at the zeros of $G(s)H(s)$; $s = -1$, ∞, ∞, and ∞ (three loci end at infinity in the s-plane).

(3) There are four separate loci.

(4) The root loci have conjugate symmetry.

(5) For large values of s, the loci are asymptotic to straight lines with angles given by Eq. (8-22).

For $$k = 0, \qquad \frac{(2k+1)\pi}{P-Z} = \frac{180°}{4-1} = 60° \qquad (8\text{-}42)$$

$$k = 1, \qquad \frac{(2k+1)\pi}{P-Z} = \frac{540°}{4-1} = 180° \qquad (8\text{-}43)$$

$$k = 2, \qquad \frac{(2k+1)\pi}{P-Z} = \frac{900°}{4-1} = 300° \qquad (8\text{-}44)$$

Thus the three separate loci that end at infinity must asymptotically approach infinity along 60 deg, 180 deg, and 300 deg respectively.

(6) The three asymptotic lines intersect at

$$\sigma_1 = \frac{\Sigma \text{ Poles of } G(s)H(s) - \Sigma \text{ Zeros of } G(s)H(s)}{P-Z}$$

$$= \frac{(0-4-1+j1-1-j1)-(-1)}{3} \qquad (8\text{-}45)$$

$$= -5/3.$$

In Fig. 8-6 are shown the asymptotes of the root loci for systems with different $G(s)H(s)$ functions.

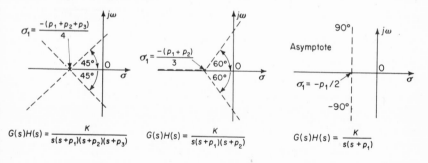

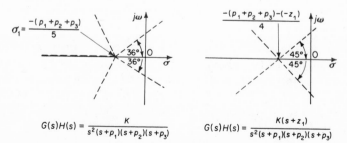

Fig. 8-6. Examples illustrating the asymptotes of root loci.

(7) Root Loci on the Real Axis

On a given section of the real axis, root loci may be found in the section only if the total number of poles and zeros of $G(s)H(s)$ to the right of the section is odd.

Proof: At any point on the real axis, the angles of the vectors from the complex poles or zeros of $G(s)H(s)$ cancel. The only contribution to the angles in Eq. (8-12) is from the poles and zeros of $G(s)H(s)$ to the right of the point on the real axis. The following example illustrates how the loci on the real axis are determined.

EXAMPLE 8-5. The root loci on the real axis corresponding to two hypothetical pole-zero configurations are shown in Fig. 8-7. It is apparent that the occurrence of the loci on the real axis is not affected by the complex open-loop poles and zeros.

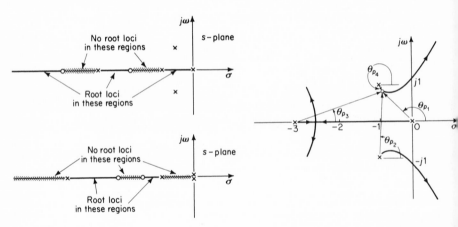

Fig. 8-7. Root loci on the real axis.   Fig. 8-8. Pole-zero configuration of
$$G(s)H(s) = \frac{K}{s(s+3)(s^2 + 2s + 2)}$$

(8) Angles of Departure (from poles) and the Angles of Arrival (at zeros) of the Root Loci

The angles of departure and arrival of the root loci can be determined readily from Eq. (8-12). For instance, in the pole-zero configuration of $G(s)H(s)$ given in Fig. 8-8, it is desired to determine the angle at which the root locus leaves the pole at $-1 + j1$. A point s_1, which is very close to the pole at $-1 + j1$, is selected on the root locus; since the point is assumed to be on the root locus, it must satisfy Eq. (8-12). Thus,

$$- (\theta_{p_1} + \theta_{p_2} + \theta_{p_3} + \theta_{p_4}) = (2k + 1)180° \qquad (8\text{-}46)$$

The θ's in the last equation are measured as shown in Fig. 8-8; we have

$$-135° - 90° - 26.6° - \theta_{p_4} = (2k + 1)180° \tag{8-47}$$

from which

$$\theta_{p_4} = -251.6° - (2k + 1)180°$$
$$= -71.6°$$

(9) *Intersection of the Root Loci with the Imaginary Axis*

The root loci shown in Fig. 8-8 apparently intersect the imaginary axis; the values of K and ω at the crossing point are normally determined by means of the Routh-Hurwitz criterion.*

EXAMPLE 8-6. Consider the pole-zero configuration given in Fig. 8-8; the corresponding loop transfer function is

$$G(s)H(s) = \frac{K}{s(s + 3)(s^2 + 2s + 2)} \tag{8-48}$$

The characteristic equation of the system is

$$s^4 + 5s^3 + 8s^2 + 6s + K = 0 \tag{8-49}$$

Applying the Routh criterion to the last equation, we have the following Routh tabulation:

$$
\begin{array}{lllll}
s^4 & 1 & 8 & K & \\
s^3 & 5 & 6 & & \\
s^2 & \frac{34}{5} & K & & \\
s^1 & \frac{\frac{204}{5} - 5K}{\frac{34}{5}} & 0 & \text{Coefficients of the auxiliary equation} \\
s^0 & K & 0 & &
\end{array}
$$

Thus, the critical value of K is determined by equating the first element of the s^1 row of the above Routh tabulation to zero; thus,

$$K = \frac{204}{25} = 8.15$$

To determine the frequency at the intersection on the imaginary axis, we write the auxiliary equation from the Routh tabulation:

$$\tfrac{34}{5} s^2 + K = 0 \tag{8-50}$$

Since $K = 8.15$, the last equation becomes

$$170s^2 + 204 = 0 \tag{8-51}$$

from which
$$s = \pm j1.095$$
and
$$\omega = \pm 1.095$$

---

*It will be shown later that, for more complex systems and for conditional stable systems, the critical values of K and ω are easily determined with the aid of the Bode plot.

(10) *Breakaway Point on the Real Axis*

The points in the s-plane where multiple roots (roots of an order higher than one) of the characteristic equation are found are called the *breakaway*

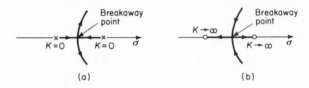

(a)   (b)

Fig. 8-9. Breakaway points on the real axis: (a) Breakaway between poles; (b) Breakaway between zeros.

points of the root locus diagram. Figure 8-9a illustrates a case in which two separate loci of a root locus diagram meet at a point on the real axis in the

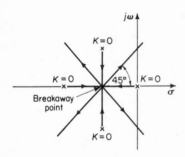

Fig. 8-10. Breakaway point of four separate loci on the real axis.

s-plane, and then break away from the real axis as the value of K is increased further. The point at which the two root loci meet and break away is a breakaway point; in this case, it represents a double root of the characteristic equation. Figure 8-9b shows a similar situation where two loci of complex roots break away at a point on the real axis in the s-plane, and then approach the two zeros. In general, a breakaway point may involve more than two root loci. For example, in Fig. 8-10, it is shown that four separate loci meet at a point on the real axis and then depart in different directions. Also, there may be more than one breakaway point for a root locus diagram, but, due to the conjugate symmetry of the root loci, the breakaway points must either lie on the real axis or occur in complex conjugate pairs.

In Fig. 8-9a and b, the root loci are shown to break away on the real axis at angles of 180 deg apart, while in Fig. 8-10 the four loci depart at angles of 90 deg apart. A general statement concerning the angles between the loci at a breakaway point can be made: *The root loci must approach and leave a breakaway point on the real axis at an angle of* 180 *deg/n apart, where n is the number of root loci approaching and leaving the point.* The proof of this statement is quite involved, and will not be given here; the interested reader can refer to the literature.*

---

*J. L. Bower, &. P. M. Schultheiss, *Introduction to the Design of Servomechanisms,* John Wiley & Sons, 1958, pp. 337–347.

The calculation of the breakaway point of the root loci is given as follows:

(a) *Breakaway Point Due to Poles and Zeros on the Real Axis.* If only the real poles and zeros of $G(s)H(s)$ are considered, and $-a$ is assumed to be the breakaway point on the real axis, the value of a is determined from the equation:

$$\sum_{\substack{\text{Zeros to the} \\ \text{left of } -a}} \frac{1}{z_i - a} - \sum_{\substack{\text{Poles to the} \\ \text{left of } -a}} \frac{1}{p_j - a}$$

$$= \sum_{\substack{\text{Zeros to the} \\ \text{right of } -a}} \frac{1}{a - z_i} - \sum_{\substack{\text{Poles to the} \\ \text{right of } -a}} \frac{1}{a - p_j} \qquad (8\text{-}52)$$

Proof: Consider the pole-zero configuration given in Fig. 8-11, in which the root loci have a breakaway point located between the two open-loop

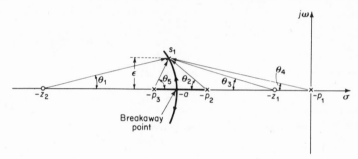

Fig. 8-11. Breakaway point on the real axis due to real poles and zeros of $G(s)H(s)$.

poles $-p_2$ and $-p_3$. Assume that a point s_1 is chosen on the locus which is very close to the breakaway point $-a$. Then, s_1 must satisfy Eq. (8-12); i.e.,

$$\sum_{i=1}^{2} \underline{/s_1 + z_i} - \sum_{j=1}^{3} \underline{/s_1 + p_j} = 180° \ (2k + 1) \qquad (8\text{-}53)$$

In terms of the angles designated in Fig. 8-11, we have

$$[\theta_1 + (\pi - \theta_3)] - [(\pi - \theta_2) + (\pi - \theta_4) + \theta_5] = \pi(2k + 1) \quad (8\text{-}54)$$

or $$\theta_1 - \theta_3 + \theta_2 + \theta_4 - \theta_5 = 0 \qquad (8\text{-}55)$$

Since the θ's are assumed to be very small angles, they can be replaced by their corresponding tangents, giving

$$\frac{\epsilon}{z_2 - a} - \frac{\epsilon}{a - z_1} + \frac{\epsilon}{a - p_2} + \frac{\epsilon}{a} - \frac{\epsilon}{p_3 - a} = 0 \qquad (8\text{-}56)$$

or $$\frac{1}{z_2 - a} - \frac{1}{p_3 - a} = \frac{1}{a - z_1} - \frac{1}{a - p_2} - \frac{1}{a - p_1} \quad (p_1 = 0) \quad (8\text{-}57)$$

It is apparent that Eq. (8-57) agrees with Eq. (8-52).

EXAMPLE 8-7. The root locus diagram sketched in Fig. 8-12 shows two breakaway points on the real axis: one between the poles 0 and -2, the other between the zeros at -4 and $-\infty$. Let the breakaway point

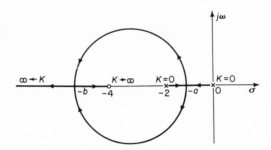

Fig. 8-12. Root loci for system with

$$G(s)H(s) = \frac{K(s+4)}{s(s+2)}$$

between the two poles be at $-a$, and that between the zeros at $-b$. Corresponding to the point $-a$, Eq. (8-52) gives

$$\frac{1}{4-a} - \frac{1}{2-a} = -\frac{1}{a} \tag{8-58}$$

Rearranging the terms in Eq. (8-58) yields

$$a^2 - 8a + 8 = 0 \tag{8-59}$$

which gives $a = 1.172$ or $a = 6.828$

Apparently, $a = 1.172$ is the significant answer to the location of the breakaway point, since we know beforehand that a should lie between the points 0 and -2 on the real axis. Similarly, for the point $-b$, we have

$$\frac{1}{b-4} - \frac{1}{b-2} - \frac{1}{b} = 0 \tag{8-60}$$

from which $b^2 - 8b + 8 = 0$

Since the last equation is essentially the same as Eq. (8-59), the second breakaway point of the root loci is at $-b = -6.828$.

(b) *Breakaway Point Due to Complex Poles and Zeros.* The contribution to the breakaway point on the real axis from the complex poles and zeros of $G(s)H(s)$ is determined from the equation:

$$\sum_{\substack{\text{Complex zeros to} \\ \text{the left of } -a}} \frac{2(\alpha_i - a)}{(\alpha_i - a)^2 + \beta_i^2} - \sum_{\substack{\text{Complex poles to} \\ \text{the left of } -a}} \frac{2(\alpha_j - a)}{(\alpha_j - a)^2 + \beta_j^2}$$

$$= \sum_{\substack{\text{Complex zeros to} \\ \text{the right of } -a}} \frac{2(a - \alpha_j)}{(a - \alpha_i)^2 + \beta_i^2} - \sum_{\substack{\text{Complex poles to} \\ \text{the right of } -a}} \frac{2(a - \alpha_j)}{(a - \alpha_j)^2 + \beta_j^2} \tag{8-61}$$

Proof: In Fig. 8-13 is shown a pair of complex conjugate poles (or zeros) located in the s-plane; the point at $-a$ is assumed to be a breakaway point of the root loci on the real axis. A point s_1 is chosen on the root locus at a very short distance from the breakaway point $-a$. From Fig. 8-13, the angles θ_1 and θ_2 are

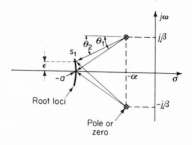

$$\theta_1 = \tan^{-1} \frac{\beta}{a - \alpha} \qquad (8\text{-}62)$$

$$\theta_2 = \tan^{-1} \frac{\beta - \epsilon}{a - \alpha} \qquad (8\text{-}63)$$

Fig. 8-13. Breakaway point on the real axis due to complex conjugate poles and zeros.

and $$\theta_1 - \theta_2 = \tan^{-1} \frac{\beta}{a - \alpha} - \tan^{-1} \frac{\beta - \epsilon}{a - \alpha} \qquad (8\text{-}64)$$

Since ϵ is very small, $\theta_1 - \theta_2$ is a very small angle which can be approximated by $\tan (\theta_1 - \theta_2)$. Thus,

$$\theta_1 - \theta_2 \approx \tan (\theta_1 - \theta_2) = \frac{\beta/(a - \alpha) - (\beta - \epsilon)/(a - \alpha)}{1 + \beta(\beta - \epsilon)/(a - \alpha)^2}$$

$$= \frac{\epsilon(a - \alpha)}{(a - \alpha)^2 + \beta^2} \qquad (a > \alpha) \quad (8\text{-}65)$$

The total angular contribution in moving from the breakaway point $- a$ to the point s_1 on the locus is

$$2(\theta_1 - \theta_2) \approx \pm \frac{2\epsilon(a - \alpha)}{(a - \alpha)^2 + \beta^2} \qquad (8\text{-}66)$$

where the plus sign is used for complex zeros and the negative sign is used for complex poles located to the right of the breakaway point $-a$.

Similarly, it can readily be shown that if a pair of complex poles or zeros is located to the left of the breakaway point $-a$, the total angular contribution in moving from the $-a$ point to s_1 on the locus is

$$2(\theta_1 - \theta_2) \approx \pm \frac{2\epsilon(\alpha - a)}{(\alpha - a)^2 + \beta^2} \qquad (8\text{-}67)$$

Usually both real and complex poles and zeros occur; hence, the breakaway point is calculated by combining Eq. (8-52) and Eq. (8-61).

EXAMPLE 8-8. Consider the root loci shown in Fig. 8-14; the breakaway point on the real axis is determined by writing

$$\frac{1}{a - 2} - \frac{2(a - 1)}{(a - 1)^2 + 1} = 0 \qquad (8\text{-}68)$$

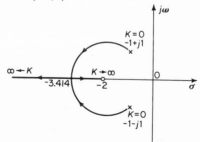

Fig. 8-14. Root loci for system in Example 8-8.

Rearranging the last equation yields

$$a^2 - 4a + 2 = 0 \qquad (8\text{-}69)$$

The real root of the last equation is found at $a = 3.414$.

(c) *Breakaway Point Not on the Real Axis.* Equations (8-52) and (8-61) can be extended to compute the breakaway points which are not located on the real axis. Consider the root loci given in Fig. 8-15; the breakaway point on the real axis is readily determined to be at -2. However, there are two conjugate breakaway points on the complex branches of the root loci. Due to the symmetry of the root loci, it is necessary to determine only one of the two points. If the axis on which the two breakaway points lie is interpreted

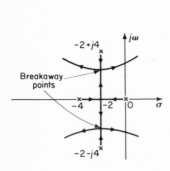

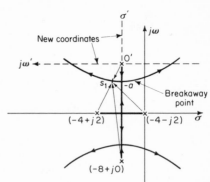

Fig. 8-15. Root loci with break-away points not located on the real axis.

Fig. 8-16. A new set of coordinates assigned to the root locus diagram given in Fig. 8-15 in order that the complex break-away points may be evaluated.

as the real axis, the two equations derived previously can be applied directly to this case. In Fig. 8-16 the pole at $-2 + j4$ is arbitrarily chosen as the new origin, and the new set of coordinates is as indicated.

If the location of the breakaway point in the upper half of the s-plane is represented as $-a$ (measured from the new origin $0'$), it is determined by the equation

$$-\frac{1}{8 - a} - \frac{2(4 - a)}{(4 - a)^2 + 2^2} = -\frac{1}{a} \qquad (8\text{-}70)$$

from which we have $a = 1.55$. Hence, the breakaway points of the complex root loci are located at $s = -2 \pm j2.45$.

(d) *Breakaway Points Computed by Analytical Method.* The breakaway points of a root locus diagram can also be computed by an analytical method. In this method, the characteristic equation is first written as

$$K = f(s) \qquad (8\text{-}71)$$

where $f(s)$ does not contain K, and the breakaway points (real and complex) of the root locus diagram are the roots of the equation obtained by taking the first derivative of K with respect to s and setting it equal to zero; i.e.,

$$\frac{dK}{ds} = 0 \qquad (8\text{-}72)$$

Proof: Assuming that the characteristic equation is a polynomial with constant coefficients, we can write it as

$$P(s) + KQ(s) = 0 \qquad (8\text{-}73)$$

where K is a positive constant, and $P(s)$ and $Q(s)$ are not functions of K. If we consider that K is varied by an increment ΔK, Eq. (8-73) reads

$$P(s) + (K + \Delta K)Q(s) = 0 \qquad (8\text{-}74)$$

Dividing both sides of Eq. (8-74) by $P(s) + KQ(s)$, we have

$$1 + \frac{\Delta K Q(s)}{P(s) + KQ(s)} = 0 \qquad (8\text{-}75)$$

which can be written

$$1 + \Delta K F(s) = 0 \qquad (8\text{-}76)$$

where

$$F(s) = \frac{Q(s)}{P(s) + KQ(s)} \qquad (8\text{-}77)$$

and the denominator of $F(s)$ is the original polynomial given by Eq. (8-73).

At points very close to a characteristic equation root s_i of multiplicity n (breakaway point of n loci), $F(s)$ can be approximated by

$$F(s) = \frac{A_i}{(s - s_i)^n} = \frac{A_i}{(\Delta s)^n} \qquad (8\text{-}78)$$

Substituting Eq. (8-78) into Eq. (8-76), we have

$$1 + \frac{\Delta K A_i}{(\Delta s)^n} = 0 \qquad (8\text{-}79)$$

from which we obtain

$$\frac{\Delta K}{\Delta s} = \frac{-(\Delta s)^{n-1}}{A_i} \qquad (8\text{-}80)$$

Taking the limit on both sides of the last equation as ΔK approaches zero, we have

$$\lim_{\Delta K \to 0}\left(\frac{\Delta K}{\Delta s}\right) = \frac{dK}{ds} = 0 \qquad (8\text{-}81)*$$

Therefore, at the breakaway points of the root loci, dK/ds is zero.

EXAMPLE 8-9. In this example, the breakaway points of the root locus diagrams shown in Figs. 8-12, 8-14, and 8-15 are calculated by use of Eq. (8-72). First, consider the locus diagram of Fig. 8-12; the characteristic equation of the system is

$$s(s + 2) + K(s + 4) = 0 \qquad (8\text{-}82)$$

which is written as

$$K = -\frac{s(s + 2)}{(s + 4)} \qquad (8\text{-}83)$$

Taking the derivative of K with respect to s and setting it equal to zero, we have

$$\frac{dK}{ds} = \frac{-(2s + 2)(s + 4) - s(s + 2)}{(s + 4)^2} = 0 \qquad (8\text{-}84)$$

and simplifying, we obtain

$$s^2 + 8s + 8 = 0 \qquad (8\text{-}85)$$

which is similar to Eq. (8-61) except for the sign of the second term. The two equations actually give the same results on the breakaway points, since b in Eq. (8-61) is considered a positive quantity, while in Eq. (8-85) the roots represent the actual location of the breakaway points. Hence, $s = -1.172$ and $s = -6.828$ are the two breakaway points of the root loci.

The breakaway point of the root locus diagram shown in Fig. 8-14 has been obtained previously at -3.414. The characteristic equation of the system is

$$(s^2 + 2s + 2) + K(s + 2) = 0 \qquad (8\text{-}86)$$

Then

$$\frac{dK}{ds} = \frac{s^2 + 4s + 2}{(s + 2)^2} = 0 \qquad (8\text{-}87)$$

---

*The quantity $ds/(dK/K)$ is defined as the "root sensitivity" of a polynomial with respect to incremental variation of the parameter K. In this case, it is proved that at the breakaway points of the root loci, the roots have infinite sensitivity. For further discussion on root sensitivity, see J. G. Truxal and I. M. Horowitz, "Sensitivity Considerations in Active Network Synthesis," *Proceedings of the Second Midwest Symposium on Circuit Theory*, East Lansing, Mich., December, 1956; and F. F. Kuo, "Pole-Zero Sensitivity in Network Functions," *IRE Transactions on Circuit Theory*, Vol. CT-5, December, 1958, pp. 372–373.

Again, the numerator of Eq. (8-87) is identical to Eq. (8-69), since a is considered a positive number in the latter equation.

The three breakaway points of the root locus plot of Fig. 8-15 can also be determined by the analytical method. We shall see that the three breakaway points are obtained in one operation from Eq. (8-72); it is no longer necessary to consider the real and complex breakaway points separately, as was done previously in the graphical analysis. The characteristic equation of the system is given by

$$s(s + 4)(s^2 + 4s + 20) + K = 0 \qquad (8\text{-}88)$$

Then $$\frac{dK}{ds} = -(4s^3 + 24s^2 + 72s + 80) = 0 \qquad (8\text{-}89)$$

simplifying, we have

$$s^3 + 6s^2 + 18s + 20 = 0 \qquad (8\text{-}90)$$

The roots of the last equation give the breakaway points of the root loci. Solving Eq. (8-90), we obtain the breakaway points at -2, $-2 + j2.45$, and $-2 - j2.45$.

(11) *Calculation of K on the Root Loci:*

Once the root loci of the characteristic equation are constructed, the value of K at any point s_1 on the loci can be determined from Eq. (8-11); that is,

$$K = \frac{1}{|\,G(s_1)H(s_1)\,|} \qquad (8\text{-}91)$$

Equation (8-91) can be evaluated either graphically or analytically. Usually, if the root locus plot is already constructed, the graphical method is more convenient. For example, in Fig. 8-17, the value of K at the point s_1 on the root locus is given by

$$K = \frac{1}{|\,G(s_1)H(s_1)\,|} = A \cdot B \cdot C \cdot D \qquad (8\text{-}92)$$

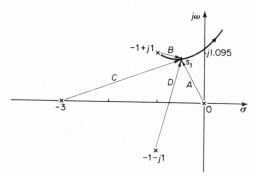

Fig. 8-17. Graphical method of evaluating the values of K on the root loci.

where A, B, C, and D are the lengths of the vectors drawn from the open-loop poles (poles of GH) to the point s_1.

The value of K at the point at which the locus intersects the imaginary axis is usually obtained by applying the Routh criterion to the characteristic equation.

EXAMPLE 8-10. In this example, the loop transfer function of a feedback control system is given as

$$G(s)H(s) = \frac{K(s + 3)}{s(s + 5)(s + 6)(s^2 + 2s + 2)} \tag{8-93}$$

The root loci of the system are to be constructed from the rules of construction.

(1) The starting points of the loci are at $s = 0$, -5, -6, $-1 + j1$, and $-1 - j1$, which are the poles of $G(s)H(s)$.

(2) One of the loci ends at $s = -3$, the others terminate at infinity.

(3) There are five separate root loci.

(4) The root loci must be symmetrical with respect to the real axis.

(5) The angles of the asymptotes of the loci at infinity are given by

$$\frac{(2k + 1)\pi}{P - Z} \tag{8-94}$$

where $k = 0$, 1, 2, 3, and $P - Z = 5 - 1 = 4$.

Hence, the four loci that terminate at infinity should approach infinity at angles of 45 deg, 135 deg, -135 deg, and -45 deg, respectively.

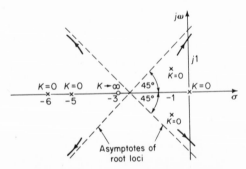

Fig. 8-18. The pole-zero configuration of

$$G(s)H(s) = \frac{K(s + 3)}{s(s + 5)(s + 6)(s^2 + 2s + 2)}$$

and the asymptotes of the root loci.

(6) The asymptotes of the loci intersect at the point

$$\sigma_1 = \frac{\Sigma \text{ Poles of } G(s)H(s) - \Sigma \text{ Zeros of } G(s)H(s)}{P - Z}$$

$$= \frac{(0 - 5 - 6 - 1 + j1 - 1 - j1) - (-3)}{4}$$

$$= -2.5$$

The results obtained from the last six steps are illustrated in Fig. 8-18.

(7) Root loci on the real axis: There are loci on the real axis between $s = 0$ and $s = -3$, $s = -5$, and $s = -6$; there are no root loci between $s = -3$ and $s = -5$, or between $s = -6$ and ∞.

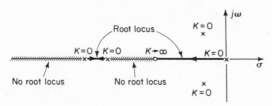

Fig. 8-19. Root loci on the real axis.

(8) Angles of departure: The angle of departure of the root locus leaving the pole at $-1 + j1$ is determined by solving for θ in the following equation:

$$26.6° - (135° + 90° + 14° + 11.4° + \theta) = (2k + 1)\pi \qquad (8\text{-}95)$$

$$\underset{\underline{/s+3}}{\uparrow} \quad \underset{\underline{/s}}{\uparrow} \quad \underset{\underline{/s+1+j1}}{\uparrow} \quad \underset{\underline{/s+5}}{\uparrow} \quad \underset{\underline{/s+6}}{\uparrow} \quad \underset{\underline{/s+1-j1}}{\uparrow}$$

from which we obtain $\theta = -43.8°$

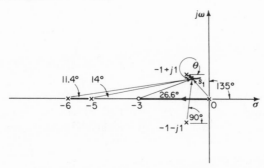

Fig. 8-20. Computation of the angle of departure of the root locus leaving the pole at $-1 + j1$.

(9) The interceptions of the root loci with the imaginary axis are determined by the Routh criterion. The characteristic equation of the system is

$$s^5 + 13s^4 + 54s^3 + 82s^2 + (60 + K)s + 3K = 0 \qquad (8\text{-}96)$$

The Routh tabulation:

s^5	1	54	$60 + K$
s^4	13	82	$3K$
s^3	47.7	$60 + 0.769K$	0
s^2	$65.6 - 0.212K$	$3K$	0
s^1	$\dfrac{3940 - 105K - 0.163K^2}{65.6 - 0.212K}$	0	0
s^0	$3K$	0	

For a stable system, the quantities of the first column in the Routh tabulation should be greater than zero. Hence,

(a) $65.6 - 0.212K > 0$ $\qquad$ or $\quad K < 309$ $\hfill$ (8-97)

(b) $3940 - 105K - 0.163K^2 > 0$ $\quad$ or $\quad K < 35$ (positive root) $\quad$ (8-98)

(c) $K > 0$

Hence, for a stable system $0 < K < 35$, and the value of K when the root loci cross the imaginary axis is 35. The frequency at the interception is determined from the auxiliary equation.

$$A(s) = (65.6 - 0.212K)s^2 + 3K = 0 \tag{8-99}$$

Substituting $K = 35$ into the last equation, we have

$$58.2s^2 + 75 = 0 \tag{8-100}$$

which yields $\qquad\qquad\qquad s = \pm j1.13$

(10) Breakaway point: There is a breakaway point between the two poles at -5 and -6, since the two loci which started from these poles meet and break toward infinity along the $+135$ deg and the -135 deg asymptotes, respectively.

The breakaway point $-a$ is readily determined from the equation

$$-\underbrace{\frac{1}{6-a}}_{\substack{(s+6) \\ \text{pole}}} = \underbrace{\frac{1}{a-3}}_{\substack{(s+3) \\ \text{zero}}} - \underbrace{\frac{1}{a-5}}_{\substack{(s+5) \\ \text{pole}}} - \underbrace{\frac{1}{a}}_{\substack{s \\ \text{pole}}} - \underbrace{\frac{2(a-1)}{(a-1)^2+1}}_{\substack{(s+1+j1)(s+1-j1) \\ \text{complex poles}}} \tag{8-101}$$

Since Eq. (8-101) is a high-order equation, it is easier to solve for a by trial and error. Since it is known that a should be somewhere between 5 and 6, as a first trial, we select $a = 5.5$. Equation (8-101) becomes

$$-\frac{1}{0.5} = \frac{1}{2.5} - \frac{1}{0.5} - \frac{1}{5.5} - \frac{9}{21.25} \qquad (8\text{-}102)$$

or $\qquad\qquad\qquad -2 \neq -2.205$

Next, we try $a = 5.6$.

$$-\frac{1}{0.4} = \frac{1}{2.6} - \frac{1}{0.6} - \frac{1}{5.6} - \frac{9.2}{22.2} \qquad (8\text{-}103)$$

or $\qquad\qquad\qquad -2.5 \neq -1.875$

It is clear now that a is between 5.5 and 5.6; the next step is to try $a = 5.52$.

$$-\frac{1}{0.48} = \frac{1}{2.52} - \frac{1}{0.52} - \frac{1}{5.52} - \frac{9.04}{21.4} \qquad (8\text{-}104)$$

or $\qquad\qquad\qquad -2.08 \approx -2.13$

Hence $\qquad\qquad\qquad a \approx 5.52$

From the information obtained in the last ten steps, the complete root locus diagram is sketched in Fig. 8-21.

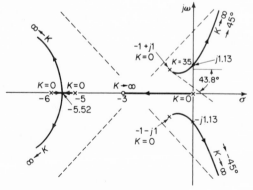

Fig. 8-21. Root loci of system with

$$G(s)H(s) = \frac{K(s+3)}{s(s+5)(s+6)(s^2+2s+2)}$$

For easy reference, the rules of contruction of root locus diagrams are tabulated in Table 8-1.

Table 8-1.

RULES OF CONSTRUCTION OF ROOT LOCUS DIAGRAMS

(1) *Starting points* $(K = 0)$	The root loci start at the poles of $G(s)H(s)$. (The poles include both those in the finite s-plane and those at infinity.)
(2) *Ending points* $(K \to \infty)$	The root loci end at the zeros of $G(s)H(s)$. (The zeros include both those in the finite s-plane and those at infinity.)
(3) *Number of separate root loci*	Number of loci $N = Z$ if $Z > P$ Number of loci $N = P$ if $Z < P$ where P = number of finite poles of $G(s)H(s)$ Z = number of finite zeros of $G(s)H(s)$
(4) *Symmetry of root loci*	The root locus plots of systems with rational transfer functions with constant coefficients are symmetrical with respect to the real axis in the s-plane.
(5) *Asymptotes of root loci as* $s \to \infty$	For large values of s, the root loci are asymptotic to straight lines with angles determined by $$\frac{(2k + 1)\pi}{P - Z}$$ where $k = 0, 1, 2, \ldots$, up to (but does not include) $k = P - Z$.
(6) *Intersection of the asymptotes*	(a) The intersection of the asymptotes lies only on the real axis in the s-plane. (b) The point of intersection of the asymptotes on the real axis is given by $$\sigma_1 = -\left(\frac{b_1 - a_1}{N}\right) = \frac{\Sigma \text{ Poles of } GH - \Sigma \text{ Zeros of } GH}{P - Z}$$
(7) *Root loci on the real axis*	On a given section of the real axis, root loci may be found in the section only if the total number of poles and zeros of $G(s)H(s)$ to the right of the section is odd.
(8) *Angles of departure and arrival*	The angle of departure of the root locus from a pole (or the angle of arrival at a zero) of $G(s)H(s)$ can be determined by assuming a point s_1 which is very close to the pole (or zero) and which is on the root locus associated with the pole (or zero), and applying the following equation: $$\underline{/G(s_1)H(s_1)} = \sum_{i=1}^{m} \underline{/s_1 + z_i} - \sum_{j=1}^{m+n} \underline{/s_1 + p_j} = (2k + 1)\pi$$
(9) *Intersection of the root loci with imaginary axis*	The values of ω and K at the crossing points on the imaginary axis of the s-plane may be obtained by use of Routh-Hurwitz criterion; for more complex cases, the Bode plot of $G(s)H(s)$ should be plotted.
(10) *Breakaway points*	All breakaway points on the root loci are determined by finding the roots of $$dK/ds = 0$$ where $K = f(s)$ is the characteristic equation.

Table 8.1. Continued

Alternate Method:

Breakaway points on the real axis:

The breakaway point $(-a)$ of the root loci on the real axis is determined from the following equation:

$$\sum_{\substack{\text{real zeros to} \\ \text{the left of } -a}} \left(\frac{1}{z_i - a}\right) - \sum_{\substack{\text{real poles to} \\ \text{the left of } -a}} \left(\frac{1}{p_j - a}\right)$$

$$+ \sum_{\substack{\text{complex} \\ \text{zeros to} \\ \text{the left} \\ \text{of } -a}} \frac{2(\alpha_k - a)}{(\alpha_k - a)^2 + \beta_k^2} - \sum_{\substack{\text{complex} \\ \text{poles to} \\ \text{the left} \\ \text{of } -a}} \frac{2(\alpha_m - a)}{(\alpha_m - a)^2 + \beta_m^2}$$

$$= \sum_{\substack{\text{real zeros to} \\ \text{the right of } -a}} \frac{1}{(a - z_i)} - \sum_{\substack{\text{real poles to} \\ \text{the right of } -a}} \left(\frac{1}{a - p_j}\right)$$

$$+ \sum_{\substack{\text{complex} \\ \text{zeros to} \\ \text{the right} \\ \text{of } -a}} \frac{2(a - \alpha_k)}{(a - \alpha_k)^2 + \beta_k^2} - \sum_{\substack{\text{complex} \\ \text{poles to} \\ \text{the right} \\ \text{of } -a}} \frac{2(a - \alpha_m)}{(a - \alpha_m)^2 + \beta_m^2}$$

Breakaway points not on the real axis:

The equation given above can also be used to locate breakaway points of the root loci that are not on the real axis of the s-plane. Simply draw a new set of coordinates with the real axis passing through the complex conjugate breakaway points, and then apply the equation given above.

(11) *Calculation of K on the root loci*	The value of K at any point s_1 on the root loci is determined graphically from the following equation: $$K = \frac{1}{|G(s_1)H(s_1)|} = \frac{\text{Product of all vector lengths drawn from the poles of } GH \text{ to } s_1}{\text{Product of all vector lengths drawn from the zeros of } GH \text{ to } s_1}$$

8.4 Some Other Important Properties of the Root Locus

The following properties of the root locus with respect to the open-loop pole-zero configurations are often helpful in the understanding of the root locus technique and its role in the design of feedback control systems.

(1) *The Effect of Adding Open-Loop Poles and Zeros*

(a) *Addition of Poles.* Let us start with the pole-zero configuration consisting of two real poles at $s = 0$ and $s = -a$; the root loci are easily constructed, as shown in Fig. 8-22a. An additional pole at $-b$ causes the loci to bend toward the right half of the s-plane, and the breakaway point is also moved to the right (Fig. 8-22b). For instance, if $a = 1$, and $b = 2$, the breakaway point is moved from -0.5 to -0.422. With the addition

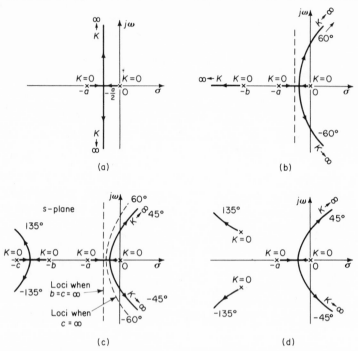

(a)

(b)

(c)

(d)

Fig. 8-22. Root locus diagrams showing the effects of adding open-loop poles.

of another pole at $-c$, the two conjugate loci near the imaginary axis are pushed farther to the right (Fig. 8-22c). Since the conjugate loci contain the roots which control the transient reponse of the closed-loop system (dominant roots), the system becomes less stable. Figure 8-22d illustrates that the addition of a pair of complex conjugate poles to the basic two-pole configuration will result in a similar effect.

Figure 8-23a shows the root locus diagram of a pair of complex poles; the system is always stable for all positive values of K. With the addition of a real pole at $-b$, the root loci are bent to the right and the system becomes unstable for large values of K (Fig. 8-23b). By adding another real pole at $-c$, it can be shown that the system will be unstable, even for a smaller value of K (Fig. 8-23c).

The root locus diagrams given in Fig. 8-22 and Fig. 8-23 simply verify the well-established fact that the addition of poles to $G(s)H(s)$ reduces the relative stability of the closed-loop system.

(b) *Addition of Zeros.* It was established from previous studies that the addition of zeros to the loop transfer function $G(s)H(s)$ produced more

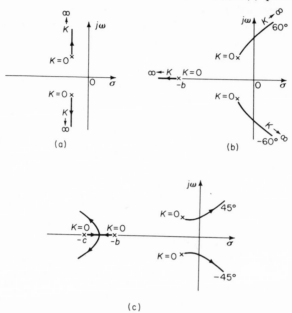

(a)   (b)

(c)

Fig. 8-23. Root locus diagrams showing the effects of adding poles.

phase lead, which had the tendency to stabilize the closed-loop system. For instance, if a real zero is added at $-b$ to the two-pole configuration shown in Fig. 8-24a, the resultant root loci bend toward the left and the

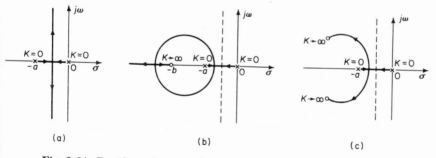

(a)   (b)   (c)

Fig. 8-24. Root locus diagrams showing the effects of adding more zeros.

stability margin is increased (Fig. 8-24b). Figure 8-24c illustrates that a similar effect will result if a pair of complex conjugate zeros is added to the left of the original loci.

(2) *The Effect of the Movements of Poles and Zeros*

Some of the uncertain factors in the sketching of the root loci can be

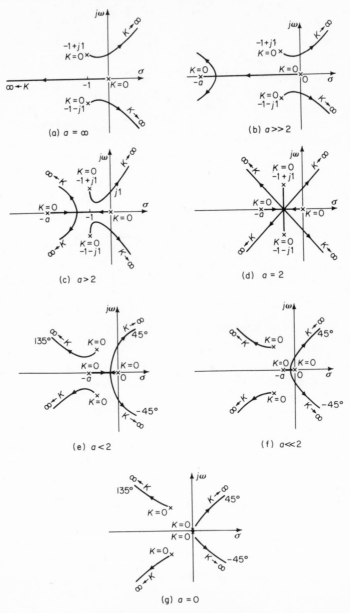

Fig. 8-25. Root locus diagrams for

$$G(s)H(s) = \frac{K}{s(s + a)(s^2 + 2s + 2)}$$

eliminated if the effects on the root locus configuration due to the movements of some poles and zeros of $G(s)H(s)$ are studied. For instance, given an open-loop transfer function of the form

$$G(s)H(s) = \frac{K}{s(s + a)(s^2 + 2s + 2)} \qquad (8\text{-}105)$$

If the value of a is chosen close to 2, the rules of root locus construction fail to indicate which pair of loci approaches the right and which pair approaches the left. This uncertainty usually puzzles the beginner. Figure

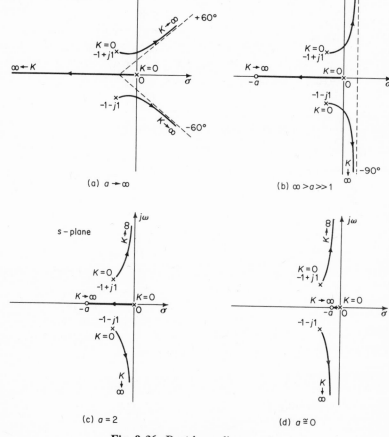

Fig. 8-26. Root locus diagrams for

$$G(s)H(s) = \frac{K(s + a)}{s(s^2 + 2s + 2)}$$

when a takes on various values.

8-25 shows the change in the root locus configurations as the pole at $-a$ is moved from $-\infty$ to the origin.

When the value of a is infinite, the two loci which start from the complex poles approach infinity asymptotic to $+60$ deg and -60 deg respectively. When a is a finite number of value greater than 2, the two loci starting from the complex poles approach infinity asymptotic to $+45$ deg and -45 deg respectively. The other two loci break away along the negative real axis and then approach infinity along $+135$ deg and -135 deg respectively. A symmetry in the loci with respect to the point $(-2, 0)$ is obtained when $a = 2$. The four loci converge on the point of symmetry at $s = -2$ and then follow the asymptotic lines, as shown in Fig. 8-25d. For values of a less than 2, the two loci originated at the two complex poles approach infinity along $+135$ deg and -135 deg respectively, and the other two loci are bent toward the right half of the s-plane.

When a zero is moved along the negative real axis toward the origin, as shown in Fig. 8-26, the effect is to pull the loci toward the left. By means of Eq. (8-40), it can be shown that when $a \geq 2$, the characteristic equation roots will always be located in the left half of the s-plane.

The study of the effects and construction of the root locus diagram when poles and zeros are varied in the s-plane can be carried out more effectively by means of the root contour diagrams, which is discussed in Sec. 8-6.

8.5 Root Locus of Conditionally Stable Systems

Consider a unity-feedback control system with the open-loop transfer function

$$G(s) = \frac{K(s + 5)(s + 40)}{s^3(s + 200)(s + 1000)} \tag{8-106}$$

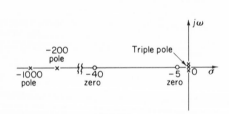

Fig. 8-27. Pole-zero configuration of
$$G(s) = \frac{K(s + 5)(s + 40)}{s^3(s + 200)(s + 1000)}$$

The pole-zero configuration of the last equation is shown in Fig. 8-27.

From the rules of construction, the following information is obtained concerning the root locus diagram:

(1) The root loci start at $s = 0$, 0, 0, -200, and -1000.

(2) The root loci end at $s = -5, -40, \infty, \infty, \infty$.

(3) There are five separate root loci.

(4) The root loci are symmetrical with respect to the real axis in the s-plane.

(5) The angles of the asymptotes of the loci are 60 deg, 180 deg, and −60 deg, respectively.

(6) The asymptotes of the loci intersect at $\sigma_1 = -385$.

(7) There is one root locus going from $s = 0$ to $s = -5$, one locus from $s = -200$ to $s = -40$, and one from $s = -1000$ to $-\infty$. Two loci of complex roots that start from the poles at the origin will eventually approach infinity along the 60 deg and the −60 deg asymptotes respectively.

(8) The two complex root loci leave the poles at the origin at angles of 60 deg and −60 deg respectively.

(9) The Routh test for critical K: The characteristic equation of the system can readily be shown as

$$s^5 + 1200s^4 + 2 \cdot 10^5 s^3 + Ks^2 + 45Ks + 200K = 0 \qquad (8\text{-}107)$$

The Routh tabulation:

s^5	1	$2 \cdot 10^5$	$45K$
s^4	1200	K	$200K$
s^3	$\dfrac{2.4 \cdot 10^8 - K}{1200}$	$\dfrac{53,800K}{1200}$	0
s^2	$\dfrac{1.7544 \cdot 10^8 K - K^2}{2.4 \cdot 10^8 - K}$	$200K$	
s^1	$\dfrac{-54,000K^3 + 9.534 \cdot 10^{12}K^2 - 11.52 \cdot 10^{18}K}{1200(2.4 \cdot 10^8 - K)}$	0	
s^0	$200K$		

For a stable system, the following conditions are required:

(a) $K < 2.4 \cdot 10^8$

$\qquad\qquad\qquad\qquad\qquad\qquad\qquad\qquad\qquad\qquad (8\text{-}108)$

(b) $K > 0, \quad K < 1.7544 \cdot 10^8$

$\qquad\qquad\qquad\qquad\qquad\qquad\qquad\qquad\qquad\qquad (8\text{-}109)$

(c) $-54,000K^2 + 9.534 \cdot 10^{12}K - 11.52 \cdot 10^{18} > 0, \qquad K > 0$ (8-110)

or $\qquad 54,000K^2 - 9.534 \cdot 10^{12}K + 11.52 \cdot 10^{18} < 0$ $\qquad\qquad$ (8-111)

The solution of the last equation is

$$(K - 1.1 \cdot 10^6)(K - 1.753 \cdot 10^8) < 0$$

from which $\qquad\qquad K > 1.1 \cdot 10^6$ $\qquad\qquad\qquad\qquad$ (8-112)

and $\qquad\qquad\qquad K < 1.753 \cdot 10^8$ $\qquad\qquad\qquad\qquad$ (8-113)

The relationships given in Eqs. (8-112) and (8-113) apparently are the more stringent restrictions on K. Since K must lie within a finite range, the system is a conditionally stable system; that is, the system is

$$\text{unstable for} \quad 0 < K < 1.1 \cdot 10^6 \qquad (8\text{-}114)$$

$$\text{stable for} \quad 1.1 \cdot 10^6 < K < 1.753 \cdot 10^8 \qquad (8\text{-}115)$$

$$\text{unstable for} \quad 1.753 \cdot 10^8 < K < \infty \qquad (8\text{-}116)$$

Substitution of the values of K given by Equations (8-112) and (8-113) into the auxiliary equation yields the critical frequencies

$$\omega = 16.6 \text{ rad/sec}$$

and

$$\omega = 212 \text{ rad/sec}$$

The root locus diagram of the system is now sketched, as shown in Fig. 8-28.

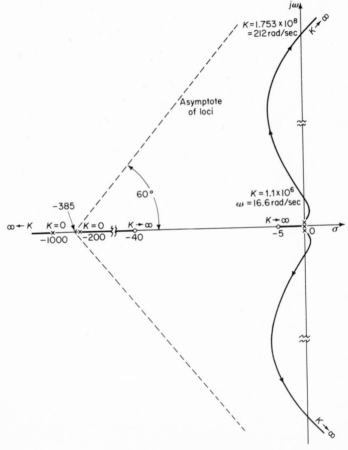

Fig. 8-28. The root loci of
$$G(s) = \frac{K(s + 5)(s + 40)}{s^3(s + 200)(s + 1000)}$$

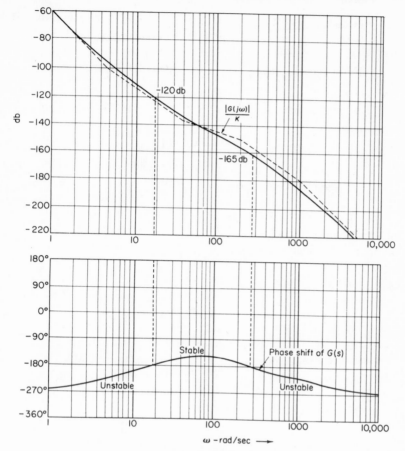

Fig. 8-29. Bode plot of

$$\frac{G(s)}{K} = \frac{5 \cdot 40}{200 \cdot 1000} \frac{[1 + (s/5)][1 + (s/40)]}{s^3[1 + (s/1000)][1 + (s/200)]}$$

The application of the Routh test to determine the critical values of K has presented two major difficulties:

(1) The process was very tedious, and error could very likely have occurred during any step of the numerical computation. There is no way of ascertaining the correctness of the results but to recheck the computation and make sure that there has been no mistake.

(2) In solving Eq. (8-111), it was necessary to use the difference between two large numbers which are almost equal to each other.

A better and easier method could have been used to determine the critical values of K and ω. In Fig. 8-29 the Bode plot of $G(s)/K$ is shown. The phase shift curve intersects the -180 deg axis at $\omega = 20$ rad/sec and $\omega = 220$ rad/sec, and the corresponding values of critical K are 10^6 and

$1.75 \cdot 10^8$, which check closely with the values obtained previously. It is easy to see that with the simple sketch of the Bode plot, not only the critical values of K and ω are obtained directly, but the root loci configuration in the vicinity of the imaginary axis in the s-plane is also indicated.

8.6 The Generalized Root Locus Diagrams (The Root Contours)

Although the root locus technique has been well developed and widely used for the analysis and design of linear feedback control systems, it was originally defined with only the open-loop gain K as the varying parameter; that is, the root locus diagram is defined as a plot of the poles of the closed-loop function $C(s)/R(s)$ as K varies from 0 to ∞. However, in most design problems, the effects on the closed-loop system poles must be studied when parameters other than K are varied; and frequently, there is more than one variable parameter. For instance, in the integral and derivative compensation by the conventional root locus technique, the proper locations of the compensating pole and zero can be determined only by plotting the root loci of all pole and zero combinations. In feedback control systems with multiple feedback loops, the forward path gain K does not appear only as a multiplying factor in the open-loop transfer function; therefore, the conventional root locus technique, again, cannot be applied directly.

In this section, a generalized root locus (root contour) technique will be introduced to construct the root loci when parameters other than K are varied in a feedback control system. The generalized root loci can be sketched simply by following the same rules of construction given in the previous sections. The term "root locus" has been used to represent the conventional plot of the closed-loop function poles when K is the variable parameter. On the other hand, the term "root contour" is used to represent the plot of the closed-loop poles when K is held constant but the open-loop function poles and zeros are varied (due to the variation of parameters other than K). It will be shown in Chapter 9 that, in the design of compensating networks for single-loop or multiple-loop systems, the generalized root loci (root contours) give a clear indication of the proper choice of the parameters of the compensating functions.

(1) *Root Contour Diagrams When a Pole of $G(s)H(s)$ Is Variable*

Let us assume first that a pole of $G(s)H(s)$ is variable but all other poles and zeros and the loop gain K are constant. The loop transfer function of the linear feedback control system shown in Fig. 8-30a can be written as follows:

$$G(s)H(s) = \frac{1}{1 + sT_a} Q(s) \tag{8-117}$$

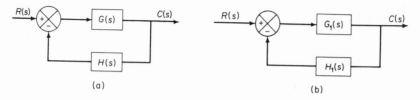

Fig. 8-30. (a) Single-loop feedback control system; (b) Equivalent system of system in (a).

where T_a is considered the variable parameter, and $Q(s)$ contains elements that are independent of T_a. The closed-loop transfer function of the system is

$$\frac{C(s)}{R(s)} = \frac{G(s)}{1 + G(s)H(s)} \tag{8-118}$$

and can be written as follows:

$$\frac{C(s)}{R(s)} = \frac{G(s)(1 + sT_a)}{1 + sT_a + Q(s)} \tag{8-119}$$

Dividing the numerator and denominator of Eq. (8-119) by $1 + Q(s)$, we have

$$\frac{C(s)}{R(s)} = \frac{\dfrac{G(s)}{1 + Q(s)}(1 + sT_a)}{1 + \dfrac{sT_a}{1 + Q(s)}} \tag{8-120}$$

If we let

$$G_1(s) = \frac{G(s)}{1 + Q(s)}(1 + sT_a) \tag{8-121}$$

and

$$H_1(s) = \frac{sT_a}{G(s)(1 + sT_a)} \tag{8-122}$$

Eq. (8-120) becomes

$$\frac{C(s)}{R(s)} = \frac{G_1(s)}{1 + G_1(s)H_1(s)} \tag{8-123}$$

Equation (8-123) implies that the system shown in Fig. 8-30b is equivalent to that of Fig. 8-30a. The loop gain of the equivalent system is

$$G_1(s)H_1(s) = \frac{sT_a}{1 + Q(s)} \tag{8-124}$$

The constant T_a in Eq. (8-124) appears only as a multiplying factor, which means that the conventional root locus technique can be applied here. The root contours must begin at $(T_a = 0)$, the poles of $G_1(s)H_1(s)$, and terminate at $(T_a \to \infty)$, the zeros of $G_1(s)H_1(s)$. Evidently, the rules of construction for the conventional root loci are still valid for the root contours.

The following examples illustrate how the root contour diagrams are constructed for feedback control systems.

Fig. 8-31. Pole-zero configuration of
$$G(s)H(s) = K/s(1 + sT_a)$$

Fig. 8-32. Pole-zero configuration of
$$G_1(s)H_1(s) = s^2 T_a/(s + K)$$

EXAMPLE 8-10. *Root contours of a second-order system.* Let

$$G(s)H(s) = \frac{K'}{s(1 + sT_a)} \qquad (8\text{-}125)$$

The problem is to investigate the effect on the poles of the closed-loop transfer function when the value of T_a is varied from 0 to ∞.

From Eq. (8-117), we have

$$Q(s) = K'/s \qquad (8\text{-}126)$$

The loop gain of the equivalent system is

$$G_1(s)H_1(s) = \frac{sT_a}{1 + Q(s)} = \frac{sT_a}{1 + K'/s} = \frac{s^2 T_a}{s + K'} \qquad (8\text{-}127)$$

The pole-zero configurations for $G(s)$ and $G_1(s)H_1(s)$ are shown in Fig. 8-31 and Fig. 8-32 respectively.

Based on the pole-zero configuration of Fig. 8-31, the conventional root locus diagrams are constructed in Fig. 8-33 for two different values of T_a.

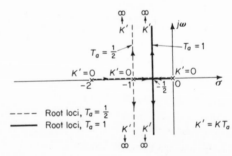

Fig. 8-33. Conventional root loci of $G(s)H(s) = K/s(1 + sT_a)$ with $T_a = \frac{1}{2}, 1$.

In Fig. 8-34 the root contours (when T_a is varied from 0 to ∞) for two different values of K' are sketched; these root contours begin at the poles of

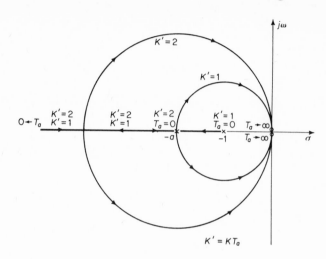

Fig. 8-34. Root contours of $G(s)H(s) = K/s\,(1 + sT_a)$ for $K' = 1$, 2. (T_a varies from 0 to ∞).

$G_1(s)H_1(s)$ and end at the zeros of $G_1(s)H_1(s)$. The arrowheads on the contours indicate the direction of increase in T_a.

EXAMPLE 8-11. Consider a unity-feedback control system with the open-loop transfer function

$$G(s) = Q(s) = \frac{K}{s(s + 1)} \tag{8-128}$$

A phase-lag network with transfer function

$$G_c(s) = \frac{1}{1 + sT_a} \tag{8-129}$$

is inserted in the forward path of the system as shown in Fig. 8-35.

The root contours will be constructed to show the effect on the closed-loop poles when the value of T_a is varied from 0 to ∞.

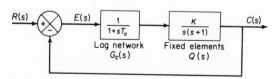

Fig. 8-35. Feedback control system with phase-lag network.

The loop gain of the equivalent system is obtained according to Eq. (8-124).

$$G_1(s)H_1(s) = \frac{sT_a}{1 + Q(s)} = \frac{s^2 T_a(s + 1)}{s^2 + s + K} \qquad (8\text{-}130)$$

It is clear that the poles of $G_1(s)H_1(s)$ are the roots of the characteristic equation of the system without the lag network. Thus the root contours begin at the poles of $G_1 H_1$, or the points on the root loci of the original system (corresponding to a given K). The root loci (K varies) of the original system are sketched in Fig. 8-36. The root contours (T_a varies)

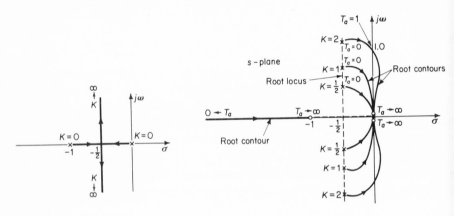

Fig. 8-36. Root loci of

$$G(s) = Q(s) = \frac{K}{s + (s + 1)}$$

Fig. 8-37. Root contours of

$$G(s)G_c(s) = \frac{K}{s(1 + sT_a)(1 + s)}$$

are sketched in Fig. 8-37. It is seen from the root contour plots that, for $K = 2$, the closed-loop system becomes unstable when T_a is greater than unity. For $1 > K \geq 0$, the system is stable for all positive values of T_a.

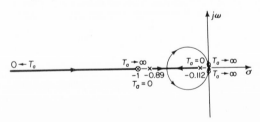

Fig. 8-38. Root contours of

$$G(s)G_c(s) = \frac{K}{s(1 + sT_a)(s + 1)}$$

for $K \leq \frac{1}{4}$.

The root contours also verify the well-established fact that a phase-lag network reduces the stability of a closed-loop system; for a given K, as the value of T_a increases, the closed-loop roots are moved toward the right half of the plane. For very small values of K ($K \leq \frac{1}{4}$), the roots of $1 + Q(s)$ are real; the root contours corresponding to this case are sketched in Fig. 8-38.

EXAMPLE 8-12. The root contour technique can theoretically be applied to systems of any order. In this example the open-loop transfer function of the system to be studied is

$$G(s) = \frac{K}{s(1 + sT_a)(s^2 + 2s + 2)} \qquad (8\text{-}131)$$

Thus

$$Q(s) = \frac{K}{s(s^2 + 2s + 2)} \qquad (8\text{-}132)$$

The loop gain of the equivalent system is

$$G_1(s)H_1(s) = \frac{sT_a}{1 + Q(s)} = \frac{s^2 T_a(s^2 + 2s + 2)}{s(s^2 + 2s + 2) + K} \qquad (8\text{-}133)$$

If the conventional root locus plots are used to show the effect of the variation of T_a, Fig. 8-39 illustrates the root loci (K varies) of $G(s)$ for

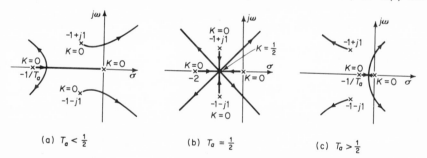

(a) $T_a < \frac{1}{2}$ (b) $T_a = \frac{1}{2}$ (c) $T_a > \frac{1}{2}$

Fig. 8-39. Root loci for

$$G(s) = \frac{K}{s(1 + sT_a)(s^2 + 2s + 2)}$$

three different values of T_a. It is apparent that a separate root locus plot must be constructed for each value of T_a.

The root contours start at the poles of G_1H_1, which are the points on the root loci for $Q(s)$; these loci are shown in Fig. 8-40. The root contours terminate at the zeros of G_1H_1 at $s = 0$, $s = 0$, and $s = -1 \pm j1$. The pole-zero configuration of $G_1(s)H_1(s)$ is shown in Fig. 8-41.

The root contours for $G(s)$ are sketched in Fig. 8-42 for three different

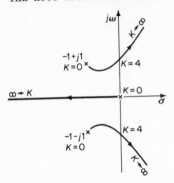 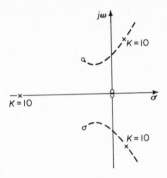

Fig. 8-40. Root loci for

$$Q(s) = \frac{K}{s(s^2 + 2s + 2)}$$

Fig. 8-41. Pole-zero configuration of

$$G_1(s)H_1(s) = \frac{s^2 T_a(s^2 + 2s + 2)}{s(s^2 + 2s + 2) + K}$$

values of K; when $K = \frac{1}{2}$ and $T_a = \frac{1}{2}$, the characteristic equation has a quadruple root at $s = -1$.

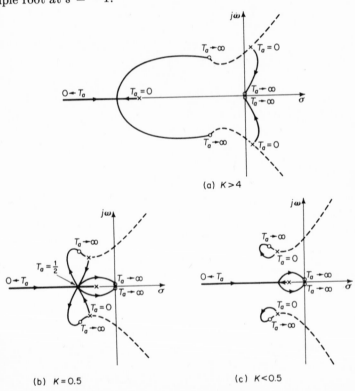

(a) $K > 4$

(b) $K = 0.5$

(c) $K < 0.5$

Fig. 8-42. Root contours for

$$G(s) = \frac{K}{s(1 + sT_a)(s^2 + 2s + 2)}$$

(2) *Root Contour Diagrams When a Zero of $G(s)H(s)$ Is Variable*

If a zero of $G(s)H(s)$ is variable, but all other poles and zeros and the loop gain K are considered constant, the loop transfer function of the system shown in Fig. 8-30a can be written as

$$G(s)H(s) = (1 + sT_1)P(s) \tag{8-134}$$

where T_1 is considered the variable parameter, and $P(s)$ contains elements that are independent of T_1. The closed-loop transfer function of the system is written as

$$\frac{C(s)}{R(s)} = \frac{G(s)}{1 + (1 + sT_1)P(s)} \tag{8-135}$$

Dividing the numerator and denominator of Eq. (8-135) by $1 + P(s)$, we have

$$\frac{C(s)}{R(s)} = \frac{\dfrac{G(s)}{1 + P(s)}}{1 + \dfrac{sT_1P(s)}{1 + P(s)}} \tag{8-136}$$

If we let

$$G_2(s) = \frac{G(s)}{1 + P(s)} \tag{8-137}$$

and

$$H_2(s) = sT_1 \frac{P(s)}{G(s)} \tag{8-138}$$

Eq. (8-136) becomes

$$\frac{C(s)}{R(s)} = \frac{G_2(s)}{1 + G_2(s)H_2(s)} \tag{8-139}$$

This implies that the feedback control system of Fig. 8-30 can be represented by an equivalent system with forward path transfer function $G_2(s)$ and feedback path transfer function $H_2(s)$. The loop transfer function of the equivalent system is

$$G_2(s)H_2(s) = \frac{T_1sP(s)}{1 + P(s)} \tag{8-140}$$

In Eq. (8-140), since the constant T_1 appears only as a multiplying factor, the root contours with T_1 as the varying parameter can be constructed, again, by means of the conventional root locus technique. The root contours in this case should start ($T_1 = 0$) at the poles and end ($T_1 \to \infty$) at the zeros of $G_2(s)H_2(s)$. The following example illustrates the construction of the root contours when a zero of the loop transfer function is variable.

EXAMPLE 8-13. Consider a unity-feedback control system with the fixed elements represented by

$$P(s) = \frac{K}{s(s + 1)(s + 2)} \tag{8-141}$$

The specification concerning the steady-state error requires that the velocity constant K_v be equal to 10 sec^{-1}. Thus, without any compensation network, $G(s) = P(s)$; the velocity constant of the system is

$$K_v = \lim_{s \to 0} sP(s) = K/2 = 10 \qquad (8\text{-}142)$$

from which $$K = 20$$

However, the result of the Routh test shows that the system is unstable for all values of $K > 6$. In order to realize a K_v of 10 and at the same time maintain a stable system, a derivative control with the transfer function $(1 + sT_1)$ is inserted in the forward path of the system. The open-loop transfer function of the compensated system becomes

$$G(s) = \frac{K(1 + sT_1)}{s(s + 1)(s + 2)} = (1 + sT_1)P(s) \qquad (8\text{-}143)$$

According to Eq. (8-140) the loop gain of the equivalent system is

$$G_2(s)H_2(s) = \frac{T_1 Ks}{s(s + 1)(s + 2) + K} \qquad (8\text{-}144)$$

The conventional root loci (K varies) of the original system are sketched in Fig. 8-43. The root contours (T_1 varies) must start ($T_1 = 0$) at the

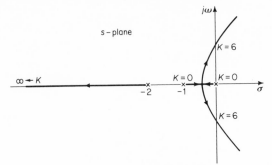

Fig. 8-43. Root loci for
$$P(s) = \frac{K}{s(s + 1)(s + 2)}$$

points on the conventional root loci corresponding to a given K. Figure 8-44 illustrates that, for $K = 20$, the three poles of $G_2(s)H_2(s)$ are at $0.425 + j2.235$, $0.425 - j2.235$, and -3.85; the finite zero is always at the origin. The asymptotes of the root contours are vertical straight lines which intersect at

$$\sigma_1 = \frac{\Sigma \text{ poles of } G_2H_2 - \Sigma \text{ zeros of } G_2H_2}{\text{No. of poles of } G_2H_2 - \text{No. of zeros of } G_2H_2}$$

$$= \frac{(-3.85 + 0.452 + 0.452) - 0}{3 - 1} = -1.5 \qquad (8\text{-}145)$$

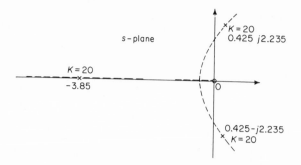

Fig. 8-44. Pole-zero configuration of

$$G_2(s)H_2(s) = \frac{T_1 K_s}{s(s+1)(s+2)+K} \quad K = 20$$

The root contours are sketched in Fig. 8-45 for three different values of K. The intersection of the asymptotes σ_1 is always at -1.5 regardless of the value of K. This is due to the fact that the sum of the poles of $G_2(s)H_2(s)$

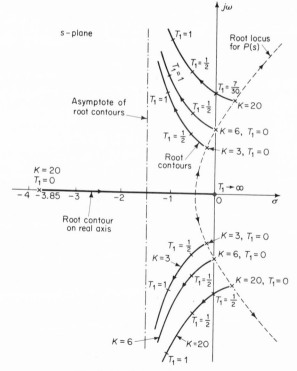

Fig. 8-45. Root contours of

$$G_2(s)H_2(s) = \frac{KT_1s}{s(s+1)(s+2)+K}$$

is always -3. The root contours shown in Fig. 8-45 verify the well-known fact that the derivative control improves the relative stability of the closed-loop system by moving the characteristic equation roots toward the left in the s-plane. The root contours also indicate an important characteristic of the lead compensation; that is, in certain cases, the contribution to the increase in band width by increasing the value of T_1 far exceeds the improvement made on the relative stability of the system. For $K = 20$ ($K_v = 10$), the system is stabilized for all values of $T_1 > 7/30$; however, the highest damping ratio that the compensated system can have by increasing the value of T_1 is about 30 per cent.

(3) *Root Contours When an Open-loop Zero and Pole Are Both Varying Parameters*

In practice, the transfer function of a simple phase-lag or a phase-lead network used for servo compensation is of the form

$$G_c(s) = \frac{1 + sT_1}{1 + sT_a} \tag{8-146}$$

The design of the compensation network essentially involves the determination of the optimum values of T_1 and T_a to satisfy the system performance specifications. The loop transfer function of the system can now be written as

$$G(s)H(s) = \left(\frac{1 + sT_1}{1 + sT_a}\right) U(s) \tag{8-147}$$

where T_1 and T_a are variable parameters, and $U(s)$ contains elements that are independent of T_1 and T_a.

The procedure of the construction of the root contours when both T_1 and T_a are variable may be described as follows:

(1) The root loci of $1 + U(s)$ are plotted from the pole-zero configuration of $U(s)$; this gives the root loci of the original system without compensation ($T_1 = T_a = 0$).

(2) Insert the function $1/(1 + sT_a)$ in the forward path of the system, setting $T_1 = 0$. The purpose of this step is to sketch the root contours when one of the variable parameters is varied while the other is set to zero. This is identical to the situation described in case (1), in which only an open-loop pole is the variable parameter. Thus the root contours are the roots of

$$[1 + G(s)H(s)]_{T_1=0} = 1 + U(s) + sT_a = 1 + Q(s) + sT_a = 0 \tag{8-148}$$

and can be constructed from the pole-zero configuration of

$$G_1(s)H_1(s) = \frac{sT_a}{1 + U(s)} \tag{8-149}$$

(3) The last step is to consider the factor $(1 + sT_1)$ and plot the root contours when T_1 is varied from 0 to ∞. This is similar to case (2) in which an open-loop zero is the varying parameter. Specifically, we are to construct the root contours of the equation

$$1 + G(s)H(s) = 1 + sT_a + U(s) + sT_1U(s) = 0 \qquad (8\text{-}150)$$

The last equation can also be written as

$$1 + \frac{T_1sU(s)}{1 + sT_a + U(s)} = 1 + G_2(s)H_2(s) = 0 \qquad (8\text{-}151)$$

where
$$G_2(s)H_2(s) = \frac{T_1sU(s)}{1 + sT_a + U(s)} \qquad (8\text{-}152)$$

Thus the root contours when T_1 varies must start at the poles of G_2H_2, which are described by the root contours when T_a is varying but $T_1 = 0$, and must end at the zeros of G_2H_2.

As an example, consider the open-loop transfer function

$$G(s) = \frac{K(1 + sT_1)}{s(1 + sT_a)(s + 1)} \qquad (8\text{-}153)$$

in which T_1, T_a, and K are all considered to be variable parameters. To show the effect of the variation of these parameters on the roots of the characteristic equation, the contours are constructed as follows:

(1) Equation (8-153) is written as

$$G(s) = \left(\frac{1 + sT_1}{1 + sT_a}\right) U(s) \qquad (8\text{-}154)$$

where
$$U(s) = \frac{K}{s(s + 1)} \qquad (8\text{-}155)$$

The root loci for $1 + U(s)$ are apparently the same as that shown in Fig. 8-36.

(2) Let $T_1 = 0$, but T_a can vary from 0 to ∞:

$$G_1(s)H_1(s) = \frac{sT_s}{1 + U(s)} = \frac{s^2T_a(s + 1)}{s^2 + s + K} \qquad (8\text{-}156)$$

The root contours of $1 + G_1H_1$ when T_a varies were given in Fig. 8-37 and Fig. 8-38.

(3) When T_1 is varied from 0 to ∞,

$$G_2(s)H_2(s) = \frac{T_1sU(s)}{1 + sT_a + U(s)} = \frac{T_1sK}{s(1 + sT_a)(s + 1) + K} \qquad (8\text{-}157)$$

The root contours of $1 + G_2H_2$ must start at the poles of G_2H_2, which are the points on the root contours shown in Fig. 8-37 or Fig. 8-38, and must end at the zero of $G_2H_2(s = 0)$.

For very small values of K and T_a, the pole-zero configuration of G_2H_2 is shown in Fig. 8-46a and the corresponding root contours are sketched in Fig. 8-46b.

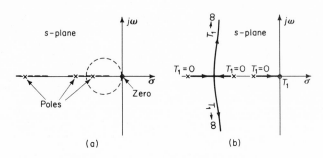

Fig. 8-46. (a) Pole-zero configuration of

$$G_2H_2 = \frac{T_1 sK}{s(1 + sT_a)(s + 1) + K}$$

($K < \frac{1}{4}$ and small T_a); (b) Root contours for

$$G_2H_2 = \frac{T_1 sK}{s(1 + sT_a)(s + 1) + K}$$

($K < \frac{1}{4}$ and small T_a).

For $K \leq \frac{1}{4}$ but large values of T_a, the pole-zero configuration of G_2H_2 is shown in Fig. 8-47a, and the corresponding root contours of $1 + G_2H_2$ are sketched in Fig. 8-47b.

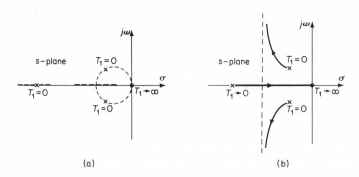

Fig. 8-47. (a) Pole-zero configuration of

$$G_2H_2 = \frac{T_1 sK}{s(1 + sT_a)(s + 1) + K}$$

($K \leq \frac{1}{4}$ and large T_a); (b) Root contours for

$$G_2H_2 = \frac{T_1 sK}{s(1 + sT_a)(s + 1) + K}$$

($K \leq \frac{1}{4}$ and large T_a).

For large values of K $(K > \frac{1}{4})$, the pole-zero configuration of G_2H_2 is of the form shown in Fig. 8-48a; the corresponding root contours are sketched in Fig. 8-48b.

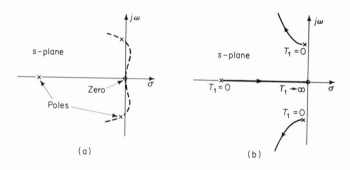

Fig. 8-48. (a) Pole-zero configuration of

$$G_2H_2 = \frac{T_1sK}{s(1 + sT_a)(s + 1) + K} \quad (K \geq \tfrac{1}{4});$$

(b) Root contours for

$$G_2H_2 = \frac{T_1sK}{s(1 + sT_a)(s + 1) + K} \quad (K \geq \tfrac{1}{4}).$$

(4) *Root Locus of Multiple Loop Systems*

In this section, the generalized root locus technique is used to construct the root loci of multiple loop feedback control systems. The chief difficulties encountered in applying the conventional root locus technique to multiple loop systems are as follows:

(1) The open-loop transfer function (or loop gain) is usually of the form

$$G(s) = \frac{C(s)}{E(s)} = \frac{Kp(s)}{q(s) + Ku(s)} \tag{8-158}$$

where $p(s)$, $q(s)$, and $u(s)$ are polynomials of s. The forward gain K appears in both the numerator and denominator of Eq. (8-158); consequently, the conventional root locus technique cannot be applied directly.

(2) There may be several variable parameters other than K whose optimum values are to be determined in a design problem.

In case (1), the characteristic equation can be written as

$$q(s) + Ku(s) + Kp(s) = 0 \tag{8-159}$$

The last equation can also be put into the following form:

$$1 + \frac{K[p(s) + u(s)]}{q(s)} = 0 \tag{8-160}$$

Since in the last equation the parameter K appears only as a multiplying factor, the root locus plot can be constructed directly from the pole-zero configuration of

$$\frac{K[p(s) + u(s)]}{q(s)} \tag{8-161}$$

In case (2), the root contours must be constructed for varying parameters other than K. The general procedure in constructing the root contours is similar to that for when an open loop zero and pole are both varying parameters described in part (3). Specifically, the root loci are first plotted for the system without any compensation network and the system is a single-loop system. The next step is to construct the root contours by adding the compensating networks one at a time.

EXAMPLE 8-14. Consider the multiple loop control system shown in Fig. 8-49. The open-loop transfer function of the system is given as

$$G(s) = \frac{C(s)}{E(s)} = \frac{\dfrac{K_1}{s(1 + sT_1)}}{1 + \dfrac{K_1 K_2 s}{s(1 + sT_1)}} = \frac{K_1}{s(1 + sT_1) + K_1 K_2 s} \tag{8-162}$$

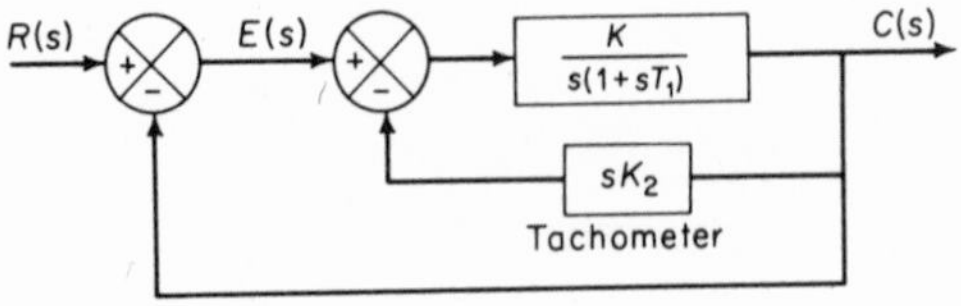

Fig. 8-49. Multiple loop control system for Example 8-15.

To illustrate case (1), we assume that the tachometer constant K_2 is held constant and only the gain K_1 can be altered. Since K_1 appears in the numerator and in the denominator of $G(s)$, we must first define an equivalent system which has a loop gain with K_1 appearing only as a multiplying factor. We write the characteristic equation of the system

$$s(1 + sT_1) + K_1 K_2 s + K_1 = 0 \tag{8-163}$$

or

$$1 + \frac{K_1(1 + K_2 s)}{s(1 + sT_1)} = 0 \tag{8-164}$$

Since K_1 appears only as a multiplying factor in the last equation, the root locus plot can now be constructed from the pole-zero configuration of

$$\frac{K_1(1 + K_2 s)}{s(1 + sT_1)} \tag{8-165}$$

where T_1 is assumed to be a fixed constant.
The root loci are sketched in Fig. 8-50a.

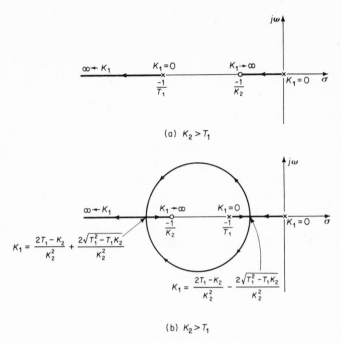

Fig. 8-50. Root loci for

$$G(s) = \frac{K_1}{s(1 + sT_1) + K_1 K_2 s}$$

For $K_2 \geq T_1$, the characteristic equation has two negative real roots for all positive values of K_1. For $K_2 < T_1$, the roots are complex for

$$\left(\frac{2T_1 - K_2}{K_2^2} - \frac{2\sqrt{T_1^2 - T_1 K_2}}{K_2^2} \right) < K_1 < \left(\frac{2T_1 - K_2}{K_2^2} + \frac{2\sqrt{T_1^2 - T_1 K_2}}{K_2^2} \right)$$
(8-166)

The root loci shown in Fig. 8-50 verify the well-known fact that the tachometer feedback improves the stability of a feedback control system.

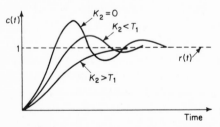

Fig. 8-51. Transient response of a tachometric feedback system.

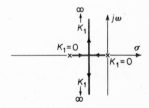

Fig. 8-52. Root loci of $G(s) = K_1/s(1 + sT_1)$ (feedback path with tachometer opened).

When K_2 is large (Fig. 8-50a), the system is overdamped ($\delta > 1$). Figure 8-51 illustrates the effect of the tachometric feedback on the transient response of the system.

To illustrate the problem described in case (2), we assume that K_1 and K_2 are both variable parameters. This is a more practical problem, since normally a tachometer with transfer function, for example, K_2s, is selected to yield satisfactory system performance. The first step in the construction of the root contours is to consider the control system when the tachometer is not in effect; the characteristic equation of the uncompensated system is

$$s(1 + sT_1) + K_1 = 0 \qquad (8\text{-}167)$$

In other words, the last equation represents the characteristic equation of the system with the tachometer feedback path opened ($K_2 = 0$). The root loci of Eq. (8-167) are sketched in Fig. 8-52. The next step is to close the tachometer feedback path; the characteristic equation given by Eq. (8-163) is in effect. The root contours, with K_2 as a varying parameter, can be obtained by writing Eq. (8-163) as

$$1 + \frac{K_2 K_1 s}{s(1 + sT_1) + K_1} = 0 \qquad (8\text{-}168)$$

in which K_2 appears only as a multiplying factor. It is recognized that the denominator of the second term in the last equation is actually the characteristic equation of the system when $K_2 = 0$; thus, the root contours when K_2 varies must start at the points on the root loci given in Fig. 8-52. The

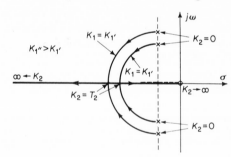

Fig. 8-53. Root contours of system with tachometer-feedback.

root contours of the system are sketched in Fig. 8-53. The concept of root contours can be extended to systems with more than two variable parameters. A more elaborate example will be given in Chapter 9.

Problems

8-1. Sketch the root locus diagram for each of the following feedback control systems. In each case determine everything about the locus of roots short of actual plotting. Indicate on each locus the starting point, the ending point, and the direction of increasing value of K. The poles and zeros of $G(s)H(s)$ of the systems are given as follows:

(a) Poles at 0, -2, -3; zeros at -5.
(b) Poles at 0, 0, -2, -3; zero at -5.
(c) Poles at $-2 + j2$ and $-2 - j2$; zero at -3.
(d) Poles at 0, $-10 + j10$, and $-10 - j10$; zero at -20.
(e) Poles at 0, -20, $-10 + j10$, and $-10 - j10$; no finite zeros.
(f) Poles at -20, $-10 + j10$, and $-10 - j10$; zero at -30.
(g) Poles at 0, 0, -12, and -12; zeros at -4, and -8.

8-2. The open-loop transfer function of a unity-feedback control system is given by

$$G(s) = \frac{K(s + 3)}{s(s^2 + 2s + 2)(s + 5)(s + 6)}$$

(a) Sketch the root locus diagram as a function of K.
(b) Determine the value of K which makes the relative damping ratio of the closed-loop complex poles equal to 0.4.

8-3. A unity-feedback control system has an open-loop transfer function

$$G(s) = \frac{K}{s(1 + 0.02s)(1 + 0.01s)}$$

(a) Sketch the root locus diagram of the system.
(b) Determine the marginal value of gain K which will cause instabilty.
(c) Determine the value of K when the system is critically damped.

8-4. A unity-feedback control system has an open-loop transfer function

$$G(s) = \frac{K(1 + 0.2s)(1 + 0.025s)}{s^3(1 + 0.001s)(1 + 0.005s)}$$

Sketch the root locus diagram for the system. Indicate the crossing points of the loci on the $j\omega$ axis, and the corresponding values of K and ω at these points.

8-5. The transfer functions of a feedback control system are given as

$$G(s) = \frac{K}{s^2(s + 2)(s + 5)} \quad \text{and} \quad H(s) = 1$$

(a) Sketch the root locus diagram and determine the stability of the system as a function of K.
(b) The transfer function of the feedback loop element is now changed to $H(s) = (1 + 2s)$. Determine the stability of the modified system as a function of K. Investigate the effect on the root locus diagram due to this change in $H(s)$.

8-6. The characteristic equation of a feedback control system is given by

$$s^3 + 3s^2 + (K + 2)s + 10K = 0$$

Sketch the root locus of this equation as a function of K.

8-7. For the following loop transfer function, sketch the root locus diagram as a function of T (T varies from 0 to ∞). Determine the value of T so that the damping ratio of the complex roots of the characteristic equation is 0.4.

$$G(s)H(s) = \frac{1000(1 + sT)}{s(1 + 0.1s)(1 + 0.001s)}$$

8-8. For the following loop transfer function, sketch the root locus diagram as a function of T. Determine the value of T so that the damping ratio of the complex roots of the characteristic equation is 0.4.

$$G(s)H(s) = \frac{30}{s(1 + 0.1s)(1 + 0.2s)(1 + sT)}$$

8-9. For the bridged-T network of Fig. 8P-9,
(a) Sketch the root locus diagrams of the zeros and poles of E_2/E_1 as a function of C_1 (C_1 varies from 0 to ∞).
(b) Sketch the root locus diagrams of the zeros and poles of E_2/E_1 as a function of C_2.

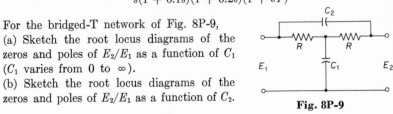

Fig. 8P-9

8-10. The characteristic equation of a closed-loop system with positive feedback may be written as $1 - G(s) = 0$, where $G(s)$ is of the form given by Eq. (8-10). The root locus plot in this case is called the "inverse root locus diagram," since it can be interpreted that the system has negative feedback but the root locus plot is constructed with K varied from 0 to $-\infty$. Determine which of the rules of root locus construction given in this chapter are still valid, which are to be modified, and how they should be modified for the inverse root locus plot.

8-11. The open-loop transfer function of a control system with positive feedback is given by

$$G(s) = \frac{K}{s(s^2 + 4s + 4)}$$

Sketch the root locus diagram of the system as a function of K.

8-12. Sketch the inverse root locus diagrams for the following systems:

(a) $G(s) = \dfrac{K}{s(s + 4)(s^2 + 2s + 4)}$

(b) $G(s) = \dfrac{K(s + 3)}{s^2(s + 4)(s^2 + 2s + 2)}$

8-13. The inverse root locus diagram described in Problem 8-10 may be used for the synthesis of servo systems. If it is desired that the closed-loop system has a transfer function

$$\frac{C(s)}{R(s)} = \frac{1}{(1 + 0.03s)(1 + 0.2s + 0.02s^2)}$$

determine the open-loop transfer function $G(s)$, assuming that unity-feedback is used.

8-14. For the system given in Fig. 8P-14, the transfer function $G_2(s)$ is given by

$$G_2(s) = \frac{K}{s(s + 2)(s^2 + 10s + 40)}$$

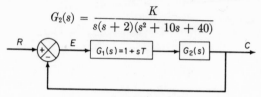

Fig. 8P-14.

The velocity error constant of the system is 5 sec^{-1}, and the damping ratio of the dominant poles is 0.4. Determine the value of T of the tandem compensation network $G_1(s)$.

9

Compensation of Feedback Control Systems

9.1 Why Is Compensation Necessary?

It is generally impossible to satisfy simultaneously the performance specifications given for the steady-state response and the transient response (stability) of a feedback control system with only the basic fixed elements, such as amplifiers, synchros, and servomotors. Usually, in order to reduce the steady-state error, the forward gain K is increased, but the transient response becomes too oscillatory or even unstable. Thus, although the adjustment of gain seems to be the most direct and the simplest way of changing the system performance, it is seldom satisfactory, except, perhaps, in very trivial cases. In the following example we shall show that a change in the gain K actually affects the system performance in a contradictory manner. Consider the open-loop transfer function $G(s)$ of a unity-feedback control system

$$G(s) = \frac{K}{s(s + 1)(s + 2)} \tag{9-1}$$

Let us assume that the steady-state error requirement specifies that the velocity constant K_v should be greater than 10 sec^{-1}. From the definition of K_v,

$$K_v = \lim_{s \to 0} sG(s) = \lim_{s \to 0} \frac{K}{(s + 1)(s + 2)} = \frac{K}{2} > 10 \tag{9-2}$$

hence, the gain constant K must be greater than 20. However, the Routh test shows that the system is unstable for all values of K greater than 6. This means that if the system is to perform according to the given specifications, some kind of corrective (compensation) network or device must be inserted into the system. Furthermore, some systems are inherently unstable, and compensation should be applied to stabilize them.

The design of the compensation of feedback control systems is usually carried out either in the frequency or the time domain. The specifications in these two domains were given previously. In the frequency domain, for instance, the specifications generally include the phase margin, the gain margin, the resonance peak, and the band width. In the time domain specification, there are the damping ratio, the rise time, the delay time, the settling time, the peak overshoot, and the steady-state error. The frequency domain design is usually conducted by means of the Bode plot, the Nyquist plot, or the Nichols chart. In general, the Bode plot is preferred to the Nyquist plot simply because the effect of the compensation network is readily evaluated by adding the magnitude and phase shift curves of the compensation network, respectively, to the magnitude and phase shift curves of the original system. The magnitude versus phase shift plot and the Nichols chart will also be used in this chapter to evaluate the resonant peak and the band width. The root contour technique developed in the last

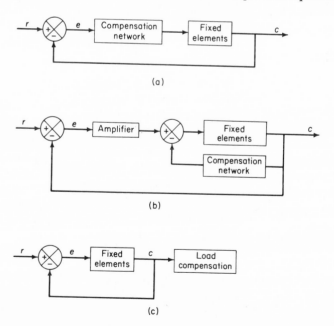

Fig. 9-1. Types of servo compensation. (a) Series compensation; (b) Feedback compensation; (c) Load compensation.

chapter is used for the s-plane design of the compensation network. It will be shown that the root contour method is particularly useful for the design of systems with multiple feedback loops.

9.2 Types of Compensation

The compensation of a feedback control system can be accomplished by the following schemes:

(1) Series compensation (tandem compensation)
(2) Feedback compensation
(3) Load compensation

The basic configurations of these three types of compensation are illustrated in Fig. 9-1.

Before beginning the discussion on the techniques of compensation, it is important to survey the nature of the feedback control systems that are to be compensated. It was pointed out in Chapter 4 that many servo systems are of the a-c or carrier type, in which the error or the actuating signal is

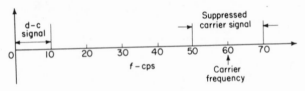

Fig. 9-2. Frequency spectrum of d-c signal and suppressed carrier signal in servo systems.

transmitted as the envelope of a modulated carrier signal. For a d-c system, the signals in the system are unmodulated. However, not all systems are purely d-c or a-c; some systems may employ both d-c and a-c components, and the signals are converted from d-c to a-c and vice versa by means of modulators and demodulators. Therefore, compensation networks should

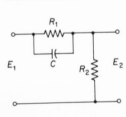

Fig. 9-3. Phase lead network as d-c compensating network.

be designed to operate on either a d-c signal which is usually in the frequency range of 0 to 15 cycles per second, or a suppressed carrier signal whose carrier frequency is usually 60 cps, 400 cps, or higher. The frequency spectra of a typical d-c signal and a suppressed carrier signal are illustrated in Fig. 9-2.

The compensation networks which are used to operate on d-c signals (hereafter called d-c compensation networks) are usually R-C filters with phase-lead, phase-lag, or combinations of lead and lag properties. Figure 9-3 shows a typical phase-lead network which can be used for d-c compensation. In general, d-c networks are relatively easy to adjust and design.

The design of networks used for the compensation of a-c signals is necessarily different from that of the d-c networks. The following discussion should help to explain the basic properties of an a-c compensation network.

If $e_s(t)$ is an error signal, and sin $\omega_c t$ is the carrier signal, the actuating signal which appears at the rotor terminals of a synchro control transformer of a servo system is described by

$$e(t) = e_s(t) \sin \omega_c t \qquad (9\text{-}3)$$

For the purpose of sinusoidal analysis, we may assume that $e_s(t)$ varies sinusoidally with time; thus, Eq. (9-3) becomes

$$e(t) = \sin \omega_s t \sin \omega_c t \qquad (9\text{-}4)$$

where, normally, $\omega_s \ll \omega_c$. By use of familiar trigonometric relations, we obtain

$$e(t) = \tfrac{1}{2} \left[\cos (\omega_c - \omega_s)t - \cos (\omega_c + \omega_s)t \right] \qquad (9\text{-}5)$$

This actuating signal is called a suppressed-carrier signal, since it is clear that $e(t)$ no longer contains the carrier frequency ω_c, but only the two side bands $\omega_c + \omega_s$ and $\omega_c - \omega_s$.

Let us assume now that this actuating signal is applied to the input of a compensating network; at the output of the network, we expect that the error signal $e_{s_1}(t)$ (envelope of the suppressed-carrier wave) is multiplied by a constant K and shifted in phase by an angle ϕ. In other words, the output of the compensator should give

$$e(t) = K \sin (\omega_s t + \phi) \sin \omega_c t \qquad (9\text{-}6)$$

It can be easily shown that Eq. (9-6) can be written as

$$e(t) = \tfrac{1}{2} K \{ \cos [(\omega_c - \omega_s)t - \phi] - \cos [(\omega_c + \omega_s)t + \phi] \} \qquad (9\text{-}7)$$

Therefore, in order that the output follow Eq. (9-6), the a-c compensating network must multiply the upper side band by K and shift it by an angle $+\phi$, and multiply the lower side band by K, but shift it by an angle of $-\phi$. Unless the lower and the upper side bands are shifted by an equal angle in opposite sense, the resulting envelop will be distorted. Passive networks which have the properties described above are of the bridged-T or twin-T type. Figure 9-4a shows a twin-T network which may be used for the compensation of a-c or carrier systems. It can be shown that, if $4C_1 R_2 > C_2 R_1$, the amplitude and phase characteristics of the network are of the

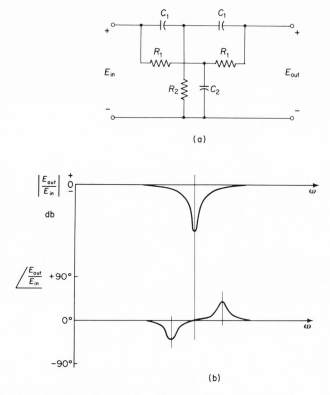

(a)

(b)

Fig. 9-4. (a) Twin-T network. (b) Magnitude and phase characteristics of twin-T network when $4R_2C_1 = R_1C_2$.

forms shown in Fig. 9-4b. It will be shown later that bridged-T networks may also be used efficiently to compensate d-c servo systems.* By properly adjusting the network parameters, it is possible to have the two complex zeros of the network cancel the unwanted poles that give excessive oscillatory response in the original system. These poles sometimes occur in systems due to effects such as structural resonances; the compensating networks are designed so that they automatically adjust to cancel these resonances.

---

*Chandaket, Rosenstein, "Bridged-T Complex Conjugate Compensation," *Trans.*, *AIEE, Part II, Application and Industry*, July, 1959, pp. 148–163.

9.3 Frequency Domain Design Versus S-Plane Design

The frequency domain design technique has been extensively developed in the past ten years. The method is still quite popular today because it is very simple and easy to comprehend. In terms of the Nyquist plot, the design technique essentially involves the shaping and reshaping of the locus until the design specifications are met. For the system represented by Eq. (9-1), for example, the Nyquist plots of $G(s)$ are sketched in Fig. 9-5 for two different values of K ($K = 20$ and $K = 2$). When $K = 20$, it was pointed out previously, the steady-state error requirement ($K_v = 10$) is satisfied, but the system is unstable. Let us assume, however, that the

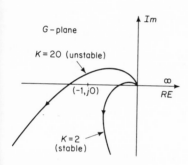

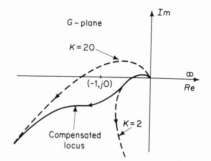

Fig. 9-5. Nyquist plot of

$$G(s) = \frac{K}{s(s + 1)(s + 2)}$$

Fig. 9-6. Nyquist plot of the compensated locus.

margin of stability is sufficient when $K = 2$, but the corresponding velocity constant is only 1 sec⁻¹. One of the methods used to satisfy the steady-state and transient requirements simultaneously is to reshape the Nyquist locus so that the high frequency (near resonant frequency) portion of the locus follows the $K = 2$ plot and the low frequency portion follows the $K = 20$ locus (Fig. 9-6). The significance of this locus reshaping is that the compensated locus will be tangent to the desired M_p circle (near the resonance frequency) while the low frequency gain is maintained at 20 to satisfy the velocity constant requirement. Evidently, by inspecting the compensated system locus given in Fig. 9-6, there are two alternate approaches in arriving at the compensated locus:

(1) Starting from the $K = 20$ locus and reshaping the locus in the region of resonance.

(2) Starting from the $K = 2$ locus and reshaping the low frequency region.

In the first approach, the high frequency portion of the $G(s)$ locus is rotated in the counterclockwise direction (while the low frequency portion is unaltered), which means that more phase is added to the system in the positive direction; this scheme is called the "phase-lead compensation." The second approach apparently involves the shifting of the low-frequency part of the $K = 2$ locus in the clockwise direction while keeping the locus near the resonance frequency untouched. This is often referred to as the "phase-lag compensation," since more phase lag is introduced to the system in the low frequency region.

One should not jump to the conclusion that a given system can always be compensated satisfactorily by either of the two schemes mentioned above. It will be shown that for systems with certain characteristics, satisfactory compensation cannot be accomplished by phase-lead networks. This, however, does not mean that proper compensation may then be achieved by using phase-lag networks, for it is quite common that neither scheme is feasible and some combination of lead and lag characteristics is needed.

The designer is usually interested in ascertaining the best compensation scheme for the particular system on which he is working. Unfortunately, the design technique in the frequency domain does not give an answer to this question. Judging from the nature of the system, the designer must depend considerably on his past experience to decide which compensation he should use, and then try it. If the scheme does not work, he simply must try something else.

The root locus method, or, in general, working with the pole-zero configuration in the s-plane, is a very powerful tool in the design of feedback control systems. The essential advantages of the root locus method are due to the fact that the locus diagram gives information about the frequency response as well as about the transient response. With the knowledge of the closed-loop poles and zeros, the transient response is determined readily by means of the inverse Laplace transform, and the frequency response is easily obtained from the Bode plot.

9.4 Series Compensation with D-C Networks

In Fig. 9-7a is shown a typical d-c servo system employing a d-c compensation network. The equivalent block diagram of the system is shown in Fig. 9-7b with the typical signal waveforms illustrated at significant points of the system. The open-loop transfer function of the system without compensation is

$$G(s) = K_s G_1(s) \tag{9-8}$$

and that of the compensated system is

$$G_c(s)G(s) = K_s G_c(s)G_1(s) \tag{9-9}$$

where $G_c(s)$ is the transfer function of the compensation network.

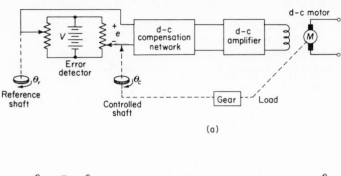

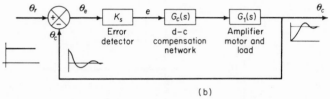

(b)

Fig. 9-7. A d-c servo system employing a d-c compensation network.

It is also quite common to replace the potentiometers in the system of Fig. 9-7 by a pair of synchros whose output is then the sine wave carrier modulated by the error signal $\theta_e(t)$. However, a demodulater must be inserted between the synchro output and the compensation network if the

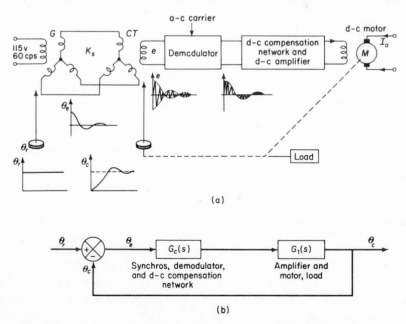

Fig. 9-8. An ac-dc servo system employing a d-c compensation network.

d-c network, d-c amplifier, and d-c motor are still used. This a-c–d-c system
is shown in Fig. 9-8a. In Fig. 9-8b is shown the equivalent block diagram
of the system. The transfer function $G_1(s)$ includes the demodulator, the
error detector, the amplifier, the motor, and the other elements involved
before compensation is added.

In Fig. 9-9 is given the schematic and block diagrams of an all a-c servo
system employing a d-c compensation network. Evidently, a demodulator

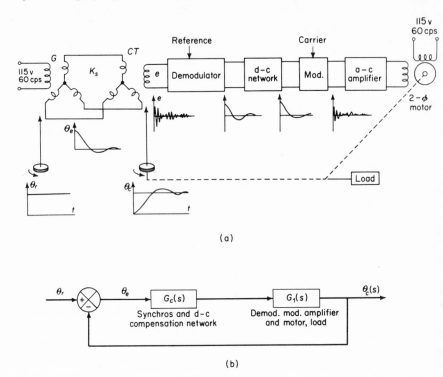

(a)

(b)

Fig. 9-9. An a-c system employing a d-c compensation network.

should be inserted in front of the d-c compensation network, and a modulator must be used to convert the d-c output signal from the network back
into an a-c signal, which is to be amplified by an a-c amplifier. Since the
transfer functions of modulators and demodulators are usually mere constants, the system may be represented by an equivalent block diagram
similar to those of the previous systems, as shown in Fig. 9-9b.

We can conclude that, when d-c compensation networks are applied to
servo systems of any kind, the design techniques are the same, provided
that the transfer functions of all the modulators used are taken into
consideration.

(1) *Phase-Lead Compensation*

In Chapter 5 a simple phase-lead compensation network with the transfer function $(1 + sT)$ was described under the name of derivative control. However, in practice, $(1 + sT)$ cannot be realized by passive

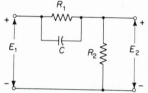

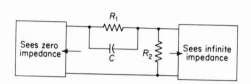

Fig. 9-10. Passive phase-lead network.

Fig. 9-11. Assumption of zero source impedance and infinite output impedance when deriving the transfer function given in Eq. (9-10).

networks; thus it is often called the transfer function of an ideal phase-lead network. A practical and simple phase-lead network* is shown in Fig. 9-10. The transfer function of the network is

$$\frac{E_2(s)}{E_1(s)} = \frac{R_2 + R_1 R_2 Cs}{R_1 + R_2 + R_1 R_2 Cs} \tag{9-10}$$

or

$$\frac{E_2(s)}{E_1(s)} = \frac{R_2}{R_1 + R_2} \frac{1 + R_1 Cs}{1 + \dfrac{R_1 R_2}{R_1 + R_2} Cs} \tag{9-11}$$

If we let

$$a = \frac{R_1 + R_2}{R_2} \qquad (a > 1) \tag{9-12}$$

and

$$T = \frac{R_1 R_2}{R_1 + R_2} C \tag{9-13}$$

hence

$$\frac{E_2(s)}{E_1(s)} = \frac{1}{a} \frac{1 + aTs}{1 + Ts} \tag{9-14}$$

It should be pointed out here that the transfer function E_2/E_1 given in Eq. (9-14) is derived under the assumption that the source impedance

---

*Although the network configuration is even simpler if, in Fig. 9-10, $R_1 = \infty$, such a network will block d-c signals completely and cannot be used in the forward path of a servo system.

which the lead network sees is zero, and the output load impedance is infinite. This assumption is, of course, made in general in the derivation of the transfer function of any four-terminal network.

Characteristics of R-C Phase-Lead Network

(1) *Pole-Zero Configuration*

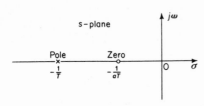

Fig. 9-12. The pole-zero configuration of

$$\frac{E_2}{E_1} = \frac{1}{a}\frac{1 + aTs}{1 + Ts}$$

The transfer function of the phase-lead network has a real zero at $s = -1/aT$, and a real pole at $s = -1/T$ (Fig. 9-12). By varying the values of a and T, the pole and zero may be located at any point on the negative real axis in the s-plane. It is seen that for $a > 1$ the zero is always located to the right of the pole, and the distance between them is determined by the constant a.

(2) *Polar Plot of the R-C Phase-Lead Network*

Since, in general, the attenuation $(1/a)$ produced by the lead network is compensated by the amplifier gain of the servo system, it is necessary to investigate only the function

$$a\frac{E_2(s)}{E_1(s)} = \frac{1 + aTs}{1 + Ts} \tag{9-15}$$

The polar plot of Eq. (9-15) is shown in Fig. 9-13 for several different values of a. For any particular value of a, the angle between the tangent

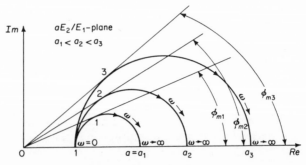

Fig. 9-13. Polar plot of

$$a\frac{E_2}{E_1} = \frac{1 + aTs}{1 + Ts}$$

line drawn from the origin to the semicircle and the real axis gives the maximum phase shift (phase lead) ϕ_m obtainable from the network. The frequency at the tangent point ω_m represents the frequency at which ϕ_m occurs. It is seen that, as a increases, the maximum phase lead ϕ_m also increases, approaching a limit of 90 deg as a approaches infinity. The frequency ω_m decreases with the increase in a.

(3) *Bode Plot of the Phase-Lead Network*

In terms of the Bode plot, the lead network has two corner frequencies: a positive corner frequency at $\omega = 1/aT$ and a negative corner at $\omega = 1/T$. The Bode plot of aE_2/E_1 is sketched in Fig. 9-14.

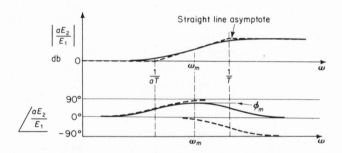

Fig. 9-14. Bode plot of the phase-lead network.

Analytically, ϕ_m and ω_m may be related to the circuit parameters a and T. Since ω_m is at the geometric mean of the two corner frequencies, we can write

$$\log \omega_m = \frac{1}{2}\left(\log \frac{1}{aT} + \log \frac{1}{T}\right) \tag{9-16}$$

hence

$$\omega_m = \frac{1}{\sqrt{a}\,T} \tag{9-17}$$

To determine the maximum phase lead ϕ_m, we first write the phase shift of aE_2/E_1 as

$$\phi = \text{Arg.}\left(a\frac{E_2}{E_1}\right) = \tan^{-1} aT\omega - \tan^{-1} T\omega \tag{9-18}$$

from which

$$\tan \phi = \frac{aT\omega - T\omega}{1 + (aT\omega)(T\omega)} \tag{9-19}$$

When $\phi = \phi_m$,

$$\omega = \omega_m = \frac{1}{\sqrt{a}\,T} \tag{9-20}$$

hence

$$\tan \phi_m = \frac{(a-1)\dfrac{1}{\sqrt{a}}}{1+1} = \frac{a-1}{2\sqrt{a}} \tag{9-21}$$

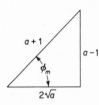

Figure 9-15

Referring to the triangle shown in Fig. 9-15, we have

$$\sin \phi_m = \frac{a-1}{a+1} \qquad (9\text{-}22)$$

Equation (9-22) is a very important and useful relationship in the frequency domain design of feedback control systems, since a is determined once the required phase lead ϕ_m is given.

Design of Phase-Lead Compensation by Bode Plot Method

The Bode plot method is generally preferred in the frequency domain design of series compensation of feedback control systems because the effect of the compensation network is easily obtained by adding its magnitude and phase shift curves, respectively, to that of the original system. For the phase-lead compensation employing the RC network shown in Fig. 9-10, the general outline of the design procedure is given as follows:

(1) The magnitude and phase versus frequency curves are plotted for $G(s)$ of the uncompensated system with the gain constant K set according to the steady-state error requirement.

(2) The phase margin and gain margin of the original system are read from the Bode plot, and the additional amount of phase lead needed to provide the specified phase margin is determined. From the maximum phase lead required, ϕ_m is estimated accordingly, and Eq. (9-22) gives the corresponding value of a.

(3) Once a is determined, it is necessary only to obtain the value of T and the design is completed. The corner frequencies of the lead network $(1/aT, 1/T)$ are usually so placed that ϕ_m is located at the new gain crossover frequency.

(4) The Bode plot of the compensated system is investigated to check that all the performance specifications are met; if not, a new value of ϕ_m must be estimated.

(5) If the specifications are all satisfied, the transfer function of the phase lead network is determined from the values of a and T.

EXAMPLE 9-1. Consider a feedback control system with the open-loop transfer function

$$G_1(s) = \frac{K}{s(s+1)} \qquad (9\text{-}23)$$

which could be the transfer function of a linearized servo system employing a two-phase servomotor. The transfer function of the modulators used to adapt d-c compensation may be assumed to be unity.

The specifications are

(1) The phase margin of the system must be greater than 45 deg.

(2) When the input is a step velocity (ramp) function, the steady-state error of the output in position should be less than 0.1 deg per deg/sec of the final output velocity.

From the second requirement, we recall that the velocity constant K_v was defined as

$$K_v = \frac{\text{Output velocity}}{\text{Steady-state error}} = \frac{1}{0.1} = 10 \text{ sec}^{-1} \qquad (9\text{-}24)$$

Also

$$K_v = \lim_{s \to 0} sG_1(s) = K = 10 \text{ sec}^{-1} \qquad (9\text{-}25)$$

which implies that if the steady-state error is to be as specified, the forward path gain must be greater than 10.

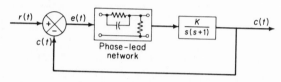

Fig. 9-16. Feedback control system with phase-lead compensation.

The following steps are followed in the design of the phase-lead compensation network:

(1) The Bode diagram of $G_1(s)$ with $K = 10$ is plotted, as shown in Fig. 9-17.

(2) The phase margin read at the gain crossover ($\omega_c = 3.16$ rad/sec) is 18 deg. The damping ratio δ and the resonance peak M_p at this gain are computed to be 15.8 per cent and 3.2 respectively. Since the phase margin is less than 45 deg, more phase lead should be added to the system. Let us assume that we choose to use the phase-lead network given in Fig. 9-10. The block diagram of the compensated system is shown in Fig. 9-16.

(3) Since the desired phase margin is 45 deg and the present phase margin with $K = 10$ is only 18 deg, the phase-lead network must provide at least an additional phase lead of 27 deg in the vicinity of the resonant frequency. However, by inserting the compensation network, the magnitude curve of the Bode plot is also affected. The gain crossover is normally shifted to a higher frequency. While it is possible to adjust the corner frequencies $1/aT$ and $1/T$ so that the maximum phase lead ϕ_m falls exactly at the new gain crossover frequency, the original phase curve at this point is no longer 18 deg; it may be decreased to a low value, for example, 15 deg.* Thus, in estimating the necessary amount of phase lead, it is essential to

---

*This is, indeed, the main difficulty encountered in the phase-lead compensation. If the phase shift decreases rapidly with increasing frequency near the gain crossover frequency, phase lead compensation becomes ineffective.

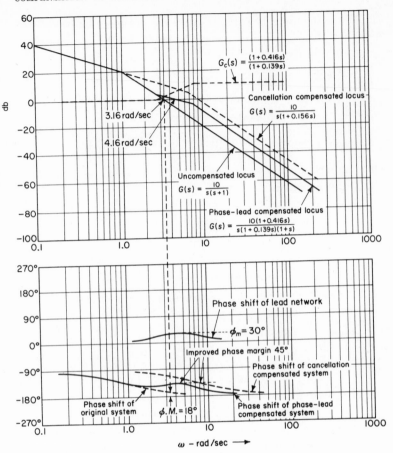

Fig. 9-17. Bode plots of $G(s)$ of system given in Example 9-1.

include a little safety factor to account for this error. Instead of selecting $\phi_m = 27$ deg, we let $\phi_m = 30$ deg. From Eq. (9-22), we have

$$\sin \phi_m = \sin 30° = 0.5 = \frac{a-1}{a+1} \tag{9-26}$$

from which $\qquad\qquad a = 3 \tag{9-27}$

(4) To determine the proper location of the two corner frequencies $1/aT$ and $1/T$: It is known that the maximum phase lead ϕ_m occurs at the geometric mean of the two corner frequencies $1/aT$ and $1/T$. To achieve maximum phase margin with a already determined, apparently, the maximum phase lead ϕ_m provided by the lead network should occur at the new gain crossover frequency ω_c', which is not known. Thus, the problem now

is to locate the two corner frequencies $1/aT$ and $1/T$, so that $\omega_m = \omega_c'$. This may be obtained graphically as follows:

(a) The zero frequency attenuation of the lead network is calculated:

$$20 \log a = 20 \log 3 = 9.55 \text{ db} \tag{9-28}$$

(b) The geometric mean ω_m of the corner frequencies $1/aT$ and $1/T$ must be located at the frequency at which the magnitude of $G_1(j\omega)$ in decibels is equal to the negative value in decibels of one half of this attenuation; i.e.,

$$|G_1(j\omega)| = \frac{-9.55}{2} = -4.78 \text{ db} \tag{9-29}$$

From the Bode plot shown in Fig. 9-17, $\omega_m = 4.16$ rad/sec.

Thus $\qquad 1/T = \sqrt{a}\,\omega_m = \sqrt{3} \times 4.16 = 7.2 \text{ rad/sec} \tag{9-30}$

and $\qquad\qquad\qquad 1/aT = 2.4 \text{ rad/sec} \tag{9-31}$

The new gain crossover frequency is at

$$\omega_c' = \omega_m = 4.16 \text{ rad/sec} \tag{9-32}$$

A check of the compensated Bode plot shows that the phase margin of the compensated system is approximately 45 deg. The design has been done here with the straight-line asymptotic plots rather than the exact curves for the magnitude plots.

(5) The transfer function of the phase-lead network is simply

$$\frac{E_2(s)}{E_1(s)} = \frac{1}{a}\frac{1 + aTs}{1 + Ts} = \frac{1}{3}\frac{1 + 0.416s}{1 + 0.139s} \tag{9-33}$$

If the amplifier gain is increased by a factor of 3, the open-loop transfer function of the compensated system becomes

$$G(s) = G_c(s)G_1(s) = \frac{10(1 + 0.416s)}{s(1 + 0.139s)(1 + s)} \tag{9-34}$$

In Fig. 9-18 the magnitude versus phase shift plot of the original and the compensated systems are plotted on the Nichols chart. These plots are obtained by taking the values of magnitude and phase shift directly from the Bode diagrams (exact values rather than asymptotes are used) shown in Fig. 9-17. From the Nichols chart, the resonance peak M_p without compensation is found to be 10 db or 3.2 in magnitude, which checks with the value computed previously. The M_p after compensation is found to be 2.7 db or 1.36, which shows quite an improvement on the system's stability. One more important point is that the resonant frequency of the system is decreased from 3.16 rad/sec to approximately 3 rad/sec and the band width is increased from 4.47 rad/sec to 6.7 rad/sec. Based on the band

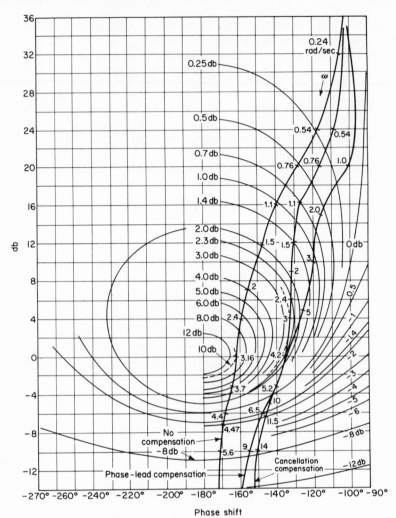

Fig. 9-18. Plots of $G(s)$ in db versus phase shift for system in Example 9-1.

width-rise time relationship, we know that the rise time is shortened by the phase-lead compensation. From the magnitude versus phase shift curves and the Nichols chart, the closed-loop frequency responses for before and after compensation are shown in Fig. 9-19. It is also interesting to investigate the effect of the phase-lead compensation on the root locus diagram of the system, which is shown in Fig. 9-20.

Cancellation Compensation

For the simple second-order system given in the last example, the compensation of the system can also be affected by a more direct approach. Since the transfer function of the phase-lead compensated system is

$$G(s) = \frac{10(1 + aTs)}{s(1 + sT)(1 + s)} \tag{9-35}$$

the zero of the lead network at $s = -1/aT$ may be so placed that it cancels the pole of the original system function at $s = -1$; thus, $aT = 1$. The compensated transfer function is

$$G(s) = \frac{10}{s(1 + sT)} \tag{9-36}$$

and we can adjust the value of T to obtain any desired amount of relative stability. If the stability requirement specifies that M_p must equal 1.36,

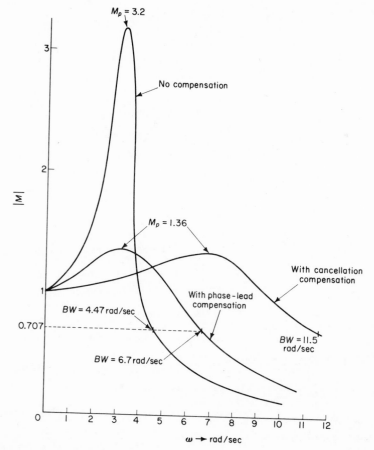

Fig. 9-19. Closed-loop frequency responses of system given in Example 9-1.

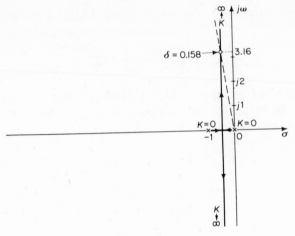

(a) Root loci of uncompensated system

$$G(s) = \frac{K}{s(1+s)}$$

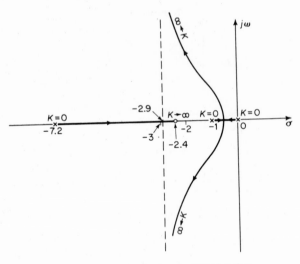

(b) Root loci of phase-lead compensated system

$$G(s) = \frac{K(1+0.416s)}{s(1+0.139s)(1+s)}$$

Fig. 9-20. Root locus diagrams of system in Example 9-1.

correspondingly, $\delta = 0.4$, from which $T = 0.156$. The transfer function of the lead network is

$$\frac{E_2(s)}{E_1(s)} = \frac{1}{6.4}\frac{1+s}{1+0.156s} \qquad (9\text{-}37)$$

The effect of the cancellation compensation is illustrated in Figs. 9-17 and 9-18. The chief difference between this cancellation compensation and the previous one is that the gain crossover frequency in the present case is considerably increased, which implies that the band width of the system is larger. As a matter of fact, the new band width is about 11.5 rad/sec, compared to 6.7 rad/sec obtained by the first method. In this particular case, the band width of the cancellation compensated system is probably still within safe tolerance, since the band width of the original system is very narrow. In most applications, the band width of the system is to be kept small so that noise and unwanted signals can be filtered out. From this point of view, the first method of compensation is certainly superior, although it is quite possible that in certain cases the additional band width provided by the lead network still exceeds the minimum band width requirement. Another point in regard to the pole-zero cancellation scheme is that, in practice, exact cancellation is seldom obtained due to the assumptions and uncertainties encountered in deriving the transfer functions.

EXAMPLE 9-2. Let us consider a third-order servo system with the open-loop transfer function

$$G_1(s) = \frac{K}{s(1 + 0.1s)(1 + 0.001s)} \tag{9-38}$$

The specifications are

(1) The phase margin of the system must be greater than or equal to 45 deg.

(2) For a velocity input, the steady-state error in the output position must be less than or equal to 0.1 per cent of the final output velocity.

From the second requirement

$$K = K_v \geq 1000 \text{ sec}^{-1} \tag{9-39}$$

which means that the gain constant of the system must be set at 1000 to meet the minimum steady-state error requirement.

The following steps are followed in the design of the compensation of the control system:

(1) As the first step, the Bode diagram of $G_1(s)$ is plotted for $K = 1000$ (Fig. 9-22).

(2) The phase margin read at the gain crossover frequency $\omega_c = 100$ rad/sec is very close to 0 deg. (The critical value of K for absolute stability determined from the Routh criterion is 1010.) This means that the pair of complex conjugate roots of the characteristic equation is practically on the $j\omega$ axis in the s-plane, and that the corresponding resonance peak M_p is almost infinite.

(3) Since additional phase is required to realize the specified phase margin, we assume that a first trial is to use the phase-lead network given

in Fig. 9-10 for series compensation (with no assurance that it will work). The configuration of the compensated system is shown in Fig. 9-21.

Evidently, the phase-lead network must provide at least an additional

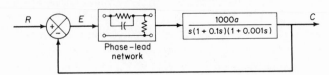

Fig. 9-21. Feedback control system with phase-lead compensation.

phase of 45 deg. However, anticipating that the new gain crossover frequency after compensation will be somewhat higher, and, at the same time, that the original phase shift decreases with the increase in frequency, it is necessary to estimate a higher value for ϕ_m; for example, 50 deg.

From Eq. (9-22), we have

$$\sin \phi_m = \sin 50° = 0.765 = \frac{a - 1}{a + 1} \tag{9-40}$$

which gives

$$a = 7.5 \tag{9-41}$$

(4) The proper location of the two corner frequencies $1/aT$ and $1/T$ is determined as follows:

(a) The attenuation of the phase-lead network is calculated:

$$20 \log a = 20 \log 7.5 = 17.5 \text{ db} \tag{9-42}$$

(b) The new gain crossover must be placed at the frequency at which the magnitude of $G_1(j\omega)$ is equal to one half of the negative value in decibels of this attenuation; i.e.,

$$|G_1(j\omega)| = -17.5/2 = -8.75 \text{ db} \tag{9-43}$$

From the Bode plot constructed in Fig. 9-22, ω_m is 164.5 rad/sec; from which we obtain

$$1/aT = 60 \text{ rad/sec} \tag{9-44}$$

hence

$$1/T = 60a = 450 \text{ rad/sec} \tag{9-45}$$

The new gain crossover frequency is at

$$\omega_c' = \omega_m = 164.5 \text{ rad/sec} \tag{9-46}$$

Hence, the transfer function of the phase lead network is

$$\frac{E_2(s)}{E_1(s)} = \frac{1}{a} \frac{1 + aTs}{1 + Ts} = \frac{1}{7.5} \frac{1 + 0.0167s}{1 + 0.00222s} \tag{9-47}$$

and the open-loop transfer function of the compensated system is

$$G(s) = \frac{1000(1 + 0.0167s)}{s(1 + 0.00222s)(1 + 0.1s)(1 + 0.001s)} \tag{9-48}$$

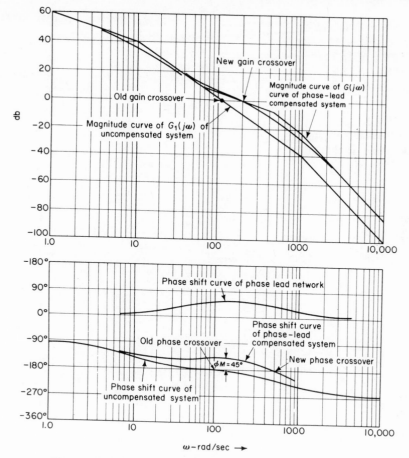

Fig. 9-22. Bode plots of control system given in Example 9-2.

A check of the Bode plot of the compensated system finds that the phase margin of the system is close to 45 deg, which is the desired value. The magnitude versus phase shift plot on the Nichols chart (Fig. 9-23) shows that the resonant peak M_p of the compensated system is 3.3 db or 1.46 in magnitude. The band width of the system, however, is increased from 150 rad/sec to 300 rad/sec.

The Nichols chart is used as an aid to the construction of the root locus diagram of the compensated system (Fig. 9-24). The loci of the complex roots of the original system intersect the imaginary axis at $\omega = \pm 100$ rad/sec ($K = 1010$), these intersections correspond to the point at which the magnitude versus phase shift curve passes through the -180 deg axis on the Nichols chart. For the compensated system, the magnitude versus phase shift curve intersects the -180 deg axis at $\omega = 612$ rad/sec and the corresponding magnitude is -17.25 db, which means that, for $K = 1000$, the gain margin is 17.25 db. By using Eq. (7-71), the marginal gain of stability (gain limit) of the compensated system is

$$G_{\text{lim}} = 17.25 + 60 = 77.25 \text{ db} \tag{9-49}$$

or $$|G_{\text{lim}}| = 7320 \tag{9-50}$$

which is the value of K where the two complex loci cross the $j\omega$ axis. The frequency at this point is 612 rad/sec.

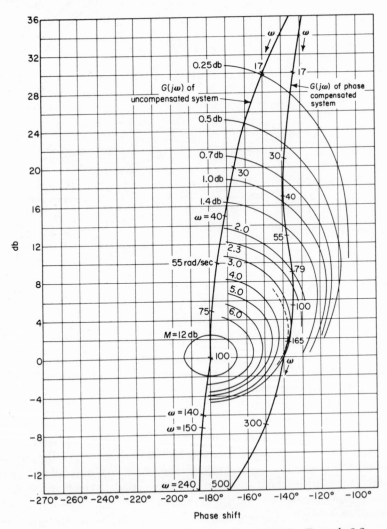

Fig. 9-23. Magnitude versus phase shift plot of $G(s)$ for Example 9-2.

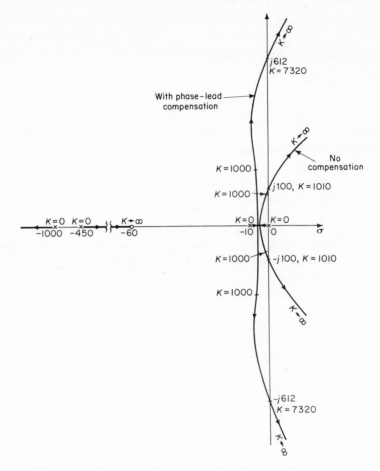

Fig. 9-24. Root locus diagrams of system given in Example 9-2.

The Effect And Limitations of the Phase-Lead Compensation

From the results obtained in the last two examples, we may summarize the general effect of the phase-lead compensation on the performance of servo systems as follows:

Frequency Response

(1) The phase shift in the vicinity of the resonant frequency is increased in the positive direction.

(2) For a given relative stability, the velocity constant usually is increased.

(3) For a given gain constant K, the slope of the magnitude curve on the Bode plot is reduced at the gain crossover; thus, the relative stability of

the system is usually improved. That is, the phase margin is increased and the resonance peak M_p is reduced.

(4) The band width is usually increased.

Time Response

(1) The overshoot is reduced.

(2) The rise time is faster.

However, it was mentioned previously that satisfactory compensation cannot always be accomplished by means of the phase-lead network. The examples given here represent two of the few types of systems on which the phase-lead compensaton is effective and practical. The successful application of the phase-lead compensation is limited by the following considerations:

(1) Band width considerations: For unstable systems, the additional phase-lead necessary to obtain a certain specified phase margin is large. This requires a large value for a; the band width of the compensated system is large accordingly, and the transmission of noise may become objectionable. In practice, the value of a is seldom chosen greater than 15; sometimes two or more cascaded lead compensators are used to achieve large phase leads.

(2) For systems with low or negative damping ratios, if the phase shift decreases rapidly near the gain crossover, phase-lead compensation becomes ineffective because the additional phase-lead at the new gain crossover is added to a much smaller phase angle than that at the old gain crossover. The desired phase margin may be realized only by using a very large value for a. The property of this rapid change in phase in general may be attributed to systems with the following characteristics:

(a) Two simple negative corners placed close to each other near the gain crossover frequency ω_c.

(b) A simple double corner $1/(1 + Ts)^2$ placed near the gain crossover frequency ω_c.

(c) A complex corner $\omega_n^2/(s^2 + 2\delta\omega_n s + \omega_n^2)$ placed near the gain crossover frequency ω_c.

EXAMPLE 9-3. Let

$$G_1(s) = \frac{K}{s(1 + 0.2s)(1 + 0.1s)} \tag{9-51}$$

be the uncompensated open-loop transfer function of a feedback control system. The frequency domain specifications are as follows:

(1) $K_v = 10$.

(2) Phase margin ≥ 40 deg.

Fig. 9-25 gives the Bode plot of $G_1(s)$ when K is set equal to 10. The phase margin at this gain is approximately -3 deg and the system is

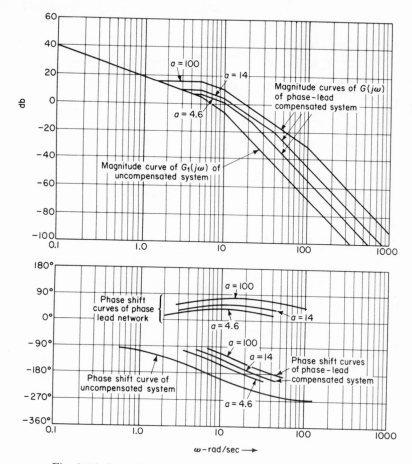

Fig. 9-25. Bode plots of control system given in Example 9-3.

unstable. (The marginal value of K for stability is 7). The rapid change in phase at the gain crossover frequency ($\omega_c = 7$ rad/sec) indicates that the phase lead compensation is ineffective. To illustrate the point, phase-lead networks with $a = 4.6$, 14, and 100 are used to compensate the system. The results are tabulated in Table 9-1. It is seen from these results that a phase margin of 40 deg can only be realized by an a greater than 100. The corresponding band width may not be too excessive, but the value of a is certainly too large. The desired specifications can be achieved for this system if one of the three following courses is followed:

(1) Use two cascaded lead compensators.

(2) Use a lag compensating network.

(3) Use auxiliary feedback loop, such as a rate feedback.

Table 9-1.

a	$1/aT$	$1/T$	ϕ_m	ω_m	Gain crossover ω_c	Band width	Phase margin
4.6	4.78	22	40°	10.3	10.3	16 rad/sec	19°
14	3.2	44.8	60°	12	12	19 rad/sec	28°
100	1.7	170	78.8°	17	17	27 rad/sec	38°

Phase Lead Compensation by Root Locus Method

The phase-lead compensation can also be effected in the s-plane; specifically, the root contour method described previously will be shown as a convenient tool in the design of feedback control systems. Consider the system given in Example 9-1. The open-loop transfer function of the compensated system is of the form:

$$G(s) = \frac{10(1 + saT)}{s(1 + s)(1 + sT)} \tag{9-52}$$

where the values of T and a are to be determined.

The root contours of the compensated system (T and a are the variable parameters) are constructed as follows:

(1) For the uncompensated system, the characteristic equation is

$$s^2 + s + 10 = 0 \tag{9-53}$$

and the roots are at $s_{1,2} = -0.5 \pm j3.12$.

(2) Consider the system is compensated by the lag factor $1/(1 + sT)$;

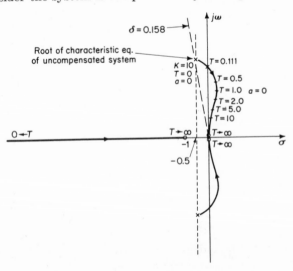

Fig. 9-26. Root contours of the control system given in Example 9-1 when $a = 0$, but T is the varying parameter ($K = 10$).

in other words, $a = 0$ for the phase lead network.   The characteristic equation of the partially compensated system is

$$s(s + 1)(1 + sT) + 10 = 0 \qquad (9\text{-}54)$$

which can be written as

$$1 + G_1 H_1 = 1 + \frac{T s^2 (s + 1)}{s^2 + s + 10} \qquad (9\text{-}55)$$

The root contours represented by the last equation with T as the varying parameter are constructed in Fig. 9-26.   These contours begin at the poles

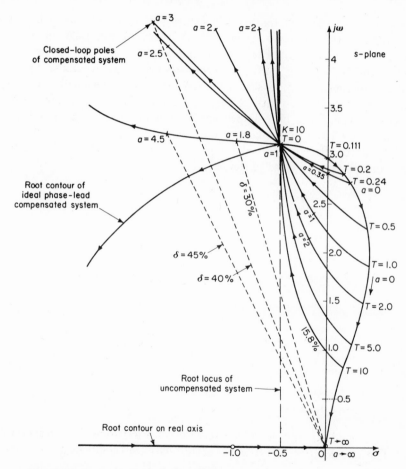

Fig. 9-27. Root contours of system given in Example 9-1 with phase-lead compensation

$$G_c(s) = \frac{1 + saT}{1 + sT}$$

of G_1H_1 and end at the zeros of G_1H_1. As the value of T is increased, the two roots of the characteristic equation move into the right half of the s-plane. The closed-loop system is unstable for all values of T greater than 0.111.

(3) The system is compensated by the phase-lead network ($a \neq 0$, $T \neq 0$). In this case, T is kept constant while a is considered a variable parameter. The characteristic equation of the compensated system is

$$s(s + 1)(1 + sT) + 10(1 + saT) = 0 \qquad (9\text{-}56)$$

which can be written as

$$1 + G_2H_2 = 1 + \frac{10aTs}{s(1 + sT)(1 + s) + 10} \qquad (9\text{-}57)$$

Thus, when a varies, the root contours start at the poles of G_2H_2, which are the points on the root contours of $1 + G_1H_1$ shown in Fig. 9-26, and end at the zero of G_2H_2 ($s = 0$). The root contours of the phase-lead compensated system are shown in Fig. 9-27. From these root contours, we can see that for effective phase lead compensation, the value of T must be small. For large values of T, the band width of the system increases very rapidly as a is increased, while very little improvement is made on the damping ratio. On the other hand, T cannot be too small, for in trying to realize the complex roots with a prescribed damping ratio, the real root on the negative real axis will be very close to the origin.

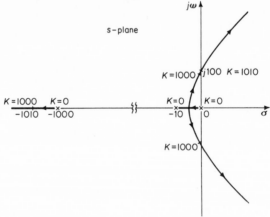

Fig. 9-28. Root loci of uncompensated system in Example 9-2 ($K = 10$).

As a second example, let us consider the control system given in Example 9-2. The open-loop transfer function of the phase-lead compensated system is

$$G(s) = \frac{1000(1 + saT)}{s(1 + 0.1s)(1 + 0.001s)(1 + sT)} \qquad (9\text{-}58)$$

The root contours of the compensated system are obtained in the same way as that described previously.

(1) The roots of the characteristic equation of the uncompensated system are shown in Fig. 9-28.

(2) When $a = 0$, but T is the varying parameter,

$$1 + G_1H_1 = 1 + \frac{Ts^2(1 + 0.1s)(1 + 0.001s)}{s(1 + 0.1s)(1 + 0.001s) + 1000} \qquad (9\text{-}59)$$

and the root contours of which are sketched in Fig. 9-29.

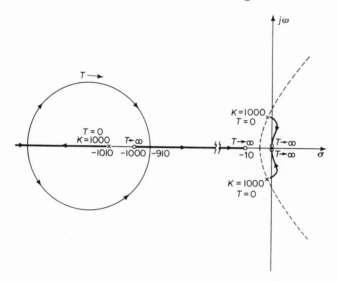

Fig. 9-29. Root contours of the control system given in Example 9-2 when $a = 0$, but T is the varying parameter.

(3) When a varies from 0 to ∞, it can readily be shown that the root contours of the compensated system are described by

$$1 + G_2H_2 = 1 + \frac{1000Tas}{s(1 + 0.1s)(1 + 0.001s)(1 + sT) + 1000} \qquad (9\text{-}60)$$

and are sketched in Fig. 9-30 for various values of T.

From the root contours shown in Fig. 9-30, it is seen that the value of T should not be too large, or the phase-lead compensation becomes ineffective. Since the two contours near the $j\omega$ axis bend into the right half of the plane, there is an upper bound for the value of a above which the compensated system will become unstable. It is clear that for large values of T, not only are the root contours very close to the $j\omega$ axis (low damping), but the stable range of a is also very small. On the other hand, the value of T should not be too small, for, although a more stable system is possible, the value of a is necessarily large and the band width is increased accordingly. Furthermore,

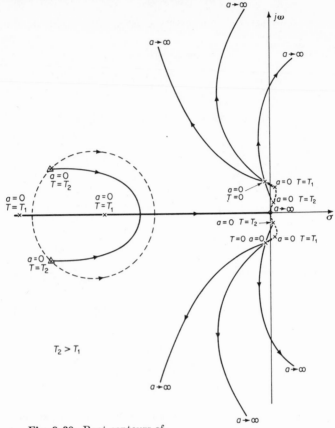

Fig. 9-30. Root contours of

$$G(s) = \frac{10(1 + saT)}{s(1 + 0.1s)(1 + 0.001s)(1 + Ts)} \quad \text{(Example 9-2)}$$

if a is large, the real zero along the real axis will move toward the origin and the oscillation of the response will be damped out more slowly.

The root contours can also be used to explain the cases for which the phase-lead compensation is entirely ineffective. For instance, consider the transfer function

$$G(s) = \frac{10(1 + sTa)}{s(1 + 0.2s)(1 + 0.5s)(1 + sT)} \quad (9-61)$$

We shall construct the root contour diagrams of this system to show that the phase-lead compensation is ineffective in improving the performance of this system.

(1) For the uncompensated system, the roots of the characteristic equation are shown in Fig. 9-31 for $K = 10$. The two complex roots are in the right half of the plane and the system is unstable.

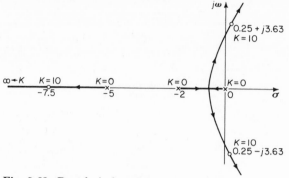

Fig. 9-31. Root loci of uncompensated system,

$$G(s) = \frac{K}{s(1 + 0.2s)(1 + 0.3s)}$$

(2) When $a = 0$, but T varies from 0 to ∞, the root contours of the compensated system are described by

$$1 + G_1H_1 = 1 + \frac{Ts^2(1 + 0.2s)(1 + 0.5s)}{s(1 + 0.2s)(1 + 0.5s) + 10} \tag{9-62}$$

The root contours are sketched in Fig. 9-32.

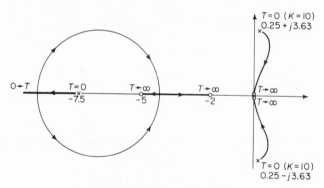

Fig. 9-32. Root contours of

$$1 + G_1H_1 = 1 + \frac{Ts^2(1 + 0.2s)(1 + 0.5s)}{s(1 + 0.2s)(1 + 0.5s) + 10}$$

(3) When the value of a is varied from 0 to ∞, the root contours of the compensated system are described by

$$1 + G_2H_2 = 1 + \frac{10Tas}{s(1 + 0.2s)(1 + 0.5s)(1 + Ts)} \tag{9-63}$$

The root contours are sketched in Fig. 9-33.

From the root contours shown in Fig. 9-33, it is easy to see that the value of T should be kept small. Large values of T do not make the system

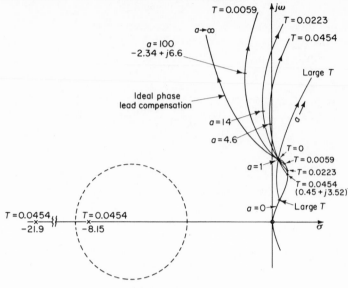

Fig. 9-33. Root contours of

$$1 + G_2H_2 = 1 + \frac{10Tas}{s(1 + 0.2s)(1 + 0.5s)(1 + Ts)}$$

stable. However, as T decreases, the root contours move very slowly into the left half of the s-plane, and then bend back into the right half of the plane. The band width of the system increases very rapidly with the increase in the value of a. All these observed phenomena are due to the fact that the two poles of G_2H_2 are close to the $j\omega$ axis; the poles have the effect of pushing the root contours toward the right half of the s-plane.

Similarly, the root contour diagram can be used to show why the phase-lead network is not recommended to compensate systems with complex

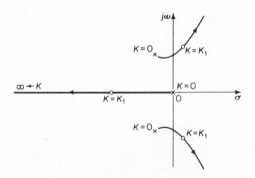

Fig. 9-34. Root loci of system with

$$G_1(s) = \frac{K}{s(s^2 + 2\delta\omega_n s + \omega_n^2)}$$

open-loop poles. Consider a feedback control system with the open-loop transfer function

$$G_1(s) = \frac{K}{s(s^2 + 2\delta\omega_n s + \omega_n^2)}$$ (9-64)

and $\delta < 1$.

The root loci of the system are shown in Fig. 9-34.

The transfer function of the phase-lead compensated system is

$$G(s) = G_c(s)G_1(s) = \frac{K(1 + sTa)}{s(1 + sT)(s^2 + 2\delta\omega_n s + \omega_n^2)}$$ (9-65)

For any fixed K, and for $a = 0$, the root contours of the partially compensated system are sketched in Fig. 9-35. It is apparent that for small values

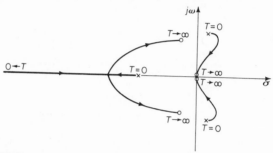

Fig. 9-35. Root contour of system represented by Eq. (9-65) with $a = 0$, but T is a varying parameter.

of T, the system can be stabilized only at the expense of large a and large band width. When the value of T is large, the roots on the two contours of the left half of the plane move toward the $j\omega$ axis and push the compensated contours toward the right half of the plane (Fig. 9-36).

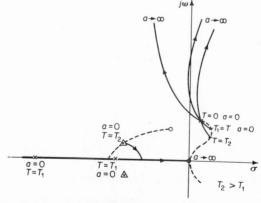

Fig. 9-36. Root contours of system represented by Eq. (9-65). The contours indicate that the phase-lead network is ineffective to compensate systems with complex open-loop poles.

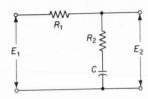

Fig. 9-37. Passive phase-lag network.

(2) Phase-Lag Compensation

Figure 9-37 shows a simple R-C network, which is often used for the phase-lag compensation of feedback control systems. If we assume that the input impedance of the network is zero and that the output impedance which the network sees is infinite, the transfer function of the lag network is

$$\frac{E_2(s)}{E_1(s)} = \frac{1 + R_2Cs}{1 + (R_1 + R_2)Cs} \tag{9-66}$$

Let

$$aT = R_2C \tag{9-67}$$

and

$$a = R_2/(R_1 + R_2) \qquad (a < 1) \tag{9-68}$$

Equation (9-66) becomes

$$\frac{E_2(s)}{E_1(s)} = \frac{1 + aTs}{1 + Ts} \tag{9-69}$$

Characteristics of the R-C Passive Phase-Lag Network

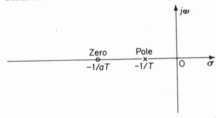

Fig. 9-38. Pole-zero configuration of $(1 + aTs)/(1 + Ts)$.

(1) Pole-Zero Configuration

The transfer function of the phase-lag network has a real zero at $s = -1/aT$ and a real pole at $s = -1/T$, as shown in Fig. 9-38. Since a is less than unity, the pole is always located to the right of the zero, and the distance between them is determined by a.

(2) Polar Plot of the R-C Phase-Lag Network

The polar plot of the transfer function represented by Eq. (9-69) is given in Fig. 9-39 for three different values of a. Just as in the case of the phase-lead network, for any given a, the angle between the tangent line drawn from the origin to the semicircle and the real axis gives the maximum phase lag ϕ_m obtainable from the network. As a is decreased, the maximum phase lag ϕ_m increases, approaching the limit of -90 deg as a approaches infinity. The frequency ω_m decreases with the increase in a.

(3) The Bode Plot of the Phase-Lag Network

The Bode plot of the phase-lag network has two corner frequencies — a positive corner at $\omega = 1/aT$, and a negative corner at $\omega = 1/T$. There is no attenuation at zero frequency.

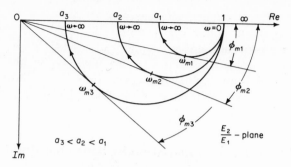

Fig. 9-39. Polar plot of
$$\frac{E_2}{E_1} = \frac{1 + aTs}{1 + Ts} \quad (a < 1)$$

Since the transfer functions of the phase-lead and phase-lag networks are identical in form except for the value of the constant factor a, the maximum phase lag of the lag network can readily be shown to be

$$\sin \phi_m = \frac{a - 1}{a + 1} \tag{9-70}$$

The design of the phase-lag compensation of feedback control systems, however, does not rely on this maximum phase shift; rather, it utilizes the attenuation of the lag network at high frequencies. It has been pointed out that, for the phase-lead compensation, the function of the lead network is to increase the phase shift of the system at the vicinity of the gain crossover

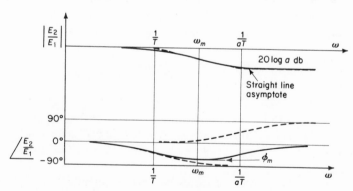

Fig. 9-40. Bode plot of the phase lag network
$$\frac{E_2}{E_1} = \frac{1 + aTs}{1 + Ts}$$

frequency while the magnitude curve of the Bode plot is kept relatively unchanged. But usually the gain crossover frequency on the magnitude curve is moved to a higher value as a consequence of the phase-lead network. The design of the lead compensation is, essentially, to find a compromise between the increase in band width and the desired amount of relative stability (phase margin). In the phase-lag compensation, the phase-lag network is used to move the gain crossover to a lower frequency while keeping the phase shift curve of the Bode plot relatively unchanged at the crossover frequency.

Design of Phase-Lag Compensation by Bode Plot Method

Just as in the case of the phase-lead compensation, the Bode plot is a very convenient tool in the design of the phase-lag compensation in the frequency domain. The design procedure may be outlined as follows:

(1) The Bode plot of the magnitude and phase shift of the open-loop transfer function $G_1(s)$ versus frequency is plotted; $G_1(s)$ is the transfer function of the uncompensated system. The gain constant K is set according to the steady-state error requirement.

(2) The phase margin and the gain margin of the original system are obtained from the Bode plot. For a certain specified phase margin, the frequency corresponding to this phase margin is found on the Bode plot; the magnitude curve must pass through the zero decibel axis at this frequency in order to realize the desired phase margin. In other words, the gain crossover of the compensated system must be located at the frequency at which the specified phase margin is found.

(3) To bring the magnitude curve down to 0 db at the new prescribed gain crossover frequency ω_c', the phase lag network must provide the amount of attenuation equal to the gain $|G_1(j\omega)|$ at the new gain crossover. Or

$$|G_1(j\omega_c')| = -20 \log a \text{ db} \qquad (9\text{-}71)$$

from which

$$a = 10^{-|G_1(j\omega_c')|/20} \qquad (a < 1) \quad (9\text{-}72)$$

(4) a having been determined (Eq. 9-72), it is necessary only to select the proper value for T to complete the design. Up to this step, we have assumed that while the gain crossover frequency is moved by attenuating the gain at ω_c, the original phase shift curve is not affected. This is not possible, however, since any modification of the magnitude curve will bring corresponding change to the phase shift curve, and vice versa. With reference to the phase characteristics of the phase lag network given in Fig. 9-40, it is apparent that, if the upper corner frequency $1/aT$ of the network is placed far below the new gain crossover frequency ω_c', the phase shift at ω_c' of $G_1(s)$ will not be appreciably affected by the lag network.

Usually the upper corner frequency $1/aT$ is placed at a frequency about one decade below the new gain crossover; i.e.,

$$\frac{1}{aT} = \frac{\omega_c'}{10} \text{ rad/sec} \tag{9-73}$$

from which

$$\frac{1}{T} = \frac{\omega_c'}{10} a \text{ rad/sec} \tag{9-74}$$

(5) The Bode plot of the compensated system is investigated to see if the performance specifications are met.

(6) If all the specifications are satisfied, the values of a and T may be substituted into Eq. (9-69) and the transfer function of the phase lag network is obtained.

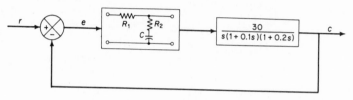

Fig. 9-41. Feedback control system with phase-lag compensation (Example 9-4).

EXAMPLE 9-4. Consider the system given in Example 9-3 for which the phase-lead compensation is ineffective. The transfer function of the uncompensated system is

$$G_1(s) = \frac{K}{s(1 + 0.1s)(1 + 0.2s)} \tag{9-75}$$

The specifications are as follows:
(1) $K_v = 30 \text{ sec}^{-1}$
(2) Phase margin ≥ 40 deg

If it is decided that the phase lag compensation is to be used, the design procedure is as follows:

(1) The Bode plot of $G_1(s)$ is plotted in Fig. 9-42 for $K = 30$.

(2) The phase margin read at the gain crossover frequency ($\omega_c = 11$ rad/sec) is -25 deg, and the system is unstable. The required phase margin is 40 deg, which can be obtained if the gain crossover frequency is moved to about 3.3 rad/sec. This means that the phase-lag network must reduce the magnitude of $G_1(j\omega)$ to zero decibels, while it does not appreciably affect the phase shift curve in the vicinity of this new gain crossover frequency. Since actually a small negative phase shift is still

introduced by the lag network at ω_c', it is a safe measure to choose the new gain crossover at a frequency some what less than 3.3 rad/sec; 3.0 rad/sec,* for example.

(3) From the magnitude curve, the gain of $G_1(j\omega)$ at $\omega_c' = 3$ rad/sec is

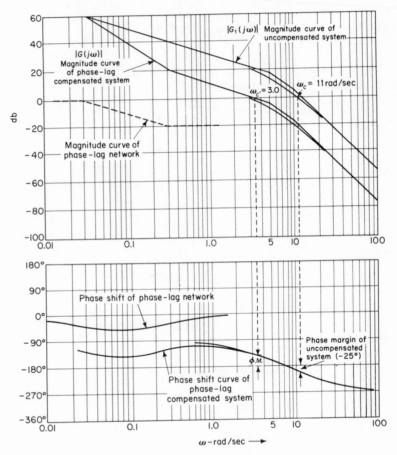

Fig. 9-42. Bode plots of open-loop transfer functions of system given in Example 9-4.

20 db, which means that the lag network must provide 20 db of attenuation at this frequency. Hence, from Eq. (9-72),

$$a = 10^{-|G_1(j\omega'c)|/20} = 10^{-1} = 0.1 \qquad (9\text{-}76)$$

---

*In other words, it is the same as selecting a safer phase margin of 45 deg.

The last equation implies that the two corners of the lag network must be placed at a distance of one decade apart in order to produce the required attenuation of 20 db.

(4) The upper corner frequency of the network, $1/aT$, is placed at the frequency one decade below the new gain crossover frequency. Thus,

$$\frac{1}{aT} = \frac{\omega_c'}{10} = \frac{3}{10} = 0.3 \text{ rad/sec} \qquad (9\text{-}77)$$

which gives $\qquad\qquad T = 33.3 \text{ sec} \qquad\qquad\qquad (9\text{-}78)$

The lower corner frequency is

$$1/T = 0.03 \qquad (9\text{-}79)$$

(5) The Bode plot of the compensated system is plotted in Fig. 9-42. It is seen that the phase margin of the compensated system is approximately 40 deg.

(6) The transfer function of the phase-lag network is

$$\frac{E_2(s)}{E_1(s)} = \frac{1 + saT}{1 + sT} = \frac{1 + 3.33s}{1 + 33.3s} \qquad (9\text{-}80)$$

and the open-loop transfer function of the compensated system is

$$G(s) = G_c(s)G_1(s) = \frac{30(1 + 3.33s)}{s(1 + 0.1s)(1 + 0.2s)(1 + 33.3s)} \qquad (9\text{-}81)$$

The magnitude versus phase shift curve of the compensated system is plotted on the Nichols chart, as shown in Fig. 9-43. It is seen that the resonant peak M_p is approximately 3 db, or a magnitude of 1.41. The band width of the system is reduced from 15 rad/sec to 5.5 rad/sec.

The root locus diagrams of the system with and without the phase-lag compensation are sketched in Fig. 9-44. It is important to note that the shape of the original root loci is hardly affected by the phase-lag compensating dipole at all. However, the critical value of K for stability is increased by a factor of 10, which is the distance between the compensating pole and zero on the Bode plot; that is, $a^{-1} = 10$. The uncompensated system becomes unstable for all values of K greater than 15, while the phase-lag compensated system will be unstable only when K is greater than 150. The compensated and the uncompensated loci cross the imaginary axis of the s-plane at approximately the same point ($\omega = 7.07$ rad/sec), since it is clear from the Bode plot in Fig. 9-42 that the phase crossover is not much affected by the phase lag characteristic.

When K is equal to 30, the roots of the characteristic equation of the compensated system are at -11.9, -0.34, and $-1.38 \pm j3.1$. The closed-loop transfer function of the compensated system can be written as

$$\frac{C(s)}{R(s)} = \frac{150(s + 0.3)}{(s + 0.34)(s + 11.9)(s + 1.38 - j3.1)(s + 1.38 + j3.1)} \tag{9-82}$$

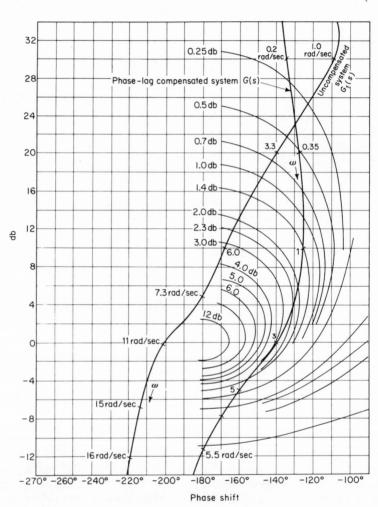

Fig. 9-43. Magnitude (db) versus phase shift of open-loop transfer function given in Example 9-4.

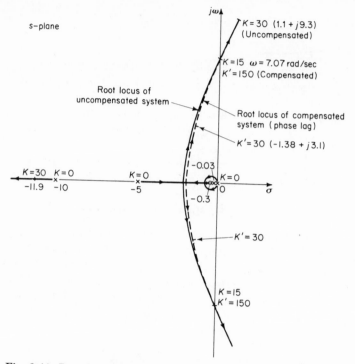

Fig. 9-44. Root locus diagrams for system in Example 9-4. Uncompensated system:

$$G_1(s) = K/s(1 + 0.1s)(1 + 0.2s)$$

Phase-lag compensated system:

$$G(s) = K(1 + 3.33s)/s(1 + 0.1s)(1 + 0.2s)(1 + 33.3s)$$

Its pole-zero configuration is shown in Fig. 9-45. It can readily be shown that, since the real zero at −0.3 and the real pole at −0.34 are very close together, they do not affect the transient response appreciably. Thus, the time response of the compensated system may be approximated by the three closed-loop poles at $s = -11.9$ and $s = -1.38 \pm j3.1$.

The Effect of the Phase-Lag Compensation

From the results of the last example, the effect of the phase lag

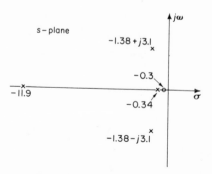

Fig. 9-45. Closed-loop poles and zeros of phase-lag compensated system in Example 9-4 ($K = 30$).

compensation on servo system performance may be summarized as follows:

Frequency Response

(1) For a given relative stability, the velocity constant is increased.

(2) The gain crossover frequency is decreased; thus, the band width of the system is reduced.

(3) For a given gain K, the magnitude curve of $G_1(s)$ is attenuated at the low frequencies, thus allowing the improvement of the phase margin and resonance peak of the system.

(4) The time response usually is slower with the lag compensation since the natural undamped frequency ω_m and the band width are decreased.

Phase-Lag Compensation by Root Locus Method

Since the transfer functions of the phase-lead and the phase-lag networks are of the same form, for the same uncompensated system, the root contour diagram may be used for either type of compensation. For the phase-lead network, the portions of the root contours corresponding to $a > 1$ are used, and those for $a < 1$ are used for the phase-lag design. To clarify this point, let us consider the second-order control system given in Example 9-1. The open-loop transfer function of the compensated system is

$$G(s) = \frac{10(1 + saT)}{s(s + 1)(1 + sT)} \qquad (9\text{-}83)$$

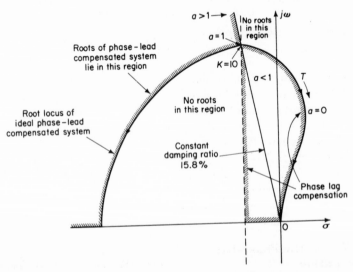

Fig. 9-46. Regions in the s-plane indicating the locations of the characteristic equation roots of phase-lag and phase-lead compensations (Example 9-1).

where, if $a < 1$, the compensation is of the phase-lag type, and if $a > 1$, the compensation is of the phase-lead type. The root contour diagram of the compensated system when a and T are variable parameters was given in Fig. 9-27. From this root contour diagram, the significance of the difference between phase-lead and phase-lag compensation in terms of the root locations is evident. Figure 9-46 shows the two regions in which the roots of the characteristic equation are found corresponding to $a < 1$ (phase-lag) and $a > 1$ (phase-lead), respectively. The straight line drawn from the origin through the $a = 1$ point represents the constant damping of 15.8 per cent, which is the damping ratio of the original uncompensated system. If the complex roots of the compensated system are to have a higher damping ratio, they must be located to the left of the $\delta = 15.8$ per cent line. From Fig. 9-46, the following facts concerning the phase-lead and phase-lag design are obtained:

(1) Improper phase-lag design may make the system less stable or even unstable. For this particular system, the value of T should be greater than 5 if the damping of the system is to be improved.

(2) Improper phase-lead compensation may also cause the system to be less stable than the original system, although it will not cause the system to become unstable.

(3) Since the distance from the complex roots to the origin in the s-plane indicates the band width of the system, the effects of the lag and lead compensations on the band width are apparent.

The servo system given in Example 9-4 serves a better purpose in the

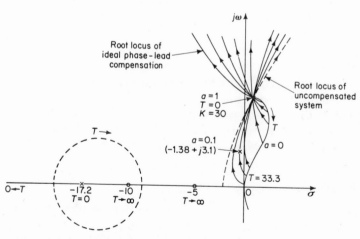

Fig. 9-47. Root contours of
$$\frac{30(1 + saT)}{s(1 + 0.1s)(1 + 0.2s)(1 + sT)}$$
(Only the two dominant root contours are shown in the diagram.)

illustration of the phase lag compensation by the root contour technique. The open-loop transfer function of the compensated system is

$$G(s) = \frac{30(1 + saT)}{s(1 + 0.1s)(1 + 0.2s)(1 + sT)} \tag{9-84}$$

where the compensation is of the phase-lag type if $a < 1$, and is of the phase-lead type if $a > 1$. The root contours of the compensated system when a and T are varied from 0 to ∞ are given in Fig. 9-47. The regions of the characteristic equation roots for lead and lag compensations are shown in Fig. 9-48. Since the root contours for $a > 1$ move rapidly upward when a

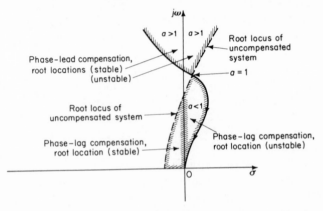

Fig. 9-48. Regions of the characteristic equation roots (dominant roots) for phase-lead and phase-lag compensation of system given in Example 9-4.

is increased, the lead compensation is apparently ineffective in this case. It is also evident that, for proper phase-lag compensation, the value of T should be large. Small values of T may not even bring the roots back into the left half of the s-plane for any value of $a < 1$. Furthermore, for large values of T, the contours travel into the left half of the s-plane, but they eventually go back to the right half of the s-plane; for each T, there is an optimum value of a which yields a maximum possible damping to the system.

(3) Lag-Lead Compensation

We have shown in the preceding sections that the phase-lead compensation usually improves the rise time and overshoot but increases the band width of a feedback control system, and that the phase-lag compensation improves the steady-state response or the stability margin, but often results in longer rise time because of reduced band width. Therefore, in regard to the effects of phase-lead and phase-lag compensations, we can say that each has its advantages and disadvantages. However, there are many systems which cannot be satisfactorily improved by the use of either scheme. We have illustrated before that feedback systems with certain characteristics cannot be effectively improveu by a phase-lead network alone. Furthermore, more stringent specifications may also make the use of pure phase-lag, as well as pure phase-lead, compensation inadequate.

A more practical and versatile arrangement is, therefore, to use a combination of the lead and lag networks. As a matter of fact, the combination of lead and lag networks, hereafter called the lag-lead compensation, contains all the advantages of both schemes, but some of the undesirable features in each are eliminated in the combined structure.

The transfer function of a lag-lead network can be written as

$$\frac{E_2(s)}{E_1(s)} = \underbrace{\frac{(1 + sT_1a)}{(1 + sT_1)}}_{\text{phase-lead}} \underbrace{\frac{(1 + sT_2b)}{(1 + sT_2)}}_{\text{phase-lag}} \qquad (a > 1),\ (b < 1) \qquad (9\text{-}85)$$

where the attenuation factor $1/a$ is not shown in the equation if we assume that adequate gain is available in the forward path of the system to compensate the loss.

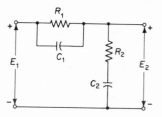

Usually it is not necessary to cascade the lead and lag networks of Figs. 9-10 and 9-37 for the realization of Eq. (9.85). A network which has the lag-lead characteristic, but a lesser number of elements, is depicted in Fig. 9-49. The transfer function of the network shown in Fig. 9-49 is

Fig. 9-49. A lag-lead network.

$$\frac{E_2(s)}{E_1(s)} = \frac{(1 + R_1C_1s)(1 + R_2C_2s)}{1 + (R_1C_1 + R_1C_2 + R_2C_2)s + R_1R_2C_1C_2s^2} \qquad (9\text{-}86)$$

Comparing Eq. (9-85) with Eq. (9-86), we have

$$aT_1 = R_1C_1 \qquad (9\text{-}87)$$

$$bT_2 = R_2C_2 \qquad (9\text{-}88)$$

$$T_1T_2 = R_1R_2C_1C_2 \qquad (9\text{-}89)$$

From Eqs. (9-87) and (9-88), we have

$$abT_1T_2 = R_1R_2C_1C_2 \qquad (9\text{-}90)$$

hence
$$ab = 1 \qquad (9\text{-}91)$$

This means that we do not have an independent choice of a and b. Once the value of b is determined, a is equal to the reciprocal of b (or vice versa).

The design of a lag-lead compensation is illustrated by the following example.

EXAMPLE 9-5. In this example, we shall again consider the system used in Examples 9-3 and 9-4. The open-loop transfer function of the uncompensated system is repeated here as

$$G_1(s) = \frac{K}{s(1 + 0.1s)(1 + 0.2s)} \tag{9-92}$$

The performance specifications are as follows:

(1) $K_v = 30 \text{ sec}^{-1}$

(2) Phase margin ≥ 40 deg

(3) After transients, the amplitude of the steady state error due to sinusoidal inputs of three units in amplitude and up to 0.1 rad/sec in frequency must not exceed 0.01 unit.

We see now that, in addition to the K_v and phase margin requirements, a third condition on the steady-state error due to low frequency signals has been added. At very low frequencies, the magnitude of the open-loop transfer function is much greater than unity; hence,

$$\left| \frac{E(j\omega)}{R(j\omega)} \right|_{\omega=0.1} = \left| \frac{1}{1 + G(j\omega)} \right|_{\omega=0.1} = \left| \frac{1}{G(j\omega)} \right|_{\omega=0.1} \tag{9-93}$$

From condition (3), we have

$$\left| \frac{E(j\omega)}{R(j\omega)} \right|_{\omega=0.1} \leq \frac{1}{300} \tag{9-94}$$

therefore $|G(j\omega)|_{\omega=0.1} \geq 300$ (9-95)

In other words, the magnitude of $G(j\omega)$ must exceed approximately 50 db at 0.1 rad/sec.

From Fig. 9-42 we see that the magnitude of $G(j\omega)$ of the phase-lag compensated system is equal to 40 db at 0.1 radian per second. We have also demonstrated in Example 9-3 that a phase-lead compensation is ineffective in this case. At this point, a lag-lead compensation seems to be the next choice. No definite procedure can be prescribed for the design of the lag-lead network. Usually a trial-and-error procedure, using the Bode plot, may provide a proper design arrangement.

We shall first determine the lag portion of the compensation by selecting proper values for T_2 and b. As a first trial, we shall move the gain crossover of $G_1(j\omega)$ from 12 rad/sec to 3 rad/sec. This corresponds to improving the phase margin from -25 deg (unstable) to 30 deg (or equivalently improving the gain margin from -10 db to $+10$ db). The lower corner of the lag network, $1/T_2$, is placed at 0.1 rad/sec, where the magnitude of $G_1(j\omega)$ is 50 db, provided that the asymptotic curves are acceptable as the final design. Since the attenuation provided by the lag network at high frequencies is 20 db, b is equal to 0.10 (Eq. 9-72). The upper corner of the lag network must then be placed at 1.0 rad/sec. The transfer function of the lag network is, therefore,

$$\frac{1 + 0.1s}{1 + s} \qquad (9\text{-}96)$$

The phase-lead portion of the compensation can be effected in much the same way as described in Sec. (1). Since b is equal to 0.10, from Eq. (9-91), a must be 10. This determines the distance between the two corners in the phase-lead network. The zero frequency attenuation of the lead network is

$$20 \log a = 20 \log 10 = 20 \text{ db} \qquad (9\text{-}97)$$

By the same method described in Eqs. (9-28) through (9-31), we obtain

$$\omega_m = 7 \text{ rad/sec} \qquad (9\text{-}98)$$

$$1/T_1 = 22 \text{ rad/sec} \qquad (9\text{-}99)$$

and $$1/aT_1 = 2.2 \text{ rad/sec} \qquad (9\text{-}100)$$

The transfer function of the lag-lead network is

$$\frac{E_2(s)}{E_1(s)} = \frac{(1 + 0.1s)(1 + 22s)}{(1 + s)(1 + 2.2s)} \qquad (9\text{-}101)$$

The Bode plots of the compensated and the uncompensated systems are depicted in Fig. 9-50. From the compensated diagram, it is clear that all the specified requirements are satisfied. The phase margin of the system is approximately 50 deg. Also, the effects of the lag and lead compensations

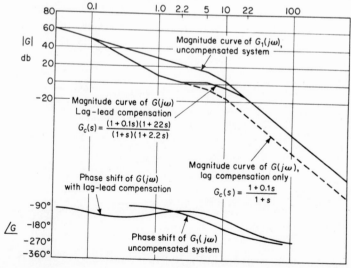

Fig. 9-50. Bode diagram for system in Example 9-5 with lag-lead compensation.

at the high frequencies cancel each other so that the band width of the system is hardly affected.

(4) Bridged-T Network Compensation

Many servo systems possess open-loop transfer functions which contain one or more pairs of complex conjugate poles. It was shown that the simple phase-lead network does not give satisfactory compensation to third- (or higher-) ordered systems with complex open-loop poles, especially if these poles are close to the imaginary axis. We may suggest the use of a compensation transfer function with two zeros and two poles. The zeros are so selected that they will cancel the undesired complex poles of the original system, and the poles are placed at more desirable locations in the s-plane. For instance, if the open-loop transfer function of the uncompensated system is

$$G_1(s) = \frac{K}{s(s^2 + s + 10)} \tag{9-102}$$

the suggested form of the compensation transfer function is

$$G_c(s) = \frac{s^2 + s + 10}{s^2 + 2\delta\omega_n s + \omega_n^2} \tag{9-103}$$

where the constants δ and ω_n are determined according to the system performance specifications. Although Eq. (9-103) can be realized by various types of passive networks, the bridged-T networks have the advantage of containing only R-C elements. The configurations of the two basic types of bridged-T R-C networks are shown in Fig. 9-51. In the

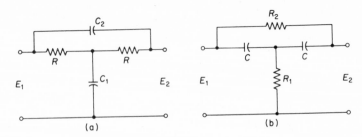

Fig. 9-51. Two basic types of bridged-T network. (a) Type 1 network; (b) Type 2 network.

following, the network shown in Fig. 9-51a is referred to as bridged-T type 1, and that shown in Fig. 9-51b is referred to as type 2.

With the assumption of zero input source impedance and infinite output load impedance, the transfer function of the bridged-T type 1 network is found to be

$$\frac{E_2(s)}{E_1(s)} = \frac{1 + 2RC_2s + R^2C_1C_2s^2}{1 + R(C_1 + 2C_2)s + R^2C_1C_2s^2} \qquad (9\text{-}104)$$

and that of the bridged-T type 2 network is

$$\frac{E_2(s)}{E_1(s)} = \frac{1 + 2R_1Cs + C^2R_1R_2s^2}{1 + C(R_1 + 2R_2)s + C^2R_1R_2s^2} \qquad (9\text{-}105)$$

When the last two equations are compared, it is apparent that the two networks have similar characteristics. If R, C_1, and C_2, in Eq. (9-104) are replaced by C, R_2, and R_1, respectively, Eq. (9-104) becomes the transfer function of the type 2 network given by Eq. (9-105).

Root Contours of the Poles and Zeros of E_2/E_1 When the Network Elements Are Varied

It is necessary to find out the behavior of the zeros and poles of the transfer functions given in Eq. (9-104) and Eq. (9-105) when the network parameters are varied. Due to the similarity of the two networks, only the type 1 will be analyzed here.

Equation (9-104) can also be written as

$$\frac{E_2(s)}{E_1(s)} = \frac{s^2 + \dfrac{2}{RC_1}s + \dfrac{1}{R^2C_1C_2}}{s^2 + \dfrac{C_1 + 2C_2}{RC_1C_2}s + \dfrac{1}{R^2C_1C_2}} \qquad (9\text{-}106)$$

If both the numerator and the denominator of the last equation are written in the standard form of a quadratic equation,

$$s^2 + 2\delta\omega_n s + \omega_n^2 = 0 \qquad (9\text{-}107)$$

We have for the numerator,

$$\omega_{nz} = \pm\frac{1}{R\sqrt{C_1C_2}} \qquad (9\text{-}108)$$

$$\delta_z = \sqrt{\frac{C_2}{C_1}} \qquad (9\text{-}109)$$

and for the denominator,

$$\omega_{np} = \pm\frac{1}{R\sqrt{C_1C_2}} \qquad (9\text{-}110)$$

$$\delta_p = \frac{C_1 + 2C_2}{2\sqrt{C_1C_2}} = \frac{1 + 2C_2/C_1}{2\sqrt{C_2/C_1}} = \frac{1 + 2\delta_z^2}{2\delta_z} \qquad (9\text{-}111)$$

By means of the root contour technique, the loci of the zeros and poles of E_2/E_1 given by Eq. (9-106) when C_1, C_2, and R vary individually are given in Fig. 9-52. When R is the varying parameter, the numerator and denominator of Eq. (9-106) contain R in the form of R^2, and the root contour method cannot be applied directly. However, the equations are of

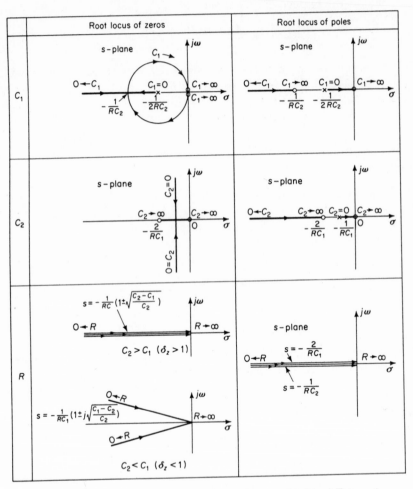

Fig. 9-52. Root contours of the poles and zeros of bridged-T type 1 network.

the second order, and the roots can be solved easily. It is seen from the zero and pole loci shown in Fig. 9-52 that the two zeros of the bridged-T network type 1 can be either real or complex. For complex zeros, C_2 must be greater than C_1. The poles can be found only on the negative real axis.

The natural undamped frequency and the damping ratio of the type 2 network may be obtained by replacing R, C_1, and C_2 in Eq. (9-108) through Eq. (9-111) by C, R_2 and R_1, respectively. Thus,

$$\omega_{nz} = \pm \frac{1}{C\sqrt{R_2 R_1}} \qquad (9\text{-}112)$$

$$\delta_z = \sqrt{\frac{R_1}{R_2}} \qquad (9\text{-}113)$$

$$\omega_{np} = \pm \frac{1}{C\sqrt{R_2 R_1}} \qquad (9\text{-}114)$$

$$\delta_p = \frac{R_2 + 2R_1}{2\sqrt{R_2 R_1}} \qquad (9\text{-}115)$$

The loci given in Fig. 9-52 can likewise be used for the type 2 bridged-T network if corresponding symbols are altered.

EXAMPLE 9-6.* The control system shown in Fig. 9-53 is selected to demonstrate the use of the bridged-T network for servo compensation. The root locus diagram of the uncompensated system is shown in Fig. 9-54.

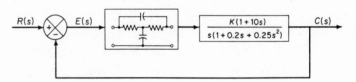

Fig. 9-53. Feedback control system with bridged-T compensation.

Evidently, the uncompensated system has a very small damping ratio and the response will be quite oscillatory. The bridged-T network used to compensate this system should possess a pair of complex zeros that will cancel the poles of the original open-loop function. Let us select the type 1 network first; the transfer function is of the form

$$\frac{E_2(s)}{E_1(s)} = \frac{s^2 + 0.8s + 4}{s^2 + 2\delta_p \omega_{np} s + \omega_{np}^2} \qquad (9\text{-}116)$$

Since

$$\omega_{nz} = \frac{1}{R\sqrt{C_2 C_1}} = \sqrt{4} = 2 \qquad (9\text{-}117)$$

and

$$\delta_z = \sqrt{\frac{C_2}{C_1}} = 0.2 \qquad (9\text{-}118)$$

---

*This example is taken from Chandaket, Rosenstein, "Notes on Bridged-t Complex Conjugate Compensation and Four-Terminal Network Loading," *AIEE Transactions, Applications and Industry*, July, 1959.

from Eq. (9-114) and Eq. (9-115) we have

$$\omega_{np} = \omega_{nz} = 2 \tag{9-119}$$

and

$$\delta_p = \frac{1 + 2\delta_z^2}{2\delta_z} = \frac{1 + 0.08}{0.4} = 2.7 \tag{9-120}$$

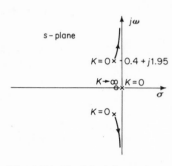

Fig. 9-54. Root loci for system with

$$G_1(s) = \frac{K(1 + 10s)}{s(1 + 0.2s + 0.25s^2)}$$

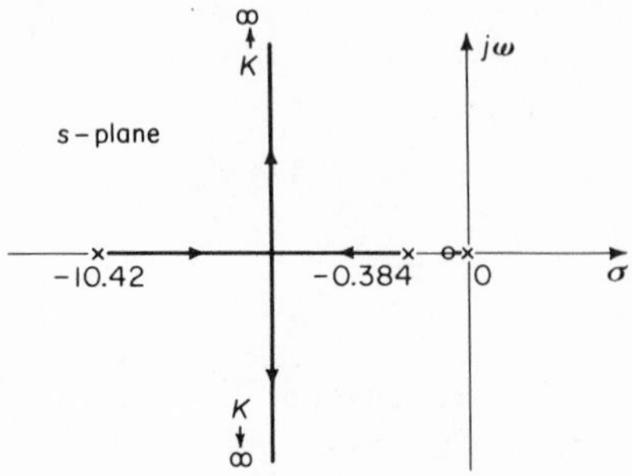

Fig. 9-55. Root loci of bridged-T compensated system (Example 9-6).

The transfer function of the bridged-T type 1 network is

$$\frac{E_2(s)}{E_1(s)} = \frac{s^2 + 0.8s + 4}{s^2 + 10.8s + 4} = \frac{s^2 + 0.8s + 4}{s(s + 0.384)(s + 10.42)} \tag{9-121}$$

The root locus diagram of the compensated system is shown in Fig. 9-55. It is apparent that the system is much improved by the bridged-T compensation.

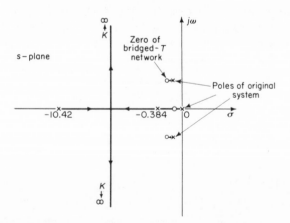

Fig. 9-56. Root loci of compensated system in Example 9-6 when pole-zero concellation is inexact.

Although this analysis is made on the basis of exact cancellation of the unwanted poles, an impossibility in physical systems, the root loci clearly show that it is not necessary to cancel the poles of $G_1(s)$ exactly. Figure 9-56 illustrates the root locus diagram with the poles and zeros close together. The system will have essentially the same performance characteristics, because the transient terms due to the closed-loop complex dipole are very small and will not affect the time response significantly.

9.5 Feedback Compensation

In general, it is common to introduce compensating networks and elements into the feedback paths of a control system. A typical application of the feedback compensation is a system with tachometer feedback or rate feedback, in which the tachometer is used to feed back a signal proportional to the first derivative of the output variable.

In Chapter 8, Example 8-14, the root loci of a system with tachometric feedback compensation were illustrated. It was shown that, by using the root contour technique, the effects of the forward gain K_1 and the tachometer constant K_2 on the roots of the characteristic equation can be determined from the root contour plots. In the following example, the root contour technique will be used to design a system with feedback compensation which involves several unknown parameters.

EXAMPLE 9-7. The multiple-loop system given in Example 8-14 is now modified by inserting a phase-lead network in the feedback path; the resultant configuration is shown in Fig. 9-57.

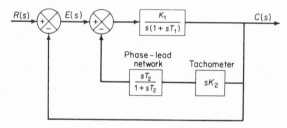

Fig. 9-57. Control system with tachometric and phase-lead feedback.

Normally, the constants T_2, K_1, and K_2 of the system are not given and must be determined to satisfy the given design specifications.

The construction of the root contours and root loci when the above-mentioned three parameters are considered to be the variable parameters is described as follows:

(1) As a first step, the feedback loop with the lead network and the

tachometer is opened. In other words, the system is considered first without any compensation. The characteristic equation of the uncompensated system is readily obtained as

$$T_1 s^2 + s + K_1 = 0 \qquad (9\text{-}122)$$

in which the value of T_1 is assumed to be given, but K_1 can be varied from 0 to ∞. The root loci of Eq. (9-122) corresponding to the uncompensated system are given in Fig. 9-58.

Let us assume that the velocity constant K_v of the compensated system is specified to be 20. The open-loop transfer function of the compensated system is

$$\frac{C(s)}{E(s)} = \frac{K_1(1 + sT_2)}{s(1 + sT_1)(1 + sT_2) + K_1 K_2 T_2 s^2} \qquad (9\text{-}123)$$

Thus, to realize $K_v = 20$, K_1 must equal 20. The two roots of Eq. (9-122) when $T_1 = 1$ are found to be at $s = -0.5 + j4.44$ and $s = -0.5 - j4.44$.

(2) The second step is to close the tachometric feedback path, but let $T_2 = 0$. The characteristic equation of the system with only tachometric feedback is

$$s(1 + sT_1) + sK_1 K_2 + K_1 = 0 \qquad (9\text{-}124)$$

or

$$1 + \frac{sK_1 K_2}{s(1 + sT_1) + K_1} = 0 \qquad (9\text{-}125)$$

Thus, the root contours when K_2 varies from 0 to ∞ must start at the points on the root loci given in Fig. 9-58, and end at $s = 0$. For $K_1 = 20$ and $T_1 = 1$, the root contours start at $s = -0.5 + j4.44$ and $s = -0.5 - j4.44$. The root contours are sketched in Fig. 9-59.

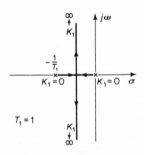

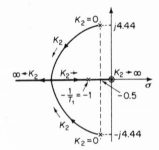

Fig. 9-58. Root loci of the control system shown in Fig. 9-57 with the tachometric feedback loop opened.

Fig. 9-59. Root contours of system shown in Fig. 9-57 with only tachometric feedback $(T_2 = 0,\ T_1 = 1,\ K_1 = 20)$.

(3) The last step in the construction of the root contours of the entire system is to consider the phase-lead network together with the tachometer $(T_2 \neq 0)$.

The characteristic equation of the completely compensated system is

$$s(1 + sT_1)(1 + sT_2) + K_1K_2T_2s^2 + K_1(1 + sT_2) = 0 \qquad (9\text{-}126)$$

rearranging, we have

$$[s(1 + sT_1) + K_1] + sT_2 + [s(1 + sT_1) + sK_1K_2 + K_1] = 0 \qquad (9\text{-}127)$$

The last equation can also be written as

$$1 + \frac{sT_2[s(1 + sT_1) + sK_1K_2 + K_1]}{s(1 + sT_1) + K_1} = 0 \qquad (9\text{-}128)$$

The root contours of Eqs. (9-126) or (9-127), when T_2 is varied from 0 to ∞, must start at the poles and end at the zeros of

$$\frac{sT_2[s(1 + sT_1) + sK_1K_2 + K_1]}{s(1 + sT_1) + K_1} \qquad (9\text{-}129)$$

Note also that one of the zeros of (9-129) is at $s = 0$ and that the rest of the zeros are the same as the roots of Eq. (9-124); the poles of (9-129) are the same as the roots of Eq. (9-122). For $T_1 = 1$ and $K_1 = 20$, the roots of Eq. (9-122) are at $s = -0.5 + j4.44$ and $s = -0.5 - j4.44$; thus, the root contours, when T_2 varies, must start at these two points. The root contours of Eq. (9-124), when K_2 varies, are sketched in Fig. (9-59), and the ending points of the root contours when T_2 varies must be found on these contours. For $K_2 = 0.25$ and $K_2 = 0.397$, the root contours when T_2 is varied are shown in Figs. 9-60 and 9-61, respectively.

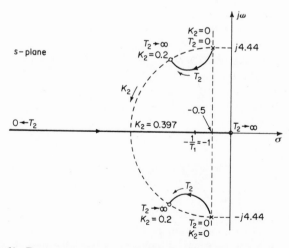

Fig. 9-60. Root contours of phase-lead network and tachometer feedback compensated system given in Example 9-7 ($K_1 = 20$, $T_1 = 1$, $K_2 = 0.2$).

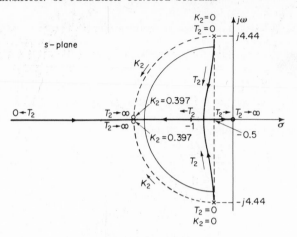

Fig. 9-61. Root contours of phase-lead network and tachometer feedback compensated system given in Example 9-7 ($K_1 = 20$, $T_1 = 1$, $K_2 = 0.397$).

Problems

9-1. The open-loop transfer function of a gun-director servomechanism is given by

$$G(s) = \frac{K}{s(1 + 0.2s)(1 + 0.5s)} \qquad H(s) = 1.$$

The maximum output velocity of the system is specified as 2 rpm, and the permissible steady-state error in the output position is to be within 2 deg. (a) Determine the smallest value of K which will satisfy the specification given above. With this value of K, analyze the system performance by evaluating the system gain margin, the phase margin, the resonance peak, and the band width.

(b) A lead compensation with transfer function $(1 + 0.4s)/(1 + 0.08s)$ is now inserted in the forward path of the system. Evaluate the values of the gain margin, the phase margin, M_p, and the band width of the system. Make comments on the effects of the lead compensation on the system performance.

(c) Sketch the root locus diagrams for the compensated and the uncompensated systems.

9-2. A unity-feedback control system has the open-loop transfer function

$$G(s) = \frac{K}{s(1 + 0.1s)(1 + 0.0005s)}$$

The following specifications on system performance are given:
(a) The velocity error constant $K_v \geq 1000$ sec^{-1}.
(b) The phase margin must be at least 45 deg.
Design a series compensating network so that the compensated system will satisfy these specifications. Compare the following quantities of the compensated and the uncompensated systems: Gain margin, phase margin, M_p, and band width.

9-3. A simple feedback control system is shown in Fig. 9P-3 in block diagram form. The system must meet the following performance specifications:
(a) Acceleration constant $K_a = 5 \sec^{-2}$
(b) The resonance peak $M_p \leq 1.5$
Design a series phase-lead compensation to satisfy these requirements. Sketch the root locus diagrams for the uncompensated and the compensated systems. What are the values of the damping ratio and the band width of the compensated system?

9-4. The open-loop transfer function of a unity-feedback control system is given as

$$G(s) = \frac{8}{s(1 + 0.1s + 0.01s^2)}$$

(a) Determine the stability of the system.
(b) Design a series compensation so that the system has a peak resonance of approximately 1.5. Plot the frequency response curves (M versus ω) for the uncompensated and the compensated systems.

9-5. A voltage regulator has an open-loop transfer function

$$G(s) = \frac{K}{(1 + 0.5s)(1 + 0.25s)} \qquad H(s) = 1$$

The output voltage is to be regulated at 1000 v ± 0.5 v. Design a series compensating network for the system so that not only is the steady-state requirement met, but also the peak resonance of the system is not greater than 1.5.

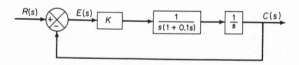

Fig. 9P-5

9-6. The block diagram in Fig. 9P-6 shows the basic components of a servomechanism before compensation. The system must meet the following specifications:
(a) Velocity constant $K_v = 20 \sec^{-1}$
(b) Phase margin ≥ 45 deg
Design a series compensating network to satisfy these requirements.

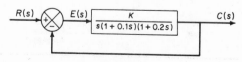

Fig. 9P-6

9-7. The feedback control system described in Problem 9-4 is to be compensated by inserting a bridged-T network in the forward path. Assuming that perfect cancellation of the undesirable poles of $G(s)$ by the zeros of the network is possible, determine the per cent overshoot of the compensated system. Plot the frequency response curve (M versus ω) for the compensated system.

9-8. Tachometer feedback is employed frequently to permit the stabilization of servomechanisms. In Fig. 9P-8 is shown a typical application of this type of feedback. Choose the tachometer constant K_t to result in a relative damping ratio of 50 per cent. How does the tachometric feedback affect the band width of the system?

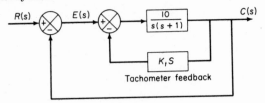

Tachometer feedback

Fig. 9P-8

9-9. For the multiple-loop feedback control system of Fig. 9-57 (Example 9-7), given $K_1 = 20$ amd $K_2 = 0.2$, determine the value of T_2 so that the relative damping of the closed-loop system is critical.

9-10. The block diagram of a servomechanism is shown in Fig. 9P-10. By means of the root contour diagram, show the effect of variation in the value of T on the location of the closed-loop poles.

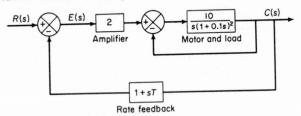

Rate feedback

Fig. 9P-10

9-11. The system described in Problem 9-3 is to be compensated by an inner positional feedback loop, as shown in Fig. 9P-11. The velocity error constant

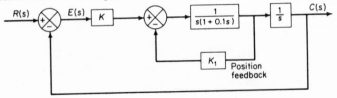

Position feedback

Fig. 9P-11

of the system is to be 5 sec^{-1}. Sketch the root contour diagram of the compensated system as a function of K_1. Determine the maximum value of the damping ratio of the complex closed-loop poles obtainable by varying the value of K_1. What is this value of K_1? What is the value of M_p for this value of K_1?

9-12. The system described in Problem 9-3 is now to be compensated by a tachometric feedback loop, as shown in Fig. 9P-12. $K_a = 5$ sec^{-2}. Sketch the root contour diagram for the compensated system as a function of K_1. Determine the value of K_1 so that the damping ratio of the complex closed-loop poles is 70 per cent. What are the band width and M_p with this value of K_1?

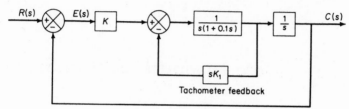

Fig. 9P-12

10

Sampled-Data Feedback Control Systems

10.1 Introduction

The conventional feedback control systems generally have variables which are continuous with respect to time. In other words, the systems considered in the previous chapters contain signals which are known at all times. In recent years there has been growing activity and interest in a new field known as the sampled-data, or digital, control systems. Usually, "sampled-data systems" refers to a more general class of systems while "digital control systems" implies the use of digital computers or digital sensing devices in a control system.

In general, a sampled-data system receives data or information only intermittently at some specific instants of time. For instance, the error signal in a control system may be supplied only intermittently in the form of pulses, in which case the control system receives no information about the error signal during the periods between two consecutive pulses. If the discrete information is received at a regular interval, the sampling is called "periodic." Conversely, if the spacing between signals is time varying or at random, the sampling is termed "aperiodic" or "random."

Why Sampled Data?

In practice, we can find many systems in which the input signal is available only in sampled or discrete form. Under certain conditions, a

360

system with sampling operation purposely introduced may give improved performance over the system with continuous data. In modern technology the applications of sampled-data systems are wide, but, on the whole, they can be divided into the following two categories:

(1) *Control Systems with Inherent Sampling*

In practice, there is a class of systems for which the signals are available only in sampled form. Some examples are as follows:

(a) *Radar Tracking System*. The input signal of a radar tracking system is in the form of a pulse train.

(b) *Time Sharing Systems*. In many systems, in order to reduce the cost of information transmission, the data transmission link is shared among several systems.

(c) *Digital Computers in Control Systems*. The use of digital computers as elements in control systems employing otherwise conventional elements has become increasingly popular in recent years.* For the same capacity, digital computers are light in weight when compared to analog devices. It will be shown later that digital computers used as compensation elements are preferable to the continuous types in the improvement of static and dynamic system characteristics. Figure 10-1 shows the block diagram of a

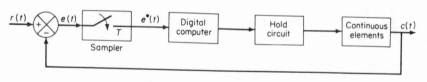

Fig. 10-1. A feedback control system employing a digital computer.

feedback control system employing a digital computer as a system component. The figure represents only one of a number of ways in which a digital computer may be incorporated in a control system. The sampling device (usually called the sampler) converts the continuous signal into digital or numerical form for the input to the digital computer. The digital computer performs a series of operations on the input sampled data and supplies the result in digital form to the data reconstruction unit (hold circuit). The hold circuit then converts the pulsed data back into continuous data which is, in turn, applied to the continuous elements.

---

*W. K. Linvill and J. M. Salzer, "Analysis of Control Systems Involving Digital Computers," *Proc. IRE*, Vol. 41, part 2, 1953.

(2) *Control Systems with Intentional Sampling*

Frequently, the sampling operation is purposely introduced to an otherwise continuous system. Under certain conditions a sampled-data control system with variable sampling periods is better in performance than conventional continuous systems. It can be shown that continuous systems with transportation lag can be stabilized by introducing sampling. In recent years, the studies of a new concept of control, the adaptive control, have become increasingly popular. The adaptive control systems, which are also called the self-optimizing systems, have the ability to change their own parameters in response to a change in operating conditions, environments, or system inputs. Systems with sampled data can, in general, facilitate the realization of the adaptive principle. For instance, the control system shown in Fig. 10-2 describes a possible scheme of the adaptive

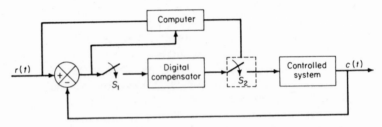

Fig. 10-2. Block diagram of a sampled-data adaptive control system.

control. The computer in the system measures the error and the input signals, and makes adjustment of the pulse transfer function of the digital compensator by varying the sampling function of the sampler S_2 so that the response of the system is optimum in some predefined sense.

Some other reasons for intentional sampling are as follows:

(a) *Improved Sensitivity.* Sometimes it is necessary to drive a load by a signal which is available at a relatively low power level. By sampling the low-power signal, the sensing device can be made extremely sensitive in terms of power gain. An example of this application is the chopper-bar galvanometer.*

(b) *Advantage in Working with Digital Signals.* Digital coded signals can usually be stored and transmitted easily and accurately.

10.2 The Sampling Process

(1) *The Sampling Switch (The Sampler)*

The device which converts a continuous signal into a sequence of pulses is called a sampling switch or sampler. A schematic representation of the

---

*J. R. Ragazzini and G. F. Franklin, *Sampled-Data Control Systems*, McGraw-Hill Book Company, Inc., New York, 1958, p. 8.

sampler is shown in Fig. 10-3a. The sampler is assumed to close for a short duration of p every T seconds. If the input to the sampler $e(t)$ is a continuous function of time, the output of the sampler, denoted by the symbol

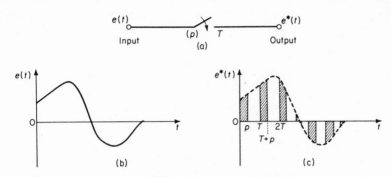

Fig. 10-3. The actual sampling process. (a) Sampler representing the sampling process; (b) Input to sampler; (c) Output of sampler.

$e^*(t)$, is a train of amplitude-modulated pulses of width p occurring at the sampling instants 0, T, $2T$, ..., nT... In other words, at $t = 0$, the sampler closes for p seconds, and during this short interval, $e^*(t) = e(t)$ After $t = p$ seconds, the sampler opens and the output signal is zero. For a repetitive uniform sampler, this process is repeated once every T seconds. In general, the sampler does not have to sample at a uniform rate. It has been shown† that a sampler with cyclic sampling rate can actually improve the stability of a sampled-data control system. The uniform sampling process is illustrated in Fig. 10-3b and c.

(2) *The Ideal Sampler (The Impulse Approximation)*

Figure 10-3 illustrates that the output of a true sampler contains a train of pulses; the amplitude of each pulse follows the amplitude variation of the input time function $e(t)$ during the pulse width p. However, the exact analysis of the sampled-data systems with finite pulse widths is quite complex.† Usually, the sampler is replaced by an "ideal sampler" whose output $e^*(t)$ contains a train of impulses. If the pulse width p of the sampler output is very small compared to the dominant time constant of the continuous part of the system and to the sampling period T, the pulse train of finite pulse width can be approximated by an impulse train.

---

*J. Tou, "Optimum Control Through Tuned Sampling," *Proc. National Electronics Conference.* 1959.

†G. Farmanfarma, "Study of Finite Pulsed Feedback Systems," *Transaction, AIEE,* part II, July, 1958. J. Tou, "Analysis of Sampled-Data Control Systems with Finite Sampling Duration," *Proc. National Electronic Conference,* 1957.

If the input to the sampler $e(t)$ is a continuous function, as shown in Fig. 10-4a, the output $e^*(t)$ of the ideal sampler is related to the input $e(t)$ by

$$e^*(t) = e(t)\delta_T(t) \tag{10-1}$$

where $\delta_T(t)$ is a unit-impulse train, or

$$\delta_T(t) = \sum_{n=0}^{\infty} \delta(t - nT) \tag{10-2}$$

where $\delta(t - nT)$ is an impulse of unit area (or strength) occurring at time $t = nT$. Hence, Eq. (10-1) can be written as

$$e^*(t) = \sum_{n=0}^{\infty} e(nT)\delta(t - nT) \tag{10-3}$$

The last equation indicates that the sampler output $e^*(t)$ is a train of impulses whose respective impulse areas (strengths) are equal to the magnitudes of $e(t)$ at the corresponding sampling instants $t = nT$. The operation of the ideal sampler is illustrated in Fig. 10-4.

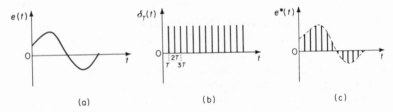

(a)   (b)   (c)

Fig. 10-4. Sampling operation of an ideal sampler. (a) Input to sampler; (b) Unit-impulse train; (c) Output of sampler.

10.3 Mathematical Analysis of the Sampling Process

In this section, the transform representation of the sampler output $e^*(t)$ will be obtained by two different methods.

(1) *The Method of Laplace Transform*

The Laplace transform of the sampler output $e^*(t)$ can be written as

$$\mathcal{L}[e^*(t)] = \mathcal{L}\left[\sum_{n=0}^{\infty} e(nT)\delta(t - nT) \right] = E^*(s) \tag{10-4}$$

Since the Laplace transform of the impulse $\delta(t - nT)$ is e^{-nTs},

$$E^*(s) = \sum_{n=0}^{\infty} e(nT)e^{-nTs} \tag{10-5}$$

In the last equation, $E^*(s)$ represents the ordinary Laplace transform of the time function $e^*(t)$. Since $e^*(t)$ describes only the values of $e(t)$ at the sampling instants, it is emphasized that $E^*(s)$ carries no information concerning the behavior of the sampled function during the sampling period T. It is important to notice that Eq. (10-5) is very similar to the definition of the Laplace transform of $e(t)$; i.e.,

$$E(s) = \int_0^\infty e(t)e^{-st}\,dt \tag{10-6}$$

Consequently, $E(s)$ is the transform of a continuous time function $e(t)$, and $E^*(s)$ is the transform of $e^*(t)$, which is a train of impulses modulated by $e(t)$. One should not be alarmed that $E^*(s)$ represented by Eq. (10-5) is an infinite series. If the Laplace transform of $e(t)$ is a rational function, $E^*(s)$ can always be written in a closed form. The following examples will illustrate this property.

EXAMPLE 10-1. Let $e(t) = u(t) =$ unit-step function. From Eq. (10-5), the Laplace transform of the sampled $e(t)$, $e^*(t)$ is

$$E^*(s) = \sum_{n=0}^\infty e(nT)e^{-nTs} = \sum_{n=0}^\infty e^{-nTs}$$

$$= 1 + e^{-Ts} + e^{-2Ts} + \cdots = \frac{1}{1 - e^{-Ts}} \tag{10-7}$$

EXAMPLE 10-2. Let $e(t) = e^{-t}$; then $e(nT) = e^{-nT}$:

$$E^*(s) = \sum_{n=0}^\infty e^{-nT}e^{-nTs} = \sum_{n=0}^\infty e^{-nT(s+1)} = \frac{1}{1 - e^{-T(s+1)}} \tag{10-8}$$

(2) *The Method of Complex Convolution (Real Multiplication)*

Alternate forms for $E^*(s)$ can be obtained from the theory of complex convolution.† The Laplace transform of $e^*(t)$ can be written as

$$\mathcal{L}[e^*(t)] = \mathcal{L}[e(t) \cdot \delta_T(t)] = \mathcal{L}[e(t)] * \mathcal{L}[\delta_T(t)] \tag{10-9}$$

or

$$E^*(s) = E(s) * \Delta_T(s) \tag{10-10}$$

where the $*$ symbol represents the complex convolution operation.

But

$$\Delta_T(s) = \mathcal{L}[\delta_T(t)] = 1 + e^{-sT} + e^{-2sT} + \cdots = \frac{1}{1 - e^{-sT}} \tag{10-11}$$

hence

$$E^*(s) = E(s) * \frac{1}{1 - e^{-sT}} \tag{10-12}$$

---

†M. F. Gardner and J. L. Barnes, *Transient in Linear Systems*, Vol. I, John Wiley & Sons, N. Y., 1942, pp. 275–278.

It follows from the definition of complex convolution that Eq. (10-12) can be written as

$$E^*(s) = \frac{1}{2\pi j} \int_{c-j\infty}^{c+j\infty} E(p)\, \frac{1}{1 - e^{-T(s-p)}}\, dp \qquad (10\text{-}13)$$

where p is a dummy variable.

The path of integration of Eq. (10-13) in the complex p-plane is along the line from $c - j\infty$ to $c + j\infty$, as shown in Fig. 10-5. The poles of $E(p)$ normally lie in the left half of the p-plane and are finite in number. The

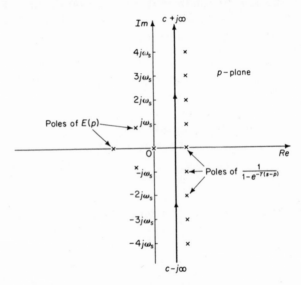

Fig. 10-5. Pole configuration of

$$\frac{1}{1 - e^{-T(s-p)}}\, E(p)$$

poles of $1/1 - e^{-T(s-p)}$ are the zeros of $1 - e^{-T(s-p)} = 0$, which are at $-T(s - p) = 2\pi nj$ for $-\infty < n < \infty$, where n is an integer. Thus, the poles of $1/1 - e^{-T(s-p)}$ are at

$$p = s + 2\pi nj/T = s + jn\omega_s \qquad (10\text{-}14)$$

where

$$\omega_s = 2\pi/T \qquad (10\text{-}15)$$

Equation (10-14) indicates that these poles are infinite in number, occurring at frequency intervals of $\pm\, n\omega_s$ along the path $Re(p) = Re(s)$ in the p-plane. Normally, the convolution integral of Eq. (10-13) can be carried out by means of the contour integration with the contour formed by the $c - j\infty$ to $c + j\infty$ line and a semicircle enclosing either the entire right half or the entire left half of the p-plane. The contour integral is then evaluated by means of the residue theorem† of complex variables. In other words, Eq. (10-13) can be written as

$$E^*(s) = \frac{1}{2\pi j} \int_{c-j\infty}^{c+j\infty} E(p) \frac{1}{1 - e^{-T(s-p)}} dp$$

$$= \frac{1}{2\pi j} \oint_{\Gamma_1} E(p) \frac{1}{1 - e^{-T(s-p)}} dp - \frac{1}{2\pi j} \oint E(p) \frac{1}{1 - e^{-T(s-p)}} dp \tag{10-16}$$

or $E^*(s) = \frac{1}{2\pi j} \int_{c-j\infty}^{c+j\infty} E(p) \frac{1}{1 - e^{-T(s-p)}} dp$

$$= \frac{1}{2\pi j} \oint_{\Gamma_2} E(p) \frac{1}{1 - e^{-T(s-p)}} dp - \frac{1}{2\pi j} \oint E(p) \frac{1}{1 - e^{-T(s-p)}} dp \tag{10-17}$$

The two possible paths Γ_1 and Γ_2 are shown in Fig. 10-6.

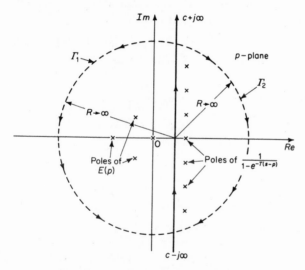

Fig. 10-6. Paths of contour integration.

If
$$\lim_{s \to \infty} E(s) = 0 \tag{10-18}$$

Eq. (10-16) can be written as

$$E^*(s) = \frac{1}{2\pi j} \oint E(p) \frac{1}{1 - e^{-T(s-p)}} dp \tag{10-19}$$

since the contour integral along the infinite semicircle vanishes. The singularity enclosed by the path Γ_1 is finite in number, and the integral

---

†R. V. Churchill, *Introduction to Complex Variables and Applications*, McGraw-Hill Book Company, New York, 1948.

along the infinite semicircle is zero. Hence, the theorem of residues can be applied to Eq. (10-19). Thus,

$$E^*(s) = \sum_{\text{poles of } E(p)} \text{Residues of } \left[E(p) \frac{1}{1 - e^{-T(s-p)}} \right] \tag{10-20}$$

If $E(p)$ has only k simple poles, and we let $E(p)$ be of the form

$$E(p) = N(p)/D(p) \tag{10-21}$$

Eq. (10-20) becomes

$$E^*(s) = \sum_{n=1}^{k} \frac{N(s_n)}{D'(s_n)} \times \frac{1}{1 - e^{-T(s-s_n)}} \tag{10-22}$$

where

$$D'(s_n) = \frac{dD(p)}{dp} \bigg|_{p=s_n} \tag{10-23}$$

and s_n is the poles of $E(s)$.

It can be shown that Eq. (10-23) and Eq. (10-5) are identical. The following examples will illustrate the applications of Eq. (10-23) and the similarity between Eqs. (10-5) and (10-23).

EXAMPLE 10-3. Let $e(t) = e^{-t}$ be the input time function to an ideal sampler with sampling period T. The Laplace transform of $e(t)$ is $E(s) = 1/(s+1)$.

In Eq. (10-22),

$$N(s) = 1 \tag{10-24}$$

$$D(s) = s + 1 \tag{10-25}$$

hence

$$D'(s) = 1 \tag{10-26}$$

Since $E(p)$ has one pole at $p = -1$,

$$D'(s_1) = 1 \tag{10-27}$$

and

$$E^*(s) = \frac{1}{1 - e^{-T(s+1)}} \tag{10-28}$$

which checks with the result obtained in Example 10-2 by using Eq. (10-5).

EXAMPLE 10-4. Let

$$e(t) = e^{-t} - e^{-2t} \tag{10-29}$$

or

$$E(s) = \frac{1}{(s+1)(s+2)} \tag{10-30}$$

By using Eq. (10-5)

$$E^*(s) = \sum_{n=0}^{\infty} e(nT)e^{-nTs}$$

$$= \sum_{n=0}^{\infty} (e^{-nT} - e^{-2nT})e^{-nTs} \tag{10-31}$$

Hence,

$$E^*(s) = \frac{1}{1 - e^{-T(s+1)}} - \frac{1}{1 - e^{-T(s+2)}} \tag{10-32}$$

By using Eq. (10-22),

$$N(s) = 1 \tag{10-33}$$

$$D(s) = (s + 1)(s + 2) \tag{10-34}$$

and

$$D'(s) = 2s + 3 \tag{10-35}$$

Hence,

$$E^*(s) = \sum_{n=1}^{2} \frac{1}{D'(s_n)} \frac{1}{1 - e^{-T(s-s_n)}}$$

$$= \frac{1}{1 - e^{-T(s+1)}} - \frac{1}{1 - e^{-T(s+2)}} \tag{10-36}$$

Care must be taken when $E^*(s)$ is evaluated according to Eq. (10-17) by following the path Γ_2 around the right half of the p-plane. Since there is an infinite number of poles enclosed by the path Γ_2 and there is a singularity on the path, strictly speaking, the residue theorem cannot be applied. Furthermore, the integral along the infinite semicircle may not even vanish. For if the degree of the denominator of $E(s)$ in s is not higher than that of the numerator by at least two, the integral along the infinite semicircle may be finite or may not converge.

Let it be assumed that $E(s)$ satisfies the condition:

$$\lim_{s \to \infty} sE(s) = 0 \tag{10-37}$$

which implies that the degree of the denominator of $E(s)$ in s is higher than that of the numerator by at least two. From the initial value theorem in ordinary Laplace transform theory, Eq. (10-37) corresponds to

$$\lim_{t \to 0} e(t) = 0 \tag{10-38}$$

If Eq. (10-37) is satisfied by $E(s)$, the integration around the semicircle of infinite radius in the right half of the plane is zero, and Eq. (10-17) becomes

$$E^*(s) = \frac{1}{2\pi j} \oint_{\Gamma_2} E(p) \frac{1}{1 - e^{-T(s-p)}} \, dp \tag{10-39}$$

Let it also be assumed that, although the path Γ_2 encloses an infinite number of simple poles, the residue theorem can still be applied.

$$E^*(s) = -\Sigma \text{ Residues of } E(p) \frac{1}{1 - e^{-T(s-p)}} \tag{10-40}$$

or

$$E^*(s) = -\sum_{n=-\infty}^{\infty} \frac{N(s_n)}{D'(s_n)} E(s_n) \tag{10-41}$$

But since $N(p) = 1$, and

$$D'(p) = \frac{d}{dp} [1 - e^{-T(s-p)}] = -Te^{-T(s-p)} \tag{10-42}$$

$$D'(s_n) = D'(p)_{p=s_n} = D'(p)_{p=s+jn\omega_s} = -T \tag{10-43}$$

substituting the last two equations into Eq. (10-41) yields

$$E^*(s) = \frac{1}{T} \sum_{n=-\infty}^{\infty} E(s + jn\omega_s) \qquad (10\text{-}44)$$

where $\omega_s = 2\pi/T$ is called the sampling frequency in radians per second.

Although the validity of Eq. (10-44) is restricted, and it is derived without mathematical rigor, it gives a clear indication of the characteristics of the ideal sampler in the frequency domain. Equation (10-44) shows that the ideal sampler is a harmonic generator. If the input function $e(t)$ is a sinusoid of frequency ω, the output of the sampler will contain frequencies $\omega \pm n\omega_s$, $(-\infty \leqslant n \leqslant \infty)$.

(3) A General Expression for $E^*(s)$

Equation (10-44) is in error if the conditions stated in Eq. (10-37) or Eq. (10-38) are not satisfied. If $e(0) = $ finite number, a general expression for $E^*(s)$ is

$$E^*(s) = \frac{1}{2} e(0^+) + \frac{1}{T} \sum_{n=-\infty}^{\infty} E(s + jn\omega_s) \qquad (10\text{-}45)$$

When $e(0^+)$ is nonzero, the expression for $E^*(s)$ given in Eq. (10-44) only samples half of the actual value of $e(t)$ at $t = 0$. However, Eq. (10-44) is entirely valid if $e(t)$ does not possess a jump at $t = 0$.

At this point, it is appropriate to summarize the various possible mathematical descriptions of the ideal sampler given in this section.

(1)
$$E^*(s) = \sum_{n=0}^{\infty} e(nT)e^{-nTs} \qquad (10\text{-}46)$$

This equation is essentially just the ordinary Laplace transform of the sampler output $e^*(t)$. The input function $e(t)$ must be a single-valued function of time defined for $t > 0$; it is Laplace transformable.

(2)
$$E^*(s) = \sum_{n=1}^{k} \frac{N(s_n)}{D'(s_n)} \times \frac{1}{1 - e^{-T(s-s_n)}} \qquad (10\text{-}47)$$

where
$$E(s) = N(s)/D(s) \qquad (10\text{-}48)$$

and
$$D'(s_n) = dD(p)/dp_{p=s_n} \qquad (10\text{-}49)$$

Equation (10-47) is valid only when

$$\lim_{s \to \infty} E(s) = 0 \qquad (10\text{-}50)$$

since otherwise, the residue theorem cannot be applied in deriving Eq. (10-47).

(3)
$$E^*(s) = \frac{1}{T} \sum_{n=-\infty}^{\infty} E(s + jn\omega_s) \qquad (10\text{-}51)$$

The last equation is valid only if

$$\lim_{s \to \infty} sE(s) = 0 \tag{10-52}$$

(4)
$$E^*(s) = \frac{1}{2} e(0^+) + \frac{1}{T} \sum_{n=-\infty}^{\infty} E(s + jn\omega_s) \tag{10-53}$$

The last equation is valid only if

$$\lim_{s \to \infty} E(s) = 0 \tag{10-54}$$

The following example serves to illustrate the difference between Eqs. (10-51) and (10-53).

EXAMPLE 10-5. Let the input to an ideal sampler be $e(t) = u(t) = $ unit step function. The Laplace transform of $e(t)$ is $E(s) = 1/s$. It is apparent that Eq. (12-51) should not be used in this case; if it is used, $E^*(s)$ reads

$$E^*(s) = \frac{1}{T} \sum_{n=-\infty}^{\infty} E(s + jn\omega_s) = \frac{1}{T} \sum_{n=-\infty}^{\infty} \frac{1}{s + jn\omega_s} \tag{10-55}$$

or
$$E^*(s) = \frac{1}{Ts} + \frac{1}{T} \sum_{n=1}^{\infty} \frac{2s}{s^2 + n^2\omega_s^2} = \frac{1}{2} \cot h\left(\frac{sT}{2}\right)$$

$$= \frac{1}{2} + \frac{1}{e^{sT} - 1} = \frac{1}{2} + e^{-sT} + e^{-2sT} + \cdots \tag{10-56}$$

Obviously, by using Eq. (10-51), only half of the value of $e(0^+)$ is sampled. The correct answer, however, can be obtained if Eq. (10-53) is used.

10.4 Interpretation of the Sampling Process in the Frequency Domain

Equation (10-51) is significant in representing the sampling process, since it gives the characteristics of the ideal sampler in the frequency domain. By substituting $s + jm\omega_s$ for s in Eq. (10-46), where m is an integer, we have

$$E^*(s + jm\omega_s) = \sum_{n=0}^{\infty} e(nT)e^{-n(s+jm\omega_s)T}$$

$$= \sum_{n=0}^{\infty} e(nT)e^{-nsT}e^{-jnm\omega_s T}$$

$$= \sum_{n=0}^{\infty} e(nT)e^{-nsT} = E^*(s) \tag{10-57}$$

Hence, $E^*(s) = E^*(s + jm\omega_s) \tag{10-58}$

Thus, $E^*(s)$ is a periodic function with period ω_s.

Fig. 10-7. Frequency spectrum of sampler input.

Assume that the input signal $e(t)$ has an amplitude-frequency spectrum as shown in Fig. 10-7. The sampler output contains the spectrum shown in Fig. 10-8. The amplitude of the output $|E^*(j\omega)|$ contains the primary frequency spectrum of the input plus other complementary components, separated by the sampling frequency ω_s. Figure 10-8 illustrates only a particular case in which the sampling frequency is slightly higher than twice the highest frequency component of the input signal; that is,

$$\omega_s > 2\omega_h \qquad (10\text{-}59)$$

where ω_h is the highest frequency component in $|E(j\omega)|$.

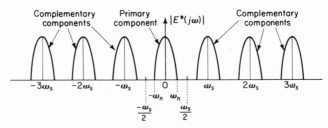

Fig. 10-8. Frequency spectrum of sampler output.

If the sampling frequency ω_s is decreased, (the sampling period T is increased) so that

$$\omega_s < 2\omega_h \qquad (10\text{-}60)$$

the complementary components overlap each other; the sampled output is a distorted picture, as shown in Fig. 10-9. It is evident that even an ideal

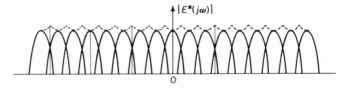

Fig. 10-9. Frequency spectrum of sampler output when $\omega_s < 2\omega_h$.

filter cannot recover the exact original input spectrum in this case. The sampling theorem developed by Shannon† states that if the sampler input $e(t)$ has a finite band width and has frequency components up to ω_h radians

---

†C. E. Shannon, "Communication in the Presence of Noise," *Proc. I.R.E.*, Vol. 37, No. 1, 1949, pp. 10–21.

per second, a complete description of $e(t)$ can be obtained by specifying the values of the signal at instants of time separated by $T = 2\pi/(2\omega_h)$ sec. This theorem is very useful in sampled-data systems, because it indicates the minimum sampling period T for the reconstruction of a signal from sampled impulses.

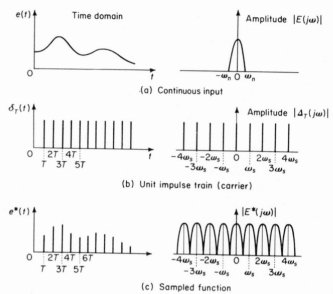

Fig. 10-10. Description of the ideal sampler in time and frequency domain.

In summary, the characteristics of the ideal sampler are shown in Fig. 10-10 by the sketches of $e(t)$, the input signal; $\delta_T(t)$, the impulse train; and $e^*(t)$, the sampled output; in both the time and the frequency domain.

10.5 Data Reconstruction (Hold Circuit)

Although the envelop of the output pulses of $e^*(t)$ corresponds to the values of the continuous input $e(t)$ at the sampling instants, the two functions were shown to be quite different in the frequency domain. In most feedback control systems, the complementary components introduced by the sampler must be removed before the signal is applied to the continuous part of the control system. A low pass filter, which may be considered a data reconstruction device or an extrapolation device, is normally used for this purpose. If it were possible to realize an ideal low pass filter, a sampled-data system would be identical to a continuous system. However, in general, a perfect hold circuit is not realizable because of the random nature of the time function which must be reconstructed. Furthermore, a very important consideration in the design of hold circuits is that a close approximation of the original time function requires a time delay, which has an adverse effect on the stability of the closed-loop system.

The approximation of the original time function between two sampling instants $t = nT$ and $t = (n + 1)T$ depends essentially on the input at the sampling instant nT and at all earlier sampling instants. One method of generating the desired approximation is based on the power series expansion of $e(t)$ in the interval between nT and $(n + 1)T$; that is,

$$e_n(t) = e(nT) + e'(nT)(t - nT) + \frac{e''(nT)}{2!} (t - nT)^2 + \cdots \quad (10\text{-}61)$$

where $e_n(t) = e(t)$ for $nT \leqslant t \leqslant (n + 1)T$ (10-62)

In Eq. (10-61) the primes indicate the derivatives of $e(t)$ at nT. To evaluate the coefficients of the series given by Eq. (10-61), it is necessary to obtain the derivatives of the function $e(t)$ at the beginning of the interval nT. Since the information concerning $e(t)$ is available only at the sampling instants, these derivatives must be estimated from the sampled data. Hence,

$$e'(nT) = \frac{1}{T} [e(nT) - e(n - 1)T] \quad (10\text{-}63)$$

$$e''(nT) = \frac{1}{T} [e'(nT) - e'(n - 1)T]$$

$$= \frac{1}{T^2} \{e(nT) - 2e[(n - 1)T] + e[(n - 2)T]\} \quad (10\text{-}64)$$

From the last two equations, it is apparent that, to obtain an estimate of the derivative of $e(t)$, the minimum number of delay pulses which must be considered is equal to the order of the desired derivative plus one. This means that the higher the order of the desired derivative, the greater the delay before a reliable estimate of that derivative can be obtained. It is for this reason that an attempt to use high-order derivatives of $e(t)$ meet with serious problems in system stability.

(1) *The Zero-Order Hold*

If only the first term of the power series given in Eq. (10-61) is used,

$$e(t) = e(nT) \quad \text{for} \quad nT \leq t < (n + 1)T \quad (10\text{-}65)$$

The last equation represents the zero-order hold. The impulse response of a zero-order hold circuit is shown in Fig. 10-11. In general, an nth order hold system is one in which the signal between two successive sampling instants is approximated by an nth order polynomial. From Fig. 10-11, it can readily be shown that the transfer function of the zero-order hold circuit is

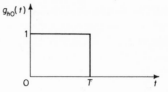

Fig. 10-11. Impulse response of zero-order hold circuit.

$$G_{h0}(s) = \frac{1 - e^{-sT}}{s} \qquad (10\text{-}66)$$

The block diagram of a sampled-data system employing a zero-order hold circuit is shown in Fig. 10-12. The input and output of the hold circuit

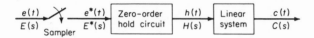

Fig. 10-12. Open-looped sampled-data system with zero-order hold circuit.

are shown in Fig. 10-13a and b. It is noticed that the value of the hold circuit output $h(t)$ at the discontinuity point nT^- is equal to $e(nT^-) = e(n-1)T$, but not equal to $e(nT^+) = e(nT)$. The frequency response of

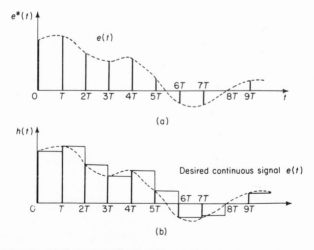

Fig. 10-13. (a) Input signal $e(t)$ and sampled signal $e^*(t)$; (b) Output wave-form of zero-order hold circuit.

the zero-order hold circuit is derived in the following. If we let $s = j\omega$, Eq. (10-66) becomes

$$G_{h0}(j\omega) = \frac{1 - e^{-j\omega T}}{j\omega}$$

$$= \frac{2e^{-j\omega T/2}(e^{j\omega T/2} - e^{-j\omega T/2})}{2j\omega}$$

$$= T \frac{\sin (\omega T/2)}{(\omega T/2)} e^{-j\omega T/2} \tag{10-67}$$

Since the sampling period T is related to the sampling frequency ω_s by Eq. (10-15), Eq. (10-67) can be written as

$$G_{h0}(j\omega) = \frac{2\pi}{\omega_s} \frac{\sin \pi(\omega/\omega_s)}{\pi(\omega/\omega_s)} e^{-j\pi(\omega/\omega_s)} \tag{10-68}$$

The gain and phase characteristics of the zero-order hold circuit are obtained as follows:

$$|G_{h0}(j\omega)| = \frac{2\pi}{\omega_s} \left| \frac{\sin \pi(\omega/\omega_s)}{\pi(\omega/\omega_s)} \right| \tag{10-69}$$

$$\underline{/G_{h0}(j\omega)} = - \pi(\omega/\omega_s) \frac{\sin \pi(\omega/\omega_s)}{|\sin \pi(\omega/\omega_s)|} \tag{10-70}$$

The frequency response (amplitude and phase) of the zero-order hold is shown in Fig. 10-14. It is apparent from these figures that the zero-order

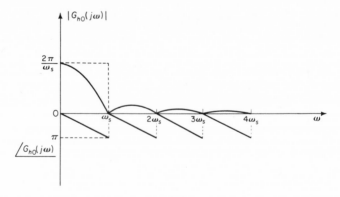

Fig. 10-14. Gain and phase characteristics of a zero-order hold circuit.

hold behaves essentially as a low pass filter. However, compared with the ideal filter characteristic, instead of cutting off sharply at the frequency of $\omega_s/2$, the amplitude of $|G_{h0}(j\omega)|$ drops only to 63.6 per cent of its initial value. Because of the sine term in Eq. (10-68), the phase shift curve of $G_{h0}(j\omega)$ is discontinuous at integral values of the sampling frequency. Since, normally, the sampling frequency is at least twice as high as the highest frequency of the continuous signal $e(t)$, the discontinuity in phase shift should have no effect in most systems.

(2) The First-Order Hold

If the first two terms of the power series of Eq. (10-61) are used to extrapolate the time function $e(t)$ between two successive sampling instants nT and $(n + 1)T$, we have

$$e_n(t) = e(nT) + e'(nT)(t - nT) \tag{10-71}$$

where
$$e'(nT) = \frac{e(nT) - e(n - 1)T}{T} \tag{10-72}$$

Equation (10-72) indicates that the output of the first-order hold between sampling instants nT and $(n + 1)T$ is a ramp function with the slope equal to the difference in amplitude of $e(t)$ at $t = nT$ and $t = (n - 1)T$. It can be shown that the gain and phase characteristics of a first-order hold circuit are as follows:

$$|G_{h1}(j\omega)| = \frac{2\pi}{\omega_s} \sqrt{\left(1 + \frac{4\pi^2\omega^2}{\omega_s^2}\right)} \left(\frac{\sin \pi\omega/\omega_s}{\omega/\omega_s}\right)^2 \tag{10-73}$$

$$\underline{/G_{h1}(j\omega)} = \tan^{-1}\left(\frac{2\pi\omega}{\omega_s}\right) - \frac{2\pi\omega}{\omega_s} \tag{10-74}$$

The frequency response curves of the first-order hold are shown in Fig. 10-15. It is seen that although the gain characteristics of the first-order hold

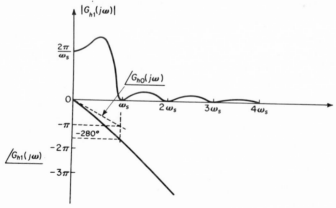

Fig. 10-15. Gain and phase characteristics of a first-order hold circuit.

cut off more sharply than those of the zero-order hold, the first-order hold produces more phase lag.† Note that at the sampling frequency, $\underline{/G_{h0}}$ is

---

† In Fig. 10-15, the phase shift of $G_{h1}(j\omega)$ is shown as a continuous curve. Strictly speaking, because of the $(\sin \pi(\omega/\omega_s)^2$ term in Eq. (10-73), the phase shift of $G_{h1}(j\omega)$ should jump by -2π at $\omega = \omega_s, 2\omega_s, 3\omega_s, \ldots$.

−180 deg, while $\underline{/G_{h1}}$ is about −280 deg. Consequently, the application of a first-order hold circuit in a feedback control system will, in general, reduce the system stability. It is for this reason that hold circuits of the order higher than zero are seldom used in feedback control systems.

(3) *Other Types of Hold Devices*

Other practical filters, such as the "partial-velocity-correction first-order hold," the "polygonal hold," and the "exponential hold," are also used as smoothing devices in sampled-data systems. The interested reader may refer to the references.†

10.6 The z-Transform Method

The Laplace transform method is a basic tool for the analysis and synthesis of linear continuous control systems. In a similar manner, the z-transform method has been quite popular for solving problems of control systems with sampled data.

Definition of the z-Transform

It has been shown that the Laplace transform of a sampled time function $e^*(t)$ is

$$E^*(s) = \sum_{n=0}^{\infty} e(nT)e^{-nTs} \tag{10-75}$$

Furthermore, the expression for $E^*(s)$ normally contains the factor e^{-sT}, which will inevitably lead to non-algebraic functions. It is, therefore, convenient to introduce a change in variable by setting

$$z = e^{sT} \tag{10-76}$$

where s is the Laplace operator and T is the sampling period. Equation (10-75) can now be written as

$$E^*\left(s = \frac{1}{T}\ln z\right) = E(z) = \sum_{n=0}^{\infty} e(nT)z^{-n} \tag{10-77}$$

or $E(z) = z$-transform of $e(t) = $ Laplace transform of $e^*(t)]_{s=(1/T)\ln z}$
$$\tag{10-78}$$

Evidently, the z-transform of the time function $e(t)$ is the same as the Laplace transform of $e^*(t)$, though disguised by the change in variable from s to z. In general, any continuous function which possesses a Laplace transform also has a z-transform.

---

†J. R. Ragazzini, and G. F. Franklin, *Sampled-Data Control Systems*, McGraw-Hill Book Company, New York, N.Y., 1958. J. Tou, *Digital and Sampled-Data Control Systems*, McGraw-Hill Book Company, New York, N.Y., 1959.

Similarly, the expression for $E^*(s)$ given in Eq. (10-47) can be written as

$$E(z) = \sum_{n=1}^{k} \frac{N(s_n)}{D'(s_n)} \frac{1}{1 - e^{s_n T} z^{-1}} \tag{10-79}$$

The last equation indicates that if $E(s)$ has a finite number of poles, the z-transform of $E(s)$ is a rational function in z; the order of $E(z)$ is the same as the order of $E(s)$. It must be pointed out that the z-transform carries information about the corresponding time function only at the sampling instants. There are other restrictions and limitations on the application of z-transforms; these will be discussed in more detail in a later section.

In general, if a time function $e(t)$ is given, the z-transform of $e(t)$, $E(z)$, is obtained by following the two steps given below:

(1) $E^*(s)$, the Laplace transform of $e^*(t)$ is obtained by using either Eq. (10-46) or Eq. (10-47).

(2) $E(z)$ is obtained by substituting $z = e^{sT}$ in $E^*(s)$.

EXAMPLE 10-6. Let

$$e(t) = e^{-at}$$

then

$$e(nT) = e^{-anT}$$

From Eq. (10-46),

$$E^*(s) = \sum_{n=0}^{\infty} e^{-anT} e^{-nTs} = \frac{1}{1 - e^{-(s+a)T}} \tag{10-80}$$

Hence, the z-transform of $e(t)$ is

$$E(z) = [E^*(s)]_{z=e^{sT}} = \frac{1}{1 - e^{-aT}z^{-1}} = \frac{z}{z - e^{-aT}} \tag{10-81}$$

EXAMPLE 10-7. Derive the z-transform of $e(t) = \sin \omega t$.
In Eq. (10-47),

$$E(s) = \mathcal{L}[e(t)] = \frac{\omega}{s^2 + \omega^2} \tag{10-82}$$

$$N(s) = \omega \tag{10-83}$$

and

$$D'(s) = 2s \tag{10-84}$$

hence,
$$E^*(s) = \sum_{n=1}^{2} \frac{N(s_n)}{D'(s_n)} \frac{1}{1 - e^{-T(s-s_n)}}$$

$$= \frac{\omega}{2j\omega} \left[\frac{1}{1 - e^{-T(s-j\omega)}} - \frac{1}{1 - e^{-T(s+j\omega)}} \right]$$

$$= \frac{1}{2j\omega} \left[\frac{e^{-sT} (- e^{-j\omega T} + e^{j\omega T})}{1 - e^{-sT} (e^{j\omega T} + e^{-j\omega T}) + e^{-2sT}} \right]$$

$$= \frac{e^{-sT} \sin \omega T}{e^{-2sT} - 2e^{-sT} \cos \omega T + 1} \tag{10-85}$$

Hence,

$$E(z) = \frac{z^{-1} \sin \omega T}{z^{-2} - 2z^{-1} \cos \omega T + 1} = \frac{z \sin \omega T}{z^2 - 2z \cos \omega T + 1} \tag{10-86}$$

The z-transforms of some common time functions are given in Table 10-1.

Table 10-1.

TABLE OF z-TRANSFORMS

Laplace transform	Time function	z-Transform
1	Unit impulse $\delta(t)$	1
$\dfrac{1}{s}$	Unit step $u(t)$	$\dfrac{z}{z-1}$
$\dfrac{1}{1-e^{-Ts}}$	$\delta_T(t) = \sum\limits_{n=0}^{\infty} \delta(t-nT)$	$\dfrac{z}{z-1}$
$\dfrac{1}{s^2}$	t	$\dfrac{Tz}{(z-1)^2}$
$\dfrac{1}{s^3}$	$\dfrac{t^2}{2}$	$\dfrac{T^2 z(z+1)}{2(z-1)^3}$
$\dfrac{1}{s^{n+1}}$	$\dfrac{t^2}{n!}$	$\lim\limits_{s\to 0} \dfrac{(-1)^n}{n!} \dfrac{\partial^n}{\partial a^n}\left(\dfrac{z}{z-e^{-aT}}\right)$
$\dfrac{1}{s+a}$	e^{-at}	$\dfrac{z}{z-e^{-aT}}$
$\dfrac{1}{(s+a)^2}$	te^{-at}	$\dfrac{Tze^{-aT}}{(z-e^{-aT})^2}$
$\dfrac{a}{s(s+a)}$	$1-e^{-at}$	$\dfrac{(1-e^{-aT})z}{(z-1)(z-e^{-aT})}$
$\dfrac{\omega}{s^2+\omega^2}$	$\sin \omega t$	$\dfrac{z \sin \omega T}{z^2 - 2z\cos \omega T + 1}$
$\dfrac{\omega}{(s+a)^2+\omega^2}$	$e^{-at}\sin \omega t$	$\dfrac{z\,e^{-aT}\sin \omega T}{z^2 e^{-2aT} - 2ze^{-aT}\cos \omega T + 1}$
$\dfrac{s}{s^2+\omega^2}$	$\cos \omega t$	$\dfrac{z(z-\cos \omega T)}{z^2 - 2z\cos \omega T + 1}$
$\dfrac{s+a}{(s+a)^2+\omega^2}$	$e^{-at}\cos \omega t$	$\dfrac{z^2 - ze^{-aT}\cos \omega T}{z^2 - 2ze^{-aT}\cos \omega T + e^{-2aT}}$

The Inverse z-Transformation

Just as in the Laplace transform method, it is often desirable to obtain the time domain response from the z-transform expression. The inverse z-transformation can be effected by one of the following methods:

(1) The z-transform is manipulated into a partial-fraction expression and the z-transform table is used to find the corresponding time function.

(2) The z-transform $E(z)$ is expanded into a power series in powers of z^{-1}. The coefficient of z^{-n} corresponds to the value of the time function $e(t)$ at the nth sampling instant. The above statement is apparent in view of Eq. (10-77).

(3) The time function $e(t)$ may be obtained from $E(z)$ by the real

inversion integral. The values of $e(t)$ at the sampling instants $t = nT$ can be obtained by the following formula:

$$e(nT) = \frac{1}{2\pi j} \oint_{\Gamma} E(z)\, z^{n-1}\, dz \qquad (10\text{-}87)$$

where Γ is a circle of radius $z = e^{cT}$ centered at the origin in the z-plane, and c is of such a value that all the poles of $E(z)$ are enclosed by the circle.

It must be emphasized here that only the values of $e(t)$ at the sampling instants can be obtained from $E(z)$, since $E(z)$ does not contain any information on $e(t)$ between sampling instants.

EXAMPLE 10-8. Given the z-transform

$$E(z) = \frac{(1 - e^{-aT})z}{(z - 1)(z - e^{-aT})} \qquad (10\text{-}88)$$

find the inverse z-transform $e^*(t)$.

(1) *Partial-Fraction Expansion Method*

Equation (10-88) may be written as

$$E(z) = \frac{z}{z - 1} - \frac{z}{z - e^{-aT}} \qquad (10\text{-}89)$$

From the z-transform table (Table 10-1), the corresponding time function at the sampling instants is

$$e(nT) = 1 - e^{-anT} \qquad (10\text{-}90)\dagger$$

hence

$$e^*(t) = \sum_{n=0}^{\infty} e(nT)\delta(t - nT)$$

$$= \sum_{n=0}^{\infty} (1 - e^{-anT})\delta(t - nT) \qquad (10\text{-}91)$$

(2) *Power Series Expansion*

Expanding $E(z)$ into a power series in z^{-1} by long division, we have

$$E(z) = (1 - e^{-aT})z^{-1} + (1 - e^{-2aT})z^{-2} + (1 - e^{-3aT})z^{-3} + \cdots$$
$$+ \cdots (1 - e^{-naT})z^{-n} + \cdots \qquad (10\text{-}92)$$

correspondingly,

$$e^*(t) = 0 \times \delta(t) + (1 - e^{-aT})\delta(t - T)$$
$$+ (1 - e^{-2aT})\delta(t - 2T) + \cdots + (1 - e^{-naT})\delta(t - nT) + \cdots$$
$$= \sum_{n=0}^{\infty} (1 - e^{-anT})\delta(t - nT) \qquad (10\text{-}93)$$

---

†It is seen that the inverse z-transform of $z/(z - 1)$ is not unique; it could be either a unit step function or a unit impulse train. In other words, the definition of the z-transform implies that the sampling of an impulse still results in an impulse of the same strength. The sampler output will still be a unit impulse train, regardless of whether the input to the sampler is a unit step function or a unit impulse train of period T.

(3) *Real Inversion Integral Method*

From Eq. (10-87) we have

$$e(nT) = \frac{1}{2\pi j} \oint_\Gamma E(z) \, z^{n-1} \, dz = \Sigma \text{ Residues of } E(z)z^{n-1} \text{ at poles of } E(z)$$
$$= 1 - e^{-aT}e^{-anT}e^{aT} = 1 - e^{-anT} \qquad (10\text{-}94)$$

hence, the same result for $e^*(t)$ is obtained.

It is important to remember that the inverse of the z-transform is not unique. For any given $E(z)$, the inverse of $E(z)$ found by any of the above-mentioned methods is not unique, since $e^*(t)$ may represent any time function $e(t)$ having the same values at the sampling instants. Figure 10-16

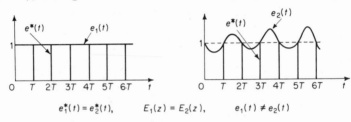

$$e_1^*(t) = e_2^*(t), \qquad E_1(z) = E_2(z), \qquad e_1(t) \neq e_2(t)$$

Fig. 10-16. Two time functions having the same z-transforms.

illustrates that the z-transforms of $e_1(t)$ and $e_2(t)$ are identical, although the two time functions are entirely different.

Some Important Theorems of the z-Transforms

(1) *Addition and Subtraction*

If $e_1(t)$ and $e_2(t)$ are Laplace transformable, and

$$E_1(z) = \mathsf{Z}[e_1(t)] \qquad E_2(z) = \mathsf{Z}[e_2(t)$$

then

$$\mathsf{Z}[e_1(t) \pm e_2(t)] = E_1(z) \pm E_2(z) \qquad (10\text{-}95)$$

Proof: By definition,

$$\mathsf{Z}[e_1(t) \pm e_2(t)] = \sum_{n=0}^{\infty} [e_1(nT) \pm e_2(nT)]z^{-n}$$

$$= \sum_{n=0}^{\infty} e_1(nT)z^{-n} \pm \sum_{n=0}^{\infty} e_2(nT)z^{-n}$$

$$= E_1(z) \pm E_2(z) \qquad (10\text{-}96)$$

(2) *Multiplication by a Constant*

$$\mathsf{Z}[ae(t)] = a\mathsf{Z}[e(t)] = aE(z) \qquad (10\text{-}97)$$

where a is a constant.

Proof: $\mathsf{Z}[a \, e(t)] = \sum_{n=0}^{\infty} a \, e(nT)z^{-n} = a \sum_{n=0}^{\infty} e(nT)z^{-n} = aE(z) \qquad (10\text{-}98)$

(3) *Real Translation*

If $e(t)$ is Laplace transformable and has the z-transform $E(z)$, then

$$\mathbb{Z}[e(t \pm nT)] = z^{\pm n} E(z) \tag{10-99}$$

where n is an integer.

Proof: By definition,

$$\mathbb{Z}[e(t \pm nT)] = \sum_{k=0}^{\infty} e(kT \pm nT)z^{-k} = \sum_{k=0}^{\infty} e(kT \pm nT)z^{-(k \pm n)} z^{\pm n}$$

$$= z^{\pm n} \sum_{k=0}^{\infty} e(kT \pm nT)z^{-(k \pm n)} = z^{\pm n} E(z) \tag{10-100}$$

(4) *Complex Translation*

$$\mathbb{Z}[e^{\mp at} e(t)] = \mathbb{Z}[E(s \pm a)] = E[ze^{\pm aT}] \tag{10-101}$$

Proof: By definition,

$$\mathbb{Z}[e^{\mp at} e(t)] = \sum_{n=0}^{\infty} e(nT)e^{\mp anT} z^{-n} \tag{10-102}$$

If we let $z_1 = ze^{\pm aT}$, Eq. (10-102) becomes

$$\mathbb{Z}[e^{\mp at} e(t)] = \sum_{n=0}^{\infty} e(nT)z_1^{-n} = E(z_1) \tag{10-103}$$

hence,

$$\mathbb{Z}[e^{\mp at} e(t)] = E(z e^{\pm aT}) \tag{10-104}$$

EXAMPLE 10-9. Apply the complex translation theorem to find the z-transform of te^{-at}.

If we let $e(t) = t$, then

$$E(z) = \mathbb{Z}[t] = \frac{Tz}{(z-1)^2} \tag{10-105}$$

From Theorem 4,

$$\mathbb{Z}[te^{-at}] = E(ze^{aT}) = \frac{T(ze^{aT})}{(ze^{aT} - 1)^2}$$

$$= \frac{Tze^{-aT}}{(z - e^{-aT})^2} \tag{10-106}$$

(5) *Initial Value Theorem*

If the function $e(t)$ has the z-transform $E(z)$, and $\lim E(z)$ exists, then

$$\lim_{t \to 0} e^*(t) = \lim_{z \to \infty} E(z) \tag{10-107}$$

(6) *Final Value Theorem*

If the function $e(t)$ has the z-transform $E(z)$, and $(1 - z^{-1})E(z)$ has no pole on or outside the unit circle centered at the origin in the z-plane, then

$$\lim_{t \to \infty} e^*(t) = \lim_{z \to 1} (1 - z^{-1})E(z) \tag{10-108}$$

EXAMPLE 10-10. Given

$$E(z) = \frac{0.792z^2}{(z-1)(z^2 - 0.416z + 0.208)} \tag{10-109}$$

determine the final value of $e^*(t)$.

Since

$$(1 - z^{-1})E(z) = \frac{0.792z}{(z^2 - 0.416z + 0.208)} \tag{10-110}$$

which does not have a pole on or outside the unit circle in the z-plane, the final value theorem can be applied.
Hence,

$$\lim_{t \to \infty} e^*(t) = \lim_{n \to \infty} e(nT) = \lim_{z \to 1} \frac{0.792z}{z^2 - 0.416z + 0.208}$$

$$= \frac{0.792}{1 - 0.416 + 0.208} = 1 \tag{10-111}$$

This result can readily be checked by expanding $E(z)$ in powers of z^{-1}.

$$E(z) = \frac{0.792z^2}{(z-1)(z^2 - 0.416z + 0.208)} = 0.792z^{-1} + 1.12z^{-2}$$

$$+ 1.091z^{-3} + 1.01z^{-4} + 0.983z^{-5} + 0.989z^{-6} + 0.99z^{-7} + \cdots (10\text{-}112)$$

The coefficients of this series converge rapidly to its final steady state value of 1.

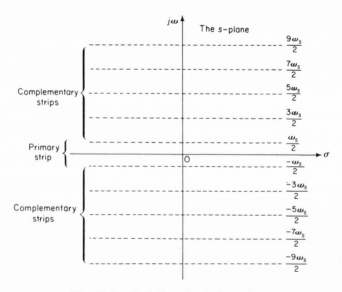

Fig. 10-17. Periodic strips in the s-plane.

The Mapping of the s-Plane into the z-Plane

The z-transformation $z = e^{sT}$ given by Eq. (10-76) transforms the infinite left half of the s-plane onto the interior of the unit circle centered at the origin in the z-plane. The s-plane is first divided into an infinite number of periodic strips, which are parallel to the real axis. The primary strip extends from $\omega = -\omega_s/2$ to $+\omega_s/2$; the other complementary strips extend from $\omega = -\omega_s/2$ to $-3\omega_s/2$, $-3\omega_s/2$ to $-5\omega_s/2$, ..., etc., for negative frequencies, and from $\omega = +\omega_s/2$ to $3\omega_s/2$ ..., etc., for positive frequencies (Fig. 10-17).

If we consider only the primary strip shown in Fig. 10-18a, the path described by (1)-(2)-(3)-(4)-(5)-(1) in the left half of the s-plane is mapped

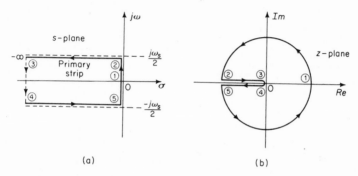

(a)   (b)

Fig. 10-18. Mapping of the primary strip in the left-half s-plane onto the z-plane by the transformation $z = e^{sT}$.

into a unit circle in the z-plane (Fig. 10-18b) by the transformation $z = e^{sT}$. Similarly, since

$$e^{(s+jn\omega_s)T} = e^{sT} e^{2\pi jn} = e^{sT} = z \qquad (10\text{-}113)$$

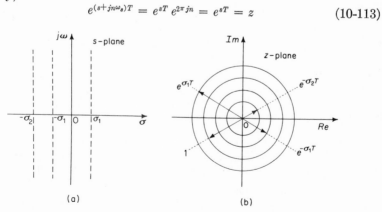

(a)   (b)

Fig. 10-19. Constant damping loof in the s-plane and the z-plane.

all the complementary strips are also mapped into the same unit circle in the z-plane.

(1) *The Constant Damping Loci*

For a constant damping factor σ_1 in the s-plane, the corresponding z-plane locus is a circle of radius $z = e^{\sigma_1 T}$ centered at the origin (Fig. 10-19).

(2) *The Constant Frequency Loci*

For any constant frequency ω_1 in the s-plane, the corresponding z-plane locus is a straight line emanating from the origin at an angle of $\theta = \omega_1 T$ measured from the positive real axis (Fig. 10-20).

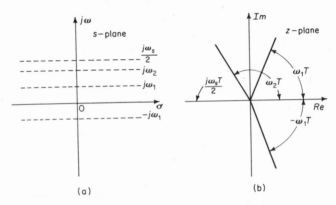

Fig. 10-20. Constant frequency loci in the s-plane and the z-plane.

(3) *The Constant Damping Ratio Loci*

For a constant damping ratio δ, the constant δ line in the s-plane which is shown in Fig. 10-21a, is represented by

$$s = -\omega \tan \beta + j\omega \tag{10-114}$$

Then

$$z = e^{sT} = e^{(-\omega \tan \beta + j\omega)T} \tag{10-115}$$

and

$$z = e^{-(2\pi/\omega_s)\omega \tan \beta} \underline{/\dfrac{2\pi\omega}{\omega_s}} \tag{10-116}$$

The constant δ path corresponding to Eq. (10-115) in the z-plane when $\beta =$ constant is a logarithmic spiral, except for $\beta = 0$ deg and 90 deg. The region shown shaded in Fig. 10-21a corresponds to the interior of the shaded region in Fig. 10-21b.

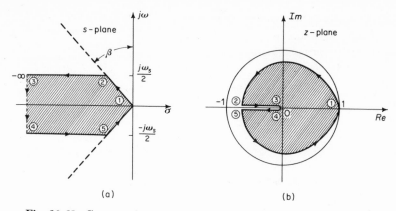

Fig. 10-21. Constant damping ratio loci in the s-plane and the z-plane.

In Fig. 10-22, the constant δ paths for $\beta = 30$ deg are shown in both the s-plane and the z-plane. Each half revolution of the logarithmic spiral corresponds to the passage of the δ path in the s-plane through a change of $j\omega_s/2$ along the $j\omega$ axis.

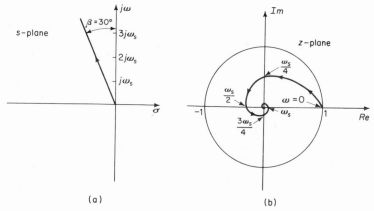

Fig. 10-22. Constant damping δ path for $\beta = 30°$ in the s-plane and the z-plane.

10.7 The Pulse Transfer Function

For a continuous open-loop system, such as that shown in Fig. 10-23a, the system characteristics are represented by the transfer function

$$G(s) = C(s)/E(s) \tag{10-117}$$

For a system with sampled data, Fig. 10-23b illustrates a network G which is connected to a sampler S_1 with sampling period T. Suppose that in the sampled-data system of Fig. 10-23b, a unit step function is applied as $e(t)$ at $t = 0$, and the sampling switch S_1 is closed and opened only once at $t = 0$ for a very short duration. Then the input to the network $e^*(t)$ is

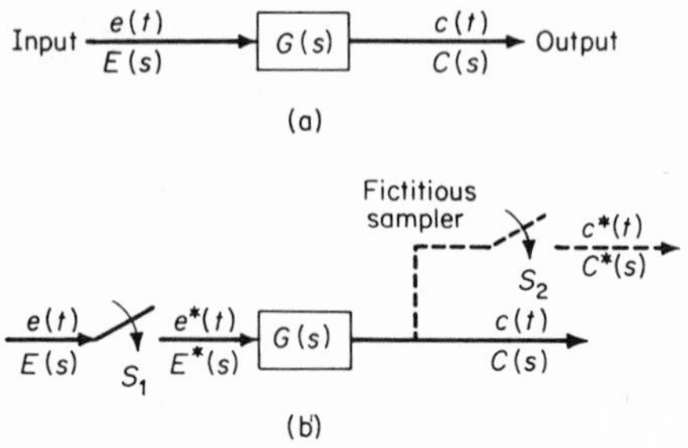

Fig. 10-23. (a) Continuous system; (b) Sampled-data system.

just a unit impulse occurring at $t = 0$. The output $c(t)$ in response to the impulse input is the impulse response of G; or

$$c(t) = g(t) = \text{impulse response of } G \qquad (10\text{-}118)$$

If a fictitious sampler S_2 with the same sampling period T as that of S_1 is placed at the output, the output of the switch S_2 is

$$c^*(t) = g^*(t) = \sum_{n=0}^{\infty} c(nT)\delta(t - nT) \qquad (10\text{-}119)$$

where $c(nT) = g(nT)$ is defined as the "weighting sequence" of G. The signals $e(t)$, $e^*(t)$, $c(t)$, and $c^*(t)$ are illustrated in Fig. 10-24.

Taking the Laplace transform of Eq. (10-119) yields

$$G^*(s) = \sum_{n=0}^{\infty} g(nT)e^{-nTs} \qquad (10\text{-}120)$$

which is the pulsed transfer function of the system G. We can sum up our findings at this point as follows: When a unit impulse is applied to a network or system G, the output is simply the impulse response of G; the output of the fictitious sampler S_2 is called the weighting sequence of the network G. The Laplace transfer function of the weighting sequence gives the pulsed transfer function $G^*(s)$.

Once the weighting sequence of a network G is defined, the output $c(t)$ and $c^*(t)$ of the system corresponding to any arbitrary input can be obtained by means of the principle of superposition. Assume that an arbitrary function $e(t)$ is applied to the system of Fig. 10-23b at $t = 0$; the sampled input to G is the sequence $e(nT)$. At the time $t = nT$, the output sample $c(nT)$ is the sum of the effects of all samples $e(nT)$, $e(n-1)T$, $e(n-2)T$, ..., $e(0)$; that is,

$$c(nT) = \Sigma \text{ Effects of all samples } e(nT), e(n-1)T, \ldots, e(0) \tag{10-121}$$

or $\quad c(nT) = e(0)g(nT) + e(T)g[(n-1)T] + e(2T)g[(n-2)T] + \cdots$
$$+ e[(n-1)T]g(T) + e(nT)g(0) \tag{10-122}$$

Multiplying both sides of the last equation by e^{-nTs}, and taking the summation for $n = 0$ to ∞, we have

$$\sum_{n=0}^{\infty} c(nT)e^{-nTs} = \sum_{n=0}^{\infty} e(0)g(nT)e^{-nTs} + \sum_{n=0}^{\infty} e(T)g[(n-1)T]e^{-nTs} + \cdots$$

$$+ \sum_{n=0}^{\infty} e[(n-1)T]g(T)e^{-nTs} + \sum_{n=0}^{\infty} e(nT)g(0)e^{-nTs} \tag{10-123}$$

or $\quad \displaystyle\sum_{n=0}^{\infty} c(nT)e^{-nTs} = [e(0) + e(T)e^{-Ts} + e(2T)e^{-2Ts} + \ldots] \sum_{n=0}^{\infty} g(nT)e^{-nTs}$
$$\tag{10-124}$$

from which

$$\sum_{n=0}^{\infty} c(nT)e^{-nTs} = \sum_{n=0}^{\infty} e(nT)e^{-nTs} \sum_{n=0}^{\infty} g(nT)e^{-nTs} \tag{10-125}$$

or simply

$$C^*(s) = E^*(s)G^*(s) \tag{10-126}$$

where $G^*(s)$ is defined as the pulsed transfer function of G, and is given by Eq. (10-120).

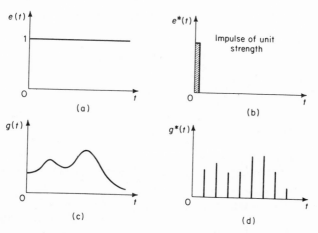

Fig. 10-24. Signals of system shown in Fig. 10-23. (a) Unit-step function; (b) Sampled-input, unit impulse; (c) Impulse response; (d) Weighting sequence.

Taking the z-transform on both sides of Eq. (10-126) yields

$$C(z) = E(z)G(z) \qquad (10\text{-}127)$$

It is important to point out that the output $c(t)$ of the sampled-data system is continuous with respect to time. However, the pulsed transform of the output $C^*(s)$ and the z-transform of the output $C(z)$ only specify the values of $c(t)$ at the sampling instants.

10.8 The z-Transform Analysis of Sampled-Data Systems

(1) Open Loop Systems

The z-transform relation given by Eq. (10-127) can also be obtained by using the simple relation between $E^*(s)$ and $E(s)$ (Eq. 10-51). From Fig. 10-23, the Laplace transform of the continuous output of the system is

$$C(s) = G(s)E^*(s) \qquad (10\text{-}128)$$

Taking the pulsed transform of the last equation, and utilizing the relation given by Eq. (10-51), we have

$$C^*(s) = \frac{1}{T} \sum_{n=-\infty}^{\infty} C(s + jn\omega_s) \qquad (10\text{-}129)$$

or

$$C^*(s) = \frac{1}{T} \sum_{n=-\infty}^{\infty} G(s + jn\omega_s)E^*(s + jn\omega_s) \qquad (10\text{-}130)$$

Since it was proved that $E^*(s)$ is a periodic function with period ω_s, and $E^*(s) = E^*(s + jn\omega_s)$, Eq. (10-130) can be written as

$$C^*(s) = \frac{1}{T} E^*(s) \sum_{n=-\infty}^{\infty} G(s + jn\omega_s) \qquad (10\text{-}131)$$

hence

$$C^*(s) = E^*(s)G^*(s) \qquad (10\text{-}132)$$

where

$$G^*(s) = \frac{1}{T} \sum_{n=-\infty}^{\infty} G(s + jn\omega_s) \qquad (10\text{-}133)$$

z-Transform of Cascaded Elements with Sampling Switches between Them. Figure 10-25a illustrates a sampled-data system with cascaded elements G_1 and G_2. The two elements are separated by a second sampling switch S_2 which is synchronized to S_1; i.e., the two switches have the same sampling period T. The z-transform relation between the output and the input signals is derived as follows:

The output signal of G_1 is

$$D(s) = G_1(s)E^*(s) \qquad (10\text{-}134)$$

and the system output is

$$C(s) = G_2(s)D^*(s) \qquad (10\text{-}135)$$

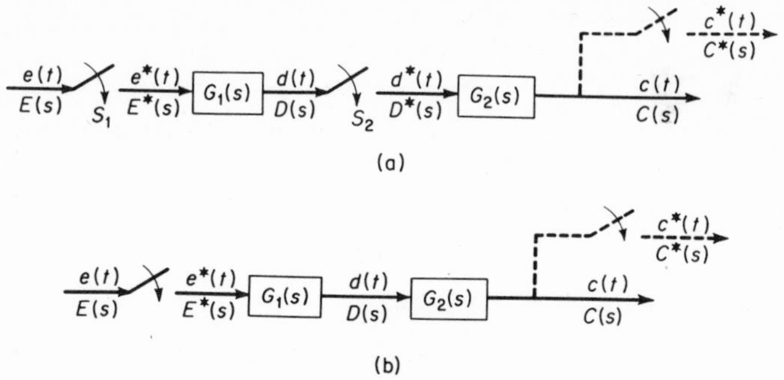

(a)

(b)

Fig. 10-25. (a) Sampled-data system with cascaded elements (sampler separates the two elements); (b) Sampled-data system with cascaded elements (no sampler between the two elements).

Taking the pulsed transform of Eq. (12-134) yields

$$D^*(s) = G_1^*(s)E^*(s) \tag{10-136}$$

and substituting $D^*(s)$ into Eq. (10-135), we have

$$C(s) = G_2(s)G_1^*(s)E^*(s) \tag{10-137}$$

Taking the pulsed transform of the last equation, we have

$$C^*(s) = G_2^*(s)G_1^*(s)E^*(s) \tag{10-138}$$

The z-transform of the above equation is

$$C(z) = G_1(z)G_2(z)E(z) \tag{10-139}$$

Consequently, the z-transform of two linear elements separated by a sampling switch is equal to the product of the z-transforms of the two individual elements.

z-Transform of Cascaded Elements with No Sampling Switches between Them. Figure 10-25b illustrates a sampled-data system with two cascaded elements; there is no sampler between the elements. The z-transform relation of the output and input signals is derived as follows: The transform of the continuous output is

$$C(s) = G_1(s)G_2(s)E^*(s) \tag{10-140}$$

The pulsed transform of the output is

$$C^*(s) = G_1 G_2^*(s) E^*(s) \tag{10-141}$$

where

$$G_1 G_2^*(s) = [G_1(s)G_2(s)]^* = \frac{1}{T} \sum_{n=-\infty}^{\infty} G_1(s + jn\omega_s)G_2(s + jn\omega_s) \tag{10-142}$$

In general,

$$G_1 G_2^*(s) \neq G_1^*(s)G_2^*(s) \tag{10-143}$$

The z-transform of Eq. (10-141) is

$$C(z) = G_1 G_2(z) E(z) \tag{10-144}$$

where $G_1 G_2(z)$ is defined as the z-transform of the product of $G_1(s)$ and $G_2(s)$. Thus, the z-transform of two cascaded elements with no sampler between them is equal to the z-transform of the product of the Laplace transform of the two elements. The following example will illustrate the difference between Eq. (10-139) and Eq. (10-144).

EXAMPLE 10-12. For the sampled-data systems shown in Fig. 10-25a and b, if $G_1(s) = 1/s$, $G_2(s) = a/(s + a)$, and $e(t)$ is a unit step function, the output of the system shown in Fig. 10-25a is

$$C(z) = G_1(z)G_2(z)E(z) = \frac{z}{z - 1} \times \frac{az}{z - e^{-aT}} \times \frac{z}{z - 1}$$

$$= \frac{az^3}{(z - 1)^2(z - e^{-aT})} \tag{10-145}$$

while the output of the system shown in Fig. 10-25b is

$$C(z) = G_1 G_2(z)E(z) = Z\left[\frac{a}{s(s + a)}\right]E(z) = \frac{z(1 - e^{-aT})}{(z - 1)(z - e^{-aT})} \times \frac{z}{z - 1}$$

$$= \frac{z^2(1 - e^{-aT})}{(z - 1)^2(z - e^{-aT})} \tag{10-146}$$

(2) *Closed-Loop Systems*

The transfer function of a closed-loop sampled-data system can also be

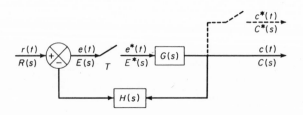

Fig. 10-26. Closed-loop sampled-data system.

obtained by the procedure used in the last section. For the system shown in Fig. 10-26, the output transform is

$$C(s) = G(s)E^*(s) \qquad (10\text{-}147)$$

The Laplace transform of the continuous error function is

$$E(s) = R(s) - C(s)H(s) \qquad (10\text{-}148)$$

Substituting Eq. (10-147) into Eq. (10-148) yields

$$E(s) = R(s) - H(s)G(s)E^*(s) \qquad (10\text{-}149)$$

Taking the pulsed transform of the last equation, we have

$$E^*(s) = R^*(s) - HG^*(s)E^*(s) \qquad (10\text{-}150)$$

from which

$$E^*(s) = \frac{R^*(s)}{1 + HG^*(s)} \qquad (10\text{-}151)$$

The output transform $C(s)$ is obtained by substituting $E^*(s)$ from Eq. (10-151) into Eq. (10-147); hence,

$$C(s) = \frac{G(s)}{1 + HG^*(s)} R^*(s) \qquad (10\text{-}152)$$

The pulsed-transform of $c^*(t)$ is

$$C^*(s) = G^*(s)E^*(s) = \frac{G^*(s)}{1 + HG^*(s)} R^*(s) \qquad (10\text{-}153)$$

Hence, the z-transform of $c(t)$ is

$$C(z) = \frac{G(z)}{1 + HG(z)} R(z) \qquad (10\text{-}154)$$

As another example of the derivation of the closed-loop transfer function of a sampled-data system, consider the sampled-data system shown in Fig. 10-27. The output transforms $C(s)$ and $C(z)$ are derived as follows:

$$C(s) = E(s)G(s) \qquad (10\text{-}155)$$

and

$$E(s) = R(s) - H(s)C^*(s) \qquad (10\text{-}156)$$

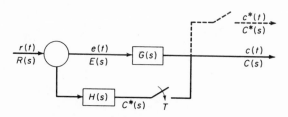

Fig. 10-27. Closed-loop sampled-data system.

Substituting Eq. (10-156) into Eq. (10-155) yields

$$C(s) = E(s)G(s) = G(s)R(s) - G(s)H(s)C^*(s) \qquad (10\text{-}157)$$

Taking the pulsed transform of the last equation, we have

$$C^*(s) = GR^*(s) - HG^*(s)C^*(s) \qquad (10\text{-}158)$$

from which

$$C^*(s) = \frac{GR^*(s)}{1 + HG^*(s)} \qquad (10\text{-}159)$$

In order to determine the continuous output $C(s)$, we substitute $C^*(s)$ in the last equation into Eq. (10-157); hence,

$$C(s) = G(s)\left[R(s) - \frac{H(s)GR^*(s)}{1 + HG^*(s)} \right] \qquad (10\text{-}160)$$

The z-transform of the output $c(t)$ is obtained from Eq. (10-159).

$$C(z) = \frac{GR(z)}{1 + HG(z)} \qquad (10\text{-}161)$$

10.9 Signal Flow Graphs of Sampled-Data Systems†

It is reasonable to expect that, for sampled-data systems with more complicated system configurations than those shown in Figs. 10-26 and 10-27, the derivation of the output transform by means of the algebraic method will be quite tedious. One probably would immediately think of the possibility of using Mason's signal flow formula, which is given in Eq. 2-128. However, an attempt to apply Mason's formula to the block diagram or equivalent signal flow graph of a system with sampled data will encounter immediate difficulty. It is not hard to see that the chief difficulty stems from the existence of the sampling switches; since we cannot replace the samplers by transfer functions describing the sampling operation, the conventional flow graph algebra cannot handle a flow graph with sampling switches. In special cases, if all the signals in a sampled-data system are of the sampled form, all the transforms are starred, and the general gain formula can still be applied directly. For instance, let us consider the

---

†R. Ash, W. H. Kim, G. M. Kranc, "A General Flow Graph Technique For the Solution of Multiloop Sampled Systems," *Trans. of ASME, Journal of Basic Engineering*, June, 1960, pp. 360–370. J. M. Salzer, "Signal Flow Reductions in Sampled Data Systems," *IRE Wescon Convention Record*, Part 4, pp. 166–170, 1957. G. G. Lendaris and E. I. Jury, "Input-Output Relationships for Multi-Sampled-loop Systems," *AIEE, Trans.*, Paper No. 59-882.

sampled-data system shown in Fig. 10-28a. It is seen that only sampled signals appear throughout the system. The signal flow graph of the system is shown in Fig. 10-28b. Since no continuous signal is found in the system,

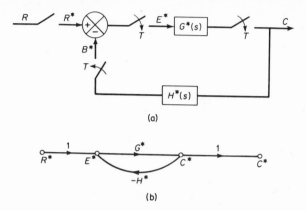

(a)

(b)

Fig. 10-28. (a) An all-sampled-data system; (b) Equivalent signal flow graph of sampled-data system in Fig. (a).

the sampling switches may be omitted from the equivalent flow graph. Applying the gain formula, we obtain the closed-loop transfer function as

$$\frac{C^*(s)}{R^*(s)} = \frac{G^*(s)}{1 + G^*(s)H^*(s)} \tag{10-162}$$

However, a majority of the systems with sampled data contain both sampled and continuous signals; therefore, the samplers cannot be omitted. We can conclude that the gain formula can be applied only when the flow graph contains nodes representing either all continuous signals or all sampled signals.

In the following we shall demonstrate that if a sampled-data system has both sampled data and continuous data, the method of determination of the output transforms of the system by use of Mason's gain formula generally involves the following steps:

(1) Using the block diagram as the starting point, the "original signal flow graph" of the system is constructed. The original flow graph is defined as the equivalent flow graph of the block diagram. For instance, the original flow graph of the system in Fig. 10-26 is constructed in Fig. 10-29.

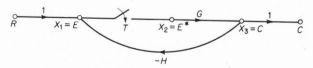

Fig. 10-29. Original signal flow graph of system in Fig. 10-26.

(2) The so-called "sampled signal flow graph" is constructed from information obtained from the original signal flow graph. This step will need some explanation. Let us consider the flow graph shown in Fig. 10-29. Note that the flow graph still contains the sampling switch, so the gain formula cannot be applied directly. However, the following set of equations may be written from the flow graph:

$$X_1 = E = R - HX_3 \tag{10-163}$$

$$X_2 = E^* = X_1^* \tag{10-164}$$

$$X_3 = C = GX_2 \tag{10-165}$$

where, for simplicity, $E^*(s)$ is represented by E^*; $R(s)$ by R; $H(s)$ and $G(s)$ by H and G, respectively. X_1, X_2, and X_3 are Laplace transforms of flow graph variables at nodes 1, 2, and 3 in Fig. 10-29. Substituting Eq. (10-164) into Eq. (10-165), and then substituting Eq. (10-165) into Eq. (10-163), we may write the last three equations in the following form:

$$X_1 = -HGX_1^* + R \tag{10-166}$$

$$X_2 = X_1^* \tag{10-167}$$

$$X_3 = GX_1^* = GX_2 \tag{10-168}$$

Careful examination of Eqs. (10-166), (10-167), and (10-168) reveals that the same set of equations may be obtained if the sampler in the origina flow graph of Fig. 10-29 is deleted, and an artificial signal source of strength $X_2 = X^* = E^*$ is applied at node 2. (Now the system has two separate inputs.) If now we take the pulsed transform of both sides of Eqs. (10-166) through (10-168), we have

$$X_1^* = -(HG)^*X_1^* + R^* \tag{10-169}$$

$$X_2^* = X_1^* \tag{10-170}$$

$$X_3^* = G^*X_1^* \tag{10-171}$$

Since the above equations contain only sampled variables, the signal flow graph constructed from these equations is called the *sampled signal flow graph* (of the system in Fig. 10-26). This sampled flow graph is shown in Fig. 10-30; note that it has only the sampled variables R^*, X_1^*, X_2^*, X_3^*, and C^*.

Now we may apply Mason's gain formula directly to the sampled flow

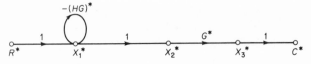

Fig. 10-30. Sampled flow graph of system in Fig. 10-26.

graph of Fig. 10-30 for the evaluation of the sampled output response $C^*(s)$ or $C(z)$. It is apparent that once the sampled flow graph is constructed, all other variables $X_1^* = E^* = X_2^*$ can also be expressed as functions of the input R^* by using the gain formula. Thus,

$$C^*(s) = \frac{G^*(s)}{1 + HG^*(s)} R^*(s) \qquad (10\text{-}172)$$

and

$$E^*(s) = \frac{1}{1 + HG^*(s)} R^*(s) \qquad (10\text{-}173)$$

where $HG^*(s) = (HG)^*$.

In general, if a multi-loop sampled-data system contains several samplers (synchronized), by deleting the samplers and adding the artificial signal sources at the nodes where the output of the samplers are connected, a set of equations similar to Eqs. (10-169) through (10-171) may be written. For instance, if the node variables of the original flow graph are represented by X, the following equation may be written for the variable X_j of node j:

$$X_j = \sum_i a_{ij} X_i^* + \sum_k b_{kj} R_k \qquad (10\text{-}174)$$

where it is assumed that a sampler is located between nodes i and j, and that the signal is transmitted from node i to node j. Therefore, x_i^* is the sampled signal from the sampler following node i which will flow to node j; a_{ij} represents the transmission between node i and node j; b_{kj} denotes the transmission from node k to node j; R_k is the signal applied at node k which will flow to node j. Taking the pulsed transform of both sides of Eq. (10-174) yields

$$X_j^* = \sum_i a_{ij}^* X_i^* + \sum_k (b_{kj} R_k)^* \qquad (10\text{-}175)$$

In the last equation, all the variables are of the sampled form. Therefore, in general, the sampled signal flow graph of a sampled-data system may be defined as a flow graph which represents the functional relationship between the sampled variables $X_1^*, X_2^*, \ldots, X_i^*, X_j^*, \ldots$ of the system.

(3) In the last step we demonstrated how the sampled variables of a sampled-data system can be evaluated from the sampled signal flow graph by direct use of Mason's formula. However, the sampled flow graph does not contain the unsampled variables $X_1, X_2, \ldots$ Since the actual output response of most sampled-data systems does not take the form of a pulse train, it is essential to determine the expression of the continuous response $C(s)$. For this purpose, we shall define a so-called *"composite signal flow graph,"* which is the composition of the original flow graph and the sampled flow graph, with the sampling switches in the original flow graph deleted; the sampling operation is described by drawing a branch of unity gain from node X_i^* of the sampled graph to node X_j on the original flow graph (since

if a sampler is located between node i and node j and the signal is transmitted from i to j, the branch of unity gain simply describes the relation $X_j = X_i^*$). From this composite signal flow graph, all the sampled and continuous output responses can be determined as functions of the input signal by means of Mason's formula. Actually, once the composite signal flow graph is constructed, there is no need to construct a separate sampled signal flow graph, because the former will contain all the information about the sampled and the unsampled variables.

Let us use the simple sampled-data system shown in Fig. 10-26 to illustrate the construction of the composite signal flow graph. The original signal flow graph of the system is shown in Fig. 10-29, and the sampled signal flow graph is already obtained, as shown in Fig. 10-30. It is apparent that the variables in the two flow graphs are related by Eq. (10-164); i.e., $X_2 = X_1^*$. Therefore, the composite flow graph is constructed by drawing a branch of unity gain from node X_1^* of the sampled graph to node X_2 on the original flow graph; this is shown in Fig. 10-31. By use of Mason's gain formula, the continuous output response of the system is

$$C(s) = \frac{G(s)}{1 + HG^*(s)} R^*(s) \qquad (10\text{-}176)$$

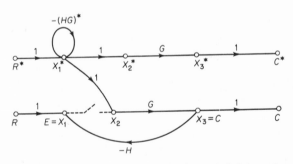

Fig. 10-31. Composite signal flow graph of sampled-data system given in Fig. 10-30.

which agrees with the result given in Eq. (10-152). The unsampled signal $R(s)$ does not appear in the expression for $C(s)$, since there is no forward path from R to C. In a similar manner, the continuous signal $E(s)$ is derived as

$$E(s) = \frac{1}{1 + HG^*(s)} R(s) \qquad (10\text{-}177)$$

It is easy to see that the sampled responses $C^*(s)$ and $E^*(s)$, given by Eqs. (10-172) and (10-173) respectively, can also be derived directly from the composite flow graph simply by use of the gain formula.

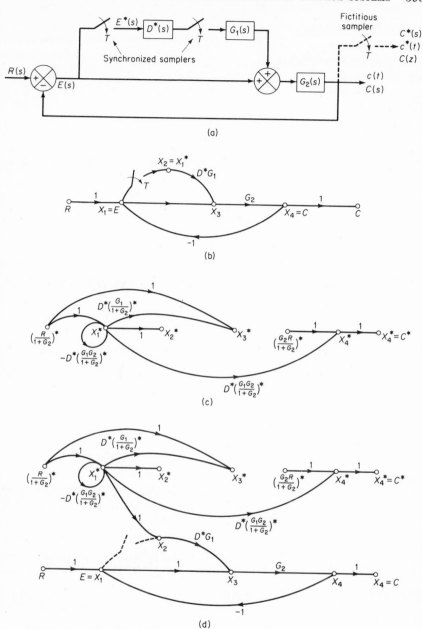

Fig. 10-32. (a) Block diagram of sampled-data system used in Ex. 10-13; (b) Original signal flow graph of sampled-data system shown in 10-32(a); (c) Sampled-signal flow graph of sampled-data system shown in Fig. 10-32(a); (d) Composite signal flow graph of sampled-data system shown in Fig. 10-33(a).

EXAMPLE 10-13. In this example, the sampled and unsampled output response of the sampled-data system shown in Fig. 10-32a will be evaluated by use of the signal flow graph technique. By following the steps outlined above:

(1) The original signal flow graph of the system is constructed, as shown in Fig. 10-32b.

(2) From the original flow graph, the following set of equations is written in accordance with the form of Eq. (10-174):

$$E = X_1 = \frac{- D^* G_1 G_2}{1 + G_2} X_1^* + \frac{R}{1 + G_2} \qquad (10\text{-}178)$$

$$X_2 = X_1^* \qquad (10\text{-}179)$$

$$X_3 = \frac{D^* G_1}{1 + G_2} X_1^* + \frac{R}{1 + G_2} \qquad (10\text{-}180)$$

$$X_4 = \frac{D^* G_1 G_2}{1 + G_2} X_1^* + \frac{G_2 R}{1 + G_2} \qquad (10\text{-}181)$$

Taking the pulsed transform of both sides of Eqs. (10-178) through (10-181) yields

$$X_1^* = - D^* \left(\frac{G_1 G_2}{1 + G_2} \right)^* X_1^* + \left(\frac{R}{1 + G_2} \right)^* \qquad (10\text{-}182)$$

$$X_2^* = X_1^* \qquad (10\text{-}183)$$

$$X_3^* = D^* \left(\frac{G_1}{1 + G_2} \right)^* X_1^* + \left(\frac{R}{1 + G_2} \right)^* \qquad (10\text{-}184)$$

$$X_4^* = D^* \left(\frac{G_1 G_2}{1 + G_2} \right)^* X_1^* + \left(\frac{G_2 R}{1 + G_2} \right)^* \qquad (10\text{-}185)$$

From these equations with sampled variables, the sampled signal flow graph of the system is constructed as shown in Fig. 10-32c; the composite flow graph of the system is shown in Fig. 10-32d.

By using Mason's gain formula, the sampled and unsampled output variables of the system are determined from the composite flow graph as follows:

$$C^* = X_4^* = \left(\frac{G_2 R}{1 + G_2} \right)^* + \frac{D^* \left(\frac{G_1 G_2}{1 + G_2} \right)^*}{1 + D^* \left(\frac{G_1 G_2}{1 + G_2} \right)^*} \left(\frac{R}{1 + G_2} \right)^* \qquad (10\text{-}186)$$

which may be simplified to the following form:

$$C^* = \frac{\left(\frac{G_2 R}{1 + G_2} \right)^* + \left[\left(\frac{G_2 R}{1 + G_2} \right)^* + \left(\frac{R}{1 + G_2} \right)^* \right] D^* \left(\frac{G_1 G_2}{1 + G_2} \right)^*}{1 + D^* \left(\frac{G_1 G_2}{1 + G_2} \right)^*} \qquad (10\text{-}187)$$

Since the following relation is true,

$$R^* = \left(\frac{RG_2}{1 + G_2}\right)^* + \left(\frac{R}{1 + G_2}\right)^* \tag{10-188}$$

Eq. (10-187) reads

$$C^* = \frac{\left(\dfrac{G_2R}{1 + G_2}\right)^* + D^*\left(\dfrac{G_1G_2}{1 + G_2}\right)^* \times R^*}{1 + D^*\left(\dfrac{G_1G_2}{1 + G_2}\right)^*} \tag{10-189}$$

The unsampled output signal $C(s)$ is

$$C = \frac{RG_2\left[1 + D^*\left(\dfrac{G_1G_2}{1 + G_2}\right)^*\right] + \left(\dfrac{R}{1 + G_2}\right)^* D^*G_1G_2}{1 + G_2 + D^*\left(\dfrac{G_1G_2}{1 + G_2}\right)^* + G_2D^*\left(\dfrac{G_1G_2}{1 + G_2}\right)^*} \tag{10-190}$$

The last equation can be simplified to read

$$C = \frac{G_2R}{1 + G_2} + \frac{G_1G_2}{1 + G_2} \times \frac{D^*\left(\dfrac{R}{1 + G_2}\right)^*}{1 + D^*\left(\dfrac{G_1G_2}{1 + G_2}\right)^*} \tag{10-191}$$

EXAMPLE 10-14. Let us consider the multisampler system shown in Fig. 10-33a. The original flow graph of the sampled-data system is constructed in Fig. 10-33b.

We observe that variables X_1 and X_5 are assigned to the input of the two samplers. Therefore, we can write directly from Fig. 10-33b:

$$X_1 = -G_1G_2X_1^* + X_5^*HG_2 + R \tag{10-192}$$

$$X_2 = X_1^* \tag{10-193}$$

$$X_3 = G_1X_1^* - HX_5^* \tag{10-194}$$

$$X_4 = X_5^* \tag{10-195}$$

$$X_5 = -G_2HX_5^* + G_1G_2X_1^* \tag{10-196}$$

Taking the pulsed transform of both sides of Eqs. (10-192) and (10-193) yields

$$X_1^* = -(G_1G_2)^*X_1^* + (G_2H)^*X_5^* + R^* \tag{10-197}$$

$$X_2^* = X_1^* \tag{10-198}$$

$$X_3^* = G_1^*X_1^* - H^*X_5^* \tag{10-199}$$

$$X_4^* = X_5^* \tag{10-200}$$

$$X_5^* = (G_1G_2)^*X_1^* - (G_2H)^*X_5^* \tag{10-201}$$

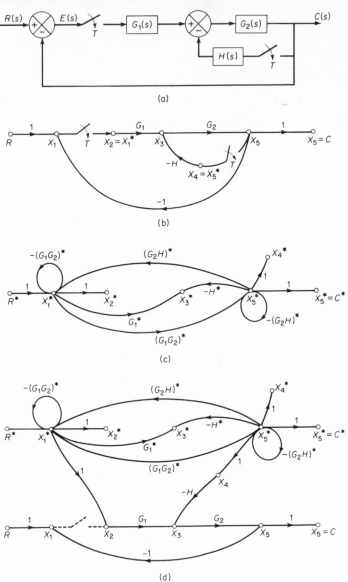

Fig. 10-33. (a) A multisampler sampled-data system; (b) Original signal flow graph of system in Fig. 10-33(a); (c) Sampled flow graph for the system of Fig. 10-33(a); (d) Composite signal flow graph of system in Fig. 10-33(a).

These equations with sampled signals can be represented by the sampled signal flow graph shown in Fig. 10-33c. If we eliminate the two samplers from the original flow graph and connect by unity gain branches nodes X_1^*

and X_5^* of the sampled flow graph to nodes X_2 and X_4 on the original flow graph, respectively, we have the composite flow graph, as shown in Fig. 10-33d.

From the composite flow graph, we compute the expressions for the sampled and the unsampled outputs, using Mason's formula as follows:

$$C^* = X_5^* = \frac{(G_1G_2)^*R^*}{1 + (G_1G_2)^* + (G_2H)^* - (G_1G_2)^*(G_2H)^* + (G_1G_2)^*(G_2H)^*} \tag{10-202}$$

or

$$C^* = \frac{(G_1G_2)^*R^*}{1 + (G_1G_2)^* + (G_2H)^*} \tag{10-203}$$

$$C = X_5 = \frac{G_1G_2[1 + (G_2H)^*] - (G_1G_2)^*G_2H}{1 + (G_1G_2)^* + (G_2H)^*} R^* \tag{10-204}$$

Two methods of deriving the transfer functions of sampled-data systems have been described in this section and in Sec. 10-8; one is the block diagram technique, or, essentially, the analytical method, and the other is the signal flow technique. It is apparent that the signal flow graph method is far more straightforward in all respects. The original signal flow graph is merely the conventional flow graph of the sampled-data system. The sampled signal flow graph contains only the sampled variables as nodes. By use of Mason's gain formula, the transform expressions of all the sampled variables which satisfy the requirement as output nodes can be evaluated by inspection from the sampled flow graph. The composite flow graph is a combination of the sampled and the original flow graph; it provides information on all the sampled and the unsampled variables of the system.

Unlike the continuous-data systems, it is frequently impossible to arrive at the so-called pulsed transfer function $C^*(s)/R^*(s)$ for a sampled-data system; it is possible that the input signal R appears in the form of $(RG)^*$, where G is the transfer function or a linear combination of some system transfer function, so that R does not appear explicitly as $R^*(s)$, and the input-output relation of the system simply cannot be expressed by a pulsed-transfer function. In this case, it is possible to describe the system input-output relation only by writing the output transform $C^*(s)$ as a function of $(RG)^*$.

It is also important to point out that the signal flow graph technique devised here can also be extended to systems with multirate sampling; i.e., samplers that are not synchronized.[†]

†R. Ash, W. H. Kim, G. M. Kranc, "A General Flow Graph Technique for the Solution of Multiloop Sampled Systems," *Trans. of ASME, Journal of Basic Engineering,* June, 1960, pp. 360–370.

Table 10-2 — sampled-data system signal flow graphs

System block diagram	Original signal flow graph	Sampled signal flow graph	Composite signal flow graph
Row 1		$C^*(s) = \dfrac{G^*(s)R^*(s)}{1+HG^*(s)}$	$C(s) = \dfrac{G(s)R^*(s)}{1+HG^*(s)}$
Row 2		$C^*(s) = \dfrac{G^*(s)R^*(s)}{1+H^*(s)G^*(s)}$	$C(s) = \dfrac{G^*(s)R^*(s)}{1+H^*(s)G^*(s)}$
Row 3		$C^*(s) = \dfrac{RG^*(s)}{1+HG^*(s)}$	$C(s) = \dfrac{R(s)G(s)[1+HG^*(s)] - RG^*(s)H(s)G(s)}{1+HG^*(s)}$
Row 4		$C^*(s) = \dfrac{RG_1^*(s)G_2^*(s)}{1+HG_1G_2^*(s)}$	$C(s) = \dfrac{RG_1^*(s)G_2(s)}{1+HG_1G_2^*(s)}$

Table 10-2.

For the purpose of reference, Table 10-2 provides the block diagrams, original flow graphs, completer flow graphs, and various forms of the output transforms of some common sampled-data system configurations.

10.10 Limitations of the z-Transform Method

It was shown in the past sections that the z-transformation is a very convenient tool for the treatment of sampled-data systems. However, the z-transform method has limitations, and in certain cases care must be taken in its applications.

(1) First of all, we must realize that the derivation of the z-transform is based upon the assumption that the sampled signal is approximated by a train of impulses whose areas are equal to the input time function of the sampler at the sampling instants. This assumption is considered to be valid only if the sampling duration of the sampler is small, compared to the significant time constant of the system.

(2) The z-transform $C(z)$ specifies only the values of the time function $c(t)$ at the sampling instants; it does not contain any information concerning the value of $c(t)$ between sampling instants. Therefore, for any $C(z)$, the inverse z-transform $c(nT)$ describes $c(t)$ only at the sampling instants $t = nT$.

(3) In analyzing a sampled-data system by the z-transform method, it is necessary that the transfer function $G(s)$ have at least two more poles than zeros [or $g(t)$, the impulse response of G, must not have a jump at $t = 0$]; otherwise, the system response obtained by the z-transform method is unrealistic or even incorrect.

In order to illustrate the points mentioned above, let us consider the R-C integrating circuit of Fig. 10-34. The transfer function of the circuit

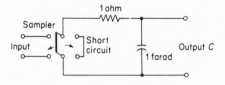

Fig. 10-34. R-C integrating network.

is $G(s) = 1/(s + 1)$, and the corresponding z-transform is $G(z) = z/(z - e^{-T})$. If the input to the sampler is a unit step function, $R(z)$ is equal to $z/(z - 1)$. The output z-transform of the network is

$$C(z) = R(z)G(z) = \frac{z^2}{(z - 1)(z - e^{-T})} = \frac{z^2}{(z - 1)(z - 0.368)}$$

$$(10\text{-}205)$$

for $T = 1$ second. The values of $c(t)$ at the sampling instants can be determined by expanding $C(z)$ in the inverse power of z, or

$$C(z) = 1 + 1.368z^{-1} + 1.5z^{-2} + 1.55z^{-3} + 1.56z^{-4} + \cdots \quad (10\text{-}206)$$

The values of $c(nT)$ are illustrated in Fig. 10-35a. It is important to note that the output transform $C(z)$ specifies the values of $c(t)$ only at the sampling instants; it does not give even a slight indication of the behavior

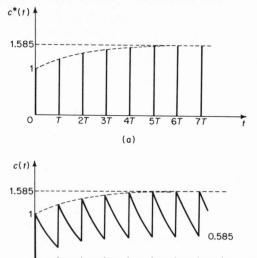

(a)

(b)

Fig. 10-35. (a) Output at sampling instants of R-C network given in Fig. 10-34 by the z-transform method; (b) Actual output between sampling instants of the R-C network given in Fig. 10-34.

of $c(t)$ between the sampling instants. As a matter of fact, we can show very easily by the impulse response or by the Laplace transform method that the actual response $c(t)$ is of the form shown in Fig. 10-35b. Furthermore, the z-transform method shows that there is a jump in $c(t)$ at $t = 0$. This phenomenon will not occur if the actual pulses of finite pulse widths are considered.

As another example, consider that the capacitor in the R-C network is replaced by an inductor of 1 henry. The transfer function of the circuit is $s/(s + 1)$, and its z-transform is

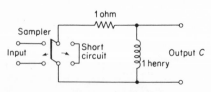

Fig. 10-36. R-L network.

$$G(z) = \frac{-e^{-T}}{z - e^{-T}} = \frac{-0.368}{z - 0.368} \quad (10\text{-}207)$$

for $T = 1$ sec. For a unit step input, the output z-transform is

$$C(z) = \frac{0.368z}{(z - 1)(z - 0.368)} \tag{10-208}$$

or

$$C(z) = -0.368z^{-1} - 0.503z^{-2} - 0.551z^{-3} - 0.568z^{-4} - \cdots \tag{10-209}$$

The values of $c(nT)$ given by Eq. (10-209) are illustrated in Fig. 10-37a. The z-transform method shows that the output response starts with a zero

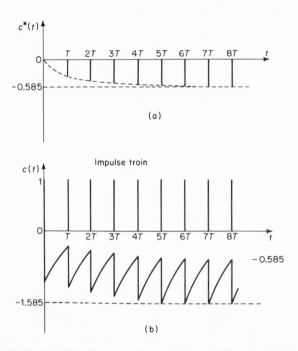

Fig. 10-37. (a) Output at sampling instants of R-L network given in Fig. 10-36 by the z-transform method; (b) Actual output of the R-L network given in Fig. 10-36.

value at $t = 0$, but if we judge from the impulse response of $G(s)$, it is apparent that $c(t)$ must contain an impulse of strength 1 at $t = 0$. By the principle of superposition, there must be impulses of unit strength for $c(t)$ st $t = 0, T, 2T, 3T, \ldots$ The actual output $c(t)$, when the input to $G(s)$ is assumed to be a train of unit impulses, is shown in Fig. 10-37b. It is seen that, in the previous example, while the z-transform does give correct output response only at the sampling instants, the z-transform technique breaks down completely in the present case.

10.11 Stability Analysis

Just as in the case of linear continuous system design, one of the most important specifications in designing a sampled-data system is stability. A sampled-data system is considered to be stable if the sampled output is bounded when a bounded input is applied. This statement is almost identical to the definition given for a continuous system, except that a bounded output at the sampling instants leaves the possibility of having the so-called hidden oscillation† between sampling instants. When the response between sampling instants becomes important, special techniques other than the z-transforms must be developed to yield information about the output at all times.

If we consider the basic system configuration of the sampled-data system given in Fig. 10-26, the closed-loop pulse transfer function is

$$\frac{C^*(s)}{R^*(s)} = \frac{G^*(s)}{1 + HG^*(s)} \tag{10-210}$$

where $1 + HG^*(s) = 0$ is the characteristic equation of the system. The stability of the sampled-data system is entirely determined by the locations of the roots of the characteristic equation. Specifically, none of the roots of the characteristic equation must be found in the right half of the s-plane, since such a root will yield exponentially growing time functions. In terms of the z-transforms, the characteristic equation of the system is written as $1 + HG(z) = 0$. Since the right half of the s-plane is mapped onto the exterior of the unit circle in the z-plane, as shown in Fig. 10-38, the stability

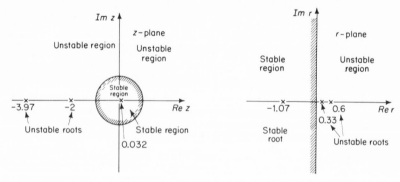

Fig. 10-38. Stable regions and unstable regions in the z- and r-planes, and the roots of the characteristic equation of Eq. (10-215).

requirement states that all the roots of the characteristic equation must lie inside the unit circle. We recall that, for continuous feedback control sys-

---

*E. I. Jury, "Hidden Oscillations in Sampled-Data Control Systems," *Trans. AIEE*, Vol. 76, part II, January, 1957, pp. 391–394.

tems, stability may be investigated by the following five well-known methods:

(1) The Routh-Hurwitz Criterion. Determines whether any roots of the characteristic equation lie in the right half of the s-plane.

(2) The Nyquist Criterion. Investigates whether the open-loop transfer function plot encircles the -1 point in the G-plane, and hence, determines the difference between the number of poles and the number of zeros of the closed-loop transfer function which are in the right half of the s-plane.

(3) The Bode Plot. Determines whether any real frequency exists at which the open-loop gain is greater than 0 db and the phase shift greater than 180 deg.

(4) Decibels of G as a Function of Phase Shift of G. Plots of the magnitude of G in decibels versus the phase shift of G. From this plot, the absolute stability as well as the relative stability of the closed-loop system may be investigated. By superimposing this plot with the Nichols chart, the frequency response of the closed-loop system may be obtained.

(5) The Root Locus Method. Determines the location of the roots of the characteristic equation when the open-loop gain K is varied.

With some modifications, each of the above techniques can be extended to determine the stability of sampled-data feedback control systems.

The Routh-Hurwitz Criterion Applied to Sampled-Data Systems

The attempt to apply the Routh test directly to the z-transform characteristic equation of a sampled-data system meets with one major difficulty. The conventional Routh test is devised to test the roots of a polynomial with respect to the left or right half of the complex s-plane. However, the stability of the sampled-data system concerns the determination of the location of the roots of the characteristic equation with respect to the unit circle in the z-plane. This difficulty is eliminated by modifying the Routh test with the bilinear transformation

$$r = \frac{z + 1}{z - 1} \tag{10-211}$$

or

$$z = \frac{r + 1}{r - 1} \tag{10-212}$$

where r is a complex variable; i.e., $r = \sigma_r + \omega_r$.

This transformation maps the interior of the unit circle in the z-plane onto the left half of the r-plane; therefore, the Routh test may be performed on the polynomial in the variable r. The following example illustrates how the modified Routh test is performed for a sampled-data feedback system.

EXAMPLE 10-15. Let the open-loop transfer function of a unity-feedback system with sampled-error signal be of the form

$$G(s) = \frac{22.57}{s^2(s + 1)} \tag{10-213}$$

If the sampling period is 1 sec, the z-transform of $G(s)$ is

$$G(z) = \frac{22.57z(0.368z + 0.264)}{(z - 1)^2(z - 0.368)} \tag{10-214}$$

The characteristic equation of the system may be written as

$$z^3 + 5.94z^2 + 7.7z - 0.368 = 0 \tag{10-215}$$

Substitution of Eq. (10-212) into the last equation yields

$$\left(\frac{r + 1}{r - 1}\right)^3 + 5.94\left(\frac{r + 1}{r - 1}\right)^2 + 7.7\left(\frac{r + 1}{r - 1}\right) - 0.368 = 0 \tag{10-216}$$

When we simplify,

$$14.27r^3 + 2.3r^2 - 11.74r + 3.13 = 0 \tag{10-217}$$

The Routh tabulation of the last equation is

$$
\begin{array}{lll}
r^3 & 14.27 & -11.74 \\
r^2 & 2.3 & 3.13 \\
r^1 & \dfrac{-27 - 44.6}{2.3} = -31.1 & 0 \\
r^0 & 3.13 &
\end{array}
$$

Since there are two changes of sign in the first column of the tabulation, the characteristic equation has two roots in the right half of the r-plane, which corresponds to two roots outside the unit circle in the z-plane. This result can be easily checked by solving Eq. (10-216); the three roots of the characteristic equation are at $z = 2$, $z = -3.97$, and $z = 0.032$. When mapped into the r-plane by Eq. (10-211), the three roots are at $r = \frac{1}{3}$, $r = 0.6$, and $r = -1.07$. The z-plane roots and the r-plane roots are illustrated in Fig. 10-38.

In principle, the bilinear r-transformation is very simple to apply. In transforming from the z to the r domain, the degree of the polynomial is not altered. However, in the case of higher degree order systems, the process of simplifying Eq. (10-216) to the form of Eq. (10-217) may be quite tedious.

The Nyquist Criterion

The stability of a sampled-data system may also be studied by using the Nyquist criterion. In the case of a sampled-data system, the characteristic equation is a function of z. It is apparent that the Nyquist path in the z-plane must be the unit circle enclosing the exterior of the circle. Then, the Nyquist plot of $HG(z)$ is the mapping of the unit circle in the z-plane to the $HG(z)$-plane. The stability of the sampled-data system is studied by investigating the encirclement of the -1 point by the $HG(z)$ locus in the

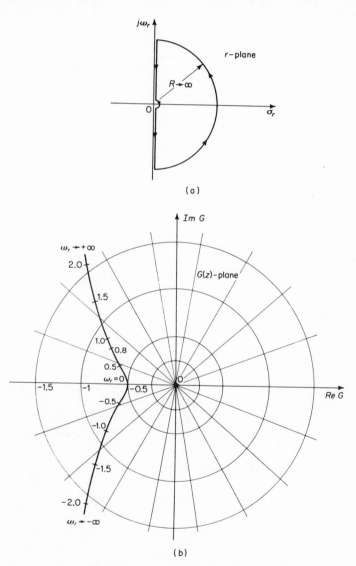

(a)

(b)

Fig. 10-39. The Nyquist path and the Nyquist plot of

$$G(z) = \frac{0.792Kz}{(z - 1)(z - 0.208)}$$

$HG(z)$-plane. All the properties and rules of the Nyquist criterion for continuous-data systems are still valid when applied to the $HG(z)$ locus. The main difference obviously exists in the new Nyquist path — the unit circle in the z-plane, and the typical forms of the $HG(z)$ locus for a sampled-data system. Actually, the Nyquist locus can easily be sketched by following the same techniques used for continuous systems if the bilinear transformation is applied. With the r-transformation, the Nyquist path in the complex r-plane is, again, composed of the imaginary axis and the semicircle with infinite radius in the right half of the r-plane, as shown in Fig. 10-39a. As an example, assume that the open-loop transfer function of a unity-feedback system with sampled-error is $G(s) = K/s(s + 1)$. If the sampling period T is 1.57 sec, the z-transform of $G(s)$ is

$$G(z) = \frac{0.792Kz}{(z - 1)(z - 0.208)} \tag{10-218}$$

Application of the bilinear transformation to $G(z)$ yields

$$G\left(z = \frac{r + 1}{r - 1}\right) = \frac{0.792K(r + 1)/(r - 1)}{\left(\frac{r + 1}{r - 1} - 1\right)\left(\frac{r + 1}{r - 1} - 0.208\right)} = \frac{K(r^2 - 1)}{2(r + 1.525)} \tag{10-219}$$

Since the system is open-loop stable, it is necessary only to construct the Nyquist plot corresponding to the positive portion of the imaginary axis in the r-plane. Therefore,

when $\qquad r = j\omega_r = j\infty, \quad G(z) = \infty\,\underline{/90°}$

$\qquad\qquad r = 0, \qquad G(z) = -K/3.05$

The Nyquist plot of $G(z)$ for $K = 1$ corresponding to values of r from $-j\infty$ to $+j\infty$ is given in Fig. 10-39b. It is seen from the Nyquist plot that for $K = 1$, the plot intersects the negative real axis at -0.328. The critical value of K is 3.05; for values of K greater than 3.05, the plot encloses the -1 point and the system is unstable. It is interesting to note that a second-order system with continuous data is known to be always stable; however, a second-order system with sampled data has introduced the possibility of becoming unstable.

The relation between the imaginary part of r and the true frequency may be derived as follows:
For $s = j\omega$, $z = e^{sT} = e^{j\omega T}$ and

$$r = j\omega_r = \frac{z + 1}{z - 1} = \frac{e^{j\omega T} + 1}{e^{j\omega T} - 1} \tag{10-220}$$

Multiplication of the numerator and denominator of the last equation by $e^{-j\omega T/2}$ yields

$$j\omega_r = \frac{e^{j\omega T/2} + e^{-j\omega T/2}}{e^{j\omega T/2} - e^{-j\omega T/2}} = \frac{2\cos\left(\dfrac{\omega T}{2}\right)}{j2\sin\left(\dfrac{\omega T}{2}\right)} \tag{10-221}$$

hence

$$\omega_r = -\cot\left(\frac{\omega T}{2}\right) \tag{10-222}$$

or

$$\omega = -\frac{2}{T}\cot^{-1}\omega_r \tag{10-223}$$

From Eq. (10-222), when $\omega = \omega_s = 2\pi/T$, $\omega_r = -\cot\pi = \infty$;

when $\omega = \omega_s/2 = \pi/T$, $\omega_r = -\cot(\pi/2) = 0$;

when $\omega = 0$, $\omega_r = -\infty$.

Therefore, when ω_r is varied from $-\infty$ through 0 to $+\infty$, the corresponding variation of the actual frequency ω is only from 0 to the sampling frequency ω_s.

The Bode Diagram

The Bode diagram also can be constructed for a sampled-data system if the bilinear transformation is applied. The Bode plot of $G(z)$ is made in terms of the magnitude of $G(z)$ in decibels and the angle of $G(z)$ as a function of ω_r. For example, Eq. (10-219) may be written as

$$G\left(z = \frac{j\omega_r + 1}{j\omega_r - 1}\right) = \frac{K(j\omega_r)^2 - 1}{2(j\omega_r + 1.525)} = \frac{K(j\omega_r + 1)(j\omega_r - 1)}{2(j\omega_r + 1.525)} \tag{10-224}$$

or

$$G(z) = \frac{K(j\omega_r + 1)(j\omega_r - 1)}{3.05(0.655 j\omega_r + 1)} \tag{10-225}$$

The corner frequencies of the plot are at $\omega_r = 1$ rad/sec, 1 rad/sec, and 1.525 rad/sec. The asymptotes of the magnitude curves of $(j\omega_r - 1)$ and $(j\omega_r + 1)$ are identical, with a slope of $+20$ db/decade of frequency. Thus, the magnitude curve of $(j\omega_r + 1)(j\omega_r - 1)$ has an asymptote with a slope of $+40$ db/decade of frequency. The intersection of the asymptote with the ω_r axis is at $\omega_r = 1$ rad/sec. The only difference between the Bode plots of the two linear terms is in the phase shift curves. The phase shift of $(j\omega_r + 1)$ varies from 0 deg to 90 deg while the phase shift of $(j\omega_r - 1)$ varies from 180 deg to 90 deg, as ω_r is varied from 0 to ∞. Thus, the net phase shift of the product of the two terms is a constant 180 deg. In Fig. 10-40, the Bode plot of Eq. (10-225) is constructed with $K = 1$. The gain limit ($=$ gain margin when $K = 1$) is found to be 3.05. The phase margin will depend on the value of K, and can be determined from the Bode plot in the usual manner. For $K = 1$, the phase margin is approximately 52 deg.

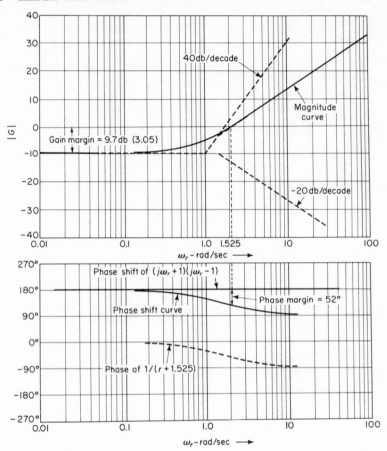

Fig. 10-40. The Bode plot of

$$G(z) = \frac{K(j\omega_r + 1)(j\omega_r - 1)}{3.05(0.655j\omega_r + 1)} \quad (K = 1).$$

Decibels of G as a Function of Phase Shift of G

The magnitude M of the ratio of C to R is usually used to represent the amplification of a closed-loop system. For a sampled-data system, M may be defined as

$$M = \frac{C(z)}{R(z)} = \frac{G(z)}{1 + HG(z)} \tag{10-226}$$

If we substitute Eq. (10-225) into the last equation and simplify, we have

$$M = \frac{-K(\omega_r^2 + 1)}{3.05 + j2\omega_r - K(\omega_r^2 + 1)} \tag{10-227}$$

Examination of the last equation shows that M can be larger than unity. Furthermore, if the real and imaginary parts of the denominator of M are equal to zero at the same frequency ω_r, the value of M will be infinite. This will occur when

$$\omega_r^2 = \frac{3.05}{K} - 1 = 0 \tag{10-228}$$

or $K = 3.05$ at $\omega_r = 0$, which checks with the result obtained from the Nyquist and the Bode plots. A plot of $G(z)$ in decibels versus phase shift is constructed on the Nichols chart in Fig. 10-41 for a value of $K = 1.57$.

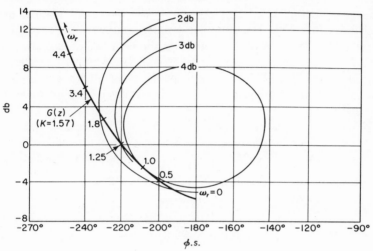

Fig. 10-41. Magnitude versus phase shift plot of
$$G(z) = \frac{K(j\omega_r + 1)(j\omega_r - 1)}{2(j\omega_r + 1.525)}$$

The resonant peak M_p is equal to 1.58, and the resonance frequency is $\omega_r = 0.966$ or, equivalently, at $\omega = 3$ rad/sec. A plot of M as a function of frequency is given in Fig. 10-42.

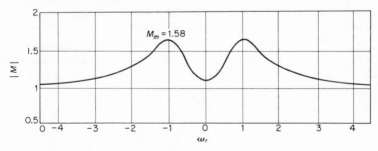

Fig. 10-42. Magnification M of sampled-data system with
$$G(z) = \frac{K(j\omega_r + 1)(j\omega_r - 1)}{2(j\omega_r + 1.525)}$$
for $K = 1.57$.

The Root Locus Technique

The root locus technique used for the analysis and design of continuous-data systems can also be easily adapted to the study of sampled-data systems. Since the characteristic equation of a simple sampled-data system may be represented by the form

$$1 + HG(z) = 0 \qquad (10\text{-}229)$$

Where $HG(z)$ is a rational function in z, the root locus method may be applied directly to the last equation without modification. The significant difference between the present case and the continuous case are that the root loci of Eq. (10-229) are constructed in the z-plane, and that in investigating the stability of the sampled-data system from the root locus plot, the unit circle rather than the imaginary axis in the z-plane should be observed.

It is clear that, in the construction of the root loci in the z-plane, all the properties of the root loci discussed in Chapter 8 are still valid. The following example shows the construction of root loci for a sampled-data system.

EXAMPLE 10-16. Consider a unity-feedback control system with sampled-error signal; the open-loop transfer function of the system is given as

$$G(z) = \frac{Kz(1 - e^{-T})}{(z - 1)(z - e^{-T})} \qquad (10\text{-}230)$$

The characteristic equation of the system is $1 + G(z) = 0$, whose root loci are to be determined when K is varied from 0 to ∞. If the sampling period T is 1 sec, $G(z)$ becomes

$$G(z) = \frac{0.632Kz}{(z - 1)(z - 0.368)} \qquad (10\text{-}231)$$

which has poles at $z = 1$, $z = 0.368$, and a zero at the origin. The pole-zero configuration of $G(z)$ is shown in Fig. 10-43a. The root loci must start at the poles $(K = 0)$ and end at the zeros $(K \to \infty)$ of $G(z)$. The complete root loci for $T = 1$ sec are constructed in Fig. 10-43. The intersection of the loci with the unit circle occurs at $z = -1$, and the corresponding value of K at that point is 4.33.

If the sampling period is changed to $T = 5$ sec, $G(z)$ becomes

$$G(z) = \frac{0.993Kz}{(z - 1)(z - 0.0067)} \qquad (10\text{-}232)$$

The root loci when $T = 5$ sec are constructed in Fig. 10-43b. The reader should not be misled by the fact that the root loci take the form of a smaller circle than that of $T = 1$ sec and conclude that with the same value of K, the system is more stable with $T = 5$ sec. The marginal value of K

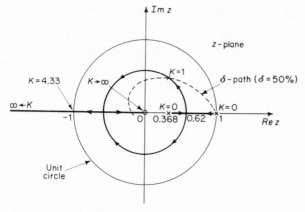

(a) Root loci for $T = 1$ sec

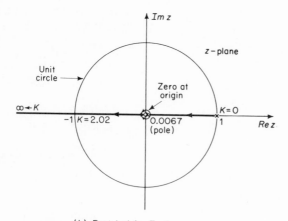

(b) Root loci for $T = 5$ sec

Fig. 10-43. Root locus diagrams of sampled-data system.

$$G(z) = \frac{Kz(1 - e^{-T})}{(z - 1)(z - e^{-T})} \; .$$

for $T = 5$ sec is found to be 2.02, as compared to the marginal K of 4.33 for $T = 1$ sec.

The constant damping ratio δ-path may be superimposed on the root loci to determine the required value of K for a certain specified damping ratio. In Fig. 10-43a, the δ-path for $\beta = 30$ deg ($\delta = 50$ per cent) is drawn, and the intersection with the root loci gives the value of $K = 1$. This means that for all values of K greater than 1, the damping ratio of the system is greater than 50 per cent.

The effect of the zero-order hold circuit on system stability may also be observed by means of the root locus plot. If zero-order hold circuit is inserted between the sampler and the controlled system $G(s)$, the open-loop transfer function is

$$G(z) = \frac{K[(T - 1 + e^{-T})z - Te^{-T} + 1 - e^{-T}]}{(z - 1)(z - e^{-T})} \qquad (10\text{-}233)$$

The root loci of the system with hold circuits for $T = 1$ sec and $T = 5$ sec are constructed in Fig. 10-44a and b, respectively. The marginal value of K is 2.3 for $T = 1$ sec, and that of $T = 5$ sec is 0.66.

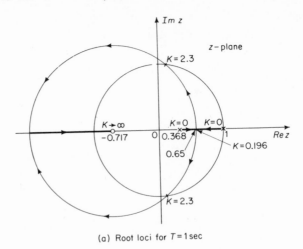

(a) Root loci for $T = 1$ sec

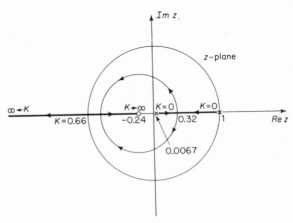

(b) Root loci for $T = 5$ sec

Fig. 10-44. Root locus diagrams of sampled-data system with zero-order hold circuit.

$$G(z) = \frac{Kz(1 - e^{-T})}{(z - 1)(z - e^{-T})}$$

10.12 Design and Compensation of Sampled-Data Systems

When the preliminary studies made on a certain sampled-data system reveal that the over-all performance is unsatisfactory with reference to the given specifications, compensation techniques for improving the system performance must be employed.

Just as in the compensation of control systems with continuous-data, the compensation of a sampled-data system is generally accomplished by inserting elements in the forward path (cascaded compensation) on the feedback path (feedback compensation), or by forming additional minor feedback loops or other more complex measures. In general, the basic purpose of compensation is to reshape the Nyquist locus of the open-loop transfer function so that the compensated system meets the required performance specifications.

In sampled-data systems, cascade compensation may be effected by the following two schemes:

(1) *Compensation by Continuous Networks.* In this scheme, continuous-data networks are connected in series with the elements in the controlled system.

(2) *Compensation by Digital Networks.* In this scheme, digital controllers or networks are employed in place of the continuous networks. Digital controllers operate only on sampled data, and, in general, can be a special-purpose digital computer or a portion of a general-purpose digital computer.

(1) *Cascade Compensation by Continuous-Data Networks*

A sampled-data control system with a continuous-data compensating element is shown in Fig. 10-45. The open-loop transfer function of the compensated system may be written as

$$z\text{-transform of } [G_{h0}(s)G_c(s)G(s)] = G_{h0}G_cG(z) \qquad (10\text{-}234)$$

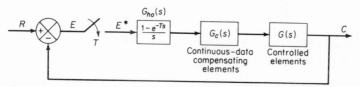

Fig. 10-45. A sampled-data feedback control system with continuous-data cascade compensation.

However, unlike the compensation of continuous-data systems, the transfer function $G_{h0}G_cG(z)$ cannot be related to $G_c(z)$ or $G_{h0}G(z)$ alone. Therefore, a different transfer locus for $G_{h0}G_cG(z)$ must be constructed each time a new compensating element $G_c(s)$ is selected. This is the major difficulty in the compensation of sampled-data systems with continuous-data networks. However, if certain appropriate approximations on the system are made, the conventional compensation techniques devised originally for the compensation of continuous systems may still be applied. For instance, the sampled-data system with zero-order hold circuit may be approximated by an equivalent continuous system with time lag.

From Eq. (10-67), the transfer function of a zero-order hold circuit is

$$G_{h0}(j\omega) = T \frac{\sin\left(\dfrac{\omega T}{2}\right) e^{-j\omega T/2}}{\dfrac{\omega T}{2}} \qquad (10\text{-}235)$$

and, by definition, $G_{h0}G_cG^*(j\omega)$ may be written as

$$G_{h0}G_cG^*(j\omega) = \frac{1}{T} \sum_{n=-\infty}^{\infty} G_{h0}(j\omega + jn\,\omega_s)G_c(j\omega + jn\omega_s)G(j\omega + jn\omega_s) \quad (10\text{-}236)$$

Substitution of Eq. (10-235) into Eq. (10-236) yields

$$G_{h0}G_cG^*(j\omega) = \frac{1}{T} \sum_{n=-\infty}^{\infty} T \frac{\sin\left(\dfrac{\omega + n\omega_s}{2}\right)T}{\dfrac{(\omega + n\omega_s)T}{2}} e^{-j\omega(+nu)T/2} G_c(j\omega + jn\omega_s)$$
$$G(j\omega + jn\omega_s) \qquad (10\text{-}237)$$

If the sampling frequency ω_s is high, and if the frequency characteristic of $G(j\omega)$ is of the low pass, all harmonics can be neglected; Eq. (10-237) can be approximated just by its first term; i.e.,

$$G_{h0}G_cG^*(j\omega) \cong e^{-j\omega T/2} G_c(j\omega)G(j\omega) \qquad (10\text{-}238)$$

Therefore, the sampler and zero-order hold circuit may be replaced by a time lag of half the sampling period. The approximating continuous

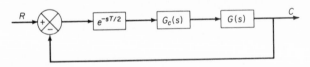

Fig. 10-46. The approximating continuous system of the sampled-data control system in Fig. 10-45.

system is shown in Fig. 10-46. Since this approximation yields a continuous system, conventional techniques of design and compensation can be used.

EXAMPLE 10-17. Assume that the transfer function of the controlled elements $G(s)$ of the sampled-data system shown in Fig. 10-45 is

$$G(s) = \frac{K}{s(s+1)} \qquad (10\text{-}239)$$

where $K = 1$, and $T = 1$ sec.

The approximating continuous model of the uncompensated system is

$$G_{h0}G^*(j\omega) \approx e^{-j\omega T/2}\, G(j\omega) = e^{-j\omega T/2}\, \frac{K}{j\omega(j\omega + 1)} \qquad (10\text{-}240)$$

the Bode plot of which is constructed in Fig. 10-47. The phase margin of the uncompensated system for $K = 1$ is approximately 17 deg. Let us

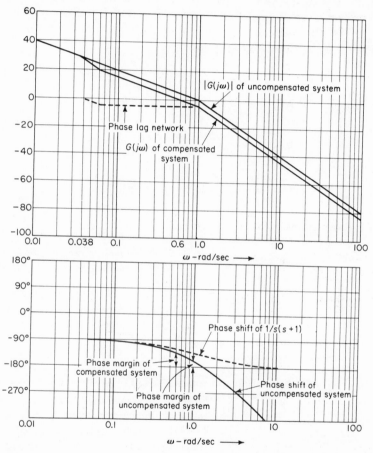

Fig. 10-47. Bode plot of sampled-data feedback control system in Example 10-16.

assume that the specification calls for a phase margin of at least 45 deg. Because of the rapid increase in phase lag as the frequency becomes higher, a phase-lead network may not be effective in improving the phase margin in this case. We may try a phase-lag network with the transfer function

$$G_c(s) = \frac{1 + a\tau s}{1 + \tau s} \qquad (a < 1) \quad (10\text{-}241)$$

where the values of a and τ are to be determined. From the Bode plot of the uncompensated system, we see that the phase margin of 45 deg may be realized if the gain crossover is moved from 1 rad/sec to a frequency of 0.65 rad/sec. As a standard practice, the new gain crossover is selected at a frequency somewhat below 0.65 rad/sec, for example, $\omega_c' = 0.6$ rad/sec. The gain of $G(j\omega)$ at this new gain crossover is about 4 db, so the phase-lag network must produce 4 db of attenuation at this frequency. By using Eq. (9-72), the distance between the two corner frequencies of the lag network can be determined. Therefore,

$$a = 10^{-G(j\omega'c)/20} = 10^{-4/20} = 0.632 \qquad (10\text{-}242)$$

and from Eq. (9-73), the upper corner frequency of the lag network is

$$\frac{1}{a\tau} = \frac{\omega_c'}{10} = 0.06\,\text{rad/sec} \qquad (10\text{-}243)$$

hence

$$\frac{1}{\tau} = 0.06 \cdot 0.632 = 0.038\,\text{rad/sec} \qquad (10\text{-}244)$$

The transfer function of the phase lag network is determined to be

$$G_c(s) = \frac{1 + 16.67s}{1 + 26.3s} \qquad (10\text{-}245)$$

The Bode plot of the compensated system is shown in Fig. 10-47. The phase margin of the compensated system is found to be approximately 45 deg.

(2) Cascade Compensation by Digital Compensators

In the preceding section the compensation of sampled-data systems by continuous-data networks is discussed. The continuous-data element is connected directly to the controlled elements, and, in order to simplify the design procedure, the sampler and the zero-order hold circuit are approximated by a time lag $e^{-sT/2}$. With this approximation, the sampled-data system is converted into a continuous-data system, and the conventional compensation technique can be applied directly.

Alternatively, the cascade compensation of a sampled-data system may also be effected by inserting a pulsed-data or digital network in the forward path. A pulsed-data or digital network is one which receives a sequence of numbers (impulses) at its input and delivers a sequence of processed numbers at the output. In general, a digital network may be a passive network preceded and followed by samplers, or a special purpose digital computer.

Figure 10-48 illustrates a sampled-data feedback control system; a digital compensating network with transfer function $D^*(s)$ or $D(z)$ is inserted in series with the controlled elements $G(s)$. The open-loop transfer function of the compensated system is $D(z)G_{h0}G(z)$. Since $D(z)G_{h0}G(z)$

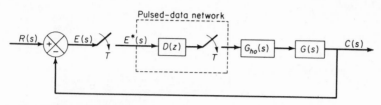

Fig. 10-48. A sampled-data feedback control system with pulsed-data network compensation.

is equal to the product of the pulse transfer function $D(z)$ of the digital controller and the z-transform of $G_{h0}(s)G(s)$, conventional design techniques may readily be used to study the effect of variation of the poles and zeros of $D(z)$ on the over-all system performance. The root locus design technique may be used effectively in the z-plane to show the effect of the digital controller on the location of the closed-loop poles. With the aid of the bilinear r-transformation, the conventional methods of reshaping the Nyquist plot and the Bode plot may also be adopted.

The a priori requirement in the design of the pulsed-data network $D(z)$ is that it be physically realizable. It would be useless if the design results in a transfer function $D(z)$ which cannot be realized by physical elements. A pulsed-data network is considered to be physically realizable if no output signal of the network will appear before an input signal is applied. In general, $D(z)$ may be expressed as the ratio of two polynomials in z.

$$D(z) = \frac{a_n z^n + a_{n-1} z^{n-1} + \cdots + a_0}{b_m z^m + b_{m-1} z^{m-1} + \cdots + b_0} \qquad (10\text{-}246)$$

If $D(z)$ is expanded in a power series in z^{-1}, the coefficients of the series represent the values of the weighting sequence of the digital network; therefore, the series should not contain any positive powers in z. A positive power in z in the series expansion of $D(z)$ will indicate "prediction," or simply, the output signal precedes the input signal. This means that for a physically realizable $D(z)$, the highest power of its denominator must be equal to or greater than the highest power of the numerator; i.e., in Eq. (10-246), $m \geqslant n$.

The following example illustrates the design of digital compensation by means of the bilinear transformation and the conventional design technique.

EXAMPLE 10-18. In this example, the same sampled-data system given in Example 10-17 is to be compensated by a digital compensator. The transfer function of the controlled elements $G(s)$ of the original sampled-data system is given by $G(s) = K/s(s + 1)$, where $K = 1$ and $T = 1$ sec. The z-transform of the open-loop transfer function of the uncompensated system is

$$\mathcal{Z}\left[G_{h0}(s)G(s) \right] = G_{h0}G(z) = \frac{0.368z + 0.264}{(z - 1)(z - 0.368)} \tag{10-247}$$

Substitution of the relation $z = (r + 1)/(r - 1)$ into the last equation and simplifying yields

$$G_{h0}G(z) = \frac{0.038(r - 1)(r/0.162 + 1)}{(1 + r/2.16)} \tag{10-248}$$

The Bode plot of the uncompensated system is constructed as shown in Fig. 10-49. The phase margin of the uncompensated system obtained from

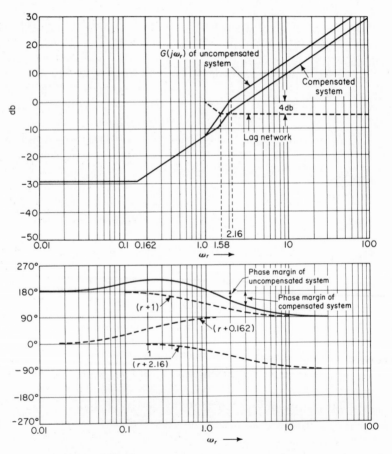

Fig. 10-49. Bode plot of sampled-data system in Example 10-17.

the plot is approximately 25 deg, as compared to the 17 deg determined in Example 10-17 by the approximation method.

Note that because the slope of the magnitude curve in Fig. 10-49 is positive in the higher frequency range, compensation of the system with a phase-lag network in the r-domain will result in a higher gain crossover frequency. It is also important to notice that since the phase margin is measured from the 180 deg axis, the phase shift of the lag network with the transfer function

$$D\left(z = \frac{r+1}{r-1}\right) = \frac{1 + a\tau r}{1 + \tau r} \qquad (a < 1) \qquad (10\text{-}249)$$

will be added to the original phase shift curve in such a manner as to further improve the phase margin. Therefore, in the design of the digital compensator $D(z)$, there is no need to put the upper corner frequency $1/a$ at a frequency of 1 decade below the new crossover frequency. As a matter of fact, the frequency $1/a\tau$ should be as high as possible.

Assume that a phase margin of 45 deg is required for the system, and that from the Bode plot shown in Fig. 10-49, the required phase margin may be obtained if the gain crossover frequency is moved up to $\omega'_{rc} = 3$ rad/sec. The gain of $G(j\omega_r)$ at this new gain crossover frequency is approximately 4 db. Therefore,

$$a = 10^{-G(j\omega rc)/20} = 10^{-4/20} = 0.632 \qquad (10\text{-}250)$$

The highest possible value for $1/a\tau$ should be found at the frequency where $|G(j\omega_r)| = -|G(j\omega_{rc})| = -4$ db. Hence, from Fig. 10-49, the upper corner frequency of the lag network is

$$\frac{1}{a\tau} = 1.7 \text{ rad/sec} \qquad (10\text{-}251)$$

from which

$$\frac{1}{\tau} = 1.7 \cdot 0.632 = 1.07 \text{ rad/sec} \qquad (10\text{-}252)$$

The transfer function of the lag network in the r-domain is

$$D(z) = \frac{1 + 0.588r}{1 + 0.934r} \qquad (10\text{-}253)$$

Substitution of $r = (z + 1)/(z - 1)$ into the last equation and simplifying yields

$$D(z) = \frac{0.805(z - 0.26)}{(z - 0.34)} \qquad (10\text{-}254)$$

Since the denominator and numerator polynomials of $D(z)$ are of the same degree, the realizability requirement is satisfied.

In the following, we shall show that $D(z)$ may be realized either by a digital computer with operations of amplifiers, summing devices, samplers, and time delays, or by a simple R-C network preceded and followed by synchronized samplers.

Eq. (10-254) may also be written as follows:

$$D(z) = \frac{E_1(z)}{E(z)} = \frac{0.805(1 - 0.26z^{-1})}{(1 - 0.34z^{-1})} \qquad (10\text{-}255)$$

or

$$0.805(1 - 0.26z^{-1})E(z) = E_1(z)(1 - 0.34z^{-1}) \qquad (10\text{-}256)$$

Taking the inverse z-transform on both sides of the last equation yields

$$0.805e(nT) - 0.209e[(n - 1)T] = e_1(nT) - 0.34e_1[n - 1]T] \qquad (10\text{-}257)$$

Solving for $e_1(nT)$ in the last equation, we have

$$e_1(nT) = 0.34e_1[(n - 1)T] + 0.805e(nT) - 0.209e[(n - 1)T] \qquad (10\text{-}258)$$

The block diagram representation of the digital computer which realizes Eq. (10-258) is constructed in Fig. 10-50.

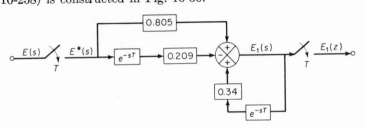

Fig. 10-50. Digital computer realizing pulse transfer function

$$D(z) = 0.805 \frac{(1 - 0.26z^{-1})}{(1 - 0.34z^{-1})}$$

It is also possible to realize the digital compensator $D(z)$ by a series zero-order hold and an R-C filter network preceded and followed by synchronized samplers, as shown in Fig. 10-51. Then

$$\mathcal{Z}\left(\frac{1 - e^{-Ts}}{s}\right)G_c(s) = D(z) = 0.805 \frac{(z - 0.26)}{(z - 0.34)} \qquad (10\text{-}259)$$

or

$$\mathcal{Z}\left[\frac{G_c(s)}{s}\right] = \frac{D(z)}{1 - z^{-1}} = 0.805 \frac{(1 - 0.26z^{-1})}{(1 - z^{-1})(1 - 0.34z^{-1})} \qquad (10\text{-}260)$$

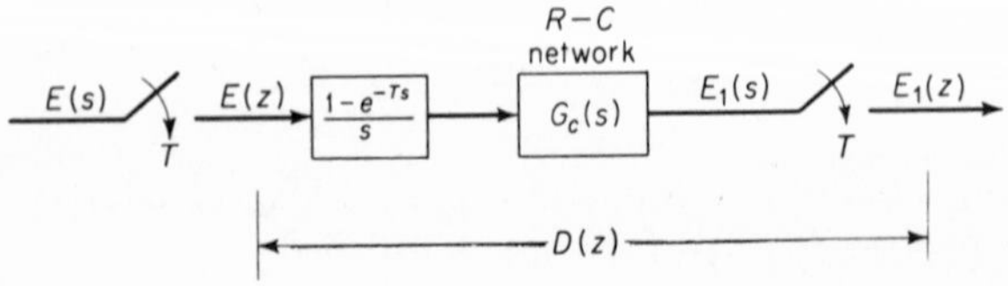

Fig. 10-51. Realization of pulsed-data controller by simple R-C filter network.

Expanding the last equation into partial fractions yields

$$Z\left[\frac{G_c(s)}{s}\right] = 0.903\,\frac{1}{(1 - z^{-1})} - \frac{0.098}{(1 - 0.34z^{-1})} \qquad (10\text{-}261)$$

Letting $0.34z^{-1} = z_1^{-1}$ and substituting into the last equation, we have

$$Z\left[\frac{G_c(s)}{s}\right] = \frac{0.903}{(1 - z^{-1})} - \frac{0.098}{(1 - z_1^{-1})} \qquad (10\text{-}262)$$

Taking the inverse z-transform on both sides of Eq. (10-262) yields

$$\frac{G_c(s)}{s} = \frac{0.903}{s} = \frac{0.098}{s_1} \qquad (10\text{-}263)$$

where

$$s_1 = \frac{1}{T}\ln z_1 \qquad (10\text{-}264)$$

Hence

$$0.34e^{-sT} = e^{-s_1 T} \qquad (10\text{-}265)$$

or

$$\ln 0.34 - sT = -s_1 T \qquad (10\text{-}266)$$

$$s_1 = s - \frac{1}{T}\ln 0.34 = s + 0.47 \qquad (10\text{-}267)$$

The transfer function of the network $G_c(s)$ is

$$G_c(s) = 0.903 - \frac{0.098s}{s + 0.47} = \frac{0.903s - 0.098s + 0.424}{s + 0.47}$$

$$= \frac{0.805s + 0.424}{s + 0.47} = \frac{0.9(1 + 1.9s)}{(1 + 2.13s)} \qquad (10\text{-}268)$$

Evidently, $G_c(s)$ can be synthesized by a simple $R\text{-}C$ network.

10.13 Response of Sampled-Data Systems Between Sampling Instants

Although the z-transform method can be applied systematically for the analysis and design of sampled-data control systems, it is known that the z-transform method does not yield any information between sampling instants. A complete description of any system response almost always necessitates a knowledge of the output waveform between sampling instants.

Several methods* have been developed in the past for the evaluation of response between sampling instants. However, among these methods, the

---

*E. I. Jury, *Sampled-Data Control Systems*, John Wiley & Sons, Inc., New York, 1958, pp. 64–72.

submultiple sampling method† and the modified z-transform method‡ are the most common and useful methods. The submultiple sampling method is discussed in detail in the following.

Consider the open-loop sampled-data system shown in Fig. 10-52a. The sampling switch S_0 samples at uniform intervals of T seconds. The ordinary z-transform of the output response $C(z)$ is obtained by taking the

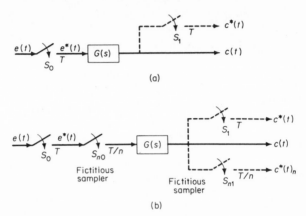

(a)

(b)

Fig. 10-52. (a) Sampled-data system; (b) Sampled-data system with fictitious samplers.

Laplace transform of the output of the fictitious sampler S_1 and making the substitution of $z = e^{sT}$. In Fig. 10-52b, fictitious samplers S_{n0} and S_{n1} with sampling period T/n, where $n = 1,2,3, \ldots$, are placed between S_0 and $G(s)$ and at the output terminal, respectively. The fictitious samplers are not physical components; they are used simply to facilitate the calculation of the system response between sampling instants.

Since the input to the fictitious sampler S_{n0} is a train of impulses spaced T sec apart, and since S_{n0} is sampling at a rate n times as fast as S_0, the insertion of the switch S_{n0} does not at all affect the original system behavior. Therefore, the two systems shown in Fig. 10-52a and b are essentially identical.

The continuous output of the system shown in Fig. 10-52b may be written as follows:

$$c(t) = \sum_{m=0}^{\infty} e(mT)g(t - mT) \qquad (10\text{-}269)$$

†W. K. Linvill and R. W. Sittler, *IRE Convention Record* New York, Part I, 1953, pp. 99–104.

‡R. H. Barker, "The Pulse Transfer Function and Its Application to Sampling Servo Systems," *Proc. I.E.E.* (London), Vol. 99, Part IV, 1952, pp. 302–317; E. I. Jury, "Synthesis and Critical Study of Sampled-Data Control Systems," *Trans. AIEE*, Vol. 75, Part II, 1956, pp. 141–151.

where $g(t)$ is the impulse response of $G(s)$. At any sampling instant $t = kT/n$ of sampler S_{n1}, $(k = 0,1,2,3, \ldots)$, the value of the output is

$$c\left(\frac{kT}{n}\right) = \sum_{m=0}^{\infty} e(mT)g\left(\frac{kT}{n} - mT\right) \tag{10-270}$$

Then, the output of the fictitious sampler S_{n1} can be written as

$$c^*(t)_n = \sum_{k=0}^{\infty} c\left(\frac{kT}{n}\right)\delta\left(t - \frac{kT}{n}\right) \tag{10-271}$$

The z-transform of the last equation is

$$C(z)_n = \mathbb{Z}[c^*(t)_n] = \sum_{k=0}^{\infty} c\,(kT/n)z^{-k/n} = C(z)]_{\substack{z=z^{1/n} \\ T=T/n}} \tag{10-272}$$

Therefore, the z-transform of the output of sampler S_{n1} is equal to the z-transform of $c^*(t)$ with z replaced by $z^{1/n}$ and T replaced by T/n. Substitution of Eq. (10-270) into Eq. (10-271) yields

$$C(z)_n = \sum_{k=0}^{\infty}\sum_{m=0}^{\infty} e(mT)g\left(\frac{kT}{n} - mT\right)z^{-k/n} \tag{10-273}$$

If we let $\left(\dfrac{k}{n} - m\right) = \dfrac{v}{n}$, where v is an integer, Eq. (10-273) may be written as

$$C(z)_n = \sum_{v=0}^{\infty} g\left(\frac{vT}{n}\right)z^{-v/n}\sum_{m=0}^{\infty} e(mT)z^{-m} \tag{10-274}$$

hence

$$C(z)_n = G(z)_n\,E(z) \tag{10-275}$$

where

$$G(z)_n = \sum_{v=0}^{\infty} g\left(\frac{vT}{n}\right)z^{-v/n} = G(z)]_{\substack{z=z^{1/n} \\ T=T/n}} \tag{10-276}$$

Equation (10-275) implies that the response between sampling instants can be evaluated by using just the ordinary z-transforms. The number of points at which the values of $c(t)$ are required determines the value of n. For instance, if in addition to the values at the normal sampling instants $t = 0, T, 2T, \ldots$, the values of $c(t)$ at two other points between sampling instants are to be determined, n is set equal to 3. In general, $n = q + 1$, where q is the number of sampled values desired between sampling instants.

EXAMPLE 10-19. Let $G(s) = 1/(s + 1)$ for the system shown in Fig. 10-52a. The ordinary z-transform of $G(s)$ is $G(z) = z/(z - e^{-T})$. Then

$$G(z)_n = G(z)]_{\substack{z=1/n \\ T=T/n}} = \frac{z^{1/n}}{z^{1/n} - e^{-T/n}} = \frac{z^{1/n}}{z^{1/n} - e^{-1/n}} \tag{10-277}$$

where $T = 1$ sec. If we let $n = 3$,

$$G(z)_3 = \frac{z^{1/3}}{z^{1/3} - 0.717} \tag{10-278}$$

The inverse transform of $G(z)_3$ yields values of the impulse response $g(t)$ not only at the actual sampling instants $t = 0,1,2,\ldots$, but also at $t = \frac{1}{3}, \frac{2}{3}, \frac{4}{3}, \frac{5}{3}, \ldots$.

If we let $z^{1/3} = z_3$, then $z = z_3^3$. Equation (10-278) is written as

$$G(z)_3 = \frac{z_3}{z_3 - 0.717} = 1 + 0.717z_3^{-1} + 0.515z_3^{-2} + 0.368z_3^{-3} + 0.264z_3^{-4}$$
$$+ 0.189z_3^{-5} + 0.1365z_3^{-6} + 0.097z_3^{-7} + \cdots \quad (10\text{-}279)$$

The values of $g(t)$ at the fictitious sampling instants are represented by the respective coefficients of the series expansion of $G(z)_3$.

Therefore $g(0) = 1$, $g(\frac{1}{3}) = 0.717$, $g(\frac{2}{3}) = 0.515$, $g(1) = 0.368$, $g(\frac{4}{3}) = 0.264$, $g(\frac{5}{3}) = 0.189$, $g(2) = 0.136$, $\ldots$

If the input $e(t)$ to the system is a unit step function, $E(z) = \dfrac{z}{z-1}$.

From Eq. (10-275), for $n = 3$,

$$C(z)_3 = G(z)_3 E(z) = \frac{z^{1/3}}{z^{1/3} - 0.717} \times \frac{z}{z - 1} \quad (10\text{-}280)$$

or

$$C(z)_3 = \frac{z_3}{z_3 - 0.717} \frac{z_3^3}{z_3^3 - 1} = \frac{z_3^4}{(z_3 - 0.717)(z_3^3 - 1)} \quad (10\text{-}281)$$

Expansion of $C(z)_3$ into a power series in z_3^{-1} yields

$$c(nT) = 1 + 0.717z_3^{-1} + 0.514z_3^{-2} + 1.368z_3^{-3} + 0.98z_3^{-4} + 0.703z_3^{-5}$$
$$+ 1.504z_3^{-6} + 1.08z_3^{-7} + 0.773z_3^{-8} + 1.55z_3^{-9} + \ldots \quad (10\text{-}282)$$

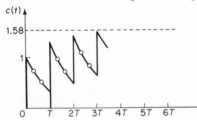

Fig. 10-53. Output response of system given in Example 10-18.

The waveform of $c(nT)$ is constructed in Fig. 10-53.

The submultiple sampling scheme may also be applied to closed-loop sampled-data systems. In Fig. 10-54, a fictitious sampler S_{n0} with sampling period $1/n$ is inserted in the forward path and a second fictitious sampler with the same sampling period S_{n1} is applied at the output terminal. At the output terminal, the actual continuouous output of the

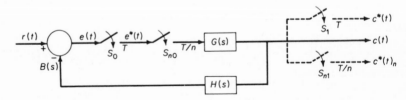

Fig. 10-54. Closed-loop sampled-data system with fictitious samplers.

system is denoted by $C(s)$; the ordinary z-transform of the output $C(z)$ is obtained from the sampler S_1. But if additional information concerning $c(t)$ between the actual sampling instants is desired, the output of S_{n1} should be used. In Fig. (10-54), the output of S_{n1} may be written as

$$C(z)_n = G(z)_n E(z) \qquad (10\text{-}283)$$

also

$$E(z) = R(z) - B(z) = R(z) - HG(z)E(z) \qquad (10\text{-}284)$$

hence

$$E(z) = \frac{R(z)}{1 + HG(z)} \qquad (10\text{-}285)$$

Substitution of the last equation into Eq. (10-283) yields

$$C(z)_n = G(z)_n \frac{R(z)}{1 + HG(z)} \qquad (10\text{-}286)$$

10.14 Summary

It is seen that because of the time-varying property, the analysis and design of sampled-data feedback control systems are generally more complex than those for continuous systems. Nevertheless, the techniques used in the studies of sampled-data systems rely to a great extent upon the extension of their continuous system counterparts.

The material presented in this chapter is intended to give the reader a general concept of feedback control systems with sampled data. No attempt is made to cover all the topics concerned in this area.

Problems

10-1. A particle of mass M is connected as shown in Fig. 10P-1, and is at rest in its equilibrium position at $t = 0$. The force is in the form of blows of impulses of strength F which are given to the particle at $t = nT$ sec $(n = 0, 1, 2, \ldots)$. Write the equation of motion for the system and solve for the displacement $x(t)$ of the particle by means of the Laplace transform method. K = linear spring constant = $M(u^2 + \omega_s^2)$; u = constant and $\omega_s = 2\pi/T$. f = viscous friction coefficient = $2Mu$.

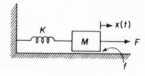

Fig. 10P-1

10-2. The following signals are sampled by an ideal sampler with sampling period T. Determine the sampler output $e^*(t)$, and evaluate the pulsed transform $E^*(s)$ by the Laplace transform method and the complex convolution method.
  (a) $e(t) = te^{-at}$
  (b) $e(t) = e^{-at} \sin \omega t \quad (a = \text{constant})$

10-3. Derive an expression for the z-transform of $1/s^n$ and $1/(s+a)^n$, and from that derive the z-transform of $1/s^3$ and $1/(s+a)^3$.

10-4. Obtain the z-transform of the following functions:

(a) $\dfrac{1}{s^3(s+2)}$ (b) $\dfrac{1}{s(s+5)^2}$

10-5. Evaluate the inverse z-transform of

$$G(z) = \frac{z(z^2 + 2z + 1)}{(z^2 - z + 1)(z^2 + z + 2)}$$

by means of the following methods:

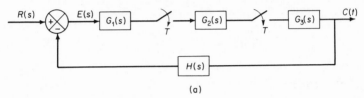

(a)

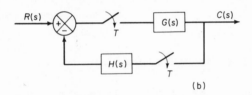

(b)

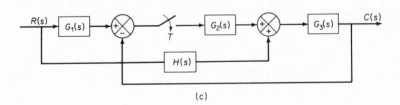

(c)

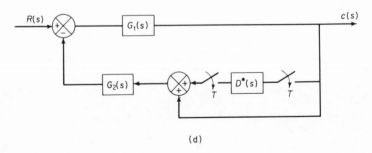

(d)

Fig. 10-P-6.

(a) the real inversion formula.

(b) the partial fraction expansion.

(c) power series expansion.

10-6. Construct the original signal flow graph, the sampled signal flow graph, and the composite signal flow graph for the following systems. Evaluate $C(s)$ and $C^*(s)$ from the flow graphs.

10-7. For the sampled-data system shown in Fig. 10-26, given

$$G(s) = \frac{1}{s^2(s + 5)}, \quad H(s) = 1, \quad \text{and} \quad T = 1 \text{ sec}$$

and for a unit step function input,

(a) obtain the z-transform of the output.

(b) obtain the output response at the sampling instants.

(c) determine the final value of the output response.

10-8. The block diagram of a sampled-data control system is shown in Fig. 10P-8, where $G_{ho}(s)$ is the transfer function of a zero-order hold circuit, and

$$G(s) = \frac{5}{s(1 + 0.2s)}$$

The sampling period is 1 sec.

(a) Plot the Nyquist diagram for a continuous system with $G(s)$ as the open-loop transfer function.

(b) Plot the Nyquist diagram for the system with sampling but without the hold circuit.

(c) Plot the Nyquist diagram for the system with sampling and zero-order hold.

(d) Discuss the effect of sampling upon the stability of the system.

(e) Discuss the effect of the hold circuit upon stability of the sampled-data system.

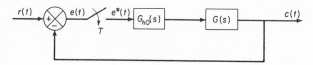

Fig. 10P-8

10-9. The sampled-data system shown in Fig. 10P-8 has a transfer function

$$G(s) = \frac{K}{s(1 + 0.2s)}$$

(a) Sketch the root locus diagrams for the system without the hold circuit for $T = 1$ sec and 5 sec respectively. Determine the marginal value of K for stability in each case.

(b) Sketch the root locus diagrams for the system with hold circuit for $T = 1$ sec and 5 sec respectively. Determine the marginal value of K for stability in each case.

10-10. For the open-loop sampled-data system shown in Fig. 10-52a, the transfer function of the system is

$$G(s) = \frac{100}{s(s^2 + 100)}$$

and the sampling period is 0.1 sec.

(a) Use the z-transform method to evaluate the output response to a unit step function input at the sampling instants.

(b) Use the submultiple sampling method to evaluate the output response at time intervals of $t = 0, T/3, 2T/3, T, 4T/3, \ldots$.

11

Nonlinear Systems

11.1 Introduction

In the preceding chapters, the analysis and design techniques discussed are restricted to linear feedback control systems only. However, all practical systems are nonlinear to some extent; most physical systems can be considered to be linear only within a limited range of operation. If a feedback control system is designed according to linear theory and methods, it is essential that the components used in the system operate in linear fashions under various operating conditions. If, under certain circumstances, the components are driven into the region of nonlinear characteristics, linear design theory may describe only approximately, or quite often may give a completely erroneous prediction of the system performance. For systems in which the linearity assumption is not valid, nonlinear differential equations must be used to describe system behavior.

Broadly speaking, a nonlinear system is one for which the principle of superposition is no longer valid. In linear systems, mathematical analysis is characterized by the fact that if the separate application of inputs $r_1(t)$ and $r_2(t)$ produces responses $c_1(t)$ and $c_2(t)$, respectively, the simultaneous application of $r_1(t) + r_2(t)$ will produce an output of $c_1(t) + c_2(t)$. This is why, in linear systems, it is necessary to analyze system response to just a few test signals, such as step function, ramp function, acceleration,

435

and sine functions, which can be combined to approximate signals of almost any kind. Unfortunately, this property does not carry over to nonlinear systems. It is also for this basic reason that nonlinear differential equations are more difficult to solve and, thus, require special attention. At present, there is no definite set of mathematical tools which may be used to solve a general class of nonlinear systems.

The study of nonlinear control systems is met with further difficulties because most of the commonly used tools and terminologies for linear systems are no longer valid. The transfer function concept of linear systems becomes insignificant for systems with nonlinear elements; poles and zeros do not have any meaning in characterizing nonlinear systems. Furthermore, the root locus diagrams which are so convenient for the study of linear systems are meaningless for nonlinear systems, simply because the characteristic equation is not defined strictly. But even if we could somehow extend the characteristic equation concept to nonlinear systems, the roots of the equation would not be stationary when the input level was changed. A simple illustration will demonstrate this behavior. Assume that the amplifier of a servo system has saturation characteristics as shown in Fig. 11-1a. The gain of the amplifier K, defined as the ratio of the amplitudes of the sinusoidal output and the input, is shown in Fig. 11-1b. The root loci of the characteristic equation as a function of K are assumed

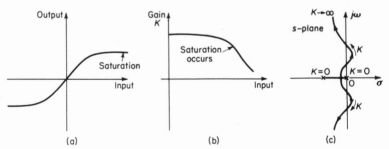

Fig. 11-1. (a) Saturation characteristic of servo amplifier; (b) Gain characteristic of servo amplifier; (c) Root loci of servo system.

to take the form of Fig. 11-1c. It is apparent that since the gain K is a function of the input amplitude, the characteristic equation roots will travel along the loci as the input level is varied.

Although nonlinearities in feedback control systems may generally be due to shortcomings of the physical components, such as saturation, hysteresis, dead zone, backlash, or variation of parameters as a function of the operating conditions, there is a class of systems in which nonlinear elements are intentionally introduced in order to improve system performance. The on-off or relay-type servo systems, such as the automobile voltage regulators and on-off furnace controls, are common examples of this class of nonlinear systems.

11.2 The Phase Plane Method

The phase plane diagram is a graphical technique of solving linear and nonlinear differential equations. However, the application of the phase plane technique to control systems has been predominant chiefly in the studies of nonlinear systems, simply because the Laplace transform method of solving linear differential equations is so convenient and straightforward that there seems to be no apparent advantage in applying this graphical analysis to linear systems.

If a second-order system is characterized by the dependent variable $c(t)$ and its first derivative with respect to time, $dc(t)/dt$, the phase plane diagram is a plot of dc/dt as a function of c. At any time t_1, the coordinate $[c(t_1),\ dc(t_1)/dt]$ in the phase plane determines the "state" of the system. As time t is varied from 0 to ∞, the representing point $(c,\ \dot{c})$ will trace out a continuous path which indicates the complete history of the system with regard to c and $dc/dt(=\dot{c})$ at all times; the path itself is called the *phase plane trajectory*. For instance, in a servo system, the phase plane diagram is a plot of the output velocity $\dot{c}$ as a function of the output displacement c. In Fig. 11-2, the typical phase plane diagram and the cor-

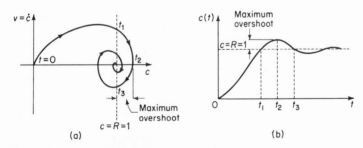

Fig. 11-2. Phase plane diagram and the corresponding step response of a second-order servo system.

responding output response of a second-order servo system with unit step input are shown. The arrows on the phase plane trajectory indicate the increase of time. For an electrical system, the plot of current i as a function of electric charge q also forms a phase plane diagram.

The phase plane concept may also be extended to third- and higher-order systems (differential equations). However, the representation of the state of the system requires three- or higher-dimensional plots. This is the principal difficulty in applying phase plane technique to systems higher than the second order; a three-dimensional "phase-space" diagram is very difficult to visualize and to construct.

In addition to the above-mentioned limitation, the phase plane technique can be used to study transient performance of systems subject only to step function and linear time function inputs, with initial conditions. No simple method is available at present to extend the phase plane technique to sinusoidally excited systems.

Phase Plane Analysis Applied to Linear Servo Systems

Consider a linear second-order servo system with unity-feedback. The open-loop transfer function of the system is given by

$$G(s) = \frac{C(s)}{E(s)} = \frac{K_m}{fs(1 + s\tau)} = \frac{K}{s(1 + s\tau)} \tag{11-1}$$

where $\tau = J/f$ = inertia/friction, and $K = K_m/f$. The differential equation which describes the relation between the input and output variables of the closed-loop system may be written as

$$Kr(t) = \tau \frac{d^2c(t)}{dt^2} + \frac{dc(t)}{dt} + Kc(t) \tag{11-2}$$

If we make the substitution of

$$v = \frac{dc}{dt} \quad \text{and} \quad \dot{v} = \frac{dv}{dt} = \frac{d^2c}{dt^2} = \frac{dv}{dc}\frac{dc}{dt} = v\frac{dv}{dc}$$

Eq. (11-2) reads

$$Kr = \tau v \frac{dv}{dc} + v + Kc \tag{11-3}$$

where r, v, and c are functions of time. Solving for dv/dc in Eq. (11-3) yields

$$\frac{dv}{dc} = -\frac{1}{\tau} + \frac{K(r - c)}{v\tau} \tag{11-4}$$

The last equation presents an analytical expression for the slope of a trajectory in the $(c, \dot{c})$ or (c, v) plane. For an input, for example, $r(t) =$ unit step function, there exists one trajectory in the phase plane for each set of initial conditions $c(0^+)$, $v(0^+)$. Frequently, the phase plane trajectories are sketched by finding the lines on which the trajectories have the same slope dv/dc; these lines are called the "isoclines" of the phase plane trajectories. For instance, by setting $dv/dc = 0$ in Eq. (11-4), we have

$$K(r - c) - v = 0$$

which represents a straight line passing through the real axis in the phase plane at $c = r(t) = 1$, with a slope of $- K$. Therefore, any phase plane trajectory which intersects this line must have a slope of zero at the intersecting point. Similarly, for any constant slope σ of the trajectory in the phase plane,

$$\frac{dv}{dc} = -\frac{1}{\tau} + \frac{K(r - c)}{v\tau} = \sigma$$

Simplifying, we have

$$v = \frac{K(r - c)}{1 + \sigma\tau} \tag{11-5}$$

which represents the equation of the isoclines in the phase plane. All the phase plane trajectories intersecting the same isocline have the same slope σ at the intersections. Figure 11-3a shows the isoclines for several

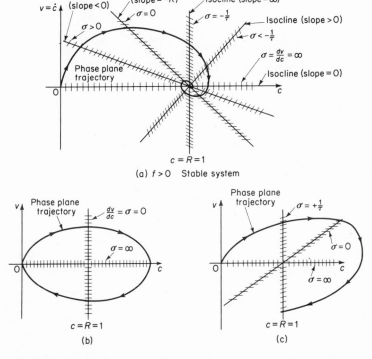

(a) $f > 0$ Stable system

(b)

(c)

Fig. 11-3. Phase plane trajectories of a second-order servo system subject to a unit-step input and zero initial conditions.

values of σ, the phase plane trajectory when the input r is a unit step function, and zero initial conditions ($c_0 = 0$, $v_0 = 0$). The arrows on the trajectory indicate increase in time.

The phase plane trajectory given in Fig. 11-3a clearly indicates the decay of the oscillatory transient response of the system; the output finally reaches a steady-state value of $c = R = 1$.

If the viscous friction coefficient f is made zero, the differential equation of the system reads

$$K_m(r - c) = J \frac{d^2c}{dt^2} \tag{11-6}$$

The isoclines in the phase plane are represented by the equation

$$v = K_m(r - c)/J\sigma \tag{11-7}$$

which are straight lines with slopes equal to $-K_m/J\sigma$, passing through the point $(c = R = 1, v = 0)$ in the phase plane. For the same magnitudes of σ but with opposite signs, the isoclines are symmetrical with respect to the isocline for $\sigma = 0$ (the $c = R = 1$ line). The corresponding phase plane trajectory with zero initial conditions is in the form of an ellipse, as shown in Fig. 11-3b.

For a negative viscous friction coefficient, the system is unstable. In this case the phase plane trajectory circles outward and eventually goes to infinity (Fig. 11-3c).

The Singular Points

The points $(c = R = 1, v = 0)$ in the phase plane of Fig. 11-3 are called singular points of the phase plane trajectories. A singular point may be classified as a focal point, saddle point, node point, or vortex. The classification depends entirely upon the variations of the coefficients of the differential equation or the roots of the characteristic equation. For instance, the singular point in Fig. 11-3a is called a stable focus; the singular point in Fig. 11-3b is a vortex; that of Fig. 11-3c is an unstable focus point.

If, in Eq. (11-2), $r(t) = 0$, the origin is the only singular point in the phase plane. The relations among coefficients and the roots of the differential equation for each type of singularity are given as follows:

$$J \frac{d^2c}{dt^2} + f \frac{dc}{dt} + K_m c = 0$$

(1) $K_m > 0$, $f > 0$, $f < 2\sqrt{JK_m}$ Two complex conjugate roots   Stable focus.
with negative real parts.

(2) $K_m > 0$, $f < 0$, $f < 2\sqrt{JK_m}$ Two complex conjugate roots   Unstable focus.
with positive real parts.

(3) $K_m > 0$, $f = 0$.   Two imaginary roots.   Vortex.

(4) $K_m > 0$, $f > 0$. $f > 2\sqrt{JK_m}$ Two negative real roots.   Stable node.

(5) $K_m > 0$, $f < 0$, $f > \sqrt{JK_m}$ Two positive real roots.   Unstable node.

(6) $K_m < 0$, $f = 0$.   Two real roots with   Saddle point.
opposite signs.

The phase plane trajectories, locations of roots in the s-plane, and the corresponding transient responses of the six cases given above are illustrated in Fig. 11-4.

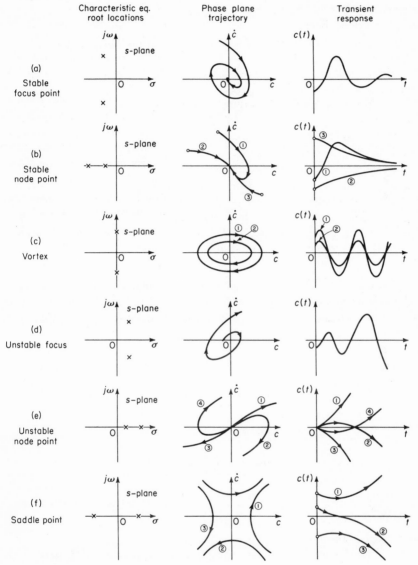

Fig. 11-4. Phase plane trajectories of second-order linear system.

11.3 Application of Phase Plane Technique to On-Off Control Systems

In the linear servo systems treated in the preceding chapters, the amount of power applied by the servomotor to the output is normally proportional to the instantaneous error $e(t)$ of the system. For linear systems with cascaded compensation element, the power applied to the output may depend on the error e, its derivatives, and its integrals, in some linear manner. There is a class of systems in which the motor develops a maximum torque at all times. Specifically, the motor applies full power to the output member whenever the error signal exceeds some predetermined value; this power is maintained until the error is reduced to some insignificant value. Since switching relays are often used to accomplish this on-off control of power, a system of this type is often referred to as a "relay-type" servo system, "on-off" servo, or "bang-bang" servo. Because of the utilization of maximum available power at all times, an on-off type of system is usually lighter and cheaper than a conventional continuous system. Also, by properly designing the switching of the relay, an on-off type of system is capable of having a minimum response time, and the response is usually called an optimum response. However, there are disadvantages in this type of system, such as its tendency to produce oscillations in its steady-state, and it is usually difficult to obtain perfect steady-state correspondence of input and output.

Relay Characteristics

Figure 11-5a shows an idealized action of a relay with double contacts. The relay controls the supply of constant power to the output member as

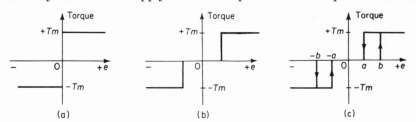

Fig. 11-5. Relay characteristics. (a) Ideal relay; (b) Relay with dead zone; (c) Relay with dead zone and hysteresis.

long as the input is non-zero. An ideal relay does not exist in practice; nor would it be desirable, since the wear on the relay contacts should be kept small. In practice, all relays possess dead zones and hysteresis effect. Figure 11-5b gives the characteristics of a relay with dead zone only. Such a dead zone is usually arranged so that when the error or actuating signal is less than D, the magnitude of the dead zone, the relay causes the motor torque to be zero. The proper magnitude of the dead zone is determined on the basis of the allowable difference between c and r in the steady state, and practical considerations of wear of relay contacts. It will be shown later than the size of the dead zone also is detrimental to the relative stability of the servo system. In Fig. 11-5c, a relay character-istic with dead zone and hysteresis is shown. A constant torque is applied in the positive direction when $e(t)$ exceeds a value of b; the torque does not drop to zero until the error signal has dropped below the level a. Similar behavior also exists for negative errors.

(1) *On-Off Servo with Ideal Relay (Step Input)*

In Fig. 11-6, a simple servo system with relay-type control is given. It is assumed that the relay has an idealized characteristic, as shown in Fig.

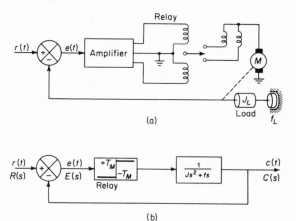

(a)

(b)

Fig. 11-6. Simple relay-type servo system. (a) Schematic diagram of relay servo system; (b) Block diagram of relay servo system.

11-5a. The differential equation describing the torque-output relationship is

$$\text{Constant motor torque} = J\frac{d^2c}{dt^2} + f\frac{dc}{dt} \tag{11-8}$$

where the motor torque is $+T_m$ or $-T_m$, depending upon whether the error e is positive or negative. For $+T_m$, and at $t = 0$, the initial conditions of the system are characterized by $c(0) = c_0$ and $v(0) = v_0$; the Laplace transform of Eq. (11-8) is

$$\frac{T_m}{s} = Js^2C(s) - Js\,c_0 - Jv_0 + fsC(s) - fc_0$$

$$= s(Js + f)C(s) - (Js + f)c_0 - Jv_0 \tag{11-9}$$

Solving for $C(s)$ in the last equation, we have

$$C(s) = \frac{T_m}{fs^2(1 + s\tau)} + \frac{c_0}{s} + \frac{Jv_0}{fs(1 + s\tau)} \tag{11-10}$$

where $\tau = J/f$ = time constant. The inverse Laplace transform of Eq. (11-10) is

$$c(t) = \frac{T_m}{f}(t - \tau + \tau e^{-t/\tau}) + c_0 + v_0\tau(1 - e^{-t/\tau}) \qquad (11\text{-}11)$$

The output velocity of the system is obtained by taking the first derivative of $c(t)$. Thus,

$$v(t) = \frac{T_m}{f}(1 - e^{-t/\tau}) + v_0 e^{-t/\tau} \qquad (11\text{-}12)$$

The equation describing the phase plane trajectory of the on-off servo system may be obtained by eliminating t from Eqs. (11-11) and (11-12). Thus, from Eq. (11-12),

$$t = -\tau \ln\left(\frac{1 - vf/T_m}{1 - v_0 f/T_m}\right) \qquad (11\text{-}13)$$

Substitution of Eqs. (11-12) and (11-13) into Eq. (11-11) yields

$$c = -\frac{T_m}{f}\tau \ln\left(\frac{1 - vf/T_m}{1 - v_0 f/T_m}\right) - \tau\frac{T_m}{f}(1 - e^{-t/\tau}) - \tau v_0 e^{-t/\tau} + c_0 + v_0\tau$$

or

$$c = -\frac{T_m}{f}\tau \ln\left(\frac{1 - vf/T_m}{1 - v_0 f/T_m}\right) - \tau v + v_0\tau + c_0 \qquad (11\text{-}14)$$

Rearranging, we have

$$c - c_0 = -\tau(v - v_0) - \frac{T_m}{f}\tau \ln\left(\frac{1 - vf/T_m}{1 - v_0 f/T_m}\right) \qquad (11\text{-}15)$$

Let $v_{\max} = T_m/f$, and $v/v_{\max} = v_n$ = normalized displacement; $t/\tau = t_n$ = normalized time. Dividing both sides of Eq. (11-15) by the factor $T_m\tau/f$ yields

$$\frac{c - c_0}{T_m\tau/f} = -\frac{(v - v_0)}{T_m/f} - \ln\left(\frac{1 - vf/T_m}{1 - v_0 f/T_m}\right) \qquad (11\text{-}16)$$

or

$$c_n - c_{0n} = -(v_n - v_{0n}) - \ln\left(\frac{1 - v_n}{1 - v_{0n}}\right) \qquad (11\text{-}17)$$

Equation (11-17) represents the relation between c_n and v_n, and thus describes a trajectory in the normalized phase plane. For the simple case, when $c_0 = 0$ and $v_0 = 0$ (zero initial conditions), Eq. (11-17) reads

$$c_n = -v_n - \ln(1 - v_n) \qquad (11\text{-}18)$$

The corresponding values of v_n, according to the last equation, when the value of c_n is varied from 0 to ∞, are tabulated in Table 11-1. The phase plane trajectory described by Eq. (11-18) is shown in Fig. 11-7 as the curve AOA'. It is seen that the trajectory is asymptotic to the line $v_n = 1$, which is the final normalized velocity when the torque is $+T_m$. The arrows on the trajectory indicate the increase in time t_n on the path.

It can be shown that for any initial conditions c_0, v_0, and positive torque $(+T_m)$, the trajectory will have the same shape as that shown in Fig. 11-7, except that it is shifted horizontally so

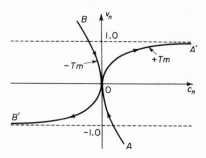

Fig. 11-7. Normalized phase plane diagram for second-order on-off servo system. Curve AOA' represents trajectory with positive torque $(+T)_m$, and curve BOB' represents trajectory when negative torque $(-T_m)$ is applied.

that it passes through the initial point (c_{0n}, v_{0n}) in the phase plane. Equation (11-17) can be written as

$$c_n = -v_n - \ln(1 - v_n) - K \qquad (11\text{-}19)$$

where

$$K = -c_{0n} - v_{0n} - \ln(1 - v_{0n}) \qquad (11\text{-}20)$$

Equation (11-19) implies that, for any initial conditions (c_0, v_0), the corresponding phase plane trajectory is obtained by shifting the zero-initial condition trajectory horizontally by K units. Whether the shift is to the left or to the right depends on the sign of K. Assume that c_{0n} and v_{0n} are

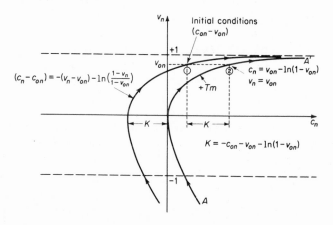

Fig. 11-8. Normalized phase plane diagram of on-off servo system with non-zero initial conditions.

represented by the point 1 in the phase plane of Fig. 11-8. The zero-initial condition trajectory is given by the curve AOA', on which point 2 is characterized by

$$c_n = -v_{0n} - \ln(1 - v_{0n}) \tag{11-21}$$

since at point 2, $v_n = v_{0n}$.

The horizontal distance between point 1 and point 2 is given by

$$K = -c_{0n} - v_{0n} - \ln(1 - v_{0n}) \tag{11-22}$$

Thus, if the trajectory AOA' is shifted to the left so that it passes through point 1, it will satisfy Eq. (11-17). This is a convenient feature of the phase plane analysis of on-off systems, since a template of the shape of AOA' can be made to aid the graphical construction of the total phase plane diagram.

By a similar method, it can be shown that for a negative applied torque $(-T_m)$, the phase plane trajectory is that of BOB', as shown in Fig. 11-7. The trajectory has the same shape as that of AOA', except that it is inverted. The trajectory is asymptotic to the line $v_n = -1$ as c_n goes to infinity.

Table 11-1.

v_n	c_n	v_n	c_n
0.1	0.0054	-0.2	0.018
0.2	0.023	-0.4	0.064
0.3	0.057	-0.5	0.095
0.4	0.112	-0.7	0.17
0.5	0.194	-0.8	0.212
0.6	0.317	-0.9	0.258
0.7	0.503	-1.0	0.307
0.8	0.81	-1.2	0.412
0.84	1.00	-1.4	0.525
0.90	1.40	-1.6	0.644
0.95	2.05	-1.8	0.72
0.98	2.93	-2.0	0.90
1.00	∞	-3.0	1.61

As an example of the construction of the phase plane diagram of the system of Fig. 11-6, assume that the reference input of the system is a step displacement of 1 radian, and $c_0 = 0$, $v_0 = 0$. The system parameters are $f = 1$ oz-in/rad/sec, and $J = 1$ oz-in/rad/sec^2; $T_m = 1$ oz-in. The normalized quantities are:

$$v_n = \frac{v}{T_m/f} = v \qquad t_n = t/\tau = t \qquad \tau = J/f = 1 \text{ sec}$$

$$c_n = \frac{c}{c_{max}} = \frac{c}{T_m\tau/f} = \frac{c}{1} \qquad R_n = \frac{R}{c_{max}} = \frac{R}{1} = 1$$

Since the error signal at $t = 0$ is positive ($e_n = R_n - c_n = 1$), a positive torque $+T_m$ is applied. The phase plane trajectory corresponding to this positive torque is shown to start at the origin in Fig. 11-9. The positive

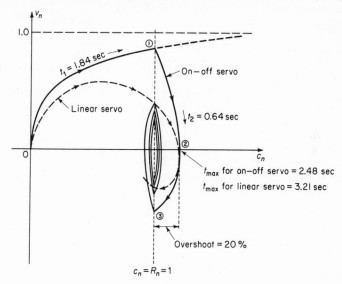

Fig. 11-9. Phase plane trajectories for relay type servo system and a linear system with the same amount of overshoot (20 per cent) (second-order system).

torque is maintained until c_n exceeds $R_n = 1$; in which case, the torque is reversed, and the trajectory corresponding to $-T_m$ (BOB' of Fig. 11-7) is used. This forms the portion of the trajectory from point 1 to point 3 in Fig. 11-9. At point 3, $c_n = R_n$ again, and the torque is reversed from $-T_m$ to $+T_m$. Each time the phase plane trajectory passes through the switching line $c_n = R_n$, the torque is reversed in direction. Finally, the oscillation is shown to decay to the steady-state amplitude of $c_n = R_n$.

One of the inconveniences in the phase plane technique is that time does not appear explicitly on the phase plane trajectory. However, this is not the case with the phase plane diagram of relay-type systems. In a relay-type system, the time required for the system to go from one state to another can be computed directly from the phase plane trajectory. Substitution of Eq. (11-13) into Eq. (11-17) and simplifying yields

$$t_n = (c_n - c_{0n}) + (v_n - v_{0n}) \qquad (11\text{-}23)$$

which gives the time required for the system to go from the state (c_0, v_0) to (c, v) on the trajectory. Similarly, for a negative torque, the analogous expression for time is

$$t_n = -(c_n - c_{0n}) - (v_n - v_{0n}) \qquad (11\text{-}24)$$

For instance, in Fig. 11-9, the time for the output response to reach the maximum overshoot is to be computed. Since the torque is reversed at point 1, it is essential to compute first the time required to go from 0 to 1, and then from point 1 to 2. The total time is the sum of the two parts. Applying Eq. (11-23), we have

$$t_{1n} = c_{1n} + v_{1n} = 1 + 0.84 = 1.84 \tag{11-25}$$

and since the time constant τ is 1 sec, the time from 0 to 1 is $t_1 = 1.84$ sec. The time required to go from point 1 to 2 is

$$t_{2n} = -(1.2 - 1) - (0 - 0.84) = -0.2 + 0.84 = 0.64 \tag{11-26}$$

or $t_2 = 0.64$ sec. The total time required for the response to reach its maximum overshoot is 2.48 sec.

It is interesting to compare the rise time of the on-off system with a second-order linear continuous system which has the same amount of overshoot. From Fig. 11-9, it is seen that the maximum overshoot of the on-off servo is 20 per cent. The open-loop transfer function of a second-order linear system may be represented by

$$\frac{C(s)}{E(s)} = \frac{K_m}{s(Js + f)} \tag{11-27}$$

The natural undamped frequency ω_n is equal to $\sqrt{K_m/J}$, and the damping ratio is

$$\delta = \frac{f/J}{2\omega_n} = \frac{1}{2\sqrt{K_m/1}} \tag{11-28}$$

By means of Eq. (5-31), the damping ratio of the second-order linear system with a maximum overshoot of 20 per cent is found to be 0.456. Thus, the corresponding value of K_m obtained from Eq. (11-28) is 1.12. The natural undamped frequency ω_n is 1.1 rad/sec. By using Eq. (5-27), the time for the output response to reach its maximum overshoot is

$$t_{\max} = \frac{\pi}{\omega_n\sqrt{1 - \delta^2}} = 3.21 \text{ sec} \tag{11-29}$$

It is apparent that, although the amounts of overshoot of the two systems are the same, the on-off system has a shorter rise time.

(2) *Phase Plane Diagram of On-Off Servo System With Dead Zone (Step Input)*

In this section, the servo system given in Fig. 11-6 is considered to employ a relay with dead zone characteristics, as shown in Fig. 11-5b. Because of the dead zone in the relay characteristics, the torque applied to the output of the system has a value of $+T_m$, 0, or $-T_m$, depending on the magnitude and sign of the error signal. The differential equation of the open-loop system may be written as

$$J \frac{d^2c}{dt^2} + f \frac{dc}{dt} = T_m \qquad \text{for } e > D$$

$$= 0 \qquad \text{for } -D < e < D \qquad (11\text{-}30)$$

$$= -T_m \qquad \text{for } e < -D$$

When the torque is either $+T_m$ or $-T_m$, the phase plane trajectories given in Fig. 11-7 are still valid; when the motor torque is zero, the error signal lies within the relay dead zone, and the system equation is of the form

$$J \frac{d^2c}{dt^2} + f \frac{dc}{dt} = 0 \qquad (11\text{-}31)$$

If the initial conditions of the system are denoted by c_0 and v_0, the solution of the last equation is

$$c = c_0 + v_0\tau(1 - e^{-t/\tau}) \qquad (11\text{-}32)$$

Or, in terms of the normalized quantities,

$$c_n = c_{0n} + v_{0n}(1 - e^{-t_n}) \qquad (11\text{-}33)$$

The normalized velocity of the output member is obtained by taking the derivative of c_n; hence,

$$v_n = v_{0n}e^{-t_n} \qquad (11\text{-}34)$$

Eliminating t_n from Eqs. (11-33) and (11-34) yields the equation of the phase plane trajectory when the torque is zero.

Thus,
$$(c_n - c_{0n}) + (v_n - v_{0n}) = 0 \qquad (11\text{-}35)$$

which represents a straight line in the normalized phase plane; the slope of the line is -1.

A normalized phase plane diagram for the second-order on-off servo with relay dead zone is shown in Fig. 11-10. For a step displacement input $r(t) = R$, the vertical strip bounded by the switching lines $c_n = R_n - D_n$ and $c_n = R_n + D_n$ represents the relay dead zone in the normalized phase plane. The trajectory from 0 to 1 is the same as curve OA' for positive torque T_m given in Fig. 11-7. When the normalized output displacement c_n enters the relay dead zone at $c_n = R_n - D_n$, the torque is switched from $+T_m$ to 0, and the phase plane trajectory, described by Eq. (11-35), is a straight line with slope equal to -1. At the end of the dead zone, $c_n = R_n + D_n$, a negative torque $-T_m$ is switched into effect, and the trajectory is described by the negative torque curve (BOB' in Fig. 11-7). In Fig. 11-10, the output response is shown to reach a final steady state after several oscillations. However, the system is capable of having a steady state error which may lie anywhere within the relay dead zone. The size of the dead zone thus has a definite bearing on the system output response. In Fig.

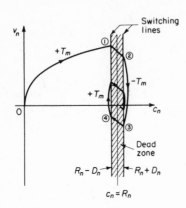

Fig. 11-10. Normalized phase plane diagram of a second-order on-off servo system with dead zone.

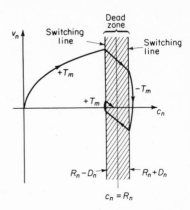

Fig. 11-11. Normalized phase plane diagram of a second-order on-off servo system with dead zone showing the effect of the variation of dead zone on system response.

11-11, it is shown that the number of oscillations is reduced by increasing the size of the dead zone, but the possible final error is also increased.

(3) *Phase Plane Diagram of On-Off Servo with Hysteresis and Dead Zone*

If the servo system of Fig. 11-6 employs a relay which has the characteristics shown in Fig. 11-5c, the differential equation which describes the torque-output relation of the system may be written as

$$J \frac{d^2c}{dt^2} + f \frac{dc}{dt} = +T_m \quad \text{when} \quad \begin{cases} e > b & \text{and } \frac{de}{dt} > 0 \\ \\ e > a & \text{and } \frac{de}{dt} < 0 \end{cases}$$

$$= 0 \qquad \text{when} \quad -a < e < +a \qquad (11\text{-}36)$$

$$= -T_m \quad \text{when} \quad \begin{cases} e < -b & \frac{de}{dt} < 0 \\ \\ e < -a & \frac{de}{dt} > 0 \end{cases}$$

Observation of the last equation and Fig. 11-5c shows that the phase plane can be divided into three regions: one where $+T_m$ is applied, one in which $-T_m$ is applied, and in the region where the torque is zero. These regions are illustrated in Fig. 11-12. It is seen that there are a total of four switching lines represented by $c = R - b, R - a, R + a, R + b$. The construction of the phase plane trajectory follows essentially the same procedure as that given for the previous cases. A typical phase plane diagram of a

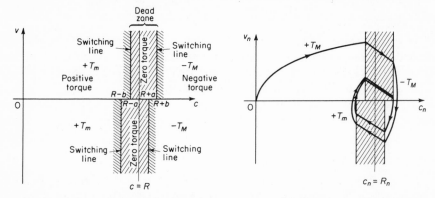

Fig. 11-12. Three regions in the phase plane indicating different torque values for relay with hysteresis and dead zone.

Fig. 11-13. Phase plane diagram of a second-order on-off system with hysteresis and dead zone.

second-order on-off system with hysteresis and dead zone and a step displacement input is illustrated in Fig. 11-13.

11.4 Application of Phase Plane Technique to Systems with Coulomb Friction

In this section, a feedback control system with coulomb friction will be considered and analyzed by means of the phase plane method. Consider a feedback control system which is characterized by an inertia load with viscous friction similar to the second-order linear system given in Sec. 11-2, except that coulomb friction in the output shaft is now considered. The differential equation of the nonlinear system with coulomb friction may be written as

$$K_m[r(t) - c(t)] = K_m e(t) = T_m = J\frac{d^2c}{dt^2} + f\frac{dc}{dt} + T_c\frac{dc}{|dc|}$$

(11-37)

where T_c is the Coulomb frictional torque. An equivalent block diagram of the closed-loop nonlinear system is shown in Fig. 11-14. Suppose that, at

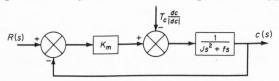

Fig. 11-14. Equivalent block diagram of a second-order feedback control system with coulomb friction.

$t = 0$, a step displacement input $r(t) = R$ is applied to the system; the output velocity of the system is positive after $t = 0$ so that $dc/|dc| = +1$, and Eq. (11-30) becomes

$$K_m R - T_c = J \frac{d^2 c}{dt^2} + f \frac{dc}{dt} + K_m c \tag{11-38}$$

The solution of the last equation is the same as that discussed previously for a linear second-order system with step input, except that the forcing function R is reduced by the amount of the coulomb frictional torque T_c/K_m. The solution of Eq. (11-38) is thus obtained as

$$c(t) = \left(R - \frac{T_c}{K_m} \right) \left[1 - \frac{e^{-\delta \omega_n t}}{\sqrt{1 - \delta^2}} \sin \left(\omega_n \sqrt{1 - \delta^2}\, t - \phi \right) \right] \tag{11-39}$$

where $\delta = f/2\sqrt{K_m J}$ and $\omega_n = \pm\sqrt{K_m/J}$.

From Eq. (11-39), it is apparent that the effect of the coulomb friction is to reduce the effective values of the input R by the amount T_c/K_m. For a critically damped or overdamped system ($\delta \geq 1$), the velocity v of the system output is always positive, and Eq. (11-39) is valid as the total solution to a step input. The output response of the system will eventually die down to the final steady-state value of $R - \dfrac{T_c}{K_m}$. However, for an underdamped system ($\delta < 1$), the output velocity v reverses when displacement c reaches its first overshoot, and the sign of T_c must be reversed. The effective value of the input to the linear system represented by the right side of Eq. (11-38) is $K_m R + T_c$. This means simply that when the velocity is negative, the oscillation appears to take place about an axis $R + \dfrac{T_c}{K_m}$, and when the velocity is positive, the output tends to oscillate about the axis $R - \dfrac{T_c}{K_m}$. Since the sign of coulomb frictional torque depends on the direction of v, in any case, the coulomb friction tends to reduce the overshoot or undershoot of the output response. If, under any condition, the output velocity reaches zero and the magnitude of the error $|e| = |r - c|$ is less than T_c/K_m, the torque developed by the motor, which is proportional to e, is insufficient to overcome the coulomb frictional torque and the output motion of the system ceases. In other words, the output will stop at the moment any overshoot or undershoot first occurs inside the region bounded by $R - T_c/K_m$ and $R + T_c/K_m$. Three typical step displacement responses of servo systems with coulomb friction are depicted in Fig. 11-15.

It can be stated that, in general, the effect of the coulomb friction is to reduce the overshoot and oscillatory property of a servo system, but the system may have a steady-state error of any value between $+T_c/K_m$ and $-T_c/K_m$ in addition to the regular amount of error.

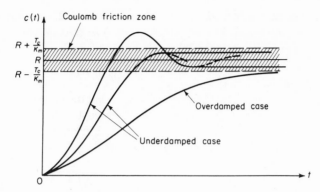

Fig. 11-15. Typical step response of servo system with coulomb friction.

The discussion given above can be verified by investigating the system in the phase plane. Equation (11-37) can be rewritten as

$$\frac{K_m}{f}(R - c) - \frac{T_c}{f}\frac{v}{|v|} = \frac{J}{f}v\frac{dv}{dc} + v \tag{11-40}$$

Solving for dv/dc in the last equation yields

$$\sigma = \frac{dv}{dc} = \frac{K_m(R - c)}{fv\tau} - \frac{T_c}{fv\tau}\frac{v}{|v|} - \frac{1}{\tau} \tag{11-41}$$

where σ is the slope of the phase plane trajectory, and $\tau = J/f$. Simplifying, and solving for v in the last equation, we have

$$v = \frac{\dfrac{K_m}{f}(R - c) - \dfrac{T_c}{f}\dfrac{v}{|v|}}{1 + \sigma\tau} \tag{11-42}$$

which defines the isoclines in the phase plane. Comparison of Eqs. (11-42) and (11-5) reveals that, similar to the linear system case, these isoclines are straight lines, except that they do not intersect the c axis at $c = R$. In fact, the comparison shows that the $\dfrac{T_c}{f}\dfrac{v}{|v|}$ term in Eq. (11-42) causes the isoclines to be shifted a distance of T_c/K_m units to the left of $c = R$ when v is positive, and to the right of $c = R$ by the same distance for negative v. Therefore, the isoclines for the second-order system with coulomb friction may be obtained directly by shifting the isoclines in the upper half of the plane $(+v)$ of Fig. 11-3 to the left by a distance of T_c/K_m, and those in the lower half of the plane $(-v)$ to the right by the same distance. Two typical phase

plane trajectories of a second-order servo system with coulomb friction are
shown in Fig. 11-16.

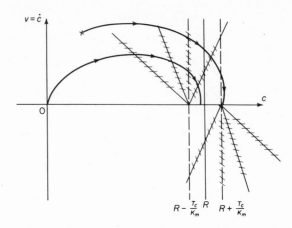

Fig. 11-16. Phase plane trajectories of second-order system with
coulomb friction.

11.5 Phase Plane Diagram of Systems with Ramp Input

The phase plane method can also be extended to analyze systems with
ramp-type inputs. For instance, in the linear feedback control system given
by Eq. (11-1), the input signal is now considered to be a ramp function
$r(t) = kt$; the system output $c(t)$ will have an error of k/K when steady
state is reached. Since the output response increases with time, it is more
significant to construct the phase plane diagram of $\dot{e}$ versus e, where
$e = r - c$. From Eq. (11-2),

$$Ke = K(r - c) = \tau\ddot{c} + \dot{c} \tag{11-43}$$

or

$$\dot{c} = \dot{r} - \dot{e} = k - \dot{e} \tag{11-44}$$

$$\ddot{c} = \ddot{r} - \ddot{e} = -\ddot{e} \tag{11-45}$$

Substitution of Eqs. (11-44) and (11-45) into Eq. (11-43) yields

$$Ke = -\tau\ddot{e} - \dot{e} + k \tag{11-46}$$

or $$\tau\ddot{e} + \dot{e} + Ke = k \tag{11-47}$$

The phase plane equation of the system is

$$\frac{d\dot{e}}{de} = -\frac{1}{\tau} + \frac{K(k/K - e)}{v\tau} \tag{11-48}$$

It is seen that Eq. (11-48) is quite similar to Eq. (11-4), except that the
input function $r(t)$ in the former equation is replaced by k/K. The phase

plane trajectory of $\dot{e}$ versus e is similar to those given in Fig. 11-3, which are given in terms of $\dot{c}$ versus c, except that the reference input is now $e = k/K$. The final value of k/K represents the steady-state error for a stable system.

By the same procedure described above, nonlinear systems (such as the relay type) with ramp function inputs, can also be analyzed by the phase plane technique.

11.6 The Describing Function Technique

From the discussions given in the preceding sections, it is seen that the major limitations of the phase-plane technique are that only second-order systems (or higher-order systems which can be approximated by second-order systems) can be effectively studied by this method, and that it cannot be extended to systems with sinusoidal inputs. The describing function method developed by Goldfarb* and Kochenburger,† on the other hand, provides sinusoidal studies of nonlinear feedback systems of any order. The describing function method is based on the following assumptions and considerations:

(1) The control system contains only one nonlinear element n; a typical form of the nonlinear system under consideration is shown in Fig. 11-17.

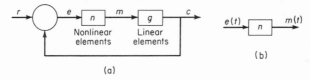

Fig. 11-17. (a) Servo system with nonlinear elements; (b) Nonlinear element.

(2) The input to the nonlinear element n is assumed to be sinusoidal. The output of the nonlinear element is, in general, not a sinusoidal wave; nevertheless, it is a periodic function, and can be represented by a Fourier series. The describing function analysis assumes that only the fundamental component of the output is significant. Actually, if the input to n is considered to be sinusoidal, the output of n contains components at the fundamental frequency, and, in general, at all higher harmonic frequencies. It can be shown that the harmonics in the outputs of most of the common types of nonlinearities in servo systems are often of smaller amplitudes than

*L. C. Goldfarb, "On Some Non-linear Phenomena in Regulatory Systems," *Avtomatika i Telemekhanika*, Vol. 8, No. 5, pp. 349–383, 1947.

†R. J. Kochenburger, "A Frequency Response Method for Analyzing and Synthesizing Contactor Servomechanisms," *Trans. AIEE*, Vol. 69, Part I, pp. 270–284, 1950.

the amplitudes of the fundamental components. Furthermore, most servo systems act as low pass filters, so that the higher harmonics in the output of the nonlinear elements are attenuated when compared to the fundamental component.

When the basic assumptions listed above are satisfied, the nonlinear element n can be represented by an equivalent transfer function called the describing function, which is defined as the ratio of the fundamental component of the output to the amplitude of the input. Therefore,

Describing function $N =$

$$\frac{\text{Fundamental component of output from Fourier analysis}}{\text{Amplitude of the sinusoidal input signal}}$$

(11-49)

Although the describing function is defined as the ratio of amplitudes of two sinusoidal signals of the same frequency, it is not a linear transfer function. It will be shown that, in general, N may be a function of the amplitude or the frequency, or both, of the input signal to n. For instance, the describing functions of simple amplifier saturation and on-off relay are functions only of the amplitude of the input sinusoid; the describing functions of friction- and inertia-controlled gear backlash depend not only on the amplitude but also on the frequency of the input signal. In addition to the above-mentioned properties, N may be a real number, as in the case of simple amplifier saturation, or ideal relay; or N may be complex, as in the case of a relay with hysteresis.

For the notation of Fig. 11-17, if the input to the nonlinear element n is assumed to be

$$e(t) = E \sin \omega t \tag{11-50}$$

the output of the nonlinear element $m(t)$ is a periodic function, and may be represented by the Fourier series

$$m(t) = \sum_{n=1}^{\infty} (A_n \cos n\omega t + B_n \sin n\omega t) \quad (n = 1,2,3,\ldots) \tag{11-51}$$

where

$$A_n = \frac{1}{\pi} \int_{-\pi}^{\pi} m(t) \cos n\omega t\, d\omega t \tag{11-52}$$

$$B_n = \frac{1}{\pi} \int_{-\pi}^{\pi} m(t) \sin n\omega t\, d\omega t \tag{11-53}$$

The constant term in the Fourier series has been omitted due to the assumption that the average value of $m(t)$ is zero; this is true provided that the nonlinear element possesses symmetrical characteristics. According to the assumptions of the describing function, we may drop all higher terms in the Fourier series of Eq. (11-51), leaving only the fundamental component. Thus,

$$m(t) = A_1 \cos \omega t + B_1 \sin \omega t$$
$$= \sqrt{A_1^2 + B_1^2} \sin (\omega t + \phi) = M_1 \sin (\omega t + \phi) \qquad (11\text{-}54)$$

where $\qquad \phi = \tan^{-1}(A_1/B_1) \quad$ and $\quad M_1 = \sqrt{A_1^2 + B_1^2}$

The describing function is then defined according to Eq. (11-49) as

$$N = \frac{M_1}{E} e^{j\phi} \qquad (11\text{-}55)$$

Therefore, N is a complex quantity when ϕ is nonzero. In other words, the describing function N generally has a magnitude of M_1/E and a phase angle of ϕ.

11.7 Describing Functions of Common Nonlinear Elements in Feedback Control Systems

(1) Describing Function of an Ideal Relay

If a sinusoidal input $e(t) = E \sin \omega t$ is applied to the nonlinear element with the ideal relay characteristics of Fig. 11-5a, the output of the relay

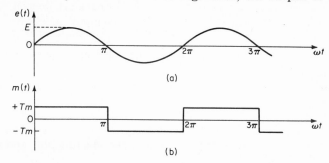

Fig. 11-18. Input-output relation of nonlinearity controlled by ideal relay.

takes the form of Fig. 11-18. Since the output $m(t)$ is a single-valued odd function of the input, it can be written as

$$m(t) = \sum_{n=1}^{\infty} M_n \sin n\omega t \cong M_1 \sin \omega t \qquad (11\text{-}56)$$

and

$$M_1 = \frac{1}{\pi} \int_0^{2\pi} m(t) \sin \omega t d\omega t = 4T_m/\pi \qquad (11\text{-}57)$$

Hence, the describing function of the ideal relay is

$$N = \frac{M_1}{E} = \frac{4T_m}{\pi E} \qquad (11\text{-}58)$$

It is apparent that, in this simple case, the describing function is only a function of the input amplitude E, and is a real number for any given values of E and T_m.

(2) *Describing Function of Relay with Dead Zone*

For the relay characteristic of Fig. 11-5b, the sinusoidal input-output relation is given in Fig. 11-19. The output of the nonlinear element is represented by

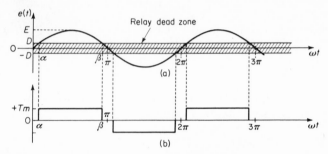

Fig. 11-19. Input-output relation of nonlinearity controlled by relay with dead zone.

$$m(t) = 0 \qquad \text{for } 0 < \omega t < \alpha$$
$$m(t) = T_m \qquad \text{for } \alpha < \omega t < \beta \qquad (11\text{-}59)$$

Due to the symmetry of $m(t)$, the magnitude of its fundamental component can be written as

$$M_1 = \frac{4}{\pi} \int_0^{\pi/2} m(t) \sin \omega t d\omega t$$

$$= \frac{4}{\pi} \int_\alpha^{\pi/2} T_m \sin \omega t d\omega t \qquad (11\text{-}60)$$

Hence, $$M_1 = \frac{4T_m}{\pi} \cos \alpha \qquad (11\text{-}61)$$

Since $\sin \alpha = D/E$, and $\cos \alpha = \sin (\pi/2 - \alpha) = \sin (\pi/2 - \sin^{-1} D/E)$

$$= \sqrt{1 - D^2/E^2}$$

hence, $$M_1 = \frac{4T_m}{\pi} \sqrt{1 - D^2/E^2}$$

The describing function of the relay with dead zone is

$$N = \frac{M_1}{E} = \frac{4T_m}{\pi E} \sqrt{1 - D^2/E^2} \qquad (11\text{-}62)$$

which is also only a function of the input amplitude E, if the dead zone D and T_m are constants.

(3) *Describing Function of Relay with Dead Zone and Hysteresis*

For the relay characteristics of Fig. 11-5c, the sinusoidal-input-output relation is given in Fig. 11-20. When the input sinusoid $e(t)$ is positive and increasing, the relay switches the output from 0 to T_m at $e = b$; when the

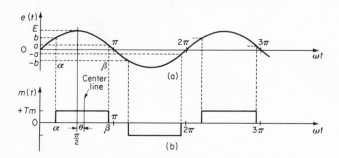

Fig. 11-20. Input-output relation of nonlinearity controlled by relay with dead zone and hysteresis.

input is positive but decreasing, the relay switches the output from T_m to 0 at $e = a$. A similar switching process is true for negative input. It is easy to see from Fig. 11-20 that the output periodic wave lags the input sinusoid by a phase angle θ, which usually implies that the describing function will be a complex number. The phase shift θ may be written as

$$\theta = \frac{\pi}{2} - \left(\frac{\alpha + \beta}{2}\right) \tag{11-63}$$

where
$$\alpha = \sin^{-1}(b/E) \tag{11-64}$$

and
$$\beta = \pi - \sin^{-1}\left(\frac{a}{E}\right) \tag{11-65}$$

The fundamental component of the relay controlled output $m(t)$ will be of the form given by Eq. (11-54), and

$$A_1 = \frac{2}{\pi} \int_\alpha^\beta T_m \cos \omega t\, d\omega t = \frac{2T_m}{\pi}(\sin \beta - \sin \alpha) \tag{11-66}$$

$$B_1 = \frac{2}{\pi} \int_\alpha^\beta T_m \sin \omega t\, d\omega t = \frac{2T_m}{\pi}(\cos \alpha - \cos \beta) \tag{11-67}$$

The magnitude of the describing function is given by

$$\frac{M_1}{E} = \sqrt{\frac{A_1^2 + B_1^2}{E}} = \frac{2T_m}{\pi E}[(\sin \beta - \sin \alpha)^2 + (\cos \alpha - \cos \beta)^2]^{1/2}$$

$$= \frac{4T_m}{\pi E} \sin \left(\frac{\beta - \alpha}{2}\right) \tag{11-68}$$

the phase angle of which is

$$\phi = \tan^{-1} \frac{A_1}{B_1} = \tan^{-1} \frac{(\sin \beta - \sin \alpha)}{(\cos \alpha - \cos \beta)} \tag{11-69}$$

From simple trigonometric relations,

$$\tan \phi = \frac{\sin \beta - \sin \alpha}{\cos \alpha - \cos \beta} = \frac{2 \sin \frac{1}{2}(\alpha - \beta) \cos \frac{1}{2}(\alpha + \beta)}{2 \sin \frac{1}{2}(\alpha + \beta) \sin \frac{1}{2}(\alpha - \beta)} = \cot \frac{\alpha + \beta}{2} \tag{11-70}$$

Hence,

$$\phi = \frac{\pi}{2} - \frac{\alpha + \beta}{2} \tag{11-71}$$

where α and β are given by Eq. (11-64) and Eq. (11-65), respectively. The describing function of the relay characteristics with dead zone and hysteresis is then

$$\overline{N} = \frac{\overline{M}_1}{E} = \frac{4 T_m}{\pi E} \sin \left(\frac{\beta - \alpha}{2} \right) e^{j \left(\pi/2 - \frac{\alpha + \beta}{2} \right)} \tag{11-72}$$

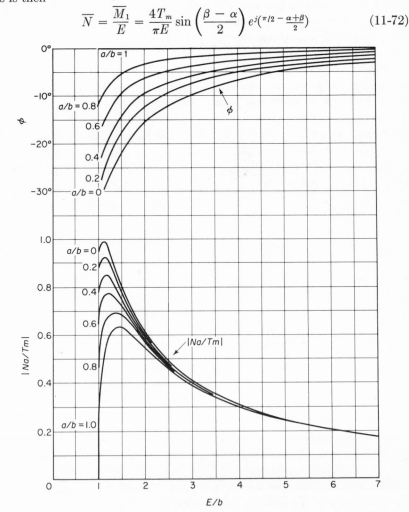

Fig. 11-21. Magnitude and phase of describing function of relay with dead zone and hysteresis.

It is evident that $\overline{N}$ is a function of E, the input amplitude, and it is also a complex quantity. The quantities $|Na/T_m|$ and ϕ are plotted in Fig. 11-21 for various values of E/b. When $a/b = 1$, the relay characteristic is reduced to that shown in Fig. 11-5b (relay with dead zone). Thus the curves of $|Na/T_m|$ and ϕ given in Fig. 11-21 for $a/b = 1$ represents the normalized describing function given by Eq. (11-62).

(4) Describing Function of Gear Backlash

The problem of gear backlash or free play becomes important when high precision feedback control systems are considered. If one observes a servomechanism with backlash in the gears, a continual oscillation or chattering may be noticed. In general, excessive amount of backlash in gears may give rise to

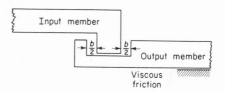

Fig. 11-22. Physical model of backlash between two bodies.

instability; it also has a tendency to wear out the gears. A physical model of backlash between an input and an output member is shown in Fig. 11-22. The amount of backlash is $b/2$ on either side of the reference position. In order to simplify the methods of analysis, the backlash between gears is assumed to be either of the friction-controlled type or of the inertia-controlled type; these are discussed in the following.

The Friction-controlled Backlash. If the moment of inertia of the output member is small compared with that of the input member, it may be neglected, and the backlash is said to be friction-controlled. This means simply that the output member cannot coast whenever there is no torque applied to it. The transfer characteristic between input and output displacement of this type of backlash is shown in Fig. 11-23a. The output member remains in contact with the input member until the velocity reaches zero; then the output member will stand still until the backlash is taken up on the other side, at which time it is assumed that the output member instantaneously takes on the velocity of the input member. It is also assumed that the collision takes place without bouncing or deformation of the two members. After collision, the output member f follows the input until the velocity again reaches zero. To illustrate the relative motion between the input and output members, let us assume that the input member is driven sinusoidally with respect to time; the waveform of the output displacement is given in Fig. 11-23b. The input member is assumed to start at the center position, as shown in Fig. 11-22. Figure 11-23c shows the waveforms of the velocities of input and output members; the output velocity is zero while the input is moving through the backlash zone b. The describing function of the friction-controlled backlash can be derived

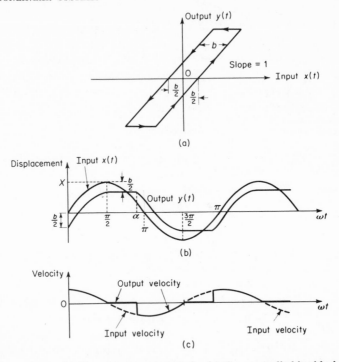

Fig. 11-23. (a) Transfer characteristic for friction-controlled backlash; (b) Input and output displacement waveforms of a friction-controlled backlash element when $x(t) = X \sin \omega t$; (c) Input and output velocity waveforms of a friction-controlled backlash element when $x(t) = X \sin \omega t$.

from the conventional Fourier analysis of the wave shapes shown in Fig. 11-23b. If the input member displacement is given as $x(t) = X \sin \omega t$, the output waveform may be represented by the following set of equations:

$$y(t) = \begin{cases} X \sin \omega t - b/2 & \text{for} & 0 < \omega t < \pi/2 \\ X - b/2 & \text{for} & \pi/2 < \omega t < \alpha \\ X \sin \omega t + b/2 & \text{for} & \alpha < \omega t < 3\pi/2 \\ -X + b/2 & \text{for } 3\pi/2 < \omega t < \pi + \alpha \\ X \sin \omega t - b/2 & \text{for} & \pi + \alpha < \omega t < 2\pi \end{cases} \quad (11\text{-}73)$$

The angle α is obtained from Fig. 11-23b as

$$\alpha = \pi - \sin^{-1}(1 - b/X) \quad (11\text{-}74)$$

The fundamental component of the output waveform $y(t)$ is

$$y(t) = A_1 \cos \omega t + B_1 \sin \omega t = M_1 \sin(\omega t + \phi) \quad (11\text{-}75)$$

where $\qquad M_1 = \sqrt{A_1^2 + B_1^2} \quad \text{and} \quad \phi = \tan^{-1}(A_1/B_1)$

Substituting $y(t)$ into Eq. (11-53) and Eq. (11-52) for $m(t)$, we have

$$B_1 = \frac{2}{\pi}\int_0^\pi y(t)\sin\omega t\,d\omega t = \frac{2X}{\pi}\left[\frac{3\pi}{4} + \left(\frac{b}{X} - 1\right)\cos\alpha - \frac{\alpha}{2} + \frac{\sin 2\alpha}{4}\right]$$

(11-76)

and

$$A_1 = \frac{2}{\pi}\int_0^\pi y(t)\cos\omega t\,d\omega t = \frac{2X}{\pi}\left[\frac{3}{4} + \sin\alpha\left(1 - \frac{b}{X}\right) + \frac{\cos 2\alpha}{4}\right]$$

(11-77)

If we let $\beta = \sin^{-1}(1 - b/X)$; then $\alpha = \pi - \beta$

Equations (11-76) and (11-77) now become

$$A_1 = \frac{2X}{\pi}\left[\frac{3\pi}{4} - \sin\beta\cos\alpha - \frac{\alpha}{2} + \frac{\sin 2\alpha}{4}\right]$$

$$= \frac{2X}{\pi}\left[\frac{3\pi}{4} + \sin\beta\cos\beta - \frac{\pi - \beta}{2} - \frac{\sin 2\beta}{4}\right]$$

$$= \frac{X}{\pi}\left[\left(\frac{\pi}{2} + \beta\right) + \frac{\sin 2\beta}{2}\right]$$

(11-78)

$$B_1 = \frac{2X}{\pi}\left(-\frac{3}{4} + \sin^2\beta + \frac{1}{4} - \frac{1}{4}\sin^2\beta\right) = \frac{2X}{\pi}\left(-\frac{1}{2} + \frac{1}{2}\sin^2\beta\right)$$

$$= \frac{2}{\pi}\left[\left(\frac{b}{X}\right)^2 - \left(\frac{b}{X}\right)\right]$$

(11-79)

In Fig. 11-24 is shown the dependence of the describing function magnitude $|N| = M_1/X$ and phase ϕ upon the value of the ratio X/b. The magnitude varies from zero at $X/b = 0.5$ to unity at $X/b = \infty$; the phase shift varies from -90 deg to 0 deg accordingly.

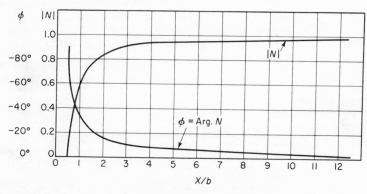

Fig. 11-24. Dependence of the magnitude and phase of describing function upon X/b for friction-controlled backlash element.

(5) *Describing Function of Inertia-controlled Gear Backlash*

When the friction on the output member of the backlash element is so small that it may be neglected so that the inertia of the output member becomes the controlling factor, the backlash is said to be inertia-controlled. In such a system, the output member remains in contact with the input member so long as the acceleration is in the direction to keep the two members together. When the acceleration goes to zero, the output member does not stop immediately, but leaves the input member and coasts at a constant velocity which is equal to the maximum velocity that the input member had attained. When the output member has traversed a distance, relative to the input member, which is equal to the full width of the backlash spacing, it will be restrained by the opposite side of the input member. It is assumed that, at this time, the output member will instantaneously take on the velocity of the input member with no bouncing or distortion of the two bodies. To illustrate the relative motion between the input and output members, let us assume that the input member is driven sinusoidally with respect to time; the waveforms of the input and output displacements are shown in Fig. 11-25a. Figures 11-25b and 11-25c show the waveforms for the velocities and accelerations of the input and output members, respectively.

To derive the describing function in this case, it is more convenient to

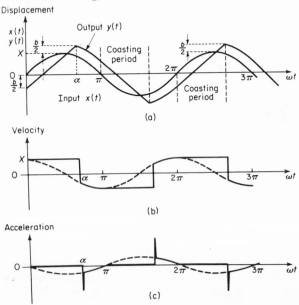

Fig. 11-25. Input-output displacement, velocity, acceleration of inertia-controlled gear backlash. The waveform of the input member is a sine wave.

use the velocity waveforms given in Fig. 11-25b. Since the fundamental component of the output displacement $y(t)$ is

$$y(t) = A_1 \cos \omega t + B_1 \sin \omega t$$

the output velocity is

$$\frac{dy}{dt} = -A_1\omega \sin \omega t + B_1\omega \cos \omega t \tag{11-80}$$

The coefficients $-A_1\omega$ and $B_1\omega$ can be evaluated by using Fig. 11-25b. Hence,

$$-A_1\omega = \frac{2}{\pi} \left[\int_0^\alpha X\omega \sin \omega t \, d\omega t + \int_\alpha^\pi X\omega \cos \omega t \sin \omega t \, d\omega t \right]$$

$$= \frac{2X\omega}{\pi} \left(1 - \cos \alpha - \frac{1}{4} + \frac{\cos 2\alpha}{4} \right) = \frac{2X\omega}{\pi} \left(\frac{3}{4} - \cos \alpha + \frac{\cos 2\alpha}{4} \right) \tag{11-81}$$

or

$$A_1 = \frac{2X}{\pi} \left(-\frac{3}{4} + \cos \alpha - \frac{\cos 2\alpha}{4} \right) \tag{11-82}$$

$$-B_1\omega = \frac{2}{\pi} \left[\int_0^\alpha X\omega \cos \omega t \, d\omega t + \int_\alpha^\pi X\omega \cos^2 \omega t \, d\omega t \right]$$

$$= \frac{2X\omega}{\pi} \left(\sin \alpha + \frac{\pi}{2} - \frac{\alpha}{2} - \frac{\sin 2\alpha}{4} \right) \tag{11-83}$$

or

$$B_1 = \frac{2X}{\pi} \left(\sin \alpha + \frac{\pi}{2} - \frac{\sin 2\alpha}{4} - \frac{\alpha}{2} \right) \tag{11-84}$$

where

$$\alpha - \sin \alpha = b/X \tag{11-85}$$

The angle α is zero when the backlash spacing is zero ($X/b = \infty$), but reaches 180 deg when $X/b = 1/\pi$. When $X/b = 1/\pi = 0.318$, the displacement of the output member is a triangular wave which lags behind the input wave by 90 deg; the velocity of the output member becomes a true rectangular wave and is in phase with the input wave. For values of X/b less than $1/\pi$, the frequency of the output member displacement becomes a submultiple of the input, rendering the describing function concept in-inapplicable.

The dependence of the describing function magnitude $|N| = \sqrt{A_1^2 + B_1^2}/X$ and phase shift $\phi = \tan^{-1}(A_1/B_1)$ upon the value of X/b is given in Fig. 11-26.

In the general case, the output member of the backlash element contains both inertia and friction; hence, the gear backlash can be considered to be neither purely friction-controlled nor purely inertia-controlled, as assumed in the foregoing cases. However, in comparing the waveforms of the output member displacements given in Fig. 11-23b and Fig. 11-25a, it is apparent that when both inertia and viscous friction are considered in the backlash element, the output waveform will fall between the friction-controlled and inertia-controlled cases. When the input member of the backlash element

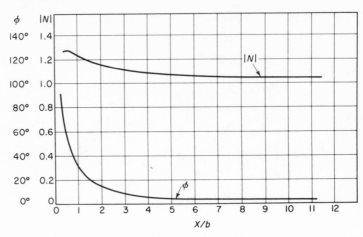

Fig. 11-26. Dependence of the magnitude and phase of describing function upon X/b for inertia-controlled backlash element.

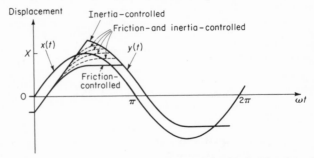

Fig. 11-27. Input and output waveforms of backlash element with friction- and inertia-controlled in the output member.

is driven sinusoidally, the waveforms of the displacement of the output member are as shown in Fig. 11-27. It is seen that the actual output waveforms depend on the ratio of inertia to friction and include the two foregoing cases as special cases.

The describing function $\overline{N}$ of gear backlash with both friction- and inertia-controlled characteristics is found* to be a complex function of X/b and $\omega\tau$, where ω is the frequency of the sinusoidal input $x(t)$ and τ is the ratio of inertia to viscous friction in the output member of the backlash element.

In the foregoing sections, the describing functions for relay and backlash types of nonlinears are derived. By similar procedures, the describing functions of common nonlinearities in servomechanisms can be derived; some of these are tabulated in Table 11-2.

---

*H. C. Brearley, Jr., "Prediction of Transient Response of Nonlinear Servomechanisms by Sinusoidal Analysis," Ph.D. thesis, University of Illinois, 1953.

Table 11-2. Characteristics and Describing Functions of Nonlinear Elements

Type of nonlinearity	Input-output transfer characteristic	Output waveform corresponding to sinusoidal input	Describing function N
(a) Saturation			$N = k \quad E < A$ $N = \dfrac{M_1}{E} = \dfrac{2k}{\pi}\left(\alpha + \dfrac{\sin 2\alpha}{2}\right) \quad E > A$ where $\quad \alpha = \sin^{-1}\dfrac{A}{E}$
(b) Saturation with dead zone			$N = \dfrac{M_1}{E} = \dfrac{2k}{\pi}\left(\beta - \alpha - \dfrac{\sin 2\alpha - \sin 2\beta}{2}\right) \quad E > \dfrac{A}{k}$ $N = 0 \quad E < D$ $N = \dfrac{2k}{\pi}\left(\dfrac{\pi}{2} - \alpha - \dfrac{\sin 2\alpha}{2}\right) \quad A > E > D$ where $\quad \alpha = \sin^{-1}\dfrac{D}{E} \quad \beta = \sin^{-1}\dfrac{A}{E}$
(c) Dead zone but no saturation			$N = 0 \quad E < D$ $N = \dfrac{2k}{\pi}\left(\dfrac{\pi}{2} - \alpha - \dfrac{\sin 2\alpha}{2}\right) \quad E > D$
(d) Ideal relay			$N = \dfrac{4T_m}{\pi E}$

Table 11-2. Characteristics and Describing Functions of Nonlinear Elements (cont.)

Type of nonlinearity	Input-output transfer characteristic	Output waveform corresponding to sinusoidal input	Describing function N
(e) Relay with dead zone			$N = 0 \quad E < D$ $N = \dfrac{4T_m}{\pi E}\sqrt{1 - \left(\dfrac{D}{E}\right)^2}$
(f) Relay with dead zone and hysteresis			$\overline{N} = \dfrac{4T_m}{\pi E}\sin\left(\dfrac{\beta - \alpha}{2}\right)\exp\left[\,j\left(\dfrac{\pi}{2} + \dfrac{\alpha + \beta}{2}\right)\right]$ $\alpha = \sin^{-1}\dfrac{b}{E} \qquad \beta = \pi - \sin^{-1}\dfrac{a}{E}$
(g) Dead zone with linear transfer characteristic			$N = 0 \quad E < D$ $N = \dfrac{2k}{\pi}\left(\dfrac{\pi}{2} - \alpha + \dfrac{\sin 2\alpha}{2}\right)$ $\alpha = \sin^{-1}\dfrac{D}{E}$

Table 11-2. Characteristics and Describing Functions of Nonlinear Elements (cont.)

Type of nonlinearity	Input-output transfer characteristic	Output waveform corresponding to sinusoidal input	Describing function N
(h) Coulomb friction plus viscous friction			$N = \dfrac{4A}{\pi E} + f$
(i) Backlash element with viscous friction			$\bar{N} = \dfrac{\overline{M_1}}{E} = \sqrt{A_1^2 + B_1^2} = \|N\|e^{j\phi} \qquad \phi = \tan^{-1}\dfrac{A_1}{B_1}$ $\|N\| = \dfrac{E}{\pi}\left[\left(\dfrac{\pi}{2} + \beta\right) + \dfrac{\sin 2\beta}{2}\right]$ $A_1 = \dfrac{E}{\pi}\cdot 2\left(\dfrac{b}{E}\right)\left[1 - \dfrac{b}{E}\right]$ $B_1 = \dfrac{E}{\pi}\left[\left(\dfrac{\pi}{2} + \beta\right) + \dfrac{\sin 2\beta}{2}\right]$ $\beta = \sin^{-1}\left(1 - \dfrac{b}{E}\right)$
(j) Backlash element with inertia			$\bar{N} = \dfrac{\overline{M_1}}{E} = \sqrt{A_1^2 + B_1^2} = \|N\|e^{j\phi} \qquad \phi = \tan^{-1}\dfrac{A_1}{B_1}$ $A_1 = \dfrac{2E}{\pi}\left(-\dfrac{3}{4} + \cos\alpha - \dfrac{\cos 2\alpha}{4}\right)$ $B_1 = \dfrac{2E}{\pi}\left(\sin\alpha + \dfrac{\pi}{2} - \dfrac{\sin 2\alpha}{4} - \dfrac{\alpha}{2}\right)$ $\alpha = \sin\alpha + b/E$

11.8 The Application of Describing Function to Stability Analysis of Nonlinear Systems

Once the describing function of the nonlinear element of a given system is determined, it can be used to study the stability of the nonlinear system. The system configuration of Fig. 11-17 is used here to illustrate the technique of stability analysis using describing function.

If the nonlinear element is properly represented by the describing function $\overline{N}$, where $\overline{N}$ is, in general, a complex number and a function of the input signal amplitude and frequency, it follows that the closed-loop system transfer function is

$$\frac{C(s)}{R(s)} = \frac{\overline{N}(E, \omega)G(s)}{1 + \overline{N}(E, \omega)G(s)} \tag{11-86}$$

The stability of the closed-loop nonlinear system depends on the zeros of

$$1 + \overline{N}(E, \omega)G(s) = 0 \tag{11-87}$$

Just as in the case of linear systems, if all the zeros of Eq. (11-87) are located in the left half of the s-plane, the system is stable; if one or more zeros are found in the right half of the plane, the system is unstable. In a problem of analysis, if $G(s)$ is a given function, the stability study of the nonlinear system essentially involves the investigation of the signal frequency ω and amplitude E, of which $\overline{N}$ is a function, in order to satisfy Eq. (11-87). The roots of Eq. (11-87) may also be interpreted as the condition when

$$G(s) = -\frac{1}{N(E, \omega)} \tag{11-88}$$

Normally, the stability analysis can be carried out by using any one of the following methods: (1) the Nyquist diagram, (2) gain versus phase shift plot, or (3) the root locus diagram.

In the case of Nyquist diagram analysis, the system stability is investigated by plotting the $G(s)$ and $-1/N$ loci in polar coordinates. The $G(s)$ plot is the ordinary frequency locus, but the $-1/N$ locus can be considered to be the locus of the critical point, which in linear theory is the $(-1, j0)$ point in the complex G-plane. It is evident that when N is a function only of the input signal magnitude E to the nonlinear element, the critical points of $-1/N$ form a locus which is a function of E. If N is a function of both E and ω, a family of loci must be constructed; on each curve ω is constant, but E is a variable parameter.

The relative position of the $G(s)$ locus and the $-1/N$ plot indicates the stability condition of the nonlinear system. When the critical points of $-1/N$ lie to the left of the $G(s)$ locus or are not enclosed by it (assuming that $G(s)$ is itself a stable system function), the closed-loop system is said to be stable, since any disturbances which appear in the system will tend to die out. Conversely, when any part of the $-1/N$ locus lies to the right of the $G(s)$ locus and, thus, is enclosed by it, it implies that any disturbances which are characterized by the values of E corresponding to the enclosed critical points will provide unstable operations. The intersection of the $G(s)$ and $-1/N$ loci corresponds to the possibility of a periodic oscillation characterized by the value of E on the $-1/N$ locus and the value of ω on the $G(s)$ locus. For the situation in which the $-1/N$ locus is a function of both E and ω, periodic oscillation is possible only if the values of ω at the intersection are identical on the two loci. The periodic solution described above may be stable or unstable with respect to a slight disturbance in amplitude E or frequency ω from the equilibrium condition. If the equilibrium state is a stable one, the amplitude of oscillation tends to return to its original value following a disturbance. If the equilibrium is unstable, the oscillation either increases or decreases depending on the direction of the disturbance; the oscillation may increase indefinitely, or enter into some other equilibrium state.

(1) *Stability of Systems with Relay-Type Control*

In this section a relay-type servo system is used to illustrate the application of describing function to the study of nonlinear systems. Assume that the transfer function of the linear part of the system is of the form

$$G(s) = \frac{K}{s(s + a)(s + b)} \tag{11-89}$$

and that the relay is of the ideal type without dead zone and hysteresis. The describing function of any ideal relay characteristic is given by case (d) of Table 11-2. Thus,

$$-1/N(E) = -\pi E/4T_m \tag{11-90}$$

Figure 11-28 shows the plots of $G(j\omega)$ for two different values of K, and the

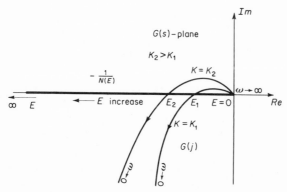

Fig. 11-28. Stability analysis of relay-type system (ideal relay).

plot of $-1/N(E)$ as a function of E. For $K = K_1$, the two loci intersect at point A on the negative real axis of the G-plane. We shall show that point A represents a stable equilibrium point which corresponds to a sustained oscillation with amplitude E_1 and frequency ω_1. Let us assume that the system is originally operated at point A so that the oscillation is characterized by amplitude E_1 and frequency ω_1 determined on the $-1/N$ and $G(j\omega)$ loci, respectively. Any slight disturbance in the direction of increasing the amplitude of oscillation moves the operating point to the left of A; thus, A is not enclosed by the $G(j\omega)$ locus; the system becomes positively damped, which tends to decrease the amplitude and eventually to move the operating point back to A. Conversely, any disturbance in the direction of decreasing the amplitude of oscillation moves the operating point to the right and thus the point is enclosed by the $G(j\omega)$ locus; the system tends to become unstable, and the amplitude of oscillation is increased, which moves the operating point back to A. If the forward gain K is increased from K_1 to K_2, for any disturbances, the system will possess sustained oscillation characterized by the same frequency ω_1, but with a larger amplitude $E_2(> E_1)$.

Figure 11-29 shows the same plots of $G(j\omega)$ as those in Fig. 11-28, except that the $-1/N(E)$ locus now corresponds to a relay with dead zone char-

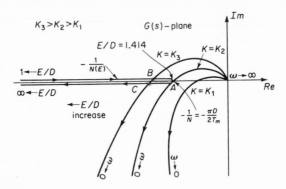

Fig. 11-29. Stability analysis of relay-type system (relay with dead zone).

acteristics. From case (e) in Table 11-2, the negative inverse describing function of this type of nonlinearity is

$$-1/N(E) = -\frac{\pi}{4T_m} \frac{D}{(D/E)} \frac{1}{\sqrt{1 - (D/E)^2}} \qquad (11\text{-}91)$$

For any given value of the dead zone D, $-1/N(E)$ depends entirely on the quantity E/D. In Fig. 11-29, the $-1/N$ locus is shown to begin at $-\infty$ for $E/D = 1$; as the value of E/D is increased further, the critical point moves toward $-\infty$ as E/D approaches infinity. The relative position of the $G(j\omega)$ and $-1/N(E)$ plots again indicate the stability condition of the system for any given set of values of K and D. When the system forward gain is of a small value, for example, K_1 , the $G(j\omega)$ locus does not intersect or enclose any portion of the $-1/N$ locus, and the system is stable. Any oscillations which may occur in the system due to any disturbances will die out. If the gain K is increased to a value of K_2 so that the $-1/N$ locus is now in touch at point A with the $G(j\omega)$ curve, (a similar result may be obtained by decreasing the relay dead zone D), the system is said to have an equilibrium operating point at A. It remains to determine whether A represents stable or unstable equilibrium. This can be determined by assuming that the system is operating at point A initially with the oscillation characterized by amplitude E on the $-1/N$ locus and the frequency determined on the $G(j\omega)$ locus. Any amplitude decrease results in the critical points being moved to the left of the $G(j\omega)$ curve (the critical point is not enclosed by $G(j\omega)$, and the system comes to rest. Any amplitude increase results in the critical points moving in the same direction and thus tends to decrease the oscillation amplitude and to move the operating point back to A. Since most disturbances are in the form of random noise, the system will likely come to rest after any disturbances from the equilibrium position represented by point A, and point A is an unstable equilibrium point, since the system cannot possibly operate at this point. However, the system is said to be on the verge of becoming unstable when $K = K_2$. If the value of K is further increased to a value of K_3 (or the relay dead zone is further decreased), Fig. 11-29 shows that the $G(j\omega)$ locus intersects the $-1/N$ locus at two points: B and C. By the same technique described above, it is easy to see that point B is an unstable equilibrium point, and that point C represents stable operation. The $-1/N(E)$ locus which lies to the left of point B corresponds to stable operation; any initial oscillations with amplitudes E which lie in this section will eventually die out. The critical points that are enclosed by the $G(j\omega)$ curve correspond to values of E for unstable operations, since any oscillations that start in this section will move the operation to point C. The values of E on the $-1/N$ curve, which is to the left of C, again, correspond to stable operations, since the oscillations decrease in magnitude and finally the system operates at point C. Thus, C is a stable equilibrium point.

The stability analysis of a control system with relay which has dead zone and hysteresis characteristics may be studied in much the same way as described in the foregoing cases. The loci of $-\dfrac{T_m}{a}\dfrac{1}{N(E)}$ for $a/b = 1.0$, 0.8, and 0.2 are plotted in the $G(s)$ plane, based on the data obtained from Fig. 11-21. It is seen that the critical loci are shifted toward the left and also toward the -180 deg axis when the value of a/b is increased. For any fixed value of a/b, the critical point on the $-1/N$ curve moves toward the left for large values of E/b. For a given $G(s)$ locus, the system is capable of having one stable equilibrium point at A, or one stable and one unstable equilibrium point (B and C), as shown in Fig. 11-30.

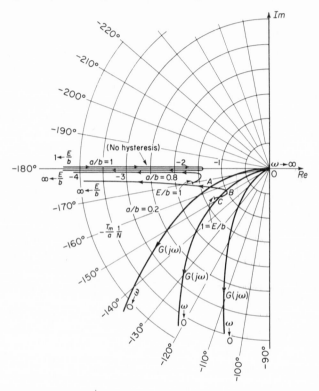

Fig. 11-30. Stability analysis of nonlinear system with relay-type control (relay with dead zone and hysteresis).

Stability Analysis in Gain-Phase Plots

The stability analysis of nonlinear systems using describing function may also be carried out in the gain versus phase shift plane. Because the use of the constant M loci in Nyquist plots is usually cumbersome, the gain-phase diagram offers convenient evaluation of the relative system stability by utilizing the Nichols chart. A simple servomechanism with gear backlash is used here to illustrate the study of stability of nonlinear systems in the gain-phase plane.

Assume that a servomechanism is entirely linear except for the backlash in the gear train between the synchro control transformer and the load. The inertia of the control transformer is considered to be negligible,

compared with that of the load; only the viscous friction of the synchro
is taken into account. Therefore, the gear backlash in this case is said to
be friction-controlled. The linear transfer function of the system is given by

$$G(s) = \frac{K}{s(s+1)} \tag{11-92}$$

and the describing function N for the friction-controlled gear backlash is
calculated in Section 11.7 (4). Figure 11-31 shows the plots of $G(j\omega)$
for $K = 1$, and the negative inverse describing function $-1/N$ for the
friction-controlled backlash. It is obvious that the system is stable and
without periodic oscillations for all values of input X to the non-linear
element n. Increasing the backlash to input ratio b/X will not make the
system unstable; however, as the value of b/X is increased, the critical
point on the $-1/N$ locus is moved closer to the $G(j\omega)$ curve. Since the
Nichols chart must also be moved along the $-1/N$ locus accordingly,
it shows that the resonance peak M_p of the system will be increased and
the system will become less stable. For example, if the backlash spacing is

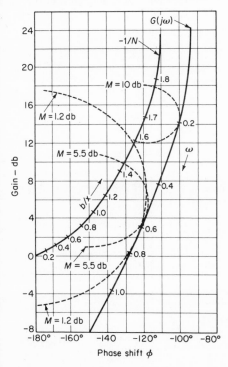

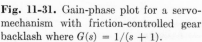

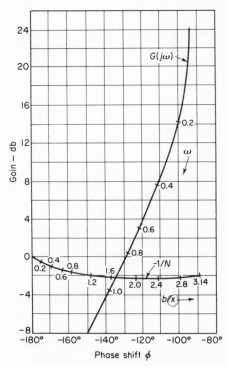

Fig. 11-31. Gain-phase plot for a servomechanism with friction-controlled gear
backlash where $G(s) = 1/(s+1)$.

Fig. 11-32. Gain-phase plot for a servomechanism with inertia-controlled gear
backlash where $G(s) = 1/(s+1)$.

zero ($b/X = 0$), the system is linear, the Nichols chart is centered at the usual critical point, and the value of M_p is about 1.2 db; but for $b/X = 1.0$, the constant M loci that is tangent to the $G(j\omega)$ locus gives an M_p of approximately 5.5 db. When the backlash is increased to $b/X = 1.7$, the resonance peak is about 10 db.

Some comments concerning the interpretation of the Nichols chart used for the study of nonlinear systems must be made here. The values of M_p determined above for a fixed value of b/X do not have the same meaning as in the linear case. For a linear system, recall that M_p is the maximum value of the closed-loop frequency response which is obtained by keeping the amplitude of the sinusoidal input to the system constant and varying the frequency. For the nonlinear system, M_p is, again, the maximum value of the closed-loop frequency response, but the response curve is obtained by varying the amplitude and frequency of the input sinusoid in such a manner that the input to the nonlinear element is a fixed value X. However, the value of M_p determined for a nonlinear system in the manner described above still gives indication of the relative stability of the system. The results obtained in the above example show that backlash in gears reduces the stability margin of a feedback control system.

Figure 11-32 shows the gain-phase diagram for $-1/N$ and $G(j\omega)$ for the same system, but with an inertia-controlled backlash in gears. A periodic solution is indicated by the intersection of the $-1/N$ and the $G(j\omega)$ loci. By means of the same method used in the previous sections, we can show that this periodic solution is a stable one.

Problems

11-1. For the linear feedback control system shown in Fig. 11P-1, plot the phase plane diagram of e versus $\dot{e}$ under the following conditions. Assume that the reference input $r(t)$ is a step displacement.

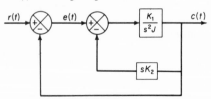

Fig. 11P-1

(a) $J = 10$ lb-ft^2 = 0.31 lb-ft-sec^2, $K_1 = 1$ ft-lb/rad, $K_2 = 2$.

Initial conditions: (1) $e(0) = 3$ rad, $\dot{e}(0) = 0$
  (2) $e(0) = 0$ rad, $\dot{e}(0) = 2$ rad/sec
  (3) $e(0) = 1$ rad, $\dot{e}(0) = -2.5$ rad/sec

(b) $J = 0.31$ lb-ft-sec², $K_1 = 1$ ft-lb/rad, $K_2 = 0.5$.

Initial conditions: (1) $e(0) = 3$ rad, $\dot{e}(0) = 0$
            (2) $e(0) = -3$ rad, $\dot{e}(0) = 0$

(c) $J = 0.31$ lb-ft-sec², $K_1 = 1$ ft-lb/rad, $K_2 = 0.5$.

Initial conditions: (1) $e(0) = 1$ rad, $\dot{e}(0) = 0$
            (2) $e(0) = 0$, $\dot{e}(0) = 0.25$ rad/sec.

(d) $J = 0.31$ lb-ft-sec², $K_1 = 1$ ft-lb/rad, $K_2 = 0$.

Initial conditions: (1) $e(0) = 1$ rad, $\dot{e}(0) = 0$
            (2) $e(0) = 0$, $\dot{e}(0) = 2$ rad/sec

11-2. A second-order relay-controlled system, shown in Fig. 11-6a, has a relay characteristic given by Fig. 11-5c with $a = 0.1$, and $b = 0.2$ and $T_m = 1$. The linear part of the system is represented by the transfer function $1/s(s + 1)$. Sketch the phase plane trajectory of c versus $\dot{c} = v$ for a step displacement input of magnitude 0.5. Sketch the phase plane trajectory of e versus $\dot{e}$ for the same system.

11-3. For the relay-type control system given in Problem 11-2, sketch the phase plane trajectory in e versus $\dot{e}$ when the reference input is $r(t) = k_0 + k_1 t$, where $k_0 = 0.5$, and $k_1 = 0.5$.

11-4. What is the effect on the phase plane diagram if static friction is considered on the output shaft in addition to coulomb friction in the nonlinear system described in Sec. 11.4?

11-5. Derive the describing function for the nonlinear element described in Table 11-2a.

11-6. Derive the describing function for the nonlinear element described in Table 11-2b.

11-7. Derive the describing function for the nonlinear element described in Table 11-2c.

11-8. Derive the describing function for the nonlinear element described in Table 11-2g.

11-9. Derive the describing function for the nonlinear element described in Table 11-2h.

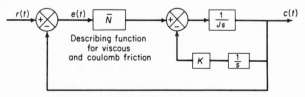

Fig. 11P-10

11-10. The differential equation of a second-order feedback control system characterized by an inertia load with viscous and coulomb frictions in the output shaft is given by Eq. (11-37). The describing function N of the combination of viscous and coulomb frictions is given in Table 11-2h. Show that for the purpose of stability study using describing function, an equivalent block diagram of the closed-loop system may be represented by Fig. 11P-10.

11-11. A servomechanism is considered to be entirely linear, except for the backlash in the gear train between the synchro control transformer and the load. The inertia of the control transformer is considered to be negligible compared with that of the load; only the viscous friction of the synchro needs to be taken into account. The linear transfer function of the amplifier-motor-load is given by

$$G(s) = \frac{K}{s(1 + 0.1s)(1 + 0.5s)}$$

The backlash spacing is given as $b = 0.5$. By means of the describing function, study the stability of the nonlinear system when $K = 4$, $K = 5$, and $K = 8$ respectively. Discuss the stability of any equilibrium points. Compare the system stability of this nonlinear system with that of a system with no backlash.

APPENDIX A

Laplace Transformation

A.1 Complex Variable and the s-Plane*

The analysis and design of feedback control systems rely to a great extent on the application of the complex variable theory.

A complex variable s is considered to have two components: a real component σ, and an imaginary component $j\omega$. Graphically, the σ component is represented in the horizontal direction, and the $j\omega$ component is measured on the vertical axis in the complex s-plane. In other words, a complex variable is always defined by a point in a plane which has a σ

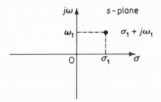

Fig. A-1. The complex s-plane.

---

*In this section, only a brief introduction to the concept of complex variable is given. For more detailed discussions, the reader should refer to a book such as R. V. Churchill, *Introduction to Complex Variables and Applications*, McGraw-Hill Book Company, New York, 1948.

479

axis and a $j\omega$ axis. Figure A-1 illustrates the complex s-plane, in which any arbitrary point $s = s_1$ is defined by the coordinates $\sigma = \sigma_1$, and $\omega = \omega_1$, or $s_1 = \sigma_1 + j\omega_1$.

Function of a Complex Variable

The function $G(s)$ is said to be a function of the complex variable s, if for every value of s there is a corresponding value (or values) of $G(s)$. Since s has real and imaginary parts, the function $G(s)$ is also represented by its real and imaginary parts; that is,

$$G(s) = Re\,G + jIm\,G \qquad (A\text{-}1)$$

Thus, the function $G(s)$ can also be represented by a complex G-plane, whose horizontal axis represents $Re\,G$ and whose vertical axis measures the imaginary component of $G(s)$. If, for every value of s (every point in the s-plane), there is only one corresponding value for $G(s)$ (one corresponding point in the $G(s)$-plane), $G(s)$ is said to be a "single-valued function," and the mapping (correspondence) from points in the s-plane into points in the $G(s)$-plane is described as "one-to-one" (Fig. A-2). If, for every point in

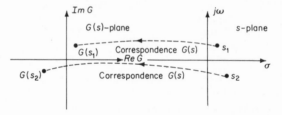

Fig. A-2. One-to-one mapping from s-plane to $G(s)$-plane.

the s-plane, there is more than one corresponding point in the $G(s)$-plane (mapped by the function $G(s)$), then $G(s)$ is called a "multi-valued function" (Fig. A-3).

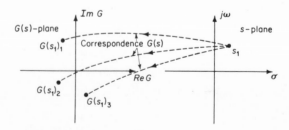

Fig. A-3. One-to-three mapping from s-plane to $G(s)$-plane illustrating that the function $G(s)$ is multi-valued.

Figure A-4 illustrates the mapping of the function $G(s) = s + 1$ from the given s-plane locus ($s = 1$); the correspondence is apparently one-to-one. The arrows on the s-plane locus and on the G-plane locus indicate the corresponding directions of the two loci.

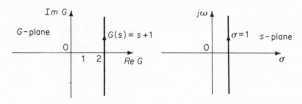

Fig. A-4. Mapping from the s-plane into the $G(s)$-plane.

Analytic Functions

Definition. A function of complex variable $G(s)$ is analytic in a region if the function and all its derivatives exist in the region. For instance, the function $G(s) = 1/(s + a)$ is analytic at every point in the s-plane except at the point $s = -a$; the function $G(s) = s + 2$ is analytic at every point in the finite s-plane.

Singularities and Poles of a Function

The singularities of a function are the points in the s-plane at which the function (or its derivatives) does not exist. A *pole* is the simplest type of singularity, and plays a very important role in the analysis and design of feedback control systems.*

Definition of a Pole. If a function $G(s)$ is analytic and single-valued in the neighborhood of s_i except at s_i, it is said to have a pole of order r at $s = s_i$ if the limit

$$\lim_{s=s_i} [(s - s_i)^r G(s)] \tag{A-2}$$

has a finite, nonzero value. In other words, the denominator of $G(s)$ must include the factor $(s - s_i)^r$, and when $s = s_i$, the function becomes infinite. If $r = 1$, the pole at $s = s_i$ is called a "simple pole." For instance, the function

$$G(s) = \frac{10(s + 2)}{s(s + 1)(s + 3)^2} \tag{A-3}$$

has a pole of order two at $s = 3$, and simple poles at $s = 0$ and $s = 1$. The function is analytic in the s-plane except at these poles.

---

*Other types of singularities are as follows: essential singularity, branch point, removable singularity, etc.

Zero of a Function

Definition. If the function $G(s)$ is analytic at $s = s_i$, it is said to have a zero of order r at $s = s_i$ if the limit

$$\lim_{s = s_i} [(s - s_i)^{-r} G(s)] \tag{A-4}$$

has a finite, nonzero value. Or, simply, $G(s)$ has a zero of order r at $s = s_i$ if $1/G(s)$ has an rth order pole at $s = s_i$. The function in Eq. (A-3), for instance, has a simple zero at $s = -2$.

If the function under consideration is a rational function, the total number of poles equals the total number of zeros (counting the multiple poles and zeros) if the poles and zeros at infinity and zero are taken into account. The function in Eq. (A-3) has four finite poles at $s = 0$, -1, -3, -3; there is one finite zero at $s = -2$, but there are three zeros at infinity, for

$$\lim_{s \to \infty} G(s) = \lim_{s \to \infty} 10/s^3 = 0 \tag{A-5}$$

A.2 The Laplace Transform*

The Laplace transformation is one of the major mathematical tools used in the solution of ordinary linear differential equations. For complex

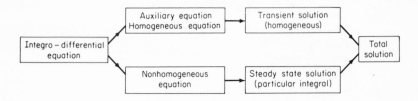

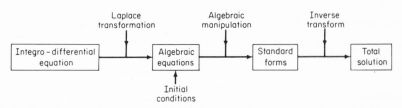

Fig. A-5. Flow diagram comparing classical and Laplace transformation methods in solving differential equations.

---

*In this section, no attempt is made to cover the Laplace transform theory with any mathematical rigor. For more extended and rigorous treatment, the reader should refer to: H. S. Carslow and J. C. Jaeger, *Operational Methods in Applied Mathematics*, Oxford University Press, Oxford, 1941; Gardner and Barnes, *Transients in Linear Systems*, John Wiley & Sons, New York, 1942.

systems, the method of Laplace transform has a definite advantage over the classical method. The philosophy behind the Laplace transform and its comparison with the classical method are illustrated by the flow diagram shown in Fig. A-5.

In order to understand the properties and definitions of the Laplace transformation, it is necessary to examine first the properties of the Fourier series and the Fourier integral.

The Fourier Series and the Fourier Integral

Let $f_T(t)$ be a single-valued periodic function of t with period T. Then $f_T(t)$ may be expanded into a Fourier series of the following form (if $f_T(t)$ satisfies certain additional mathematical conditions):

$$f_T(t) = \frac{a_0}{T} + \frac{2}{T} \sum_{n=1}^{\infty} (a_n \cos \omega_n t + b_n \sin \omega_n t) \tag{A-6}$$

where

$$\omega_n = \frac{2\pi n}{T} = \text{angular frequency} \tag{A-7}$$

and the coefficients a_0, a_n, and b_n are defined by

$$a_n = \int_{-T/2}^{T/2} f_T(t) \cos \omega_n t \, dt \quad n = 0,1,2,3,\ldots \tag{A-8}$$

$$b_n = \int_{-T/2}^{T/2} f_T(t) \sin \omega_n t \, dt \quad n = 1,2,3,\ldots \tag{A-9}$$

Since a_n and b_n are functions of frequency but not of time, Eq. (A-6) expresses $f_T(t)$ in terms of all its frequency components. The amplitude of a frequency component is given by $\sqrt{a_n^2 + b_n^2}$ and the phase is measured by $\tan^{-1}(-b_n/a_n)$. Specification of the amplitude and phase of all frequency components is thus entirely equivalent to a description of the time function $f_T(t)$.

A more compact expression may be obtained for the Fourier series in the complex form. Eq. (A-6) can be written

$$f_T(t) = \frac{a_0}{T} + \frac{2}{T} \sum_{n=1}^{\infty} \left[\frac{a_n}{2}(e^{j\omega_n t} + e^{-j\omega_n t}) - j\frac{b_0}{2}(e^{j\omega_n t} - e^{-j\omega_n t}) \right] \tag{A-10}$$

or $\qquad f_T(t) = \dfrac{a_0}{T} + \dfrac{1}{T} \displaystyle\sum_{n=1}^{\infty} [(a_n - jb_n)e^{j\omega_n t} + (a_n + jb_n)e^{-j\omega_n t}] \qquad$ (A-11)

Using Eqs. (A-8) and (A-9), we obtain

$$a_n - jb_n = \int_{-T/2}^{T/2} f_T(t)e^{-j\omega_n t} \tag{A-12}$$

and

$$a_n + jb_n = \int_{-T/2}^{T/2} f_T(t)e^{j\omega_n t} \tag{A-13}$$

Since ω_n is given by Eq. (A-7), we see that Eqs. (A-12) and (A-13) differ by a sign in n; i.e.,

$$(a_n - jb_n) = [(a_n + jb_n)]_{n=-n} \tag{A-14}$$

Eq. (A-11) can be written as

$$f_T(t) = \frac{1}{T} \sum_{n=-\infty}^{\infty} \int_{-T/2}^{T/2} f_T(t) e^{-j\omega_n t}\, dt\; e^{j\omega_n t} \tag{A-15}$$

or

$$f_T(t) = \frac{1}{T} \sum_{n=-\infty}^{\infty} C_n e^{j\omega_n t} \tag{A-16}$$

where

$$C_n = \int_{-T/2}^{T/2} f_T(t) e^{-j\omega_n t} \tag{A-17}$$

Equation (A-16) gives the complex Fourier series of $f_T(t)$, and C_n is the complex Fourier coefficient. As an example of the utility of the complex

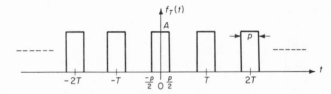

Fig. A-6. A periodic pulse train.

Fourier series, let us consider the train of periodic pulses shown in Fig. A-6. The complex Fourier coefficient of the periodic wave is

$$C_n = \int_{-p/2}^{p/2} A\, e^{-j\omega_n t}\, dt = -\frac{A}{j\omega_n} e^{-j\omega_n t} \Big|_{-p/2}^{p/2} = \frac{2A}{\omega_n} \sin \frac{\omega_n p}{2} \tag{A-18}$$

Equation (A-18) can also be written as

$$C_n = Ap \left(\frac{\sin \dfrac{\omega_n p}{2}}{\dfrac{\omega_n p}{2}} \right) \tag{A-19}$$

The plot of C_n for values of frequency ranging from $-\infty$ to $+\infty$ is shown in Fig. A-7. The envelop of C_n follows the well-known function $\sin \theta/\theta$. The spacing between successive lines in the C_n plot is equal to

$$\Delta\omega_n = \frac{2\pi}{T} \tag{A-20}$$

Therefore the number of lines between the interval $n\pi$ and $(n + 1)\pi$ depends on the period T; more lines for higher T. As T approaches infinity, C_n approaches a continuous function, described by the envelop shown in Fig. A-7.

Many functions of interest in our work are not periodic and, therefore,

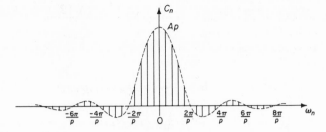

Fig. A-7. The complex Fourier coefficient for the pulse train of Fig. A-6.

cannot be represented by a Fourier series. However, we shall use the Fourier integral to represent this type of function. Let us consider the non-periodic function $f(t)$ shown in Fig. A-8. We can certainly construct

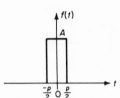

Fig. A-8. A pulse signal.

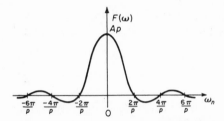

Fig. A-9. The Fourier transform of the pulse signal of Fig. A-8.

a periodic function $f_T(t)$, using $f(t)$ as the fundamental function during a period. The Fourier series of the periodic function $f_T(t)$ can be written, and, as the period of $f_T(t)$ approaches infinity, $f_T(t)$ approaches $f(t)$. Therefore the Fourier series of $f_T(t)$ as T approaches infinity is a sufficient representation of $f(t)$. Usinq Eq. (A-20), we can write Eq. (A-16) as

$$f_T(t) = \frac{1}{2\pi} \sum_{n=-\infty}^{\infty} C_n e^{j\omega_n t} \, \Delta\omega_n \qquad \text{(A-21)}$$

If we take the limit as T approaches infinity, then $\omega_n \to 0$, and the discrete lines in the C_n spectrum merge into a continuous frequency spectrum, as shown in Fig. A-9.
We have

$$\lim_{\substack{T \to \infty \\ \omega_n \to 0}} f_T(t) = \lim_{\substack{T \to \infty \\ \omega_n \to 0}} \frac{1}{2\pi} \sum_{n=-\infty}^{\infty} C_n e^{j\omega_n t} \, \Delta\omega_n$$

$$= \frac{1}{2\pi} \int_{-\infty}^{\infty} C_n e^{j\omega t} \, d\omega \qquad \text{(A-22)}$$

Also, as $T \to \infty$,

$$C_n = \int_{-\infty}^{\infty} f(t) e^{-j\omega t} \, dt = F(\omega) \qquad \text{(A-23)}$$

which is defined as the *Fourier transform* of the non-periodic function $f(t)$ and is designated by $F(\omega)$. The condition for the existence of the Fourier transform of the time function $f(t)$ is that $f(t)$ satisfies the following condition:

$$\int_{-\infty}^{\infty} |f(t)|\, dt < \infty \tag{A-24}$$

Therefore, before taking the Fourier integral (transform) of a time function, it is essential to find out if the function satisfies the absolute convergence condition stated in Eq. (A-24).

As an example, let us consider the time function

$$\begin{aligned} f(t) &= e^{at} \quad \text{for } t > 0 \\ &= 0 \quad \text{for } t < 0 \end{aligned} \tag{A-25}$$

where a is considered to be a constant. The Fourier transform of $f(t)$ is obtained by use of Eq. (A-23). Thus,

$$F(\omega) = \int_{-\infty}^{\infty} e^{at}e^{-j\omega t}\, dt = \left. \frac{e^{at}\, e^{-j\omega t}}{a - j\omega} \right|_{0}^{\infty} \tag{A-26}$$

If a is a negative number, substitution of the upper limit in the last equation will result in zero; therefore, Eq. (A-26) becomes

$$F(\omega) = \frac{-1}{a - j\omega} \qquad a < 0 \quad \text{(A-27)}$$

However, if $a > 0$, $F(\omega)$ becomes infinite at the upper limit and the Fourier transform does not exist. We could have obtained the same conclusion from Eq. (A-24), since for $a > 0$, $f(t)$ diverges as $t \to \infty$.

Although the Fourier transform is applicable to a large variety of functions, and is widely used as a mathematical tool in engineering science, because of the restriction stated by Eq. (A-24), many time functions which are of interest in engineering work cannot be handled by the Fourier transform method. For instance, the Fourier transform of a unit-step function is not defined;* other functions, such as t, t^2, etc., are also not Fourier transformable. In order to handle functions of this type, we modify our transformation by introducing a convergence factor $e^{-\sigma t}$, where σ is a real number large enough to insure absolute convergence. Therefore,

$$F(c, \omega) = \int_{0}^{\infty} f(t)\, e^{-\sigma t}\, e^{-j\omega t}\, dt \tag{A-28}$$

---

*Although it may seem that the Fourier transform of a unit-step function could be obtained by taking the limit as $a \to 0$ in Eq. (A-26) or Eq. (A-27), a unit-step function does not satisfy Eq. (A-24). Strictly speaking, the Fourier transform of a step function will exist if the impulse function is admitted. For further information, refer to S. J. Mason and H. J. Zimmermann, *Electronic Circuits, Signals, and Systems*, John Wiley & Sons, Inc., New York, 1960, Chap. 6.

The lower limit of the integral is forced to be taken as zero rather than $-\infty$, since for $\sigma > 0$, the convergence factor $e^{-\sigma t}$ will diverge when $t \to -\infty$. The transformation in Eq. (A-28) now ignores all information contained in $f(t)$ prior to $t = 0$. This does not put any serious limitation upon the new transformation, since in the usual transient studies, time reference is normally chosen at the instant $t = 0$. If we let $s = c + j\omega$, Eq. (A-28) becomes

$$F(s) = \int_0^\infty f(t) e^{-st} \, dt \qquad (A\text{-}29)$$

$F(s)$ is called the Laplace transform of $f(t)$, and is denoted by

$$F(s) = \mathscr{L}[f(t)] \qquad (A\text{-}30)$$

Also, the condition for the Laplace transform to exist is changed from that of Eq. (A-24) to

$$\int_{-\infty}^\infty |f(t) e^{-\sigma t}| \, dt < \infty \qquad (A\text{-}31)$$

for some finite c.

EXAMPLE A-1. If $f(t)$ is a unit-step function (defined for $t > 0$),

$$f(t) = u(t) \qquad (A\text{-}32)$$

The Laplace transform of $f(t)$ is

$$F(s) = \mathscr{L}[f(t)] = \int_0^\infty u(t) e^{-st} \, dt$$

$$= -\frac{1}{s} \left[e^{-st} \right]_0^\infty = \frac{1}{s} \qquad (A\text{-}33)$$

if $Re(s) = \sigma > 0$. Therefore, the Laplace transform of a step function is defined only in the right half of the s-plane.

EXAMPLE A-2. If

$$f(t) = e^{-at} \quad \text{for} \qquad\qquad\qquad t > 0 \quad (A\text{-}34)$$

$$F(s) = \int_0^\infty e^{-at} e^{-st} \, dt = \left[\frac{e^{-(s+a)t}}{s+a} \right]_0^\infty = \frac{1}{s+a} \qquad (A\text{-}35)$$

if $Re(s) > -a$. Therefore, the Laplace transform of $f(t)$ exists in the region to the right of the line $Re(s) = -a$ in the s-plane.

Inverse Laplace Transformation

A function $f(t)$ can be obtained from its Laplace transform by the relation

$$f(t) = \mathscr{L}^{-1}[F(s)] = \frac{1}{2\pi} \int_{c-j\infty}^{c+j\infty} F(s) e^{st} \, ds \qquad (A\text{-}36)$$

where c is a real constant greater than the real part of any singularity of

$F(s)$. Although the evaluation of the integral in Eq. (A-36) is usually difficult, the inverse transformations are usually performed by referring to the Laplace transform tables.

Important Theorems of the Laplace Transformation

Some of the important theorems of the Laplace transformation are given in the following:

(1) *The Laplace transform of the product of a constant A and a time function $f(t)$ is the constant A multiplied by the Laplace transform of $f(t)$; that is,*

$$\mathcal{L}[Af(t)] = AF(s) \qquad (A\text{-}37)$$

where $F(s)$ is the Laplace transform of $f(t)$.

(2) *The Laplace transform of the sum (or difference) of two time functions is the sum (or difference) of the Laplace transforms of the time functions; that is,*

$$\mathcal{L}[f_1(t) \pm f_2(t)] = F_1(s) \pm F_2(s) \qquad (A\text{-}38)$$

where $F_1(s)$ and $F_2(s)$ are the Laplace transforms of $f_1(t)$ and $f_2(t)$, respectively.

(3) *The Laplace transform of the first derivative of a time function $f(t)$ is s times the Laplace transform of $f(t)$ minus the limit of $f(t)$ as $t \to 0^+$; that is,*

$$\mathcal{L}\left[\frac{df(t)}{dt}\right] = sF(s) - \lim_{t \to 0^+} f(t) = sF(s) - f(0^+) \qquad (A\text{-}39)^*$$

In general, we have

$$\mathcal{L}\left[\frac{d^n f(t)}{dt^n}\right] = s^n F(s) - \lim_{t \to 0^+}\left[s^{n-1}f(t) + s^{n-2}\frac{df(t)}{dt} + \cdots + \frac{d^{n-1}f(t)}{dt^{n-1}}\right]$$

$$= s^n F(s) - s^{n-1}f(0^+) - s^{n-2}f'(0^+) - \cdots - f^{(n-1)}(0^+) \qquad (A\text{-}40)$$

(4) *The Transform of Integral. The Laplace transform of the first integral of a function $f(t)$ with respect to time is the Laplace transform of $f(t)$ divided by s plus the value of the integral of $f(t)$ as t approaches zero from the right divided by s; that is,*

$$\mathcal{L}\left[\int_0^t f(t)\,dt\right] = \frac{F(s)}{s} + \lim_{t \to 0^+}\frac{\int_0^t f(t)dt}{s} = \frac{F(s)}{s} + \frac{f^{-1}(0^+)}{s} \qquad (A\text{-}41)$$

where

$$f^{-1}(0^+) = \lim_{t \to 0^+}\int_0^t f(t)dt \qquad (A\text{-}42)$$

In general,

$$\mathcal{L}\left[\int\int\cdots\int f(t)dt^n\right] = \frac{F(s)}{s^n} + \frac{f^{-1}(0^+)}{s^n} + \frac{f^{-2}(0^+)}{s^{n-1}} + \cdots \frac{f^{-n}(0^+)}{s} \qquad (A\text{-}43)$$

---

*$t \to 0^+$ means time approaches zero from the right.

(5) *Shifting Theorem. The Laplace transform of a time function $f(t)$ delayed by time T is equal to the Laplace transform of $f(t)$ multiplied by e^{-sT};* that is,

$$\mathcal{L}[f(t - T) \cdot u(t - T)] = e^{-sT} F(s) \tag{A-44}$$

where $u(t)$ is a unit step function.

(6) *Initial Value Theorem. If the Laplace transform of $f(t)$ is $F(s)$, and $f(t)$ is Laplace transformable, then*

$$\lim_{t \to 0} f(t) = \lim_{s \to \infty} sF(s) \tag{A-45}$$

if the limit exists.

(7) *Final Value Theorem. If the Laplace transform of $f(t)$ is $F(s)$, and if $sF(s)$ is analytic on the imaginary axis and in the right half of the s-plane, then*

$$\lim_{t \to \infty} f(t) = \lim_{s \to 0} sF(s) \tag{A-46}$$

The final value theorem is a very useful relation in the analysis and design of feedback control systems, since it gives the final value of a time function by determining the behavior of its Laplace transform as s tends to zero. However, the final value theorem is not valid if the denominator of $sF(s)$ contains any root whose real part is zero or positive, which is equivalent to the analytic requirement of $sF(s)$ given above.

EXAMPLE A-3. Let

$$F(s) = \frac{5}{s(s^2 + s + 2)} \tag{A-47}$$

Since $sF(s)$ is analytic on the imaginary axis and in the right half of the s-plane, the final value theorem may be applied.

$$\lim_{t \to \infty} f(t) = \lim_{s \to 0} sF(s) = \lim_{s \to 0} \frac{5}{(s^2 + s + 2)} = \frac{5}{2} \tag{A-48}$$

EXAMPLE A-4. Let

$$F(s) = \frac{\omega}{s^2 + \omega^2} \tag{A-49}$$

The function $sF(s)$ has two poles on the imaginary axis; thus, although the final value theorem gives a final value of zero for $f(t)$, the result is incorrect because the theorem cannot be applied in this case.

Application of Laplace Transforms to Solving Differential Equations

With the aid of the theorems concerning Laplace transforms given in the last section and a table of transforms, linear differential equations can now be solved by the Laplace transform method.

EXAMPLE A-5. Consider the equation

$$\frac{d^2x}{dt^2} + 3\frac{dx}{dt} + 2x = 5 \tag{A-50}$$

with initial conditions: $x'(0^+) = 2$, $x(0^+) = -1$. Taking the Laplace transform of both sides of Eq. (A-50), we have

$$s^2X(s) - sx(0^+) - x'(0^+) + 3sX(s) - 3x(0^+) + 2X(s) = \frac{5}{s} \tag{A-51}$$

Substituting the values of $x'(0^+)$ and $x(0^+)$ into Eq. (A-51) and solving for $X(s)$, we have

$$X(s) = \frac{-s^2 - s + 5}{s(s^2 + 3s + 2)} = \frac{-s^2 - s + 5}{s(s + 1)(s + 2)} \tag{A-52}$$

Equation (A-52) is expanded by partial fraction expansion.

$$X(s) = \frac{5}{2s} - \frac{5}{s + 1} + \frac{3}{2(s + 2)} \tag{A-53}$$

The inverse transform of Eq. (A-53) is

$$x(t) = \frac{5}{2} - 5e^{-t} + \frac{3}{2}e^{-2t} \tag{A-54}$$

The first term of Eq. (A-54) is the steady-state solution, and the last two terms are the transient solution. Unlike the classical method, the Laplace transform gives the total solution of a differential equation in one operation. In the last example, if only the magnitude of the steady-state solution is of interest, the final value theorem may be applied; thus,

$$\lim_{t \to \infty} x(t) = \lim_{s \to 0} sX(s) = \lim_{s \to 0} \frac{-s^2 - s + 5}{(s^2 + 3s + 2)} = \frac{5}{2} \tag{A-55}$$

EXAMPLE A-6. Consider the equation

$$\frac{d^3x}{dt^3} + 5\frac{d^2x}{dt^2} + 8\frac{dx}{dt} = 0 \tag{A-56}$$

The initial conditions are as follows: at $t = 0$, $x(0^+) = 5$, but all higher derivatives are zero. Taking the Laplace transform of both sides of Eq. (A-56) we have

$$s^3X(s) - s^2x(0^+) - sx'(0^+) - x''(0^+) + 5s^2X(s) - 5sx(0^+) - 5x'(0^+)$$
$$+ 8sX(s) - 8x(0^+) = 0 \quad \text{(A-57)}$$

Substituting the initial conditions yields

$$(s^3 + 5s^2 + 8s)X(s) = (s^2 + 5s + 8)5 \tag{A-58}$$

or

$$X(s) = 5/s \tag{A-59}$$

The inverse transform of $X(s)$ is simply

$$x(t) = x(0^+) = 5 \tag{A-60}$$

At first glance, it is hard to believe that the solution is correct since the system essentially stays at its initial condition. However, from the physical point of view, the differential equation represents a system with no element for potential energy storage (no spring or capacitance); thus, with no external disturbance, the system can only stay in its initial state $x(0^+)$.

A.3 Partial Fraction Expansions

Example A-5 indicates that, in applying the inverse Laplace transformation, it is usually necessary to expand the algebraic transfer function $X(s)$ into simple terms of standard forms whose inverse transforms may be found in the Laplace transform table. The usual form of the Laplace transform solution of a differential equation is a quotient of polynomials in s; that is,

$$X(s) = \frac{p(s)}{q(s)} \tag{A-61}$$

The denominator of the polynomial, $q(s)$, may be written as

$$q(s) = a_0 s^n + a_1 s^{n-1} + \cdots + a_{n-1} s + a_n$$

$$= a_0 (s + s_1)(s + s_2) \cdots (s + s_n) \tag{A-62}$$

If the coefficients $a_0, a_1, a_2, \ldots, a_n$ are real numbers, the roots of $q(s)$ must be real or in complex conjugate pairs; in simple or multiple order.

The methods of partial fraction expansion will now be given for (1) simple roots, (2) multiple roots, (3) complex roots of $q(s)$.

Partial Fraction Expansion When All the Roots of $q(s)$ Are Simple

If all the roots of $q(s)$ are simple, Eq. (A-61) may be written as

$$X(s) = \frac{p(s)}{q(s)} = \frac{p(s)}{(s + s_1)(s + s_2)(s + s_3) \cdots (s + s_n)}$$

$$= \frac{K_{s_1}}{(s + s_1)} + \frac{K_{s_2}}{(s + s_2)} + \cdots + \frac{K_{s_n}}{(s + s_n)} \tag{A-63}$$

Any of the coefficients $K_{s_1}, K_{s_2}, \ldots K_{s_n}$ can be evaluated by multiplying

$X(s)$ in Eq. (A-63) by the corresponding denominator factor and setting s equal to the root. Thus, to find the coefficient K_{s_1}, for instance,

$$K_{s_1} = \left[(s + s_1) \frac{p(s)}{q(s)} \right]_{s=-s_1} = \frac{p(-s_1)}{(s_2 - s_1)(s_3 - s_1) \cdots (s_n - s_1)}$$

$$(A\text{-}64)$$

As an example, consider the function

$$X(s) = \frac{5s + 3}{(s + 1)(s + 2)(s + 3)} \tag{A-65}$$

which may be written in the partial-fraction form

$$X(s) = \frac{K_{-1}}{s + 1} + \frac{K_{-2}}{s + 2} + \frac{K_{-3}}{s + 3} \tag{A-66}$$

Then,

$$K_{-1} = [(s + 1)X(s)]_{s=-1} = \frac{5(-1) + 3}{(2 - 1)(3 - 1)} = -1 \tag{A-67}$$

$$K_{-2} = [(s + 2)X(s)]_{s=-2} = \frac{5(-2) + 3}{(1 - 2)(3 - 2)} = 7 \tag{A-68}$$

$$K_{-3} = [(s + 3)X(s)]_{s=-3} = \frac{5(-3) + 3}{(1 - 3)(2 - 3)} = -6 \tag{A-69}$$

Hence,

$$X(s) = \frac{-1}{s + 1} + \frac{7}{s + 2} - \frac{6}{s + 3} \tag{A-70}$$

Partial Fraction Expansion When Some Roots of $q(s)$ Are of Multiple Order

If r of the n roots of $q(s)$ are alike, the function $X(s)$ becomes

$$X(s) = \frac{p(s)}{q(s)} = \frac{p(s)}{(s + s_1)(s + s_2) \cdots (s + s_i)^r (s + s_n)} \tag{A-71}$$

which is expanded as

$$X(s) = \frac{K_{s_1}}{s + s_1} + \frac{K_{s_2}}{s + s_2} + \cdots + \frac{K_{sn}}{s + s_n} + \frac{A_1}{s + s_i} + \frac{A_2}{(s + s_i)^2} + \cdots$$

$$+ \frac{A_r}{(s + s_i)^r} \quad (A\text{-}72)$$

$|\leftarrow (n-r) \text{ terms of simple roots} \rightarrow |\leftarrow r \text{ terms of repeated roots} \rightarrow|$

The n-r coefficients, corresponding to the simple roots $K_{s_1}, K_{s_2}, \ldots, K_{sn}$, may be evaluated by the method described by Eq. (A-64).

The following equations may be used for the evaluation of the coefficients of repeated roots.

$$A_r = \left[(s + s_i)^r \frac{p(s)}{q(s)} \right]_{s=-s_i} \tag{A-73}$$

$$A_{r-1} = \frac{d}{ds} \left[(s + s_i)^r \frac{p(s)}{q(s)} \right]_{s=-s_i} \tag{A-74}$$

$$A_{r-2} = \frac{1}{2!} \frac{d^2}{ds^2} \left[(s + s_i)^r \frac{p(s)}{q(s)} \right]_{s=-s_i} \tag{A-75}$$

$$A_1 = \frac{1}{(r-1)!} \frac{d^{r-1}}{ds^{r-1}} \left[(s + s_i)^r \frac{p(s)}{q(s)} \right]_{s=-s_i} \tag{A-76}$$

EXAMPLE A-7. Let

$$X(s) = \frac{p(s)}{q(s)} = \frac{1}{s(s+1)^3(s+2)} \tag{A-77}$$

then,

$$X(s) = \frac{K_0}{s} + \frac{K_{-2}}{s+2} + \frac{A_1}{s+1} + \frac{A_2}{(s+1)^2} + \frac{A_3}{(s+1)^3} \tag{A-78}$$

From Eq. (A-64),

$$K_0 = [sX(s)]_{s=0} = \tfrac{1}{2} \tag{A-79}$$

$$K_{-2} = [(s+2)X(s)]_{s=-2} = \tfrac{1}{2} \tag{A-80}$$

The coefficients of the repeated roots at $s = -1$ are

$$A_3 = [(s+1)^3 X(s)]_{s=-1} = -1 \tag{A-81}$$

$$A_2 = \frac{d}{ds} [(s+1)^3 X(s)]_{s=-1} = \frac{d}{ds} \left[\frac{1}{s(s+2)} \right]_{s=-1}$$

$$= \left[\frac{-(2s+2)}{s^2(s+2)^2} \right]_{s=-1} = 0 \tag{A-82}$$

$$A_1 = \frac{1}{2!} \frac{d^2}{ds^2} [(s+1)^3 X(s)]_{s=-1} = \frac{1}{2} \frac{d}{ds} \left[\frac{-2(s+1)}{s^2(s+2)^2} \right]_{s=-1}$$

$$= \left[-\frac{1}{s^2(s+2)^2} + \frac{2(s+1)}{s^2(s+2)^3} + \frac{2(s+1)}{s^3(s+2)^2} \right]_{s=-1} = -1 \tag{A-83}$$

The complete expansion is

$$X(s) = \frac{1}{2s} + \frac{1}{2(s+2)} - \frac{1}{s+1} - \frac{1}{(s+1)^3} \tag{A-84}$$

Partial Fraction Expansion of Complex Conjugate Roots

Suppose that $q(s)$ contains a pair of complex roots:

$$s = -\alpha + j\omega \quad \text{and} \quad s = -\alpha - j\omega$$

Since these roots are simple, the corresponding coefficients are

$$K_{-\alpha+j\omega} = (s + \alpha - j\omega) \left.\frac{p(s)}{q(s)}\right|_{s=-\alpha+j\omega} \tag{A-85}$$

$$K_{-\alpha-j\omega} = (s + \alpha + j\omega) \left.\frac{p(s)}{q(s)}\right|_{s=-\alpha-j\omega} \tag{A-86}$$

For example, consider the function

$$X(s) = \frac{\omega_n^2}{s(s^2 + 2\delta\omega_n s - \omega_n^2)} = \frac{K_0}{s} + \frac{K_{-\alpha+j\omega}}{(s + \alpha - j\omega)} + \frac{K_{-\alpha-j\omega}}{(s + \alpha + j\omega)} \tag{A-87}$$

where $\alpha = \delta\omega_n$ and $\omega = \omega_n\sqrt{1 - \delta^2}$

Then, $$K_0 = [sX(s)]_{s=0} = 1 \tag{A-88}$$

$$K_{-\alpha-j\omega} = [(s + \alpha - j\omega)X(s)]_{s=-\alpha+j\omega}$$

$$= \frac{\omega_n^2}{2j\omega(-\alpha + j\omega)} = \frac{\omega_n}{2\omega} e^{-j(\theta+\pi/2)} \tag{A-89}$$

where $\theta = \tan^{-1} (\omega/-\alpha)$ $\tag{A-90}$

Also,

$$K_{-\alpha-j\omega} = [(s + \alpha + j\omega)X(s)]_{s=-\alpha-j\omega}$$

$$= \frac{\omega_n^2}{-2j\omega(-\alpha - j\omega)} = \frac{\omega_n}{2\omega} e^{j(\theta+\pi/2)} \tag{A-91}$$

The complete expansion is

$$X(s) = \frac{1}{s} + \frac{\omega_n}{2\omega} \left[\frac{e^{-j(\theta+\pi/2)}}{(s + \alpha - j\omega)} + \frac{e^{j(\theta+\pi/2)}}{(s + \alpha + j\omega)} \right] \tag{A-92}$$

The inverse transform of $X(s)$ is

$$x(t) = 1 + \frac{\omega_n}{2\omega} [e^{-j(\theta+\pi/2)}e^{(-\alpha+j\omega)t} + e^{j(\theta+\pi/2)}e^{(-\alpha-j\omega)t}]$$

$$= 1 + \frac{\omega_n}{2\omega} e^{-\alpha t}[e^{j[(\omega t-\theta)-\pi/2]} + e^{-j[(\omega t-\theta)-\pi/]}]$$

$$= 1 + \frac{\omega_n}{\omega} e^{-\alpha t} \sin (\omega t - \theta) \tag{A-93}$$

or, $$x(t) = 1 + \frac{1}{\sqrt{1 - \delta^2}} e^{-\delta\omega_n t} \sin (\omega_n\sqrt{1 - \delta^2}\, t - \theta) \tag{A-94}$$

Table A.1. LAPLACE TRANSFORM

Laplace transform $F(s)$	Time function $f(t)$
$\dfrac{1}{s}$	$u(t)$ (unit step function)
$\dfrac{1}{s^2}$	t
$\dfrac{n!}{s^{n+1}}$	t^n (n = integer)
$\dfrac{1}{s+a}$	e^{-at}
$\dfrac{1}{(s+a)(s+b)}$	$\dfrac{e^{-at} - e^{-bt}}{b-a}$
$\dfrac{\omega_n^2}{s^2 + 2\delta\omega_n s + \omega_n^2}$	$\dfrac{\omega_n}{\sqrt{1-\delta^2}} e^{-\delta\omega_n t} \sin \omega_n\sqrt{1-\delta^2}\,t$
$\dfrac{1}{(1+sT)^n}$	$\dfrac{1}{T^n(n-1)!} t^{n-1} e^{-t/T}$
$\dfrac{\omega_n^2}{(1+Ts)(s^2 + 2\delta\omega_n s + \omega_n^2)}$	$\dfrac{T\omega_n^2 e^{-t/T}}{1 - 2\delta T\omega_n + T^2\omega_n^2} + \dfrac{\omega_n e^{-\delta\omega_n t} \sin (\omega_n\sqrt{1-\delta^2}\,t - \phi)}{\sqrt{(1-\delta^2)(1 - 2\delta T\omega_n - T^2\omega_n^2)}},$ where $\phi = \tan^{-1} \dfrac{T\omega_n\sqrt{1-\delta^2}}{1 - T\delta\omega_2}$
$\dfrac{\omega_n}{(s^2 + \omega_n^2)}$	$\sin \omega_n t$
$\dfrac{\omega_n}{(1+Ts)(s^2 + \omega_n^2)}$	$\dfrac{T\omega_n}{1 + T^2\omega_n^2} e^{-t/T} + \dfrac{1}{\sqrt{1 + T^2\omega_n^2}} \sin (\omega_n t - \phi)$ where $\phi = \tan^{-1} \omega_n T$
$\dfrac{\omega_n^2}{s(s^2 + 2\delta\omega_n s + \omega_n^2)}$	$1 + \dfrac{1}{\sqrt{1-\delta^2}} e^{-\delta\omega_n t} \sin (\omega_n\sqrt{1-\delta^2}\,t - \phi)$ where $\phi = \tan^{-1} \dfrac{\sqrt{1-\delta^2}}{-\delta}$
$\dfrac{\omega_n^2}{s(s^2 + \omega_n^2)}$	$1 - \cos \omega_n t$
$\dfrac{1}{s(1+Ts)}$	$1 - e^{-t/T}$
$\dfrac{1}{s(1+Ts)^2}$	$1 - \dfrac{t+T}{T} e^{-t/T}$
$\dfrac{\omega_n^2}{s(1+Ts)(s^2 + 2\delta\omega_n s + \omega_n^2)}$	$1 - \dfrac{T^2\omega_n^2}{1 - 2T\delta\omega_n + T^2\omega_n^2} e^{-t/T} +$ $\dfrac{e^{-\delta\omega_n t} \sin (\omega_n\sqrt{1-\delta^2}\,t - \phi)}{\sqrt{1-\delta^2(1 - 2\delta T\omega_n + T^2\omega_n^2)}}$ where $\phi = \tan^{-1} (\sqrt{1-\delta^2}/-\delta)$ $+ \tan^{-1}[T\omega_n\sqrt{1-\delta^2}/(1 - T\delta\omega_n)]$
$\dfrac{\omega_n^2}{s^2(s^2 + 2\delta\omega_n s + \omega_n^2)}$	$t - \dfrac{2\delta}{\omega_n} + \dfrac{1}{\omega_n\sqrt{1-\delta^2}} e^{-\delta\omega_n t} \sin (\omega_n\sqrt{1-\delta^2}\,t - \phi)$ where $\phi = 2\tan^{-1} (\sqrt{1-\delta^2})/-\delta$

Table A.1. LAPLACE TRANSFORM (cont.)

Laplace transform $F(s)$	Time function $f(t)$
$\dfrac{\omega_n^2}{s^2(1 + Ts)(s^2 + 2\delta\omega_n s + \omega_n^2)}$	$t - T - \dfrac{2\delta}{\omega_n} + \dfrac{T^3\omega_n^2}{1 - 2\delta\omega_n T + T^2\omega_n^2}\,\epsilon^{-t/T}$ $\qquad + \dfrac{e^{-\delta\omega_n t}\sin(\omega_n\sqrt{1-\delta^2}\,t - \phi)}{\omega_n\sqrt{(1-\delta^2)}(1 - 2\delta\omega_n T + T^2\omega_n^2)}$ where $\phi = 2\tan^{-1}(\sqrt{1-\delta^2}/-\delta) +$ $\tan^{-1}[T\omega_n\sqrt{1-\delta^2}/(1 - T\omega_n\delta)]$
$\dfrac{1}{s^2(1 + Ts)^2}$	$t - 2T + (t + 2T)\epsilon^{-t/T}$
$\dfrac{\omega_n^2(1 + as)}{s^2 + 2\delta\omega_n s + \omega_n^2}$	$\omega_n\sqrt{\dfrac{1 - 2a\delta\omega_n + a^2\omega_n^2}{1 - \delta^2}}\,\epsilon^{-\delta\omega_n t}\sin(\omega_n\sqrt{1-\delta^2}\,t + \phi)$ where $\phi = \tan^{-1}\dfrac{a\omega_n\sqrt{1-\delta^2}}{1 - a\delta\omega_n}$
$\dfrac{\omega_n^2(1 + as)}{(s^2 + \omega_n^2)}$	$\omega_n\sqrt{1 + a^2\omega_n^2}\sin(\omega_n t + \phi)$ $\qquad$ where $\phi = \tan^{-1}a\omega_n$
$\dfrac{\omega_n^2(1 + as)}{(1 + Ts)(s^2 + 2\delta\omega_n s + \omega_n^2)}$	$\dfrac{\omega_n}{\sqrt{1-\delta^2}}\sqrt{\dfrac{1 - 2a\delta\omega_n + a^2\omega_n^2}{1 - 2T\delta\omega_n + T^2\omega_n^2}}\,\epsilon^{-\delta\omega_n t}\sin(\omega_n\sqrt{1-\delta^2}\,t + \phi)$ $\qquad + \dfrac{(T-a)\omega_n^2}{1 - 2T\delta\omega_n + T^2\omega_n^2}\,\epsilon^{-t/T}$ where $\phi = \tan^{-1}\dfrac{a\omega_n\sqrt{1-\delta^2}}{1 - a\delta\omega_n} - \tan^{-1}\dfrac{T\omega_n\sqrt{1-\delta^2}}{1 - T\delta\omega_n}$
$\dfrac{\omega_n^2(1 + as)}{(1 + Ts)(s^2 + \omega_n^2)}$	$\dfrac{\omega_n^2(T-a)}{1 + T^2\omega_n^2}\,\epsilon^{-t/T} + \dfrac{\omega_n\sqrt{1 + a^2\omega_n^2}}{\sqrt{1 + T^2\omega_n^2}}\sin(\omega_n t + \phi)$ where $\phi = \tan^{-1}a\omega_n - \tan^{-1}\omega_n T$
$\dfrac{\omega_n^2(1 + as)}{s(s^2 + 2\delta\omega_n s + \omega_n^2)}$	$1 + \dfrac{1}{\sqrt{1-\delta^2}}\sqrt{1 - 2a\delta\omega_n + a^2\omega_n^2}\,\epsilon^{-\delta\omega_n t}$ $\qquad\qquad\qquad \sin(\omega_n\sqrt{1-\delta^2}\,t + \phi)$ where $\phi = \tan^{-1}\dfrac{a\omega_n\sqrt{1-\delta^2}}{1 - a\delta\omega_n} - \tan^{-1}\dfrac{\sqrt{1-\delta^2}}{-\delta}$
$\dfrac{\omega_n^2(1 + as)}{s(1 + Ts)(s^2 + \omega_n^2)}$	$1 + \dfrac{T\omega_n^2(a - T)}{1 + T^2\omega_n^2}\,\epsilon^{-t/T} - \sqrt{\dfrac{1 + a^2\omega_n^2}{1 + T^2\omega_n^2}}\cos(\omega_n t + \phi)$ where $\phi = \tan^{-1}a\omega_n - \tan^{-1}\omega_n T$
$\dfrac{\omega_n^2(1 + as)}{s(1 + Ts)(s^2 + 2\delta\omega_n s + \omega_n^2)}$	$1 + \sqrt{\dfrac{1 - 2a\delta\omega_n + a^2\omega_n^2}{(1-\delta^2)(1 - 2T\delta\omega_n + T^2\omega_n^2)}}\,\epsilon^{-\delta\omega_n t}$ $\qquad \sin(\omega_n\sqrt{1-\delta^2}\,t + \phi) + \dfrac{\omega_n^2 T(a - T)}{1 - 2T\delta\omega_n + T^2\omega_n^2}\,\epsilon^{-t/T}$ $\phi = \tan^{-1}[a\omega_n\sqrt{1-\delta^2}[(1 - a\delta\omega_n)] -$ $\tan^{-1}[T\omega_n\sqrt{1-\delta^2}/(1 - T\delta\omega_n)] - \tan^{-1}(\sqrt{1-\delta^2}/-\delta)$
$\dfrac{1 + as}{s^2(1 + Ts)}$	$t + (a - T)(1 - \epsilon^{-t/T})$
$\dfrac{s\omega_n^2}{s^2 + 2\delta\omega_n s + \omega_n^2}$	$\dfrac{\omega_n^2}{\sqrt{1-\delta^2}}\,\epsilon^{-\delta\omega_n t}\sin(\omega_n\sqrt{1-\delta^2}\,t + \phi$ $\qquad\qquad\qquad$ where $\phi = \tan^{-1}\dfrac{\sqrt{1-\delta^2}}{-\delta}$

Table A.1. LAPLACE TRANSFORM (cont.)

Laplace transform $F(s)$	Time function $f(s)$
$\dfrac{s}{s^2 + \omega_n{}^2}$	$\cos \omega_n t$
$\dfrac{s}{(s^2 + \omega_n{}^2)^2}$	$\dfrac{1}{2\omega_n}\, t \sin \omega_n t$
$\dfrac{s}{(s^2 + \omega_{n1}{}^2)(s^2 + \omega_{n2}{}^2)}$	$\dfrac{1}{\omega_{n2}{}^2 - \omega_{n1}{}^2}\, (\cos \omega_{n1} t - \cos \omega_{n2} t)$
$\dfrac{s}{(1 + Ts)(s^2 + \omega_n{}^2)}$	$\dfrac{-1}{(1 + T^2\omega_n{}^2)}\, \epsilon^{-t/T} + \dfrac{1}{\sqrt{1 + T^2\omega_n{}^2}} \cos (\omega_n t - \phi)$ where $\quad \phi = \tan^{-1} \omega_n T$
$\dfrac{1 + as + bs^2}{s^2(1 + T_1 s)(1 + T_2 s)}$	$t + (a - T_1 - T_2) + \dfrac{b - aT_1 + T_1{}^2}{T_1 - T_2}\, \epsilon^{-t/T} -$ $\qquad\qquad\qquad\qquad \dfrac{b - aT_2 + T_2{}^2}{T_1 - T_2}\, \epsilon^{-t/T_2}$
$\dfrac{\omega_n{}^2(1 + as + bs^2)}{s(s^2 + 2\delta\omega_n s + \omega_n{}^2)}$	$1 + \sqrt{\dfrac{(1 - a\delta\omega_n - b\omega_n{}^2 + 2b\delta^2\omega_n{}^2)^2 + \omega_n{}^2(1 - \delta^2)(a - 2b\delta\omega_n)^2}{(1 - \delta^2)}}$ $\qquad\qquad\qquad \epsilon^{-\delta\omega_n t} \sin (\omega_n\sqrt{1 - \delta^2}\, t + \phi)$ $\phi = \tan^{-1} \dfrac{\omega_n\sqrt{1 - \delta^2}(a - 2b\delta\omega_n)}{b\omega_n(2\delta^2 - 1) + 1 - a\delta\omega_n} - \tan^{-1}\dfrac{\sqrt{1 - \delta^2}}{-\delta}$
$\dfrac{s^2}{(s^2 + \omega_n{}^2)^2}$	$\dfrac{1}{2\omega_n}\, (\sin \omega_n t + \omega_n t \cos \omega_n t)$

Index

A

Acceleration error, 149
Acceleration error constant, 149
Acceleration input, 121
Active networks, equations for, 17
Actuating signal, 147
Adaptive control systems, 36
Admittance function, 80
Amplifier:
  feedback, 46
  servo, 115
  single-stage RC-coupled, 63
Analytic functions, 191, 481
Argument principle, 197
Asymptote:
  Bode plot, 173, 176
  root locus, 252–55
Automatic control, 1
Autosyn, 92
Auxiliary equation, 160

B

Back emf, 103, 131
Backlash:
  friction-controlled, 461
  inertia-controlled, 464
Bandwidth, 63, 185
Block diagram, 37
  reduction procedure, 40
  terminology, 38
Blocked rotor torque, 108
Bode plot (corner plot), 172–81
Bridged-T network, 303
  compensation, 348–53

C

Carrier frequency, 116
Characteristic equation, 70, 123, 246
Chopper, 113

Closed-loop control systems, 2
Cofactor, 16
Command signal, 5
Compensation:
  a-c, 303
  bridged-T network, 348–53
  cancellation, 316–22
  feedback, 353–56
  frequency-domain versus s-plane, 305
  lead-lag, 344
  phase-lag:
    Bode plot method, 336
    effect of, 341
    root locus method, 342
  phase-lead:
    Bode plot method, 312
    effect and limitations, 323–26
    root locus method, 326–34
    series d-c network, 306
  types of, 302
Complex variable, 479
  functions of, 480
Composite signal-flow graph, 397
Conditional frequency, 126
Conditionally stable system, 229–31
Constant M loci, 231–35
Constant phase-shift loci, 235
Contour integration, 366
Controlled signal, 5
Control system:
  closed-loop, 2
  open-loop, 2
Convolution, 36
  complex, 365
Corner plot (Bode plot), 172
Coulomb friction, 23
  phase plane diagram for, 451–54
Cramer's rule, 15
Criterion:
  Nyquist, 194, 410
  Routh-Hurwitz, 156, 409
Critically damped, 126
Critical point, 203
Cut-off rate, 186

D

Damped sinusoid, 125, 129
Damping constant, 126
  ratio, 123, 126
    and natural undamped frequency, 186
Data reconstruction, 373–78

Decades of frequency, 175
Decibels:
  per decade of frequency, 175
  versus phase shift plot, 181
Demodulators, 112
Derivative control, effects on transient
    response, 138–41
Describing function:
  application to stability analysis, 470
  definition, 455–57
  gear backlash, friction-controlled, 461
    inertia-controlled, 464
  ideal relay, 457
  relay with dead zone, 458
  relay with dead zone and hysteresis, 459
Diehlsyn, 92
Differential operator, 14
Differential transmitter, 98
Digital compensators, 422
Digital computer in control systems, 361
Direct transmission, 79, 82
Displacement input, 121
Distortion effect, 61
Dominant roots, 125

E

Electrical systems, equations of, 11
Encircled, 196
Enclosed, 196
Equilibrium state, 26
  stable, 473
  unstable, 473
Error, steady-state, 145
Error coefficients, generalized definition,
    151
Error constants:
  acceleration, 149
  positional, 147
  velocity, 148
Error detector, 90
  sensitivity of, 91
Error-sensing device, 89
Error series, 151
Extraneous signal, 61

F

Feedback:
  definition, 58, 72
  degenerative, 66

Feedback, (Cont.):
  effect on bandwidth, 63
  effect on distortion, 61
  effect on gain, 60
  effect on impedance, 66
  effect on sensitivity, 60
  effect on transient response, 68
  negative, 60, 72
  positive, 60
  regenerative, 66
Feedback amplifier, single-stage RC, 64
Feedback control systems, 2
  analysis and design of, 6
  block diagram, 38, 88
  compensation of, 302
  components of, 89
  continuous-data, 6, 360
  frequency response, 182
  magnification of, 183
  relay-type, 6, 443
  sampled-data, 6, 360
  stability of, 155
  steady-state response, 145
  time-domain performance
      characteristics, 122
  time response, 120
Fictitious sampler, 428
Fourier coefficient, 484
Fourier integral, 483
Fourier series, 456, 483
Fourier transform, 486
Free body diagram, 26, 31
Friction:
  coulomb, 23, 451
  static, 22
  viscous, 23
$F(s)$-plot, 197, 202

G

Gain:
  current, 19
  loop, 38
  voltage, 19
Gain crossover frequency, 228–29, 336
Gain limit, 228, 322
Gain margin:
  definition, 223–26
  from the Bode plot, 228
Gear train, 29
GH-plot, 201
$G(s)$, classification of, 150

H

Hidden oscillation, 408
Hold device, 373
  first-order hold, 377
    gain and phase characteristics, 377
  zero-order hold, 374
    gain and phase characteristics, 376
    impulse response, 375
Hurwitz determinant, 157

I

Ideal sampler, 363
Impedance, 80
  driving point, 81–82
  input, 19
  output, 20
Impulse response, of linear systems,
    32, 388
Induction motor:
  torque-speed characteristic of:
    constant-current source, 111
    constant-voltage source, 107
Initial conditions, 439, 449, 490
Initial value theorem, 383, 489
Integral control, 138
  effect on transient response, 141
Intentional sampling, 362
Isocline, 438

K

Kirchhoff's current law, 11
Kirchhoff's voltage law, 11

L

Laplace transform, 15
  application to solving differential
      equations, 489–91
  definition, 482–87
  important theorems, 488–89
  inverse, 487
  table, 495–97
Lead-lag compensation, 344
Linear equations, 12
Linear systems, 10, 32–37

M

Magnification, 183
Magnitude versus phase plot, 181
Mason's formula (general gain formula),
    48, 74, 398, 400
    application to block diagrams, 52
Mechanical systems, equations of, 25
Minor, 16
Modulators, 112
Motion:
    rotational, 24
    translational, 21
Multirate sampling, 403

N

Network determinant, 15
Newton's force equations, 28
Nichols chart, 236–42, 474
Nonlinear equations, 12
Nonlinear system, 435
Nyquist criterion:
    application, 204–13
    definition, 202
    features, 194
    sampled-data system, 410
Nyquist path, 200
Nyquist plot, 211
    effects of adding poles and zeros, 213–18
    relative stability from, 222

O

Octave of frequency, 175
On-off servo:
    with dead zone, 448
    with ideal relay, 443
Open-loop control system, 2
Overshoot, 8, 122, 129

P

Partial fractions:
    complex conjugate roots, 493
    multiple order poles, 492
    simple poles, 491
Passive network, equations of, 11
Phase crossover frequency, 228
Phase-lag network, 302
    Bode plot, 334

Phase-lag network, (Cont.):
    polar plot, 334
    pole-zero configuration, 334
Phase-lead network, 302, 309
    Bode plot, 311
    polar plot, 310
    pole-zero configuration, 226–29
Phase plane diagram:
    comparison of linear and on-off
        systems, 447
    on-off systems with ideal relay, 443
    on-off system with dead zone, 448
    on-off system with hysteresis and dead
        zone, 400
    singular point, 440
    systems with ramp inputs, 454
Phase plane method:
    applied to linear systems, 438
    applied to on-off systems, 441
    applied to systems with coulomb
        friction, 451
    definition, 437
Phase plane trajectory:
    definition, 437
    isoclines of, 438
Polar plot, 171
Potentiometer:
    as error-sensing device, 89
    resolution, 91
    wirewound, 92
Pulse transfer function, 387–90

R

Radar tracking system, 361
Ramp input (see velocity input)
Rate feedback, 144
Residues, 369
Resonance peak, 185
Resonant frequency, 186
Return difference:
    definition, 72–74
    null, 83
    physical interpretation, 77
Return ratio:
    definition, 72
    physical interpretation, 77
Root contours:
    pole of $G(s)H(s)$ variable, 280
    second-order systems, 282
    zero and pole of $G(s)H(s)$ both
        variable, 290

Root contours, (Cont.):
  zero of $G(s)H(s)$ variable, 287
Root locus, 70, 137, 143, 246
  angle of departure, 256
  asymptotes of, 252
  breakaway point, 258
  calculation of K, 265
  conditionally stable systems, 276–80
  construction of, 250
  definition, 248
  effect of adding poles, 271
  effect of adding zeros, 273
  effects of movements of poles and
      zeros, 274
  generalized (*see* root contours)
  important properties, 271–76
  intersection of, 253
  multiple-loop systems, 293
  on the real axis, 256
  rules of construction, tabulation, 270
  symmetry of, 252

S

Sampled-data systems:
  Bode diagram, 413
  decibel versus phase shift plot, 414
  design and compensation:
    continuous-data networks, 419–22
    digital compensators, 422
  Nyquist criterion, 410
  response between sampling instants,
      427–31
    modified z-transform method, 428
    submultiple sampling method, 428
  root locus technique, 416
  Routh-Hurwitz criterion, 409
  signal flow graphs, 394–405
  with inherent sampling, 361
  with intentional sampling, 362
  z-transform analysis, 390
Sampler, ideal, 363
  frequency spectrum of output, 372
Sampling process, 362–64
  impulse approximation (*see*
      ideal sampler)
  interpretation in frequency domain,
      371–73
  mathematical analysis, 364
Sampling theorem, 372
Saturation characteristic, 436
Second-order system, 127

Selsyn, 92
Sensitivity, 60, 78
Servo amplifier, 115
Servomechanisms:
  basic elements of, 4
  definition, 5
  types of, 6
Servomotors:
  armature-controlled, 103
  field-controlled, 101
  two-phase, 105–12
Settling time, 123
Signal flow graphs:
  algebra, 45
  application to block diagrams, 52
  basic properties, 44
  composite, 397
  definition, 44
  gain formula, 48
  original, 395
  sampled, 396
Signal-to-noise ratio, 62
Singularity, 481–82
Specifications:
  frequency domain, 185
  time domain, 122
s-plane, 479
  complementary strips, 385
  primary strip, 385
Stability, definition, 155–56
Static friction, 22
Steady-state error, 122, 145
Stiffness, 28
Superposition principle, 435
Suppressed carrier signal, 112, 303
Synchros:
  a-c, 92
  control transformer, 94
  differential transmitter, 98
  transmitter, 92

T

Tachometer:
  a-c, 98
  d-c, 100
Telesyn, 92
Time delay, 122.
Time sharing system, 361
Transfer function, 32
  closed-loop, 38
  feedback path, 38

Transfer function, (Cont.):
  forward path, 38
  of linear systems, 32
  open-loop, 38
  pseudo-linear, 32
  pulse, 387
Transfer immittance, 81
Transient response:
  feedback control system, 123
    positional servomechanisms, 130
  second-order system, 127
  third-order system, 136
Transmission function, 42
Transportation lag, 218–22
Twin-T network, 304
Two-phase induction motor, 106
  torque-speed characteristics, 111

U

Undamped natural frequency, 126
Undershoot, 129
Unit impulse train, 364

V

Velocity error, 148
Velocity error constant, 148, 313
Velocity input, 121
Viscous friction, 23

W

Weighting sequence, 388

Z

Zero, definition, 482
z-plane, mapping from the s-plane, 385
z-transform:
  definition, 378
  important theorems, 382–83
    addition and subtraction, 382
    complex translation, 383
    final value, 383
    initial value, 383
    multiplication by a constant, 382
    real translation, 383
  inverse, 380
  limitations of, 405–07
  table of, 380